WORKING MEN'S COLLEGE.

LIBRARY REGULATIONS.

The Library is open every week-day evening (except Saturday), from 6.30 to 10 o'clock.

This book may be kept for three weeks. If not returned within that period, the borrower will be liable to a fine of one penny per week.

If lost or damaged, the borrower will be required to make good such loss or damage.

Only one book may be borrowed at a time.

A TEXT-BOOK OF ZOOLOGY

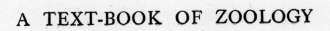

A TEXTBOOK OF ZOOLOGY

A TEXT-BOOK OF ZOOLOGY

BY THE LATE
T. JEFFERY PARKER, D.Sc., F.R.S.
PROFESSOR OF BIOLOGY IN THE UNIVERSITY OF OTAGO, DUNEDIN, N.Z.

AND THE LATE
WILLIAM A. HASWELL, M.A., D.Sc., F.R.S.
EMERITUS PROFESSOR OF BIOLOGY IN THE UNIVERSITY OF SYDNEY, N.S.W.

SIXTH EDITION

IN TWO VOLUMES

VOL. II

REVISED BY
C. FORSTER–COOPER, M.A., Sc.D., F.R.S.
LATE DIRECTOR OF THE UNIVERSITY MUSEUM OF ZOOLOGY
SOMETIME FELLOW OF TRINITY HALL, CAMBRIDGE
DIRECTOR OF THE BRITISH MUSEUM (NATURAL HISTORY)

WITH ILLUSTRATIONS

MACMILLAN AND CO., LIMITED
ST. MARTIN'S STREET, LONDON
1949

PRINTED IN GREAT BRITAIN

PREFACE TO THE SIXTH EDITION

In the preparation of this new edition, with its change of type and format, it was felt that the time had come for a considerable alteration of the text not only by the incorporation of new material but also by the omission of certain parts that appeared no longer to serve a useful purpose.

In the time that has elapsed since this text-book was first published in 1898 vertebrate zoology has grown in every direction. Particularly is this the case in its palæontology. So many new forms have been discovered and described that previous ideas on the evolution of many lines of vertebrates have become not only enlarged but also much modified. Especially noticeable in this respect is the increase in our knowledge of the Agnatha, the Palæozoic Fishes, the early Amphibia and Reptilia and, though still to an insufficient extent, the Mesozoic and Palæocene Mammals.

It has not been thought desirable, even if it were possible, to alter the general plan of a text-book that has served well so many generations of students. New material therefore has been inserted wherever it seemed best to fit. The difficulty of making large alterations in a standard text without producing some disturbance is obvious and some inequality of treatment and some occasional repetition have been unavoidable. It is hoped, however, that the continuity of the text has not been materially impaired.

The main alterations are as follows. The small sections in the previous editions on the Agnatha and Palæozoic Fishes which were formerly printed as an appendix in small type have been rewritten and enlarged and have been placed in appropriate positions in the general text. A new classification of Fishes in which four classes are recognised is brought into use. The Amphibia and Reptilia have suffered a less drastic modification, but some changes—the result of a wider knowledge of their early history—have been introduced. Except for minor points the section on the Birds has been little altered. In the section on the Mammals there will now be found a somewhat fuller treatment of the orders together with some brief account of extinct forms without which the position of the living animals cannot properly be understood. The text here has been altered in appearance by the transposition of certain parts as, for example, the descriptions of the osteology of the orders formerly placed together under the heading " General Organisation " have been divided and each placed with its own order. The remainder of the section on general organisation remains but additions have been made to it.

Consideration of space has necessitated the withdrawal of the sections on

Geographical Distribution, on the Philosophy of Zoology and on the History of Zoology. To bring these subjects up to date would render the volume unwieldy. As it is there has had to be a good deal of compression as well as excision, but it is hoped that the student will find enough to serve as a general account of the Chordata. No one text-book, if it is to be of reasonable size, can possibly cover all the ground, so that for further and more detailed information the student must turn either to original papers or to such books as " The Structure and Development of Vertebrates " by Goodrich for questions of morphology and for the palæontological aspect to the " Vertebrate Palæontology " by Romer, to mention only two. A list of books and papers which are recommended is given in an appendix.

No text-book can hope to be free from some errors, and such might have been more numerous had I not drawn freely on the help of many colleagues both at home and in the United States. I have to thank for much advice and assistance the following gentlemen: Dr. L. A. Borradaile, Dr. P. M. Butler, Professor H. A. Harris, Dr. J. E. Harris, Mr. F. R. Parrington, M.A., Mr. W. J. Heasman, M.A., H.M.I., Dr. P. Whiting, and Dr. W. Graham Smith, all of the University of Cambridge. To Professor W. K. Gregory and Dr. G. G. Simpson of the American Museum. To Professor D. M. S. Watson, Professor C. H. O'Donoghue, Dr. T. S. Westoll and Dr. Moy-Thomas, and finally to my colleagues in the British Museum, Dr. A. T. Hopwood, Mr. J. R. Norman, Mr. N. B. Kinnear, Dr. W. E. Swinton, Dr. E. Trewavas and Dr. E. I. White. I have to thank Mr. H. A. Toombs, of the British Museum, for undertaking the arduous task of compiling the index.

C. FORSTER-COOPER.

CONTENTS

CONTENTS

LIST OF ILLUSTRATIONS

VOL. II

ZOOLOGY

PHYLUM CHORDATA

In the arrangement which it has been found convenient to follow in the present work, the Vertebrate animals (Fishes, Amphibians, Reptiles, Birds, and Mammals), together with the Cephalochorda or Lancelets, the Urochorda or Ascidians, and the Hemichorda or Balanoglossus and its allies, are all grouped together in a single phylum—the Chordata. The main groups comprised in this assemblage, however, differ so widely from one another in certain essential points, and the common features uniting them together are so few, that it has been thought advisable to depart from the plan of arrangement followed in connection with the invertebrate phyla, and to make a primary division in this case not into classes, but into sub-phyla. In accordance with this scheme the phylum Chordata is regarded as made up of three sub-phyla—the Hemichorda, the Urochorda, and the Euchorda, the last-mentioned comprising the two sections Acrania and Craniata or Vertebrata, each of which receives separate treatment.

The name Chordata is derived from one of the few but striking common features by which the members of this extensive phylum are united together—the possession, either in the young condition or throughout life, of a structure termed the *chorda dorsalis* or *notochord*. This is a cord of specially modified vacuolated cells extending along the middle line on the dorsal side of the enteric cavity and on the ventral side of the central nervous system. In the lower Chordates (the Urochorda and Cephalochorda) the notochord is developed directly and unmistakably from the endoderm, and in the Hemichorda it remains permanently in continuity with that layer. But in the Craniata its origin is by no means so definite, and it may originate from cells which are not obviously of endodermal derivation. It may be enclosed in a firm sheath and thus be converted into a stiff, but elastic, supporting structure. In the Craniata (with a few exceptions among lower forms) it becomes in the adult replaced more or less completely by a segmented bony or cartilaginous axis—the spinal or vertebral column. Another nearly universal common feature of the Chordata is the perforation of the wall of the pharynx, either in the

B

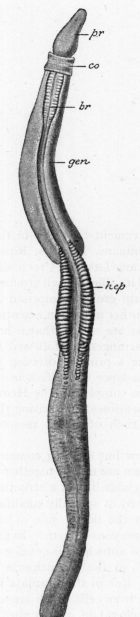

embryonic or larval condition only, or throughout life, by a system of clefts—the branchial clefts; and a third characteristic is the almost universal presence at all stages, or only in the larva, of a cavity or system of cavities, the *neurocœle* in the interior of the central nervous system.

The Chordata are Cœlomata, and the mode of development of the cœlome in the lower sub-phyla is essentially the same as in the Echinodermata (Section XI), the Chætognatha (Section X), and Brachiopoda: it is derived, that is to say, by direct outgrowth from the archenteron. In the Craniata this enterocœlic origin of the cavity is no longer definitely traceable, though what appear to be indications of it may be detected in some cases. The Urochorda are not divided [1] : in the Hemichorda there is a division of the cœlome into three parts, each occupying a definite region of the body, so that the view is sometimes maintained that these animals are tri-segmented : in the Cephalochorda and Craniata there are numerous segments, the nature of which will be referred to later.

SUB-PHYLUM I AND CLASS.—HEMICHORDA (ADELOCHORDA).

A number of worm-like, simply organised animals possessing a structure which is commonly regarded as of the nature of a rudimentary notochord, comprising *Balanoglossus* and certain allied genera, are so widely removed from the other members of the Chordata that, if we accept them as Chordates, it is advisable to consider them as constituting an independent sub-phylum, and to this the name of Hemichorda or Adelochorda has been applied. Resembling Balanoglossus in the condition of the supposed notochord, in the division of the body into three regions, sometimes looked upon as representing three segments, and in certain other features, are two genera of small marine animals—*Cephalodiscus* and

FIG. 1.—**Balanoglossus.** Entire animal. *br.* branchial region ; *co.* collar ; *gen.* genital ridges ; *hep.* prominences formed by hepatic cæca ; *pr.* proboscis. (After Spengel.)

[1] Though faint indications of serial repetition of parts are traceable in certain cases.

Rhabdopleura. These are probably more nearly related to one another than they are to Balanoglossus, from which they are separated by well-marked differences, and the Hemichorda may, therefore, best be regarded as divisible into two classes—one, the *Enteropneusta*, comprising only Balanoglossus[1] and its immediate allies; the other, the *Pterobranchia*, including Cephalodiscus and Rhabdopleura.

External Characters and Cœlome of Enteropneusta.—Balanoglossus (Fig. 1) is a soft-bodied, cylindrical, worm-like animal, the surface of which is

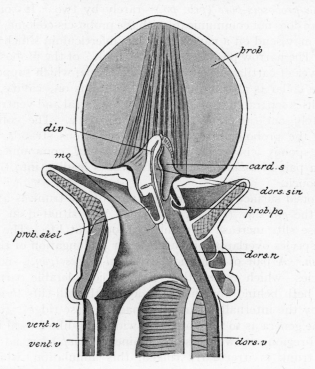

Fig. 2.—**Balanoglossus.** Diagrammatic sagittal section of anterior end. *card. s.* cardial sac; *div.* diverticulum (supposed notochord); *dors. n.* dorsal nerve-strand; *dors. sin.* dorsal sinus; *dors. v.* dorsal vessel; *mo.* mouth; *prob.* proboscis; *prob. po.* proboscis-pore; *prob. skel.* proboscis-skeleton; *vent. n.* ventral nerve-strand; *vent. v.* ventral vessel. (After Spengel.)

uniformly ciliated. The size varies extremely in the different species, some being quite small—2 or 3 centimetres—while other species are of comparatively large size and may be as much as 2½ metres in length. It is divisible into three regions: in front there is a large club-shaped hollow organ—the *proboscis* (*pr.*); immediately behind the proboscis and encircling its base is a prominent

---

[1] The name Balanoglossus is here used as a general designation rather than as a strictly generic term.

fold—the *collar* (*co.*) ; the third region or *trunk* is long and nearly cylindrical, but somewhat depressed.

Balanoglossus lives in the sea, usually in shallow water, burrowing in sand or mud by means of its proboscis : one species has been found swarming on the surface of the sea. Numerous glands in the integument secrete a viscid matter to which grains of sand adhere in such a way as to form a fragile temporary tube. The proboscis (Fig. 2, *prob.*) has muscular walls ; its cavity (proboscis-cœlome) opens on the exterior usually by a single minute aperture—the *proboscis-pore* (*prb. po.*)—rarely by two. In some species the proboscis-pore does not communicate with the proboscis-cœlome, but terminates blindly, and may send off a narrow tubular diverticulum which opens into the neurocœle. The narrow posterior part or " neck " of the proboscis is strengthened by a layer of cartilage-like or *chondroid* tissue, which supports the blood-vessels. The collar is also muscular, and contains one cavity, or two (right and left) cavities separated from one another by dorsal and ventral mesenteries, and completely cut off from the proboscis-cavity. The collar-cavity and also that of the proboscis are crossed by numerous strands of connective-tissue of a spongy character. The collar-cavity communicates with the exterior by a pair of *collar-pores*—ciliated tubes leading into the first gill-slit or first gill-pouch.

On the dorsal surface of the anterior part of the trunk is a double row of small slits—the *gill-slits* (Fig. 1, *br.*)—each row situated in a longitudinal furrow ; these slits increase in number throughout life. The most anterior are in some species overlapped by a posterior prolongation of the collar called the *operculum.* A pair of longitudinal *genital ridges* (*gen.*)—not recognisable in some species—which extend throughout a considerable part of the length of the body both behind and in the region of the gill-slits (*branchial region*), are formed by the internally situated gonads : these ridges are so prominent in some of the genera as to form a pair of wide wing-like lateral folds. Behind the branchial region are two rows of prominences (*hep.*) formed by the hepatic cæca. The trunk is irregularly ringed, this annulation, which is entirely superficial and does not correspond to an internal segmentation, being most strongly marked behind. The cœlome of the trunk is divided into two lateral closed cavities by a vertical partition (dorsal and ventral mesenteries).

Digestive Organs.—The mouth (Fig. 2, *mo.*) is situated ventrally at the base of the proboscis, within the collar. Into the dorsal half of the anterior portion of the alimentary canal open the internal gill-openings. Each of these is in the form of a long narrow U, the two limbs separated by a narrow process—the *tongue*—which contains a prolongation of the body-cavity. In most of the Enteropneusta the internal gill-openings lead into *gill-pouches* which in turn communicate with the exterior by the gill-slits. But in the genus *Ptychodera* (Fig. 3) there are no gill-pouches, the U-shaped internal gill-openings leading directly to the exterior. The gill-pouches are supported by a chitinoid skeleton consisting of a number of separate parts. Each of these consists of a dorsal basal portion and three long narrow lamellæ, a median and two lateral; the median, which is bifurcated at the end, lies in the septum or interval between two adjoining gill-sacs; the two lateral lie in the neighbouring tongues. In most species a number of transverse rods—the *synapticulæ*—connect together the tongues and the adjoining septa, and are supported by slender processes of the skeleton.

The posterior part of the alimentary canal is a nearly straight tube, giving off, in its middle part, paired *hepatic cæca*, which bulge outwards in the series of external prominences already mentioned. Posteriorly it terminates in an anal aperture situated at the posterior extremity of the body. In the posterior part of its extent in some Enteropneusta the intestine presents a ventral median ridge-like outgrowth of its epithelium—the *pygochord*. Throughout its length the intestine lies between the dorsal and ventral divisions of the vertical partition, which act as mesenteries.

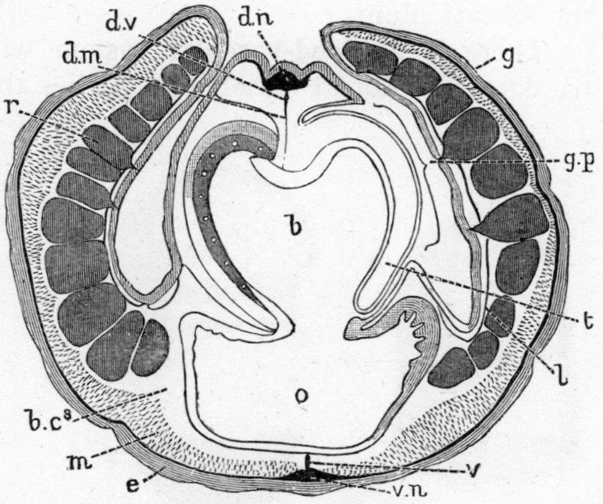

As the animal forces its way through the sand, a quantity of the latter enters the digestive canal through the permanently open mouth, and is eventually

FIG. 3.—**Ptychodera bahamensis.** Transverse section of the branchial region. *b.* branchial part of alimentary canal; *b.* c³, cœlome of trunk; *d. m.* dorsal mesentery; *d. n.* dorsal nerve; *d. v.* dorsal vessel; *e.* epidermis with nerve layer (black) at its base; *g.* genital wing; *g. p.* branchial aperture encroached upon by tongue (*t*); *l.* lateral septum; *m.* longitudinal muscles; *o.* digestive part of œsophagus; *r.* reproductive organ; *t.* tongue; *v.* ventral mesentery and ventral vessel; *v. n.* ventral nerve. (From Harmer, *Cambridge Natural History*, after Spengel.)

passed out again by the anus in the shape of castings, which may be thrown out on the surface of the sand in a form resembling that taken by the castings of earthworms.

A series of pores (*gastro-cutaneous pores*), variously arranged in the different genera, connect the intestine with the surface.

Notochord or **œsophageal diverticulum.**—The dorsal wall of the part of the digestive canal immediately following upon the mouth gives off a *diverticulum* (*div.*) that runs forward some distance into the basal part of the proboscis after giving off a short ventral branch. The diverticulum contains a narrow lumen, and its wall is composed of a single layer of long and very narrow cells, each of which contains a vacuole. This layer of cells forming the wall of the diverticulum is continuous with the epithelium of the digestive canal itself, the cells being somewhat modified by the presence of the vacuoles. The diverticulum, owing partly to its structure, partly to its relations, is usually regarded as representing the notochord of the typical Chordata. In close relation with this on its ventral surface is the chitinoid *proboscis-skeleton* (*prob. skel.*), which consists of a median part of an hour-glass shape, and with a tooth-shaped process, bifurcating behind into two flattened bars which lie in the anterior region of the œsophagus and support the opening into the lumen of the diverticulum.

There is a **blood-vascular system** with dorsal and ventral longitudinal trunks. The dorsal vessel (*dors. v.*) lies above the notochord, and ends in front

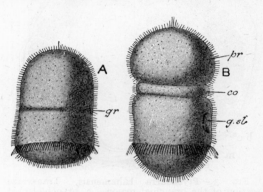

FIG. 4.—Development of **Balanoglossus.** *A*, stage of the formation of the first groove (*gr.*). *B*, stage in which the second groove has appeared, and the first gill-slit has become developed. *co.* collar; *g. sl.* gill-slit; *pr.* proboscis. (After Bateson.)

in a sinus, the *dorsal sinus* or *heart* (*dors. sin.*), situated in the anterior part of the collar and the neck of the proboscis, in close contact with the notochord. From the posterior part of the sinus is given off a vessel which bifurcates to supply the proboscis. In communication with the sinus in front are a number of vessels of a bilateral plexus in the *glomerulus*, a glandular organ, probably excretory, situated at the anterior end of the œsophageal diverticulum. From the posterior end of each half of the glomerulus there passes backwards an efferent vessel which breaks up into a plexus; the two plexuses unite ventrally to form a median ventral plexus continuous behind with the ventral vessel. The dorsal sinus, having no definite walls, is not contractile; but a closed sac, the *cardiac sac* (*card. s.*), situated on the dorsal side of the sinus, has a muscular ventral wall, by the contractions of which the blood may be propelled.

The **nervous system** consists of dorsal and ventral strands (*dors. n., vent. n.*) which extend throughout the length of the body. These are merely thickenings of a layer of nerve-fibres which extends over the entire body in the deeper part of the epidermis. Here and there are giant nerve-cells. The part of the dorsal strand which lies in the collar (collar-cord) is detached from the epidermis; it contains a larger number of the giant nerve-cells than the rest; in some species it encloses a canal, the neurocœle, opening in front and behind; in others a closed canal; in most a number of separate cavities. At the posterior extremity of the collar the dorsal and ventral strands are connected by a ring-like thickening, and there is a thickening also round the neck of the proboscis. There are no organs of special sense; but some cells of the epidermis on certain parts of the proboscis and on the anterior edge of the collar seem to be of the character of sensory cells.

Reproductive Organs.—The sexes are separate, and often differ in shape and colour; the ovaries and testes are simple or branched saccular organs arranged in a double row along the branchial region of the trunk and farther back; they open on the exterior by a series of pores.

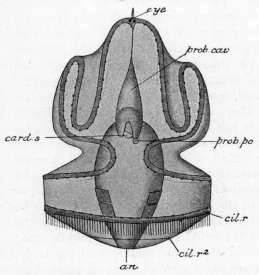

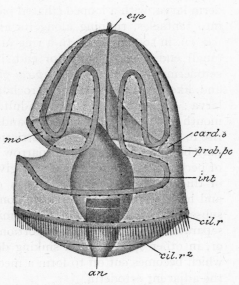

FIG. 5.—**Tornaria.** Dorsal view. *an.* anus; *card. s.* cardiac sac; *cil. r.* post-oral ciliated band (membranellæ); *cil. r².* posterior ciliated ring; *eye,* eye-spots on apical plate; *prob. cav.* proboscis-cavity; *prob. po.* proboscis-pore. (After Spengel.)

FIG. 6.—**Tornaria.** Lateral view. Lettering as in Fig. 718; in addition, *int.* intestine; *mo.* mouth. (After Spengel.)

The course of the **development** (Figs. 4–6) differs in different species. In some it is comparatively direct; in others there is a metamorphosis. Impregnation is external. Segmentation is complete and fairly regular, resulting in the formation of a blastula, which is at first rounded, then flattened. On one side of the flattened blastula an invagination takes place. The embryo at this stage is covered with short cilia, with a ring of stronger cilia. The aperture of invagination closes and the ectoderm and endoderm become completely separate. The embryo elongates and a transverse groove (*gr.*) appears (*A*): the mouth is formed by an invagination in the position of the groove. The anus is developed in the position formerly occupied by the blastopore. Before the mouth appears there are formed two diverticula of the archenteron which become completely separated off, their cavities subsequently giving rise to the cœlomic cavities of the proboscis and of the collar, and the body-cavity of the trunk. By the appearance of a second transverse groove (*B*) the body of the embryo becomes divided into three parts—an anterior, a middle, and a posterior —these being the beginnings respectively of the proboscis, the collar, and the trunk. The branchial region is marked off by the appearance of a pair of apertures—the first pair of branchial slits (*g. sl.*)—and other pairs subsequently develop behind these.

In the species that undergo a metamorphosis the embryo assumes a larval form termed *Tornaria* (Figs. 5 and 6). This is somewhat like an Echinoderm larva, with a looped ciliated band, sometimes lobed, sometimes produced into tentacles, running along its anterior part, and a ring of membranellæ (*cil. r.*), in some cases with a ring of smaller cilia (*cil. r².*), round the posterior (anal) end. At the anterior end, in the middle of the pre-oral lobe, is an ectodermal thickening—the *apical plate*—containing nerve-cells and eye-spots, and, like the apical plate of a trochophore, constituting the nerve-centre of the larva : this disappears in the adult. There is a short alimentary canal with mouth and anus. The ciliated bands are lost ; an outgrowth is formed to give rise to the proboscis, and a constriction separates it from the collar ; the hinder part becomes elongated and narrow to form the body of the animal ; a series of perforations from the exterior give rise to the branchial pouches. A band of thickened epithelium has been described on the wall of the œsophagus and has been supposed to correspond to the structure termed *endostyle* to be subsequently met with in the Tunicata. The collar-cord is formed by the separating off of the deeper portion of the ectoderm along the middle line : or, in other species, by a sinking down of the whole thickness of the layer, which becomes cut off to form a medullary plate with its edges overlapped by the adjacent ectoderm.

Constituting the class **Pterobranchia** are only the two genera *Cephalodiscus* and *Rhabdopleura*. These both resemble Balanoglossus in having the body divided into three parts or regions—a *proboscis* with a proboscis-cavity, a *collar* with a collar-cavity communicating with the exterior by a pair of collar-pores (nephridia in Rhabdopleura), and a *trunk* with two distinct lateral cavities ; and in the presence of a structure resembling a notochord with the same relations to the nervous system as in Balanoglossus. They both differ from Balanoglossus in having the alimentary canal bent on itself, so that the anal opening is situated not far from the mouth ; in the presence of arms bearing tentacles arising from the collar ; and in the comparatively small size of the proboscis. Cephalodiscus, moreover, has only a single pair of apertures which may be regarded as representing the gill-slits ; while in Rhabdopleura such openings are entirely absent, their places being taken, apparently, by a pair of ciliated grooves. Both forms occur in associations or colonies secreting a common case or investment. Both occur in the sea at various depths.

Cephalodiscus has an investment (Fig. 7) in the form of a branching gelatinous structure, which is in some species beset with numerous short filiform processes, and contains a number of tubular cavities with external openings, occupied by zooids. The latter (Fig. 7) are not in organic continuity, so that, though enclosed in a common investment, they do not form a colony in the sense in which the word is used of the Polyzoa or the Hydroid Zoophytes.

They have a feature in common with such a colony that they multiply by the formation of buds; but these become detached before they are mature. With the collar-region are connected a series of usually eight to sixteen arms, each beset, except in the case of the male of one species, with numerous very fine pinnately-arranged tentacles, and containing a prolongation of the collar-cavity. The proboscis (Fig. 9, *ps.*) is a shield-shaped lobe overhanging the mouth; its cavity communicates with the exterior by two proboscis-pores (*p. p.*). The cavity of the collar communicates with the exterior by a pair of ciliated passages opening by the collar-pores. Behind the collar-region on each side is a small area in which the body-wall and that of the pharynx are coalescent; this area is perforated by an opening—the *gill-slit.* Cilia occur only on the arms, proboscis, and lateral lips. A nerve-strand, dorsal ganglion, or collar-cord, containing nerve-fibres and ganglion-cells, is situated on the dorsal side of the collar below the epidermis, and is prolonged on to the dorsal surface of the proboscis and the dorsal surface of the arms; it is not hollow. On the ventral side of this nerve-strand is a very

Fig. 7.—**Cephalodiscus dodecalophus.** Gelatinous investment. (After McIntosh.)

slender cylindrical cellular cord (*nch.*) continuous behind with the epithelium of the pharynx: this is homologous with the diverticulum of Balanoglossus, and thus homologous with the notochord of the Chordata. A blood-vascular system with heart and cardiac sac like those of the Enteropneusta is present. In some species of Cephalodiscus the sexes are united, in most they are separate. The posterior end of the body is drawn out into a sort of stalk on which the buds are developed (Fig. 8). A pair of ovaries (Fig. 9, *ov.*) lie in the trunk-cavity, and there is a pair of oviducts (*ovd.*) lined by elongated, pigmented epithelium. The development, which is direct, without a free-swimming larval stage, takes place in passages in the investment. According to one account, the segmentation is complete, but unequal, and a gastrula is

Fig. 8.—**Cephalodiscus dodecalophus.** Entire zooid. (After McIntosh.)

formed by invagination: according to another, the segmentation is incomplete, and gastrula is formed by delamination. The larva bears a striking resemblance to that of Ectoproct Polyzoa.

Rhabdopleura (Fig. 10) occurs in colonies of zooids organically connected together, and enclosed in, though not in organic continuity with, a system of branching membranous tubes connected with a creeping stolon. The collar-region bears a pair of hollow arms, each carrying a double row of slender tentacles—the whole supported by a system of firm internal (cartilaginous?) rods. There are two collar-pores, each leading into a ciliated canal with an internal funnel, and a pair of proboscis-pores. The "notochord" and the nervous system resemble those of Cephalodiscus. The sexes are united.

Cephalodiscus, of which there are three sub-genera with fifteen species, has been found at various widely separated localities in the Southern Hemisphere (Straits of Magellan, Borneo, Celebes, the Antarctic) : species occur also off the coast of Japan and Korea. Some live in shallow water : none have been found at a greater depth than about 300 fathoms. Rhabdopleura has been found at moderate depths in Norway, Shetland, the North Atlantic, France, the Azores, Tristan d'Acunha, Celebes, and South Australia. It seems doubtful if more than one species occurs.

Affinities.—The inclusion of the Hemichorda in the phylum Chordata is an arrangement the propriety of which is not universally admitted, and is carried out here partly to obviate the inconvenience of erecting the class into a separate phylum. On the whole, however, there seems to be sufficient evidence

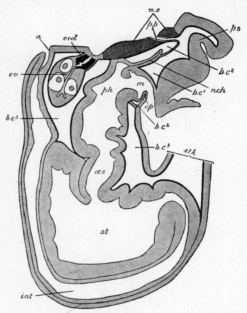

FIG. 9.—**Cephalodiscus.** Diagram of longitudinal section. *a.* anus ; *bc¹.* cœlome of proboscis ; *bc².* cœlome of collar ; *bc³.* cœlome of trunk ; *int.* intestine ; *m.* mouth ; *nch.* supposed notochord ; *n. s.* nerve-strand ; *op.* operculum ; *œs.* œsophagus ; *ov.* ovary ; *ovd.* oviduct ; *ph.* pharynx ; *p. p.* proboscis-pore ; *ps.* proboscis ; *st.* stomach ; *stk.* stalk. (After Harmer.)

for the view that, if not the existing representatives of ancestral Chordates, they are at least a greatly modified branch, taking its origin from the base of the chordate tree. The presence of the presumed rudimentary representative of a notochord and of the gill-slits seems to point in this direction. It should, however, be stated that, by some of those zoologists by whom the members of this group have been most closely studied, their chordate affinities are altogether denied. If the Hemichorda are primitive Chordates, the fact is of special interest that they show remarkable resemblances in some points to a phylum—that of the Echinodermata—which it has been the custom to place very low down in the invertebrate series. The tornaria larva of Balanoglossus

exhibits a striking likeness to an echinopædium (Vol. I., p. 422), and, though this likeness between the larvæ does not establish near connection, it suggests, at least, that an alliance exists. Between actinotrocha and tornaria there are some striking points of resemblance; and a pair of gastric diverticula in the former have sometimes been compared with the single notochord or œsophageal diverticulum of the Hemichorda.

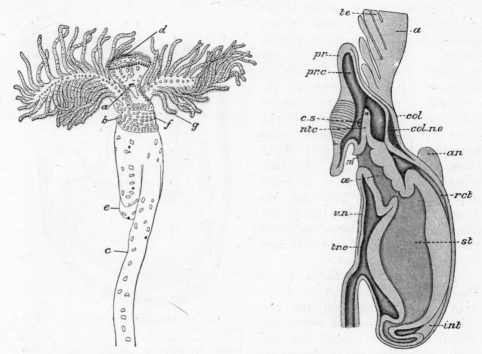

Fig. 10.—**Rhabdopleura.** *A*, Entire zooid. *a*, mouth; *b*, anus; *c*, stalk of zooid; *d*, proboscis; *e*, intestine; *f*, anterior region of trunk; *g*, one of the tentacles. (After Ray Lankester.) *B*, Diagram of the organisation: median longitudinal section, seen from the left. *a*. arm; *an*. anal prominence; *col*. collar; *col. ne*. collar-nerve; *c. s.* cardiac sac; *int*. intestine; *m*. mouth; *ntc*. "notochord"; *œ*. œsophagus; *pr*. proboscis; *pr. c*. proboscis-cœlome; *rct*. rectum; *st*. stomach; *te*. tentacles; *tr. c*. trunk-cœlome; *v. n*. ventral nerve. (After Schepotieff.)

SUB-PHYLUM II AND CLASS.—UROCHORDA.

The Class Urochorda or Tunicata comprises the Ascidians or Sea-Squirts, which are familiar objects on every rocky sea-margin, together with a number of allied forms, the Salpæ and others, all marine and for the most part pelagic. The Urochorda are specially interesting because of the remarkable series of changes which they undergo in the course of their life-history. Some present us with as marked an alternation of generations as exists among so many lower forms; and in most there is a *retrogressive metamorphosis* almost, if not quite, as striking as that which has been described among the parasitic Copepoda or the Cirripedia. In by far the greater number of cases it would be quite impossible by the study of the adult animal alone to guess at its relationship with the Chordata ; its affinities with that phylum are only detected when the life-history is followed out, the notochord and other higher structures becoming lost in the later stages of the metamorphosis. Multiplication by budding, so common in the lower groups of Invertebrata, but exceptional or absent in the higher, is of very general occurrence in the Urochorda.

1. EXAMPLE OF THE CLASS—THE ASCIDIAN OR SEA-SQUIRT.
(*Ascidia*.)

Sea-squirts are familiar objects on rocky sea-shores, where they occur, often in large associations, adhering firmly to the surface of the rock. When touched the Ascidian ejects with considerable force two fine jets of sea-water, which are found to proceed from two apertures on its upper end. The shape of the Ascidian, however, can only be profitably studied in the case of specimens that are completely immersed in the sea-water, specimens not so immersed always undergoing contraction. In an uncontracted specimen (Fig. 11), the general shape is that of a short cylinder with a broad base by which it is fixed to the rock. The free end presents a large rounded aperture, and some little distance from it on one side is a second of similar character ; the former aperture is termed the *oral*, the latter the *atrial*. A strong current of water will be noticed, by watching the movements of floating particles, to be flowing steadily in at the former and out of

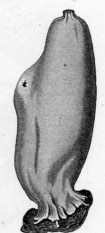

FIG. 11.—**Ascidia,** entire animal seen from the right side. (After Herdman.)

the latter. When the animal is removed from the water both apertures become narrowed, so as to be almost completely closed, by the contraction of sphincters of muscular fibres which surround them. At the same time the walls of the body contract, streams of water are forced through the apertures, and the bulk is considerably reduced.

Body-wall and Atrial Cavity.—The outer layer of the body-wall is composed of a tough translucent substance forming a thick *test* or *tunic* (Fig. 12, *test*). This proves when analysed to consist largely of a substance called *tunicine*, which is related to, though not identical with, *cellulose*, a characteristic plant product itself not found in the animal kingdom, except in the ' plant-like ' forms of Protozoa. The test of an Ascidian is frequently referred to as a cuticle, and it is a cuticle in the sense that it lies outside the ectoderm and is derived from that layer in the first instance. The cells, however, by the action of which its substance is added to in later stages, seem to be chiefly derived, not from the ectoderm, but from the underlying mesoderm, from which they migrate through the ectoderm to the outer surface. These formative cells of the test are to be found scattered through its substance. Running through it are also a number of branching tubes lined with cells, each terminal branch ending in a little bulb-like dilatation. The interior of each tube is divided into two channels by a longitudinal septum, which, however, does not completely divide the terminal bulb. Through these tubes (which are of the nature of looped blood-vessels) blood circulates, passing along one channel, through the terminal bulb, and back through the other channel.

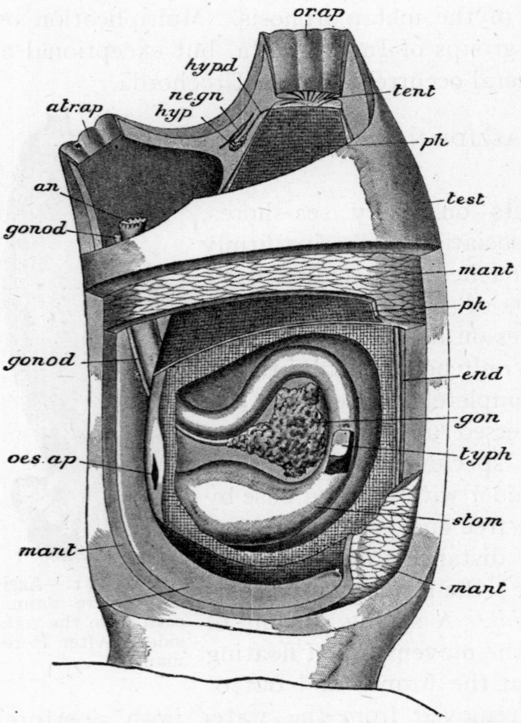

When the test is divided (Fig. 12), the soft wall of the body or *mantle* (*mant.*), as it is termed, comes into view; and the body is found to be freely suspended within the test, attached firmly to the latter only round the oral and atrial apertures. The mantle (body-wall) consists of the ectoderm with underlying layers of connective-tissue enclosing muscular fibres. It follows the general shape of the test, and at the two apertures is produced into short and wide tubular prolongations, which are known respectively as the *oral* and *atrial siphons* (Fig. 14, *or, siph., atr. siph.*). These are continuous at their margins with the margins of the apertures of the test, and round the openings are the strong sphincter muscles by which closure is effected. In

FIG. 12.—Dissection of **Ascidia** from the right side. The greater part of the test and mantle has been removed from that side so as to bring into view the relation of these layers and of the internal cavities and the course of the alimentary canal, etc. *an.* anus; *atr. ap.* atrial aperture; *end.* endostyle; *gon.* gonad; *gonod.* gonoduct; *hyp.* neural gland; *hyp. d.* duct of neural gland; *mant.* mantle; *ne. gn.* nerve-ganglion; *œs. ap.* aperture of œsophagus; *or. ap.* oral aperture; *ph.* pharynx; *stom.* stomach; *tent.* tentacles; *test,* test. (After Herdman.)

the rest of the mantle the muscular fibres are arranged in an irregular network, crossing one another in all directions, but for the most part either longitudinal or transverse. Within the body-wall is a cavity, the *atrial* or *peribranchial cavity* (*atr. cav.*), communicating with the exterior through the atrial aperture : this is not a cœlome, being formed to a great extent by involution from the outer surface.

Pharynx.—The oral aperture leads by a short and wide oral passage (*stomo-dæum*) into a chamber of large dimensions, the *pharynx* or *branchial chamber* (Fig. 725, *ph.*). This is a highly characteristic organ of the Urochorda. Its walls, which are thin and delicate, are pierced by a number of slit-like apertures, the *stigmata* (Fig. 14, *stigm.*), arranged in transverse rows. Through these the cavity of the pharynx communicates with the atrial or peribranchial cavity,[1] which completely surrounds it except along one side. The edges of the stigmata are beset with numerous strong cilia, the action of which is to drive currents of water from the pharynx into the atrial cavity. It is to the movements of these cilia lining the stigmata that are due the currents of water already mentioned as flowing into the oral and out of the atrial aperture, the ciliary action drawing a current in through the oral aperture, driving it through the stigmata into the atrial cavity, whence it reaches the exterior through the atrial aperture. The stigmata (Fig. 13) are all vertical in position; those of the same row are placed close together, separated only by narrow vertical bars; neighbouring rows are separated by somewhat thicker horizontal bars; in all of these bars run blood-vessels. Extending

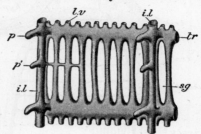

Fig. 13.—**Ascidia,** a single mesh of the branchial sac, seen from the inside. *i. l.* internal longitudinal bar; *l. v.* longitudinal vessel; *p. p'.* papillæ projecting inwards from the branchial bar; *sg.* stigma; *tr.* transverse vessel. (After Herdman.)

across the atrial cavity from the body-wall to the wall of the pharynx are a number of bands of vascular mesodermal tissue, the *connectives*.

It has been already mentioned that the atrial cavity does not completely surround the pharynx on one side. This is owing to the fact that on the side in question, which is ventral in position, the wall of the pharynx is united with the mantle along the middle line (Fig. 15). Along the line of adhesion the inner surface of the pharynx presents a thickening in the form of a pair of longitudinal folds separated by a groove: to this structure, consisting of the two ventral longitudinal folds with the groove between them, the term *endostyle* (*end.*) is applied. The cells covering the endostyle are large cells of two kinds—*ciliated cells* and *gland-cells*—the former beset at their free ends with cilia, the action of which is to drive floating particles that come within their influence outwards towards the oral aperture, the latter secreting and discharging a viscid mucous matter. Anteriorly the endostyle is continuous with a ciliated ridge which runs circularly round the anterior end of the pharynx. In front of this circular ridge, and running parallel with it, separated from it only by a

---

[1] A distinction is sometimes made between the lateral parts of this space (*peribranchial cavities*, right and left) and the median unpaired (dorsal) part (*atrial cavity*, or *cloaca*), in which the two peribranchial cavities coalesce, and which leads to the exterior through the atrial aperture.

narrow groove, is another ridge of similar character : these are termed the *peripharyngeal ridges* ; the groove between them is the *peripharyngeal groove.* Dorsally, *i.e.* opposite the endostyle, the posterior peripharyngeal ridge passes into a median, much more prominent, longitudinal ridge, the *dorsal lamina* (*dors. lam.*), which runs along the middle of the dorsal surface of the pharynx to the opening of the œso-phagus. In the living animal the lamina is capable of being bent to one side in such a way as to form a deep groove. The mucus secreted by the gland-cells of the endostyle forms viscid threads which entangle food-particles (microscopic organisms of various kinds) ; the cilia of its ciliated cells drive these laterally across the basket-work to the dorsal lamina, and the cilia on the cells of the latter drive them backwards to the opening of the œsophagus.

Some little distance in front of the anterior peri-pharyngeal ridge, at the inner or posterior end of the oral siphon, is a circlet of delicate *tentacles* (Fig. 12, *tent.*).

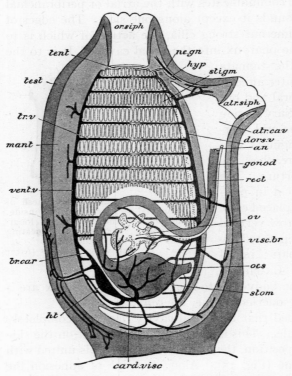

FIG. 14.—**Ascidia,** diagram of longitudinal section from the left side, the test and mantle removed. *an.* anus ; *atr. cav.* atrial cavity ; *atr. siph.* atrial siphon ; *br. car.* branchio-cardiac vessel ; *card. visc.* cardio-visceral vessel ; *dors. v.* dorsal vessel ; *gonod.* gonoduct ; *ht.* heart ; *hyp.* neural gland ; *mant.* mantle ; *ne. gn.* nerve-ganglion ; *œs.* œsophagus ; *or. siph.* oral siphon ; *ov.* ovary ; *rect.* rectum ; *stigm.* stigmata ; *stom.* stomach ; *tent.* tentacles ; *test,* test ; *tr. v.* transverse vessel ; *vent. v.* ventral vessel ; *visc. br.* viscero-branchial vessel. (From Herdman, after Perrier.)

Enteric Canal.—The œso-phagus (Figs. 12–14, *œs.*) leads from the pharynx (near the posterior end of the dorsal lamina) to the stomach (*stom.*), which, together with the in-testine, lies embedded in the mantle on the left-hand side.

The stomach is a large fusiform sac with tolerably thick walls. The intes-tine is bent round into a double loop and runs forwards to terminate in an anal aperture (*an.*) situated in the atrial cavity. Along its inner wall is a thickening—the *typhlosole.* There is no liver ; but the walls of the stomach are glandular, and a system of delicate tubules, which ramify over the wall of the intestine and are connected with a duct opening into the stomach, is supposed to be of the nature of a digestive gland.

The Ascidian has a well-developed **blood-system.** The heart (Fig. 14, *ht.*) is a simple muscular sac, situated near the stomach in the pericardium—a cavity entirely cut off from the surrounding spaces in which the blood is contained. Its mode of pulsation is very remarkable. The contractions are of a peristaltic character, and follow one another from one end of the heart to the other for a certain time; then follows a short pause, and when the contractions begin again they have the opposite direction. Thus the direction of the current of blood through the heart is reversed at regular intervals. There are no true vessels, the blood circulating through a system of channels or sinuses devoid of epithelial lining, and of spaces or lacunæ, forming a hæmocœle: in the description that follows, therefore, the word vessel is not used in its strict sense. At each end of the heart is given off a large " vessel." That given off ventrally, the *branchio-cardiac vessel* (*br. car.*), runs along the middle of the ventral side of the pharynx below (externally to) the endostyle and gives off a number of branches which extend along the bars between the rows of stig-

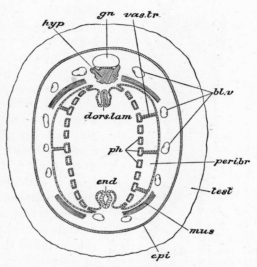

FIG. 15.—**Ascidia,** tranverse section. *bl. v.* blood-vessels; *dors. lam.* dorsal lamina; *epi.* epidermis; *end.* endostyle; *gn.* ganglion; *hyp.* neural gland; *mus.* muscular layer of wall of body; *peribr.* peribranchial cavity; *ph.* pharynx; *test,* test; *vas. tr.* vascular trabeculæ. (After Julin.)

mata, and give off smaller branches passing between the stigmata of each row. The vessel given off from the dorsal end of the heart—the *cardio-visceral* (*card. visc.*)—breaks up into branches which ramify over the surface of the alimentary canal and other organs. This system of visceral vessels or lacunæ opens into a large sinus, the *viscero-branchial* vessel, which runs along the middle of the dorsal wall of the pharynx externally to the dorsal lamina, and communicates with the dorsal ends of the series of transverse branchial vessels. In addition to these principal vessels there are numerous lacunæ extending everywhere throughout the body, and a number of branches, given off both from the branchio-cardiac and cardio-visceral vessels, ramify, as already stated, in the substance of the test. The direction of the circulation through the main vessels differs according to the direction of the heart's contractions.

When the heart contracts in a dorso-ventral direction, the blood flows through the branchio-cardiac trunk to the ventral wall of the pharynx, and through the transverse vessels, after undergoing oxygenation in the finer branches between the stigmata, reaches the viscero-branchial vessel, by which it is carried to the system of visceral lacunæ, and from these back to the heart by the cardio-visceral vessel. When the contractions take the opposite direction, the course of this main current of the blood is reversed.

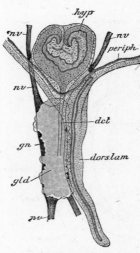

FIG. 16.—**Ascidia.** Dorsal tubercle, nerve-ganglion, and associated parts as seen from below. *dct.* duct of neural gland; *dors. lam.* dorsal lamina; *gld.* neural gland; *gn.* ganglion; *hyp.* dorsal tubercle; *nv., nv.* nerves; *periph.* peripharyngeal band. (After Julin.)

The **nervous system** is of an extremely simple character. There is a single nerve-ganglion (Figs. 12 and 14, *ne. gn.*, 16, *gn.*, and 17, *n. g.*) which lies between the oral and atrial apertures, embedded in the mantle. This is elongated in the dorso-ventral direction, and gives off at each end nerves which pass to the various parts of the body.

Lying on the ventral side of the nerve-ganglion is a body—the **neural gland** (Figs. 12, 14, *hyp.*; Fig. 16, *gld.*, and Fig. 17, *n. gl.*)—which has sometimes been correlated with the *hypophysis* of the Craniata. A duct (Fig. 16, *dct.*, and Fig. 17, *gl. d.*) runs forward from it and opens into the cavity of the pharynx; the termination of the duct is dilated to form the *ciliated funnel*, and this is folded on itself to form a prominence, the *dorsal tubercle*, which projects into the cavity of the pharynx. The dorsal tubercle may be a sensory organ: the neural gland may have to do with excretion.

The **excretory system** seems to be mainly represented by a single mass of clear vesicles, without a duct, lying in the second loop of the intestine. In the interior of these are found concretions containing uric acid.

Reproductive System.—The sexes are united. The ovary and the testis are situated close together on the left-hand side of the body in the intestinal loop. Continuous with the gonad is a duct—oviduct or sperm-duct, as the case may be—which opens into the atrial cavity close to the anus.

The **development** of the Ascidian is described below (p. 30).

2. DISTINCTIVE CHARACTERS AND CLASSIFICATION.

The Urochorda are Chordata in which the notochord is confined to the tail region, and, in all but the Larvacea, is found only in the larva. The adults, which for the most part are retrogressively metamorphosed in other respects besides the abortion of the notochord, are sometimes sessile, sometimes free and pelagic; they frequently form colonies (fixed or free) by a process of budding, and in some instances exhibit a well-marked alternation of generations. The body is enclosed in a test consisting largely of cellulose. The proximal part of the enteric canal (pharynx) is enlarged to form a spacious sac with perforated walls, acting as an organ of respiration. There is a simple heart with a system of sinuses, all devoid of epithelial lining. The cœlome is not

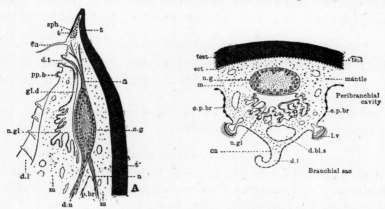

FIG. 17.—Anterio-dorsal part of **Ascidia,** showing the relations of the layers of the body and of the nervous system, *A*, in sagittal section; *B*, in transverse section. *d. bl. s.* dorsal bloodsinus; *d. l.* dorsal lamina; *d. n.* dorsal nerve; *d. t.* dorsal tubercle; *ect.* ectoderm; *en.* endoderm; *e. p. br.* epithelium of peribranchial cavity; *gl. d.* duct of neural gland; *l. v.* points to the ciliated epithelium covering a longitudinal vessel of branchial sac (pharynx); *m.* mantle; *n.* nerve; *n. g.* ganglion; *n. gl.* neural gland; *p. br.* peribranchial cavity; *pp. b.* periphargyngeal bands; *sph.* oral sphincter; *t., t'.* test; *tn.* tentacle. (After Herdman.)

recognisable. The sexes are united. The larva is always free-swimming, and is nearly always provided with a caudal appendage.

Three orders of Urochorda are recognised :—

ORDER I.—LARVACEA.

Free-swimming pelagic Tunicata with a caudal appendage supported by a skeletal axis or notochord. The test is represented by a relatively large temporary envelope, the " house," formed with great rapidity as a secretion from the surface of the ectoderm and frequently thrown off and renewed. The pharynx has only two stigmata, and these lead directly to the exterior. There is no atrial or peribranchial cavity. The principal nerve-ganglion gives off a nerve-cord with ganglionic enlargements running to the tail, along the dorsal aspect of which it passes to the extremity. There is no reproduction by budding, and development takes place without metamorphosis.

This order contains only a single family, the *Appendiculariidæ,* with about nine genera, including *Appendicularia* and *Oikopleura.*

Order 2.—Thaliacea.

Free-swimming Tunicata, sometimes simple, sometimes colonial, never provided with a caudal appendage in the adult condition. The test is a permanent structure. The muscular fibres of the body-wall are arranged in complete or interrupted ring-like bands, or diffusely. The pharynx has either two large or many small stigmata leading into an atrial cavity which communicates with the exterior by the atrial aperture. There is usually an alternation of generations; there may or may not be a tailed larval stage.

Sub-Order a.—Cyclomyaria.

Thaliacea with a cask-shaped body, having the oral and atrial apertures at opposite ends, and surrounded by a series of complete rings of muscular fibres. There is a tailed larval stage.

This sub-order contains only one family, the *Doliolidæ*, with the three genera, *Doliolum*, *Anchinia*, and *Dolchinia*.

Sub-Order b.—Hemimyaria.

Thaliacea with a more or less fusiform body, with sub-terminal oral and atrial apertures. The muscular fibres are arranged in bands which do not form complete rings. There is no tailed larval stage.

This sub-order is probably best looked upon as comprising only one family, the *Salpidæ*.

Order 3.—Ascidiacea.

Mostly fixed Tunicata, either simple or forming colonies by a process of budding, and, in the adult condition, never provided with a tail. The test is a permanent structure, usually of considerable thickness. The muscular fibres of the mantle (body-wall) are not arranged in annular bands. The pharynx is large, and its walls are perforated by numerous stigmata leading into a surrounding atrium or peribranchial cavity, which communicates with the exterior by an atrial aperture. Most undergo a metamorphosis, the larva being provided with a caudal appendage, supported by a notochord similar to that of the Larvacea.

Sub-Order a.—Ascidiæ simplices.[1]

Ascidians in which, when colonies are formed, the zooids are not embedded in a common gelatinous mass, but possess distinct tests of their own. They are nearly always permanently fixed and never free-swimming.

Including all the larger Ascidians or Sea-Squirts.

---

[1] This classification into " simple " and " compound " Ascidians is one of convenience. The more modern classification is very complicated.

Sub-Order b.—Ascidiæ compositæ.

Fixed Ascidians which form colonies of zooids, embedded in a common gelatinous material without separate tests.

This order includes *Botryllus*, *Amaræcium*, *Diazona*, and a number of other genera.

ORDER 4.—LUCIDA.

Pelagic Tunicata which reproduce by budding, so as to give rise to hollow cylindrical colonies, open at one or both ends, having the zooids embedded in the gelatinous wall in such a manner that the oral apertures open on the outer, the atrial on the inner surface of the cylinder. There is no tailed larval stage.

This order comprises only one family, the *Pyrosomidæ*, with one genus, *Pyrosoma*.

Systematic Position of the Example.

The genus *Ascidia*, of which there are very many species, is a member of the family *Ascidiidæ* of the *Ascidiæ simplices*. The Ascidiidæ differ from the other families of simple Ascidians by the union of the following characters: The body is usually sessile, rarely elevated on a peduncle. The oral aperture is usually 8-lobed and the atrial 6-lobed. The test is always of gelatinous or cartilaginous consistency. The wall of the pharynx is not folded; the tentacles are simple and filiform. The gonads are placed close to the intestine.

The genus Ascidia is characterised by having the oral and atrial apertures not close together, by the dorsal lamina being a continuous undivided fold, and by the ganglion and neural gland being situated at a little distance from the dorsal tubercle.

3. GENERAL ORGANISATION.

General Features.—The Larvacea are minute transparent animals, in shape not unlike tadpoles, with a rounded body and a long tail-like appendage attached to the ventral side. At the extremity of the body most remote from the tail is the aperture of the mouth. This leads into a tolerably wide pharynx (Fig. 19, *ph.*), in the ventral wall of which (except in *Kowalevskia*) is an endostyle similar to that of the simple Ascidian, but comparatively short. Round the pharynx there run obliquely two bands covered with strong cilia—the *peripharyngeal bands*, which join a median dorsal ciliated band. On the ventral side of the pharynx there are two ciliated openings—the *stigmata* (*stig.*), which communicate with the exterior by short passages—the *atrial canals*, situated on either side behind the anus. The axis of the tail is occupied by a cylindrical rod—the *notochord* or *urochord* (*noto.*).

A remarkable peculiarity of the Larvacea is the power which they possess of secreting from the surface, by the agency of certain specially modified

epidermal cells, a transparent envelope which is frequently discarded and quickly renewed. The chief object of this structure seems to be the capture of the very minute plankton-organisms on which the Larvacea feed. In *Oikopleura* (Fig. 18) the "house" is a comparatively large structure within which the animal is enclosed : undulatory movements of the tail cause a current of water to flow in through a pair of incurrent apertures and out through a single excurrent aperture ; the former are closed by lattice-work of fine threads, preventing the passage of any but the smallest organisms. In the interior is an elaborate apparatus for filtering out the minute organisms from the water as it passes through. In *Appendicularia* and *Kowalevskia* the house also encloses the animal : in *Fritillaria* it does not do so.

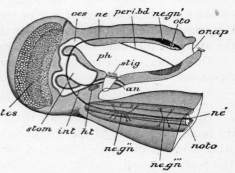

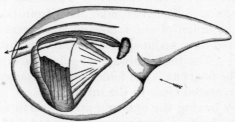

FIG. 18.—**Oikopleura** in "house." The arrows show the course of the current. (From Herdman, after Fol.)

FIG. 19.—Diagram of **Appendicularia** from the right side. *an.* anus ; *ht.* heart ; *int.* intestine ; *ne.* nerve ; *ne'.* caudal portion of nerve ; *ne. gn'.* principal nerve-ganglion ; *ne. gn.'*, *ne. gn.'''* first two ganglia of nerve of tail ; *noto.* notochord ; *œs.* œsophagus ; *or. ap.* oral aperture ; *oto.* otocyst (statocyst) ; *peri. bd.* peripharyngeal band ; *ph.* pharynx ; *tes.* testis ; *stig.* one of the stigmata ; *stom.* stomach. (After Herdman.)

Among the simple Ascidians there is a considerable degree of uniformity of structure, and little need be added here to the account given of the example. The shape varies a good deal : it is sometimes cylindrical, sometimes globular, sometimes compressed ; usually sessile and attached by a broad base, often with root-like processes, but in other cases (*e.g Boltenia*) elevated on a longer or shorter stalk. Most are solitary ; but some (the so-called *social Ascidians*) multiply by budding, stolons being given off on which new zooids are developed, so that associations or colonies are formed ; but the connection between the zooids is not close, and their tests remain distinct and separate. The test varies considerably in consistency, being sometimes almost gelatinous, transparent or translucent, sometimes tough and leathery, occasionally hardened by encrusting sand-grains or fragments of shells, or by spicules of carbonate of lime. Calcareous spicules may be developed in the substance of the mantle. The apertures always have the same position and relations, varying only in their relative prominence. The pharynx varies in its size as compared with the rest of the internal organs, in the position which it occupies with regard to the various parts of the alimentary canal, and in the number and arrangement of the stigmata. The tentacles are sometimes simple, sometimes compound; and the dorsal lamina may or may not be divided up into a system of lobes or *languets* (Fig. 21, *lang.*).

In the composite Ascidians the zooids are embedded in a common gelatinous mass formed of their united tests. The gelatinous colony thus formed is sometimes flat and encrusting, sometimes branched or lobed, sometimes elevated on a longer or shorter stalk. In certain forms the gelatinous substance is hardened by the inclusion in it of numerous sand-grains. The arrangement of the zooid presents great differences. Sometimes they occur irregularly,

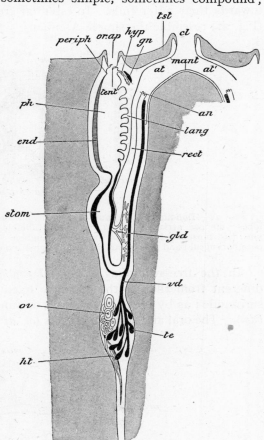

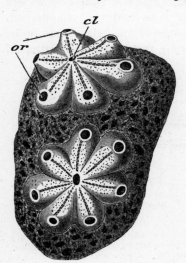

FIG. 20.—**Botryllus viola-ceus.** *or.* oral apertures; *cl.* opening of common cloacal chamber. (After Milne-Edwards.)

FIG. 21.—Diagram of a zooid of a colony of **Composite Ascidians,** in which the zooids are in pairs, as seen in a vertical section of the colony. *an.* anus; *at.* atrium; *at'.* atrium of adjoining zooid; *cl.* cloaca common to the two zooids; *end.* endostyle; *gld.* digestive gland; *gn.* nerve-ganglion; *ht.* heart; *hyp.* neural gland; *lang.* languets; *mant.* mantle; *or. ap.* oral aperture; *ov.* ovary; *periph.* peripharyngeal band; *ph.* pharynx; *rect.* rectum; *stom.* stomach; *te.* testis; *tent.* tentacles; *tst.* test, or common gelatinous mass; *v. d.* vas deferens. (After Herdman.)

dotted over the entire surface without exhibiting any definite arrangement; sometimes they are arranged in rows or regular groups; in *Botryllus* (Fig. 20) they form star-shaped, radiating sets around a common cloacal chamber into which the atrial apertures of the zooids lead, while the oral apertures are towards their outer ends. In essential structure the zooids of such colonies (Fig. 21) resemble the simple Ascidians.

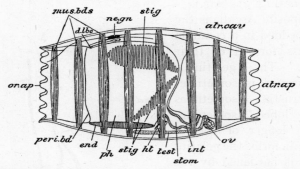

FIG. 22.—**Doliolum.** Diagram of the sexual form. *atr. ap.* atrial aperture surrounded by lobes; *atr. cav.* atrial cavity; *d. tbc.* dorsal tubercle; *end.* endostyle; *ht.* heart; *int.* intestine; *mus. bds.* muscular bands; *ne. gn.* nerve-ganglion; *or. ap.* oral aperture; *ov.* ovary; *peri. bd.* peripharyngeal band; *ph.* pharynx; *stig.* stigma; *stom.* stomach; *test.* testis. (After Herdman.)

In the free-swimming pelagic *Doliolum* (Fig. 22) the shape is widely different from that of the ordinary fixed forms. The body is cask-shaped, surrounded as by hoops, by a series of annular bands of muscular fibres (*mus. bds.*). The oral and atrial apertures (*or. ap., atr. ap.*), instead of being situated

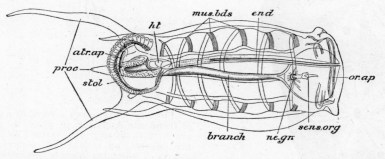

FIG. 23.—**Salpa democratica,** asexual form, ventral view. *atr. ap.* atrial aperture; *branch.* dorsal lamina; *end.* endostyle; *ht.* heart; *mus. bds.* muscular bands; *ne. gn.* nerve-ganglion; *or. ap.* oral aperture; *proc.* processes at the posterior end; *sens. org.* sensory organ (ciliated funnel and languet); *stol.* stolon. (After Vogt and Jung.)

near together at the same end of the body, are placed at opposite extremities, and the relations of the various organs have undergone a corresponding modification. The test is thin and transparent. Surrounding each opening is a series of lobes—the *oral* and *atrial lobes*—in which there are sense-organs; and the first and last of the muscular hoops serve as sphincters for the two orifices.

The oral aperture leads into a wide pharyngeal sac (*ph*) occupying at least the anterior half of the body ; the posterior wall of the pharynx alone is usually perforated by stigmata (*stig.*). An endostyle (*end.*) is present, and a peripharyngeal band ; but there is no dorsal lamina. Doliolum moves through the water by the contractions of the muscular bands, which have the effect of driving the water backwards out of the branchial sac.

Salpa (Figs. 23–24) is nearly allied to Doliolum in its external features and internal structure. It has a fusiform body, usually somewhat compressed laterally, and with the oral and atrial apertures terminal ; but the muscular bands do not form complete hoops. The pharyngeal and atrial

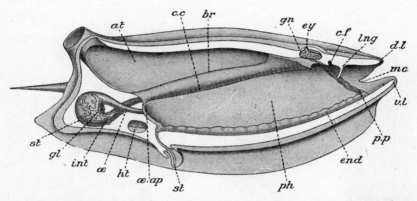

FIG. 24.—**Salpa.** Lateral view of a section—which is sagittal (longitudinal, vertical, and median) in the oral two-thirds, and oblique in the atrial third. *at.* atrial cavity ; *br.* branchia ; *c.c.* ciliated crests on the edge of the branchia ; *c. f.* ciliated funnel ; *d. l.* dorsal lip ; *end.* endostyle ; *ey.* eye ; *gl.* digestive gland ; *gn.* ganglion ; *ht.* heart ; *int.* intestine ; *lng.* languet ; *mo.* mouth ; *œ.* œsophagus ; *œ. ap.* œsophageal aperture ; *ph.* pharynx ; *pp.* peripharyngeal band ; *st.* (right) stolon ; *st.* (left) stomach ; *v. l.* ventral lip. (After Delage and Hérouard.)

cavities take up the greater part of the space in the interior of the body, where they form an almost continuous cavity, being separated from one another only by an obliquely running vascular band, which represents the dorsal lamina of the fixed Ascidians and is frequently termed the *branchia*.

Octacnemus, sometimes regarded as allied to Salpa appears to be fixed, is colonial in one species, and has the oral and atrial apertures towards one end of the body, which is somewhat discoid, with its margin produced into eight tapering processes. It has no eye. In all probability Octacnemus is more nearly related to the social Ascidians (p. 23) than to Salpa.

Pyrosoma (Fig. 25) is a colonial Tunicate, the colony assuming the form of a cylinder, the internal cavity of which, closed at one end, open at the other, serves as the common cloaca for all the zooids. The oral apertures (Fig. 26, *or. ap.*) of the zooids are situated on the outer surface of the cylinder

on a series of papillæ.   The colonies of Pyrosoma, which may be from two or
three inches to four feet in length, are pelagic, and are brilliantly phosphorescent.

The **enteric canal** in Appendicularia (Fig. 19) consists, in addition to the
pharynx, of a narrow œsophagus, a bilobed stomach, and a straight intestine
(*int.*) which opens directly by an oral aperture (*an.*) situated on the ventral
side.   The alimentary canal of the simple Ascidians has already been described,
and there are few differences of consequence in the various families, except
that in some cases there is a well-developed digestive gland or " liver " ; in
the composite forms the arrangement of the parts is the same in all essential

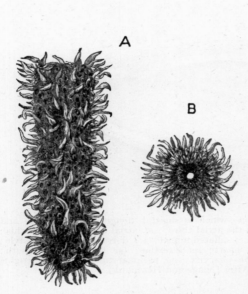

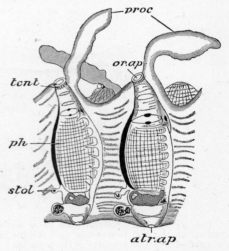

Fig. 25.—Colony of **Pyrosoma**.   *A*, side view,
B, end view.   (After Herdman.)

Fig. 26.—Part of a section through a
Pyrosoma colony. *atr. ap.* atrial aperture ;
or. ap. oral aperture ; *proc.* processes of test
on outer surface of colony ; *ph.* pharynx ;
stol. stolon on which are developed buds
giving rise to new zooids ; *tent.* tentacles.
(After Herdman.)

respects as in the simple.   In the Salpæ and in Doliolum and Octacnemus the
alimentary canal forms a relatively small dark mass—the so-called *nucleus*—
towards the posterior end of the body ; it consists of œsophagus, stomach,
and intestine, the anal aperture being situated in the peribranchial or atrial
part of the internal cavity.

The **heart** in all has the simple structure already described in the simple
Ascidian.   In one of the genera of Larvacea (*Kowalevskia*) it is absent.

The **nervous system** in Appendicularia consists of a *cerebral ganglion* (Fig.
19, *ne. gn'.*) on the dorsal side of the mouth, of a dorsal nerve which passes
from this to a *caudal ganglion* (*ne. gn".*) at the root of the tail, and of a caudal
nerve (*ne'.*) which extends from this to the extremity of the tail, presenting at

intervals slight enlargements from which nerves are given off. An otocyst or statocyst (*oto.*) is placed in close relation to the cerebral ganglion, and close to it also is a ciliated funnel; but there is no neural gland opening into the pharynx. In one species of Oikopleura a simple light-perceiving organ, without pigment, is incorporated with the statocyst. In the simple Ascidians, as we have seen, there is a single flattened ganglion, representing the cerebral ganglion of Appendicularia, situated between the oral and atrial apertures; and the same holds good of the composite forms. Many of the simple Ascidians have pigment-spots, probably of a sensory character, around the oral and atrial apertures. The dorsal tubercle is always present, but varies in shape in accordance with variations in the form of the ciliated funnel, which opens on it usually in conjunction with the duct of the neural gland, of which it forms the terminal

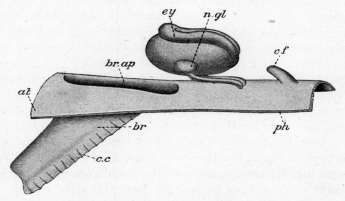

FIG. 27.—**Salpa.** Diagrammatic lateral view of the ganglion and neighbouring parts. *at.* wall of atrial cavity; *br.* branchia; *br. ap.* aperture of branchia; *c. c.* ciliated crests of branchia; *c. f.* ciliated funnel; *ey.* eye; *n. gl.* gland (paired) that may represent neural gland; *ph.* wall of pharynx. (After Delage and Hérouard.)

part. The opening may be divided into several smaller apertures by fusion of its lips: rarely the duct gives off branches with independent openings. The tubercle with the ciliated funnel is supplied with nerve-fibres from the ganglion, and is probably a sensory organ of some kind. The neural gland is usually below the ganglion, but may be situated above it or on one side. Sometimes it coalesces with it.

In Salpa and Doliolum there is also a single ganglion (Figs. 22, 23, 24, and 27) situated dorsally, giving off nerves to the various parts of the body. Salpa has a single tentacle, the so-called languet (Fig. 24, *lng.*), absent in Doliolum. In the asexual (solitary) form of Salpa there is a median horseshoe-shaped eye (Figs. 24, 27), and sometimes smaller accessory eyes. In Doliolum an eye is not developed, but there is a pair of otocysts or statocysts. A neural gland and duct with ciliated funnel are present in Doliolum; but in

Salpa, though there are a pair of glands which occupy a position similar to that occupied by the neural gland (Fig. 27, *n. gl.*), their correspondence with the latter is not established, and their ducts have no connection with the ciliated funnel.

In the simple Ascidian we have seen that the **renal organ** consists of a number of large clear vesicles situated in the loop of the intestine and devoid of duct. In some forms the terminal portion of the sperm-duct has glandular walls in which concretions of uric acid have been found. The neural gland is by some zoologists looked upon as having an excretory function, but there is no positive evidence in favour of this view, and no definite conclusion has yet been reached as to the function which it performs.

Reproductive System.—The Urochorda are hermaphrodite. Ovary and testis are in all cases simple organs placed in close relation with one another. In Appendicularia (Fig. 19) they are situated in the aboral region of the body. In the simple Ascidians they may be either single or double, and their ducts, sometimes very short, sometimes more elongated, open close together into the atrial cavity. In Pyrosoma there are no gonoducts, the ovary—which contains only a single ovum—and the testis being lodged in a diverticulum of the peribranchial cavity. In Salpa also the ovary contains usually only a single ovum : ovary and testis lie in close relation to the alimentary canal in the " nucleus," and their short ducts open into the peribranchial cavity. In Doliolum the elongated testis and oval ovary have a similar position to that which they occupy in Salpa, but the ovary consists of a number of ova.

Development and Metamorphosis.—In the Ascidiacea impregnation usually takes place after the ova have passed out from the atrial cavity. But in a few simple, and most, if not all, compound forms impregnation takes place in the atrium or in a special outgrowth of the latter serving as a brood-sac, and the ovum remains there until the tailed larval stage is attained. In certain composite forms there is a coalescence of the investing layers of the ovum with the wall of the atrium, forming a structure analogous to the *placenta* of Mammals and designated by that term. Self-impregnation is usually rendered impossible by ova and sperms becoming mature at different times ; but sometimes both ripen simultaneously, and self-impregnation is then possible.

A somewhat complicated series of membranes invests the ovum. The immature ovarian ovum is enclosed in a layer of flat cells—the primitive *follicle-cells*—derived from indifferent cells of the ovary. On the surface of this is developed a structureless basal membrane. The follicle-cells increase by division and soon form a sphere of cubical cells. Certain of the cells migrate into the interior of the sphere so as to form a layer on the surface of the ovum. Others penetrate into the latter so as to lie in the superficial strata of the yolk. The layer of cells on the surface of the ovum are termed the *test-cells* (Fig. 28, *e*) : they afterwards develop on the outer surface a thin structureless layer, the *chorion* (*d*), and internal to them is formed a gelatinous layer (*x*) through which the test-cells in a degenerated condition become scattered. Meantime, external to the follicle-cells, between them and the basal membrane, has appeared a layer of flattened epithelial cells ; this, with the basal membrane, is lost before the egg is discharged.   In all the simple Ascidians, with the exception of the few in which development takes place internally, the protoplasm of the follicle-cells (Fig. 28, *c*) is greatly vacuolated, so as to appear frothy, and the cells become greatly enlarged, projecting like papillæ on the surface and buoying up the developing ovum.

Segmentation is complete and approximately equal, but in the eight-cell stage four of the cells are smaller and four larger : the smaller, situated on the future dorsal side, are the beginning of the endoderm ; the four larger form the greater part, if not the whole, of the ectoderm.   In the following stages the ectoderm cells multiply more rapidly than the endoderm, so that they soon become the smaller.   In the sixteen-celled stage the embryo (Fig. 29, *A*) has the form of a flattened blastula (*placula*) with ectoderm on one side and endoderm on the other, and with a small segmentation-cavity. The transition to the gastrula stage is in most Ascidians effected by a process intermediate in character between embolic and epibolic invagination ; in some the invagination is of a distinctly epibolic character.   In the former case the ectoderm cells continue to increase more rapidly than the endoderm, the whole

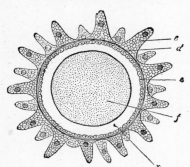

FIG. 28.—**Ascidian** (**Ciona**).   Mature egg from the oviduct after the basal membrane and layer of flattened cells have been thrown off. *c.* follicle-cells ;   *d*, chorion ;   *e*, test-cells ;   *f*, ovum ;   *x*, gelatinous layer, (From Korschelt and Heider, after Kupffer.)

embryo becomes curved, with the concavity on the endodermal side, and the ectoderm extends over the endoderm, the two layers coming to lie in close contact and the segmentation-cavity thus becoming obliterated.   The concavity deepens until the embryo assumes the form of a saucer-shaped gastrula with an archenteron and a blastopore which is at first a very wide aperture extending along the whole of the future dorsal side.   The blastopore gradually becomes constricted (Fig. 29, *B*)—the closure taking place from before backwards, and the opening eventually being reduced to a small pore at the posterior end of the dorsal surface.

The embryo elongates in the direction of the future long axis.   The dorsal surface becomes recognisable by being flatter, while the ventral remains convex.   The ectoderm cells bordering the blastopore are distinguished from the rest by their more cubical shape ; these cells, which form the earliest rudiment of the nervous system, become arranged, as the blastopore undergoes con-

traction, in the form of a plate—the *medullary plate*—on the dorsal surface.
On the surface of this plate appears a groove—the *medullary groove*—bounded
by right and left *medullary folds*, which pass into one another behind the
blastopore.

The medullary folds grow upwards and inwards over the medullary groove,
and unite together (*D*), the union beginning behind and progressing forwards
in such a way as to form a canal, the *neurocœle*, in the hinder portion of which

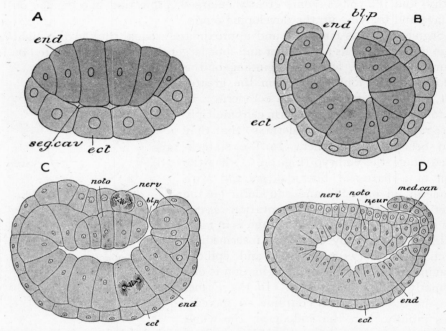

FIG. 29.—Early stages in the development of **Clavellina.** *A,* flattened blastula; *B,* early
gastrula; *C,* approximately median optical section of more advanced gastrula in which the
blastopore has become greatly reduced and in which the first rudiment of the notochord is discernible; *D,* similar view of a later larva in which the medullary canal has begun to be closed in
posteriorly. *bl. p.* blastopore; *ect.* ectoderm; *end.* endoderm; *med. can.* medullary canal; *nerv.*
cells destined to give rise to the nerve-cord; *neur.* neuropore; *noto.* notochord; *seg. cav.* segmentation cavity. (*A* and *B* from Korschelt and Heider, after Seeliger; *C* and *D* after Van Beneden
and Julin.)

is the opening of the blastopore. In this process of closing-in of the medullary
groove the fold which passes round behind the blastopore takes an important
part, growing forwards over the posterior portion of the canal. The blastopore, thus enclosed in the medullary canal, persists for a time as a small opening
—the *neurenteric canal*—by which the neurocœle and enteric cavity are placed
in communication. At the anterior end of the medullary canal, owing to its
incomplete closure in this region, there remains for a time an opening—the
neuropore (Fig. 30, *neur.*)—leading to the exterior.

A *notochord* (Figs. 29, *C*, *D*, 30 and 31, *noto.*) is formed from certain of the cells of the wall of the archenteron along the middle line of the dorsal side. These are arranged to form an elongated cord of cells which becomes com-

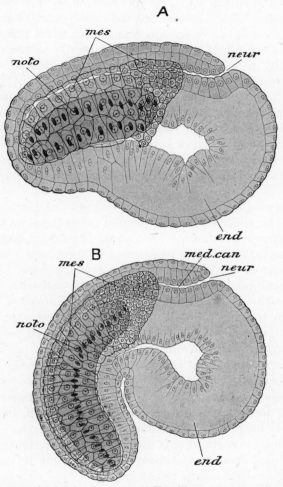

FIG. 30.—Later stages in the development of **Clavellina.** *A*, approximately median optical section of a larva in which the medullary canal (neurocœle) has become enclosed throughout, communicating with the exterior only by the neuropore at the anterior end and with the archenteron by the neurenteric canal; *B*, larva with a distinct rudiment of the tail and well-formed mesoderm-layer and notochord. Letters as in preceding figure; in addition, *mes.* mesoderm. (After Van Beneden and Julin.)

pletely constricted off from the endoderm of the wall of the archenteron, and comes to lie between the latter and the medullary groove. Laterally certain cells of the endoderm divide to give rise to a pair of longitudinal strands of

cells—the rudiments of the mesoderm (Fig. 30, *mes.*).   During this process of mesoderm-formation, there are no diverticula developed from the archenteron.

The embryo (Fig. 30, *B*) now becomes pear-shaped, the narrow part being the rudiment of the future tail.   As this narrow portion elongates, the part of the enteric cavity which it contains soon disappears, coming to be represented only by a strand of endoderm cells, which gives rise in the middle to the extension backwards of the notochord, laterally to the mesoderm of the tail, and ventrally to a cord of endoderm cells continuous with the wall of the enteric cavity in front.

The caudal region increases in length rapidly, and the anterior or trunk region, at first round, becomes oval.   At its anterior end there appear three processes of the ectoderm, the rudiments of the *adhesive papillæ* (Fig. 31, *adh.*), organs by which the larva subsequently becomes fixed.   The ectoderm cells at an early stage secrete the rudiments of the cellulose test ; in the caudal region this forms longitudinal dorsal and ventral flaps having the function of unpaired fins.

The medullary canal becomes enlarged at its anterior end.   A vesicular outgrowth from this enlarged anterior portion forms the *sense-vesicle* (*sens. ves.*). The posterior narrow part forms the caudal portion of the central nervous system (spinal cord).   Masses of pigment in relation to the sense-vesicle early form the rudiment of the two larval sense-organs, otocyst (or statocyst) and eye.   The part behind this presents a thickened wall with a narrow lumen. This is known as the *ganglion of the trunk*.   The rudiment of the neural gland early appears on the ventral wall of a ciliated diverticulum (*cil. gr.*) of the anterior end of the archenteron (future pharynx), which subsequently unites with an outgrowth from the medullary canal.

The embryonic alimentary canal consists of two regions, a wide region situated altogether in front of the notochord, and a narrower portion situated behind in the region of the notochord.   The wider anterior part gives rise to the pharynx, the posterior part to the œsophagus, stomach, and intestine.   The mouth-opening is formed shortly before the escape of the embryo from the egg ; an ectodermal invagination is formed at the anterior end, and an endodermal diverticulum from the archenteron grows out to meet it ; the two coalesce, and the oral passage is thus formed.

The rudiments of the heart and pericardial cavity first appear as a hollow outgrowth from the archenteron : this subsequently becomes constricted off and involuted to form a double-walled sac, the inner layer of which forms the wall of the heart, while the outer gives rise to the wall of the pericardium.

The first beginnings of the atrial cavity appear as a pair of invaginations of the ectoderm which grow inwards and form a pair of pouches, each opening on the exterior by an aperture.   There is a difference of opinion as to some points in the history of these atrial pouches, and it remains uncertain to what extent the ectoderm and endoderm respectively share in the formation of the atrial cavity. Eventually spaces, into the formation of which the two ecto-dermal diverticula at least largely enter, grow round the pharynx and give rise to the atrial cavity; and perforations, the stigmata, primarily two in number, place the cavity of the pharynx in communication with the sur-rounding space. The two openings of the atrial pouches subsequently coalesce to form one—the permanent atrial aperture.

It will be useful now, at the cost of a little repetition, to summarise the various characteristics of the larval Ascidian at the stage when it escapes from the egg and becomes free-swimming (Fig. 31). In general shape it bears some resemblance to a minute tadpole, consisting of an oval trunk and a long laterally-compressed tail. The tail is fringed with a caudal fin, which is merely a delicate outgrowth of the thin test covering the whole of the surface; run-ning through the delicate fringe is a series of striæ, presenting somewhat the

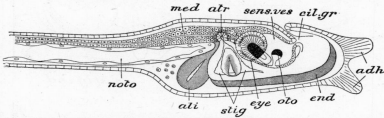

FIG. 31.—Free-swimming larva of **Ascidia mammillata,** lateral view. *adh.* adhesive papillæ; *ali.* alimentary canal; *atr.* atrial aperture; *cil. gr.* ciliated diverticulum, becoming ciliated funnel; *end.* endostyle; *eye,* eye; *med.* nerve-cord (ganglion of trunk); *noto.* notochord; *oto.* otocyst; *sens. ves.* sense-vesicle; *stig.* earliest stigmata. (From Korschelt and Heider, after Kowalewsky.)

appearance of the fin-rays of a Fish's fin. In the axis of the tail is the noto-chord (*noto.*), which at this stage consists of a cylindrical cord of gelatinous substance enclosed in a layer of cells. Parallel with this runs, on the dorsal side, the narrow caudal portion of the nerve-cord, and at the sides are bands of muscular fibres. In the trunk the nerve-cord is dilated to form the ganglion of the trunk, and, further forwards, expands into the sense-vesicle (*sens. ves.*) with the otocyst or statocyst (*oto.*) and eye (*eye*). A prolongation of it unites, as already stated, with the ciliated diverticulum from the anterior part of the pharynx. From the walls of this at a later stage are developed, on the dorsal side, the ganglion, and, on the ventral, the neural gland; the pharyngeal opening (*cil. gr.*) becomes the ciliated funnel. The enteric canal is distinguish-able into pharynx, œsophagus, stomach, and intestine. The pharynx opens on the exterior by the mouth: in its ventral floor the endostyle (*end.*) has become developed; its walls are pierced by stigmata, the number of which varies. The atrial cavity has grown round the pharynx, and opens on the exterior by a single aperture only (*atr.*). The heart and pericardial cavity have been formed. In this tailed free-swimming stage the larva remains only a few hours; it soon becomes fixed by the adhesive papillæ and begins to undergo the *retrogressive metamorphosis* by which it attains the adult condition.

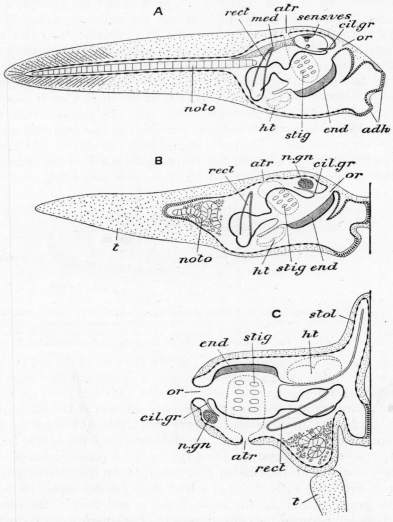

FIG. 32.—Diagram of the metamorphosis of the free-tailed larva into the fixed Ascidian. *A*, stage of free-swimming larva; *B*, larva recently fixed; *C*, older fixed stage. *adh.* adhesive papillæ; *atr.* atrial cavity; *cil. gr.* ciliated diverticulum, becoming ciliated funnel; *end.* endostyle; *ht.* heart; *med.* ganglion of trunk; *n. gn.* nerve-ganglion; *noto.* notochord; *or.* oral aperture; *rect.* rectum; *sens. ves.* sense-vesicle; *stig.* stigmata; *stol.* stolon; *t.* tail. (From Korschelt and Heider, after Seeliger.)

The chief changes involved in the retrogressive metamorphosis (Fig. 32) are the increase in the number of pharyngeal stigmata, the diminution, and eventually the complete disappearance, of the tail with the contained notochord and caudal part of the nerve-cord, the disappearance of the eye and the otocyst, the dwindling of the central part of the nervous system to a single ganglion, and the formation of the reproductive organs. Thus, from an active free-swimming larva, with complex organs of special sense, and provided with a notochord and well-developed nervous system, there is a retrogression to the fixed inert adult, in which all the parts indicative of affinities with the Vertebrata have become aborted.

In some simple Ascidians, and in the composite forms in which development takes place within the body of the parent, the metamorphosis may be considerably abbreviated, but there is always, so far as known, a tailed larva, except in the genus *Anwiella* of the *Molgulidæ*—a family of the simple forms—in which the tailed stage is wanting and there is only an obscure endodermal rudiment to represent the notochord.

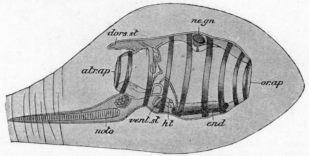

FIG. 33.—**Doliolum,** late stage in the development of the tailed larva.   *atr. ap.* atrial aperture ; *dors. st.* cadophore ; *end.* endostyle ; *ht.* heart ; *ne. gn.* nerve-ganglion ; *noto.* notochord ; *or. ap.* oral aperture ; *vent. st.* ventral stolon.   (After Uljanin.)

In Pyrosoma development is direct, without a tailed larval stage, and takes place within the body of the parent. The ovum contains a relatively large quantity of food-yolk, and the segmentation is meroblastic. A process, developed at an early stage, elongates to form the so-called *stolon*, which divides, by the formation of constrictions, into four parts, each destined to give rise to a zooid (*tetrazooid*). The primary zooid (*cyathozooid*) undergoes atrophy, and at this stage the young colony, composed of four tetrazooids with the remains of the cyathozooid enclosing a mass of yolk—the whole invested in a common cellulose test—passes out from the brood-pouch in which it was developed and reaches the exterior through the cloaca of the parent colony. By a process of budding from the four primary tetrazooids, the entire adult colony is produced.

The development of *Doliolum* is, in all essential respects, very like that of the simple Ascidians. There is total segmentation, followed by the formation of an embolic gastrula ; the larva (Fig. 33) has a tail with a notochord (*noto.*),

and a body in which the characteristic muscular bands soon make their appearance. This tailed larva becomes the asexual stage or " nurse." By and by
the tail aborts, and two processes, one postero-dorsal, the other ventral, known
respectively as the *cadophore* (*dors. st.*) and the *ventral stolon* (*vent. st.*), grow out
from the body of the larva. On the latter are formed a number of slight projections or buds. These become constricted off, and in the form of little groups
of cells, each consisting of seven strings of cells with an ectodermal investment, creep over the surface of the parent (Fig. 34, *e*, and Fig. 35) till they
reach the cadophore, to which they attach themselves after multiplying by
division. The cadophore soon becomes elongated, and the bud-like bodies
attached to it develop into zooids. As the long chain of zooids thus established
is further developed, the parent Doliolum (Fig. 34) loses its branchiæ, its

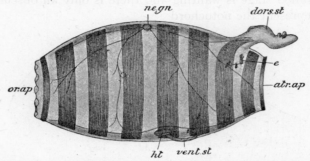

FIG. 34.—**Doliolum,** lateral view of asexual stage, showing the early development of the buds.
atr. ap. atrial aperture ; *dors. st.* cadophore ; *e.* embryos passing over the surface from the ventral
stolon to the cadophore ; *ht.* heart ; *ne. gn.* nerve-ganglion ; *or. ap.* oral aperture ; *vent. st.* ventral
stolon. (After Uljanin.)

endostyle, and its alimentary canal ; at the same time the muscle-bands increase
in thickness and the nervous system attains a higher development, until the
whole parent comes to play a part like that of the nectocalyx of a Siphono-
phore (Vol. I., Section IV), its exclusive function being to propel the colony
through the water by its contractions.

The zooids of the cadophore consist of two sets, differing from one another
in position and in future history—the *lateral zooids* and the *median zooids*.
The lateral zooids serve solely to carry on the nourishment and respiration of
the colony, and do not undergo any further development. Some of the median
buds, on the other hand, become detached and take on the special character
of *phorozooids*. When free, each phorozooid carries with it the stalk by means
of which it was attached to the stolon ; on this stalk there have previously
become attached a number of buds which are destined after a time to be
developed into the sexual zooids.

The succession of stages in the life-history of Doliolum thus briefly sketched
will be seen to succeed one another in the following order : **(1)** sexual form ;

(2) tailed larva developed sexually from (1); (3) first asexual form or " nurse," the direct outcome of (2); (4) second asexual form (phorozooid) developed on the cadophore of (3) from buds originating on the ventral stolon; (5) the young of the sexual form (1) which are developed on the stalk of (4).

Salpa, also Doliolum, presents a remarkable alternation of generations. In the sexual form, which has already been described, only one ovum is developed. The testis becomes mature later than the ovum, and the latter is impregnated by sperms from the testis of an individual of an older chain. The development is direct and takes place within the body of the parent, the embryo as it grows projecting into the branchial cavity. The nourishment of the developing embryo (Fig. 36) is effected by the formation of a structure—

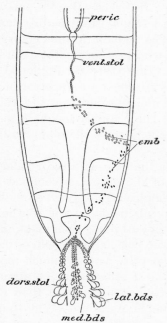

FIG. 35.—**Doliolum,** dorsa view of the posterior part of the body of an asexual zooid, showing the course taken by the buds (*emb.*) over the surface from the ventral stolon (*vent. stol.*) to the cadophore (*dors. stol.*) and their growth on the latter. *lat. bds.* lateral buds; *med. bds.* median buds; *peric.* pericardium. (After Barrois.)

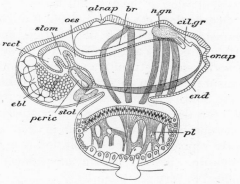

FIG. 36.—Late stage in the development of **Salpa,** showing the placental connection with the parent. *atr. ap.* atrial aperture; *br.* branchia; *cil. gr.* ciliated groove; *ebl.* elæoblast (mass of tissue probably representing a vestige of the tail); *end.* endostyle; *n. gn.* nerve-ganglion; *œs.* œsophagus; *or. ap.* oral aperture; *peric.* pericardium; *pt.* placenta; *rect.* rectum; *stol.* stolon; *stom.* stomach. (From Korschelt and Heider, after Salensky.)

the *placenta*—through which a close union is brought about between the vascular system of the parent and that of the embryo. The placenta of Salpa is partly formed from follicle-cells and ectoderm-cells of the embryo, partly from the cells of the wall of the oviduct. Segmentation is complete. The study of the earlier stages is complicated by the very remarkable and unusual circumstance that during segmentation there is a migration inwards of some of the cells of the follicle and of the wall of the oviduct, which enter the segmenting ovum and pass among the blastomeres. There is uncertainty as to what part these inwardly migrating cells play in the development of the embryo ; but probably they act merely as carriers of nourishment, and become broken up and eventually completely absorbed.

There is no tailed larval stage, and the embryo develops the muscle-bands and all the characteristic parts of the adult while still enclosed within the body of the parent and nourished by means of the placenta.   This sexually-developed embryo, however, does not give rise to a form exactly like the parent, but to one which differs from the latter in certain less important features and notably in the absence of reproductive organs.   The sexually formed embryo, in other words, gives rise to an asexual generation, which escapes to the exterior and becomes free-swimming (Fig. 34).   After a time there is developed a process or stolon (*stol.*), on the surface of which are formed a number of bud-like projections.   These increase in size as the stolon elongates, and each eventually assumes the form of a sexual Salpa.   The chain of zooids formed on the stolon breaks off in lengths which swim about intact while reproductive organs develop in the individuals.

Distribution, etc.—The pelagic forms are, as is the case with most pelagic organisms, of very wide distribution, and none of the genera is confined to particular oceanic areas.   The fixed forms, both simple and composite, are also of world-wide distribution ;   they are much more abundant in the southern hemisphere than in the northern—the composite forms attaining their maximum in the South Pacific area.   The depth to which the pelagic forms extend has not been determined.   Fixed forms occur at all depths, but are much more numerous in shallow water than in deep, and at great depths are comparatively poorly represented, the simple forms extending to a greater depth than the composite.   Several genera of pedunculated simple Ascidians seem to be confined to very great depths.

Though placed so high in the animal series, the Urochorda exhibit very low functional development.   This is chiefly connected with the sessile condition of most of them.   The movements performed by a fixed Ascidian are slow and very limited in character, being confined to contractions of the mantle ;   when the animal is detached, such contractions may sometimes be observed to result in a slow creeping locomotion.   Even in the free forms the movements are limited to the contractions, of the tail muscles in Appendicularia, of the muscle-bands of the body-wall in Doliolum, by which swimming is effected.   The mode of obtaining food resembles that which has already been described in the case of the Pelecypoda (Vol. I., Section IX), the currents which subserve respiration also bringing in microscopic organic particles to the mouth.

Affinities.—That the Urochorda are degenerate descendants of primitive Chordates admits of little doubt ; the history of the development of the Ascidians, taken in connection with the occurrence of permanently chordate members of the group (Appendicularia and its allies), is quite sufficient to point to this conclusion. But the degree of degeneration which the class has undergone—the point on the line of development of the higher Chordata from which it diverged—is open to question. According to one view the Urochorda are all extremely degenerate, and have descended from ancestors which had all the leading features of the Craniata ; according to another, the ancestors of the class were much lower than any existing Craniate—lower in the scale than even Amphioxus—and had not yet acquired the distinctive higher characteristics of the Craniates. The complete want of segmentation and the virtual absence of a cœlome seem to point in the latter direction : the presence in the larva of highly-developed central nervous system and sense-organs to the former. Appendicularia is hardly to be regarded as representing a primitive ancestral type ; its close resemblance to the larva of the sessile Ascidians rather seems to indicate that it is a persistent larval form—a form in which sexual maturity has been reached at earlier and earlier stages in the life-history, and in which the final sessile stage has at last been lost, the animal having become completely adapted to a pelagic life. Probably the other pelagic forms— Salpa, Doliolum, Pyrosoma—were also descended from sedentary ancestors : none of them shows any character that can be interpreted as primitive.

The nearest existing ally of the Urochorda among lower forms is probably Balanoglossus. The similarity in the character of the pharynx, or anterior segment of the enteric canal, perforated by branchial apertures, is alone sufficient to point to such a connection ; and further evidence is afforded by the occurrence of a " notochord " in both, and by the similarity in the development of the central part of the nervous system. But the notochord of the larval Ascidian, almost confined to a post-intestinal tail-region, differs very widely from the structure in Balanoglossus supposed to correspond to it, which is situated anteriorly and directed forwards ; moreover, the other differences are so great that the alliance cannot be a close one, and Balanoglossus and its allies can only be looked upon as very remotely connected with the stock from which the Urochorda are descended.

SUB-PHYLUM III AND CLASS.—ACRANIA.

We have seen that the fundamental characters of the Chordata are the presence of a notochord, of a dorsal, hollow, nervous system, and of a pharynx perforated by apertures or gill-slits. In none of the lower Chordata, however, are these structures found in a typical condition, at least in the adult. In Balanoglossus, Cephalodiscus, and Rhabdopleura the " notochord " is rudimentary, and in nearly all Tunicata it is present only in the embryo. In Rhabdopleura the gill-slits are absent, and in that genus as well as in Cephalodiscus and the adult Tunicata the nervous system is represented by a single solid nerve-centre or ganglion, the neurocœle being absent.   In Balanoglossus, moreover, there is a ventral as well as a dorsal nerve-cord, and it is only in the anterior portion of the latter that the neurocœle is represented.

In higher Chordates, on the other hand, what have been called the three fundamental chordate peculiarities are fully and clearly developed.   There is always a distinct notochord extending as a longitudinal axis throughout the greater part of the elongated body, and either persisting throughout life, or giving place to an articulated *vertebral column* or backbone.   The central nervous system remains throughout life in the form of a dorsal nerve-tube or *neuron* containing a longitudinal canal or neurocœle, and the pharynx is always perforated, either throughout life or in the embryonic condition, by paired branchial apertures or gill-slits.   In addition to these characters, the mouth is ventral and anterior, the anus ventral and posterior; the muscular layer of the body-wall is primarily segmented, and the renal organs arise as a series of paired tubules which may represent either nephridia or cœlomoducts. Moreover, there is always an important digestive gland, the *liver*, developed as a hollow outpushing of the gut, and distinguished by the fact that the blood from the alimentary canal circulates through it before passing into the general current, thus giving rise to what is called the *hepatic portal system* of blood-vessels.

These higher Chordates comprise sections of very unequal extent, viz., the sub-phyla Acrania, Agnatha, and Gnathostomata.

The section Acrania includes only two families, the *Branchiostomidæ*—containing the genera *Branchiostoma* (usually known by the name of one of its sub-genera, *Amphioxus*), *Epigonichthys*, and perhaps some others; and the *Amphioxididæ*—containing the pelagic genus *Amphioxides*, which, however, may not be an adult form.   The differences between the genera and species of Branchiostomidæ are comparatively insignificant, and the following description will deal exclusively with the best known and most thoroughly investigated species, the Lancelet, *Amphioxus lanceolatus*, found in the English Channel, the North Sea, and the Mediterranean.

Amphioxus is a small transparent animal, occurring near the shore and burrowing in sand; its length does not exceed 5·8 cm., or less than two inches. Its form will be obvious from Fig. 37 and from the transverse sections, Fig. 38, *A* and *B*.   The body is elongated, pointed at either end, and compressed. The anterior two-thirds is roughly triangular in transverse section, presenting right and left sides, inclined towards one another above, and a convex ventral surface.   The posterior third is nearly oval in section, the right and left sides meeting above and below in a somewhat sharp edge.

Extending along the whole of the dorsal border is a median longitudinal fold, the *dorsal fin* (*dors. f.*) : this is continued round the posterior end of the body and extends forwards, as the *ventral fin* (*vent. f.*), as far as the region where the oval transverse section passes into the triangular. The portion of the continuous median fold which extends round the pointed posterior

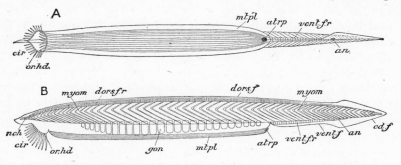

FIG. 37.—**Amphioxus lanceolatus.** *A*, ventral, *B*, side view of the entire animal. *an*. anus. *atrp*. atriopore; *cd. f*. caudal fin; *cir*. cirri; *dors. f*. dorsal fin; *dors. f. r*. dorsal fin-rays; *gon*. gonads; *mtpl*. metapleure; *myom*. myomeres; *nch*. notochord; *or. hd*. oral hood; *vent. f*. ventral fin; *vent. f. r*. ventral fin-rays. (After Kirkaldy.)

extremity of the body is somewhat wider than the rest, and may be distinguished as the *caudal fin* (*cd. f*.). In the anterior two-thirds of the body there is no median ventral fin, but at the junction of each lateral with the ventral surface

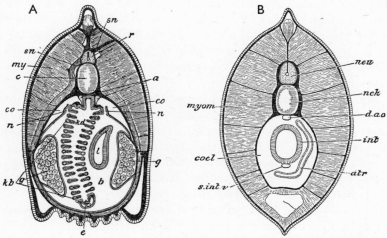

FIG. 38.—**Amphioxus lanceolatus.** *A*, transverse section of the pharyngeal region. *a*. dorsal aorta; *b*. atrium; *c*. notochord; *co*. cœlome; *e*. endostyle; *g*. gonad; *kb*. branchial lamellæ; *kd*. pharynx; *l*. liver; *my*. myomere; *n*. nephridium; *r*. neuron; *sn*. spinal nerves; *B*, transverse section of the intestinal region. *atr*. atrium; *cœl*. cœlome; *d. ao*. dorsal aorta. *int*. intestine; *myom*. myomere; *nch*. notochord; *neu*. neuron; *s. int. v*. sub-intestinal vein. (*A*, from Hertwig, after Lankester and Boveri; *B*, partly after Rolph.)

is a paired longitudinal fold, the *metapleure* (*mtpl*.), which extends forwards to the oral hood mentioned in the next paragraph.

Below the pointed anterior extremity is a large median aperture surrounded

by a frill-like membrane, the *oral hood* (*or. hd.*), the edge of which is beset with numerous tentacles or *cirri* (*cir.*). The oral hood encloses a cup-shaped cavity or *vestibule*, at the bottom of which is the *mouth* (Fig. 39, *mth.*). On the wall of the oral hood is a specially modified tract of the epithelium divided into finger-shaped lobes. The cells of this tract, which is known as the *wheel-organ*, are provided with long cilia, the movements of which drive currents of water with floating food-particles backwards into the pharynx. Along the roof of the vestibule runs a ciliated groove—the *groove of Hatschek*. Immediately in front of the anterior termination of the ventral fin and partly enclosed by the metapleures is a rounded aperture of considerable size, the *atriopore* (*atrp.*), and a short distance from the posterior extremity of the body is the *anus* (*an.*), placed unsymmetrically on the left side of the ventral fin. The post-anal portion of the body is distinguished as the *tail*.

Amphioxus ordinarily lives with the greater part of the body buried in sand, only the anterior end with the expanded oral hood protruding. It also swims in the vertical position, and frequently lies on one side on the sand : it burrows, head foremost, with great rapidity. A current of water is constantly passing in at the mouth and out at the atriopore.

Body-wall.—The body is covered with an *epidermis* (Fig. 38) formed of a single layer of columnar epithelial cells, some of which are provided with sensory hairs, while some are unicellular glands. On the surface of the epidermis is a *cuticle* perforated by pores. The epithelium of the buccal cirri presents at intervals regular groups of sensory cells, some of them bearing stiff sensory hairs, others cilia. Beneath the epidermis is the *dermis*, formed mainly of soft connective-tissue

The *muscular layer* (*my.*, *myom.*) is remarkable for exhibiting metameric segmentation. It consists of a large number—about sixty—of muscle-segments or *myomeres*, separated from one another by partitions of dense connective-tissue, the *myocommas*, and having the appearance, in a surface view, of a series of very open V's with their apices directed forwards (Figs. 37 and 39). Each myomere is composed of numerous flat, striated *muscle-plates*, arranged longitudinally, so that each is attached to two successive myocommas. In virtue of this arrangement the body can be bent from side to side with great rapidity. The myomeres of the right and left sides of the body are not opposite to one another, but have an alternate arrangement. A special set of *transverse muscles* (Fig. 38, *A*) extends across the ventral surface of the anterior two-thirds of the body, lying in the floor of the atrial cavity presently to be described.

One striking and characteristic feature of the muscular layer of the body-wall is the immense thickness of its dorsal portion. In the higher Worms and many other Invertebrates the muscles form a layer of approximately equal thickness surrounding the body-cavity, which contains, amongst other organs, the central nervous system. In Vertebrates, on the other hand, the dorsal body-wall is greatly thickened, and in it are contained both the nervous system and the notochord.

Skeleton.—The chief of the skeletal or supporting structures of the Lancelet is the *notochord* (Figs. 38 and 39, *c.*, *nch.*), a cylindrical rod, pointed at both ends, and extending from the anterior to the posterior end of the body in the median plane. It lies immediately above the enteric tract and between the right and left myomeres. It is composed of a peculiar form of cellular tissue known as *notochordal tissue*, formed of large vacuolated cells extending from side to side of the notochord, and having the nuclei confined to its dorsal and ventral regions. Around these cells is a structureless layer, secreted by the cells, enclosed in a *notochordal sheath* of connective-tissue, which is produced dorsally into an investment for the canal enclosing the central nervous system. The notochord, like the parenchyma of plants, owes its resistant character to the vacuoles of its component cells being tensely filled with fluid, a condition of turgescence being thus produced.

The oral hood is supported by a ring (Fig. 39, *sk.*) of cartilaginous consistency, made up of separate rod-like pieces arranged end to end, and corresponding in number with the cirri. Each piece sends an offshoot into the cirrus to which it is related, furnishing it with a skeletal axis.

The pharynx is supported by delicate oblique rods of a firm material, apparently composed of agglutinated elastic fibres, the *gill-rods* (*br. r.*). These will be most conveniently discussed in connection with the pharynx itself. The dorsal fin is supported by a single series and the ventral fin by a double series of *fin-rays* (*dors. f. r.*, *vent. f. r.*), short rods of connective-tissue, continuous with the investment of the neural canal and separated from one another by small cavities (*lymph-spaces*).

Digestive and Respiratory Organs.—The mouth (*mth.*), as already mentioned, lies at the bottom of the vestibule or cavity of the oral hood (*or. hd.*). It is a small circular aperture surrounded by a membrane, the *velum* (*vl.*), which acts as a sphincter, and has its free edge produced into a number of *velar tentacles* (*vl. t.*).

The mouth leads into the largest section of the enteric canal, the *pharynx* (*ph.*), a high, compressed chamber extending through the anterior half of the body. Its walls are perforated by more than a hundred pairs of narrow oblique clefts, the *gill-slits* or *branchial apertures* (*br. cl.*), which place the cavity of the pharynx in communication with the atrium (see below). From the posterior end of the pharynx goes off the tubular *intestine* (*int.*), which extends backwards almost in a straight line to the anus.

On the ventral wall of the pharynx is a longitudinal groove, the *endostyle* (Fig. 38, *A*, *e.*), lined by ciliated epithelium containing groups of gland-cells Like the homologous organ in Ascidia (p. 15), the glands secrete a cord of mucus in which food-particles are entangled and carried by the action of the cilia to

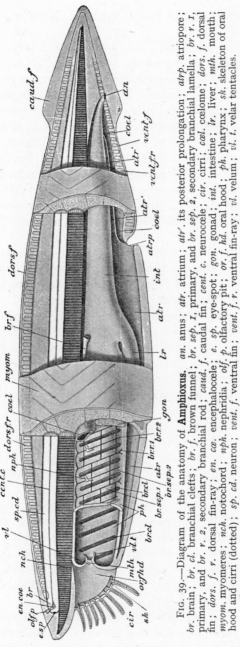

FIG. 39'.—Diagram of the anatomy of **Amphioxus.** *an.* anus; *atr.* atrium; *atr'.* its posterior prolongation; *atrp.* atriopore; *br.* brain; *br. cl.* branchial clefts; *br. f.* brown funnel; *br. sep.* 1, primary, and *br. sep.* 2, secondary branchial lamella; *br. v. 1,* primary, and *br. v. 2,* secondary branchial rod; *caud. f.* caudal fin; *cent. c.* neurocœle; *cir.* cirri; *cœl.* cœlome; *dors. f.* dorsal fin; *dors. f. r.* dorsal fin-ray; *en. cœ.* encephalocœle; *e. sp.* eye-spot; *gon.* gonad; *int.* intestine; *lr.* liver; *mth.* mouth; *myom.* myomeres; *nch.* notochord; *nph.* nephridia; *olf. p.* olfactory pit; *or. f. hd.* oral hood; *ph.* pharynx; *sk.* skeleton of oral hood and cirri (dotted); *sp. cd.* neuron; *vent. f.* ventral fin; *vent. f. r.* ventral fin-ray; *vl.* velum; *vl. t.* velar tentacles.

the intestine. A somewhat similar structure, the *epipharyngeal groove,* extends along the dorsal aspect of the pharynx : its sides are formed by ciliated cells, which, at the anterior end of the groove, curve downwards, as the *peripharyngeal bands,* and join the anterior end of the endostyle.

From the ventral region of the anterior end of the intestine is given off a blind pouch, the liver (*lr.*) or *hepatic cæcum,* which extends forwards to the right of the pharynx : it is lined with glandular epithelium and secretes a digestive fluid.

The *gill-slits* (*br. cl.*) are long narrow clefts, nearly vertical in the expanded condition, but very oblique in preserved and contracted specimens—hence the fact that a large number of clefts always appear in a single transverse section (Fig. 38, *A, kb.*). The clefts are more numerous than the myomeres in the adult, but correspond in number with them in the larva : hence they are fundamentally metameric, but undergo an increase in number as growth proceeds.

The *branchial lamellæ* (Fig. 39, *br. sep.,* Fig. 38, *A, kb.*), or portions of the pharyngeal wall separating the clefts from one another, are covered by an epithelium which is for the most part endodermal in origin, and is composed of greatly elongated and ciliated cells. On the outer face of each lamella, however, the cells are shorter and not ciliated, and are, as a matter of fact, portions of the epithelial lining of the atrium, and of ectodermal origin. Each lamella is supported towards its outer edge by one of the *branchial rods* (Fig. 39

br. r.) already referred to. These are narrow bars united with one another dorsally by loops, but ending below in free extremities which are alternately simple and forked. The forked bars are the *primary* (*br. r.* 1), those with simple ends the *secondary* (*br. r.* 2) *branchial rods*, and the lamellæ in which they are contained are similarly to be distinguished as *primary lamellæ* (*br. sep.* 1) and *secondary* or *tongue-lamellæ* (*br. sep.* 2). In the young condition the two clefts between any two primary lamellæ are represented by a single aperture : as development proceeds a downgrowth takes place from the dorsal edge of the aperture, forming, as in Balanoglossus (p. 4), a *tongue* which extends downwards, dividing the original cleft into two, and itself becoming a secondary lamella. A further complication is produced by the formation of transverse *branchial junctions* or *synapticulæ*, supported by rods connecting the primary septa with one another at tolerably regular intervals.

The Atrium.—The gill-clefts lead into a wide chamber occupying most of the space between the body-wall and the pharynx, and called the *atrium* (Figs. 38, *B*, and 39, *atr.*). It is crescentic in section, surrounding the ventral and lateral regions of the pharynx, but not its dorsal portion. It ends blindly in front ; opens externally, behind the level of the pharynx, by the atriopore (*atrp'.*) ; and is continued backwards by a blind, pouch-like extension (*atr.*) lying to the right of the intestine (Fig. 38, *B*, *atr.*). The whole cavity is lined by an atrial epithelium of ectodermal origin. As in Ascidia, the cilia lining the gill-clefts produce a current setting in at the mouth, entering the pharynx, passing thence by the gill-slits into the atrium, and out at the atriopore. The current, as in Tunicata and Balanoglossus, is both a respiratory and a food current, the animal feeding passively on the minute organisms in the surrounding water.

Cœlome.—Owing to the immense size of the atrium, the body-cavity, which is a true cœlome, is much reduced. It is represented, in the pharyngeal region, by paired cavities (Fig. 38, Fig. 39, *cœl.*, *A*, *co.*, Fig. 40, *sc.*) lying one on either side of the dorsal region of the pharynx above the atrium, and connected by narrow canals in the primary branchial lamellæ (Fig. 40, right side) with a median longitudinal space below the endostyle (*ec.*). In the intestinal region it entirely surrounds the intestine, but is much reduced on the right side, being displaced by the backward extension of the atrium (Fig. 38, *B*, *atr.*, Fig. 39, *atr*[1].) ; on the left side a forward extension of it surrounds the liver (Fig. 38, *A*, *l.*). Separate cavities lie in the metapleures. The whole series of spaces is lined by cœlomic epithelium.

Blood-System.—The blood-vessels of Amphioxus are all of one kind, but, owing to certain undoubted homologies with the more complex vessels of the Craniata (see below), some of them receive the name of *arteries*, others of *veins*.

Lying in the ventral wall of the pharynx, below the endostyle, is a median

longitudinal vessel, the *ventral aorta* (Fig. 40, *si.*, Fig. 41, *v. ao.*) ; it is contractile, and drives the blood forwards. From it are given off, on each side, lateral
branches, the *afferent branchial arteries* (Fig. 40, *k.* ; Fig. 41, *af. br. a.*), with

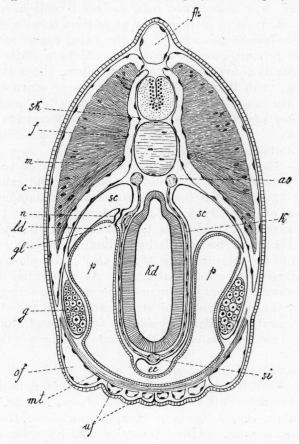

FIG. 40.—**Amphioxus lanceolatus.** Diagrammatic transverse section of the pharyngeal region,
passing on the right through a primary, on the left through a secondary branchial lamella.
ao. dorsal aorta ; *c.* derm ; *ec.* endostylar portion of cœlome ; *f.* fascia or investing layer of
myomere ; *fh.* compartment containing fin-ray ; *g.* gonad ; *gl.* glomerulus (modified part of
branchial artery in relation to nephridium) ; *k.* branchial artery ; *kd.* pharynx ; *ld.* combined atrial
and cœlomic wall (ligamentum denticulatum) ; *m.* myomere ; *mt.* transverse muscle ; *n.*
nephridium ; *of.* metapleural lymph-space ; *p.* atrium ; *sc.* cœlome ; *si.* ventral aorta ; *sh.* sheath
of notochord and neuron ; *uf.* spaces in ventral wall. (From Korschelt and Heider, after Boveri
and Hatschek.)

small contractile dilatations at their bases, which pass up the primary branchial
lamellæ and communicate by cross-branches with similar vessels (*af. br. a¹.*)
in the secondary or tongue-lamellæ. The blood is exposed, while traversing
these vessels, to the aërating influence of the respiratory current, and leaves

the branchial lamellæ dorsally by *efferent branchial arteries* (*ef. br. a.*), which open on each side into paired longitudinal vessels, the *right* and *left dorsal aortæ* (*d. ao.*), lying one on either side of the epipharyngeal groove. Anteriorly both dorsal aortæ are continued forwards to the region of the snout, the right being much dilated; posteriorly they unite with one another, behind the level of the pharynx, into an *unpaired dorsal aorta* (*d. ao'.*), which extends backwards in the middle line, immediately below the notochord and above the intestine.

The unpaired dorsal aorta sends off branches to the intestine, in the walls of which they break up to form a network of microscopic vessels or *capillaries* (*cp.*). From these the blood is collected and poured into a median longitudinal vessel, the *sub-intestinal vein* (Figs. 38, *B*, and 41, *s. int. v.*), lying beneath the intestine : in this trunk the blood flows forwards, and, at the origin of the liver, passes insensibly into a *hepatic portal vein* (*hep. port. v.*), which extends

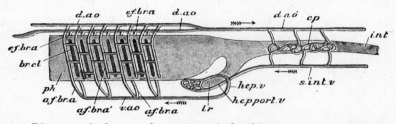

FIG. 41.—Diagram of the vascular system of **Amphioxus.** *af. br. a.* afferent branchial arteries; *br. cl.* branchial cleft; *cp.* intestinal capillaries; *d. ao.* paired dorsal aortæ; *d. ao'.* median dorsal aorta; *e.f br. a.* efferent branchial arteries; *hep. port. v.* hepatic portal vein; *hep. v.* hepatic vein; *int.* intestine; *lr.* liver; *ph.* pharynx; *s. int. v.* sub-intestinal vein; *v. ao.* ventral aorta.

along the ventral side of the liver and breaks up into capillaries in that organ. From the liver the blood makes its way into a *hepatic vein* (*hep. v.*), which extends along the dorsal aspect of the digestive gland, and, turning downwards and forwards, joins the posterior end of the ventral aorta.

It will be seen that the vascular system of Amphioxus consists essentially of (*a*) a dorsal vessel represented by the paired and unpaired dorsal aortæ, (*b*) a ventral vessel represented by the subintestinal vein and the ventral aorta, and (*c*) commissural vessels represented by the afferent and efferent branchial arteries and the intestinal capillaries. So far the resemblance to the vascular system of Annulata is tolerably close; but two important differences are to be noted. The blood in the ventral vessel travels forwards, that in the dorsal vessel backwards—the precise opposite of what occurs in worms—and the ventral vessel is broken up, as it were, into two parts, by the interposition in its course of the capillaries of the liver, so that all the blood from the intestine has to pass through that organ before reaching the ventral aorta. This passage of the intestinal blood through the vessels of the liver constitutes what is called the *hepatic portal system*, and is eminently characteristic of Vertebrata.

The *blood* is almost colourless, with a few red corpuscles, and appears to contain no leucocytes. It is not confined to the true blood-vessels just described, but occurs also in certain cavities or *lymph-spaces*, the most important of which are the cavities in the dorsal and ventral fins containing the fin-rays (Fig. 40, *fh.*), and paired canals in the metapleures (*of.*).

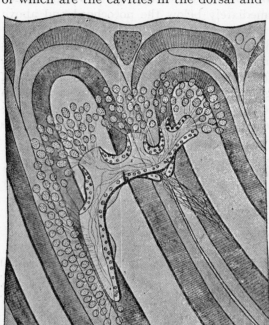

Excretory Organs.—The principal organs of excretion are about ninety pairs of peculiarly modified *nephridia* (Fig. 39, *neph*). situated above the pharynx and in relation with the main cœlomic cavities. Each nephridium (Fig. 42) is a bent tube consisting of an anterior vertical and a posterior horizontal limb. The vertical limb terminates in a large group of solenocytes (Vol. I., Section VII), and there are several smaller groups on the horizontal limb. The organ thus closely corresponds to the type of nephridium with closed inner end bearing solenocytes already described as occurring in certain of the Polychæta. On the ventral surface of the horizontal limb, opposite a secondary branchial

FIG. 42.—**Amphioxus lanceolatus.** Nephridium of the left side with part of the wall of the pharynx. (From Willey, after Boveri.)

lamella, is a single aperture bearing long cilia and opening into the atrium : this corresponds with the *nephridiopore* or external aperture of the typical nephridium.

An excretory function has also been assigned to a single pair of organs called the *brown funnels* (Fig. 39, *br. f.*), also situated on the dorsal aspect of the pharynx at its posterior end. Their wide backwardly-directed ends open into the atrium ; their narrow anterior ends probably communicate with the cœlome. There are also groups of columnar excretory cells on the floor of the atrium.

Nervous System.—The central nervous system is a rod-like organ, the *neuron* or *dorsal nerve-tube* (Fig. 38, *A*, *n.* ; *B*, *neu.*, Figs. 39, 41), contained within and completely filling a median longitudinal *neural canal* which lies immediately above the notochord. It is roughly triangular in transverse section : anteriorly it ends abruptly, some distance behind the anterior end of the notochord, while posteriorly it tapers to a point over the hinder end of the latter. It is traversed by an axial cavity, the *neurocœle* (Fig. 39, *cent. c.*), connected with the mid-dorsal region by a longitudinal cleft—the *dorsal fissure*. At the fore-end of the nerve-tube the neurocœle becomes dilated, forming a considerable cavity, the *encephalocœle* or *cerebral ventricle* (Fig. 32, *en. cœ.*, Fig. 43, *c.v.*), and a little behind this the dorsal fissure widens out above to form a trough-like *dorsal dilatation* (*dil.*) covered only by the delicate connective-tissue sheath which invests the whole nerve-tube.

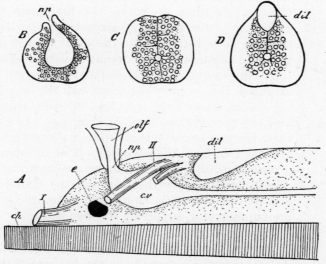

FIG. 43.—**Amphioxus lanceolatus.** *A*, brain and cerebral nerves of a young specimen ; *B*, transverse section through neuropore ; *C*, behind cerebral ventricle ; *D*, through dorsal dilatation. *ch.* notochord ; *c. v.* cerebral ventricle ; *dil.* dorsal dilatation ; *e.* eye-spot ; *np.* neuropore ; *olf.* olfactory pit ; *I, II*, cerebral nerves. (From Willey, after Hatschek.)

The anterior end of the neuron, containing these two cavities, is to be looked upon as the *brain*, although not distinguishable externally from the remaining portion or *spinal cord*.

The anterior and dorsal region of the brain is produced into a small, hollow, pointed pouch which comes into relation with the olfactory organ and is called the *median olfactory lobe*. In its posterior and ventral region a depression has been described which appears to correspond with the *infundibulum* of the Craniata (*vide,* p. 99). In the young animal the cerebral ventricle opens above by an aperture, the *neuropore* (Fig. 43, *B, np.*), which subsequently closes up.

The neuron is mainly composed of longitudinal nerve-fibres with abundant nerve-cells mostly grouped around the neurocœle. At intervals *giant nerve-cells* occur—multipolar cells of immense proportional size, connected with nerve-fibres of unusual thickness—the *giant fibres*. The latter appear to correspond with the giant fibres of Chætopods (Vol. I., Section VII), which have sometimes been supposed to have no nervous function and to be mere supporting structures.

The peripheral nervous system consists of the *nerves* given off from the neuron. They are divisible into two sets, the first consisting of two pairs of *cerebral nerves* (Fig. 43, *I.* and *II.*) arising from the brain, the second of a large number of *spinal nerves* arising from the spinal cord. The cerebral nerves take their origin in front of the first myomere, the first from the anterior extremity of the brain, the second from its dorsal region : they are both distributed to the snout, their branches being provided towards their extremities with numerous ganglia containing nerve-cells. The spinal nerves are segmentally arranged, and, in correspondence with the disposition of the myomeres, those of the right and left sides arise alternately, and not opposite one another (Fig. 44). In each segment there are two nerves on each side, a *dorsal nerve*, arising by a single root from the dorsal aspect of the spinal cord, and a *ventral nerve*, arising by numerous separate fibres : the dorsal nerves supply the skin and the transverse muscles and are therefore both sensory and motor, the ventral nerves are purely motor, supplying the myomeres.

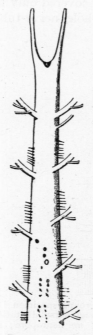

Fig. 44.—**Amphioxus lanceolatus.**—Anterior portion of neuron from above, showing nerves. (From Willey, after Schneider.)

Sensory Organs.—At the level of the anterior end of the brain is a narrow ciliated depression, the *olfactory pit* (Fig. 43, *olf.*), opening externally on the left side of the snout and connected at its lower end with the median olfactory lobe. This structure is supposed to be an organ of smell : in the larva its cavity is in direct communication with the neurocœle through the *neuropore* (*np.*).

An unpaired *pigment-spot* (*e.*) in the front wall of the brain is usually referred to as a median *cerebral eye*. There is no lens or other accessory apparatus, and experimental evidence seems to show that this so-called eye is not sensitive to light. Smaller eye-like organs with or without pigment occur in the spinal cord throughout the greater part of its length. There is no trace of auditory organs. The *groove of Hatschek*, on the roof of the buccal cavity, is supposed to have a sensory function, but this is very doubtful. Lastly, the sensory cells on the cirri of the oral hood give those organs an important tactile function.

Reproductive Organs.—The sexes are separate, but there is no distinction,

apart from the organs of reproduction, between male and female. The *gonads*
(Figs. 38, *A*, Fig. 39, *gon.*, and 40, *g.*) are about twenty-six pairs of pouches
arranged metamerically along the body-wall, and projecting into the atrium
so as largely to fill up its cavity. The inner or mesial face of each pouch is
covered by atrial epithelium pushed inwards by the growth of the gonads;
within this, and completely surrounding the reproductive organ, is a single

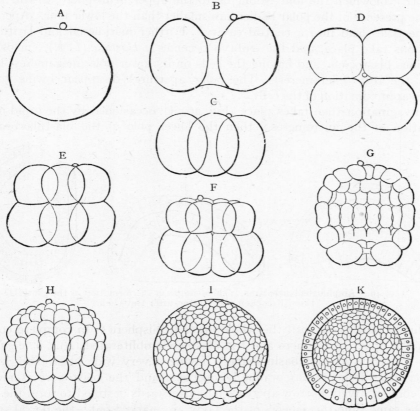

FIG. 45.—**Amphioxus lanceolatus.** Segmentation of the oosperm. *D*, the four-celled stage
(*C*) from above; *G*, vertical section of *H*; *K*, vertical section of the blastula stage *I*. (From
Korschelt and Heider, after Hatschek.)

layer of epithelium which is shown by development to be cœlomic. Hence
each gonad is surrounded by a closed cœlomic sac.

When ripe the inner walls of the gonadic pouches burst, and the ova or
sperms make their way into the atrium and thence by the atriopore to the
external water. The laid eggs are covered by a thin *vitelline membrane*, to
which a second, inner *peri-vitelline membrane* is added, the substance of which
is derived from droplets in the protoplasm.

Development.—After maturation (Fig. 45, *A*) and impregnation, the membranes separate from the oosperm, leaving a wide space around the latter. Segmentation is complete, there being very little yolk; it begins by a meridional cleft dividing the oosperm into two (*B*), and followed by a second cleft, also meridional, at right angles to the first (*C*, *D*). Next, an (approximately) equatorial cleavage takes place, the embryo coming to be formed of eight cells (*E*), of which the four belonging to the upper hemisphere, distinguished by the presence of the polar bodies, are smaller than the lower four. Apertures at the poles lead into a central cavity. Further meridional and latitudinal divisions take place, and the embryo becomes a *blastula* (*I*, *K*), enclosing a spacious blastocœle, and having the cells on its lower pole (megameres) larger than the rest (micromeres). The polar apertures disappear owing to the closer approximation of the cells.

Invagination then takes place (Fig. 46, *A*), occasioned by the rapid multiplication of the micromeres; then the lower pole of the blastula becomes

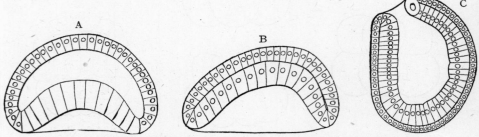

FIG. 46.—**Amphioxus lanceolatus.** Three stages in the formation of the gastrula.
(From Korschelt and Heider, after Hatschek.)

gradually pushed in until the whole lower hemisphere is in complete contact with the upper hemisphere and the blastocœle obliterated (*B*). The *gastrula* thus formed is at first basin-shaped, having a very wide blastopore, but its cavity (the archenteron) gradually deepens, and the blastopore is reduced to a comparatively narrow aperture (*C*), afterwards destined to form the anus. At the same time the aspects of the body are marked out; the dorsal surface becomes flattened, the ventral convex; the blastopore marks the posterior end and is distinctly dorsal in position. Cilia are developed from the ectoderm cells, and by their vibration cause the embryo to rotate within its membrane.

The ectoderm cells forming the median portion of the flattened dorsal surface now become differentiated and sink below the rest, giving rise to the *medullary plate* (Fig. 47, *A*, *mp.*). The ordinary ectoderm cells on each side of this plate rise up as a pair of longitudinal *medullary folds* (*hb.*), extend towards the middle line and unite (*B*, *hb.*), covering over the medullary plate. The latter bends upwards at the sides so as to become trough-like instead of flat

(*C*), and, its two sides coming in contact with one another above, the plate is converted into a tube, the *neuron* (*D*, *n.*), enclosing a central canal, the *neurocœle*, continued dorsally into a narrow cleft. The medullary folds extend behind the blastopore so that, when they unite, the latter aperture opens into the neurocœle by a *neurenteric canal* (Fig. 48, *A*, *cn.*). Anteriorly the folds remain apart up to a late period, so that the neurocœle opens externally in front by a wide aperture, the *neuropore* (Figs. 48, 49, and 50, *np.*).

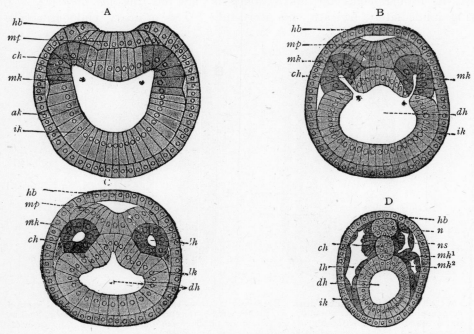

FIG. 47.—**Amphioxus lanceolatus.** Four stages in the development of the notochord, nervous system, and mesoderm. *ak.* ectoderm; *ch.* notochord; *dh.* cavity of archenteron; *hb.* ridge of ectoderm growing over medullary plate; *ik.* endoderm; *lh.* cœlome; *mk.* cœlomic pouch; *mk¹.* parietal layer of mesoderm; *mk².* visceral layer; *mp.* medullary plate; *n.* neuron; *ns.* proto-vertebra. (From Korschelt and Heider, after Hatschek.)

While the central nervous system is thus being formed, the endodermal wall of the archenteron develops dorso-laterally a pair of longitudinal folds (* in Fig. 47, *A* and *B*), the cavities in which, continuous with the archenteron, are the beginnings of the enterocœlic system. Transverse folds which appear divide the longitudinal folds into segments, with the result that the archenteron comes to have appended to it dorso-laterally a paired series of offshoots, the *enterocœlic* or *cœlomic pouches* (Fig. 47, *mk.*), arranged metamerically. In this way segmentation is established, and it is at this period that the embryo ruptures its containing membrane and begins free existence. Before long the cœlomic pouches separate from the archenteron and take on the form of a series of closed *cœlomic sacs* or *somites* (Fig. 47, *C, D*), lying between ectoderm and endoderm.   From the walls of these sacs the mesoderm is derived : their cavities uniting become the cœlome, which is therefore an *enterocœle*, like that of Sagitta and the Echinodermata.

While the cœlomic sacs are in course of formation a median groove appears along the dorsal wall of the archenteron (Fig. 47, *B, C, ch.*): it deepens, loses its tubular character, and becomes a solid rod, the *notochord* (*D, ch.*), lying immediately beneath the nerve-tube.   The ordinary endoderm cells

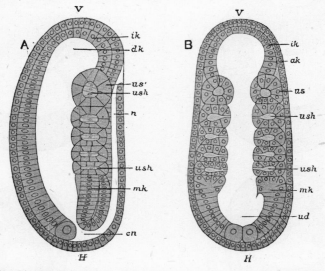

FIG. 48.—**Amphioxus lanceolatus.** Embryo. *A*, from the side ; *B*, in horizontal section.
ak. ectoderm ; *cn.* neurenteric canal ; *dk.* archenteron ; *ik.* endoderm ; *mk.* mesodermal folds ;
n. neural tube ; *ud.* archenteron ; *us.* first cœlomic pouch ; *ush.* cœlomic cavity ; *V.* anterior ;
H. posterior end.   (From Korschelt and Heider, after Hatschek.)

soon unite beneath it and so shut it off from the archenteron.   It will be seen that the notochord, like the neuron, never exhibits any trace of segmentation. At its first formation it stops short of the anterior end of the archenteron : its final extension to the end of the snout is a subsequent process.

The significance of these early stages in the development of Amphioxus has been variously regarded by different embryologists, and it is impossible to give here more than a statement of the ascertained facts, leaving the question of their interpretation, which can only be profitably discussed on the broadest basis, as a matter for more advanced study.   Since, however, the gastrulation and mesoderm-formation in Amphioxus are, almost universally, made the starting-point in the process of interpreting the phenomena of early development in all Vertebrates, it may be desirable at the present stage to state that though in the foregoing account the cells which are invaginated are referred to throughout simply as endoderm, this view of their nature is not the only one that may reasonably be held.   If the inner layer of the gastrula be composed of endoderm and of endoderm only, certain consequences necessarily follow : the notochord must be purely endodermal in origin, and so must the whole of the mesoderm.   This is the terminology which has been followed in the preceding pages.   But it may be held that the process of invagination is not so simple, and that the inner layer of the resulting gastrula is made up of two distinct parts : a dorsal part, which is ectodermal, and a ventral part, which consists of endoderm.   On this view the notochord and the mesoderm, derived from the dorsal part of the invaginated layer, would both be of ectodermal origin, and only the enteric epithelium would be endodermal.   These points will be referred to again at a later stage.

A further point about which there may be room for differences of opinion is the detailed development of the cœlome.   According to one view of the facts the cœlome of Amphioxus may at one stage be compared to that of Balanoglossus (p. 7) :—with an unpaired anterior part, destined to form the head-cœlome and representing the proboscis-cavity of Balanoglossus ; a middle pair of pouches which form the first pair of somites, and a pair of canal-like backward extensions, which may be compared to the collar-cavities ; and a posterior pair corresponding with the trunk-cœlome of the Enteropneust—the last becoming divided up to form the cœlomic sacs.

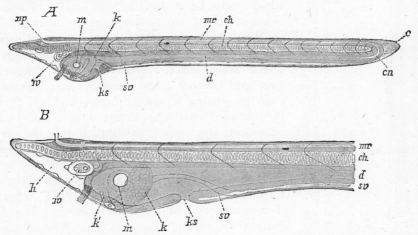

FIG. 49.—**Amphioxus lanceolatus.**   *A*, young larva ;   *B*, anterior end more highly magnified. *c*. provisional tail-fin ;   *ch*. notochord ;   *cn*. neurenteric canal ;   *d*. enteric canal ;   *h*. cœlome of head ; *k*. club-shaped gland ;   *k'*. its external aperture ;   *ks*. first gill-slit ;   *m*. mouth ;   *mr*. neuron ;   *n.p.* neuropore ;   *sv*. sub-intestinal vein ;   *w*. pre-oral pit.   (From Korschelt and Heider, after Hatschek.)

New cœlomic pouches are formed in regular order from before backwards, the embryo at the same time elongating and becoming laterally compressed and pointed fore and aft.   At the anterior end the *mouth* (Fig. 49, *m*.) appears on the left side of the body as a small aperture, which soon increases greatly in size.   On the ventral surface another small aperture, the *first gill-slit* (*ks*.), makes its appearance, and soon shifts over to the right side : it forms a direct communication between the pharynx and the exterior, like the stigmata of Appendicularia (p. 21) : there is at present no trace of the atrium.

The anterior end of the archenteron has meanwhile grown out into a pair of pouches, which become shut off as closed sacs : of these the right gives rise to the cœlome of the head (*h*.), the left to a depression called the *pre-oral pit* (*w*.), which opens on the exterior and from which the groove of Hatschek

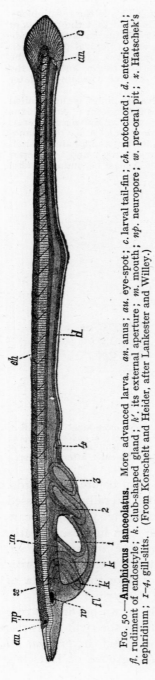

FIG. 50.—**Amphioxus lanceolatus.** More advanced larva. *an.* anus; *au.* eye-spot; *c.* larval tail-fin; *ch.* notochord; *d.* enteric canal; *fl.* rudiment of endostyle; *k.* club-shaped gland; *k'.* its external aperture; *m.* mouth; *np.* neuropore; *w.* pre-oral pit; *x.* Hatschek's nephridium; *1–4.* gill-slits. (From Korschelt and Heider, after Lankester and Willey.)

and the wheel-organ are afterwards formed. The pre-oral pit also gives rise to *Hatschek's nephridium* (Fig. 50, *x.*), a narrow ciliated tube which opens into the anterior part of the pharynx, and runs forwards to terminate blindly in the roof of the oral hood: it disappears completely in the adult except in Amphioxides, in which it is said to contain solenocytes.

On the floor of the archenteron in the neighbourhood of the mouth a depression appears giving rise to a structure known as the *club-shaped gland* (*k.*), which may be a modified gill-cleft. Posteriorly the neurenteric canal closes and the anus appears.

We left the mesoderm in the form of separate paired somites, arranged metamerically in the dorsal region of the embryo. These increase in size, and extend both upwards and downwards, each presenting a *somatic layer* (Fig. 47, *D, mk.*[1]) in contact with the external ectoderm, and a *splanchnic layer* (*mk.*[2]) in contact with the nervous system and notochord dorsally, and with the enteric canal ventrally. At about the level of the ventral surface of the notochord a horizontal partition is formed in each cœlomic sac (Fig. 47, *D*), separating it into a dorsal and ventral portion. The dorsal section is distinguished as the *protovertebra* or *myotome* (*ns.*), and its cavity as the *myocœle* or muscle-cavity: the ventral section is called the *lateral plate* or *splanchnotome*, and its cavity forms a segment of the cœlome.

The later plates now unite with one another in pairs below the enteric canal, their cavities becoming continuous: at the same time the cavities of successive lateral plates are placed in communication with one another by the absorption of their adjacent (anterior and posterior) walls. In this way the cavities of the entire series of ventral plates, right and left, unite to form the single unsegmented cœlome of the adult, their walls giving rise to the cœlomic epithelium.

At the same time the cells of the splanchnic layer of the protovertebræ become converted into muscular fibres, which nearly fill the myocœle, and give rise to the myomere : the myocommas arise from the adjacent anterior and posterior walls of the protovertebræ. An outpushing of the splanchnic layer, at about the level of the ventral surface of the notochord, grows upwards between the myomere externally and the notochord and nerve-tube internally : from the cells lining this pouch the connective-tissue sheath of the notochord and neural canal arises, and perhaps also the fin-rays. From the parietal layer of the pro-tovertebræ is formed the derm or connective-tissue layer of the skin.

The larva increases in size, and becomes very long and narrow, with a pointed anterior end and a provisional caudal fin posteriorly (Fig. 50, c). As growth proceeds, new segments are added behind those already formed, the notochord grows forwards to the anterior end of the snout, and the eye-spot

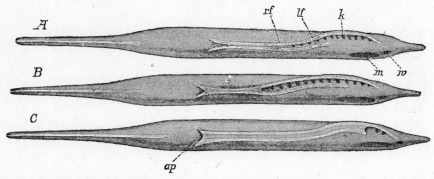

FIG. 51.—**Amphioxus lanceolatus.** Ventral aspect of three larvæ showing the development of the atrium. *ap.* atriopore ; *k.* gill-slits ; *lf.* left metapleural fold ; *m.* mouth ; *rf.* right meta-pleural fold ; *w.* pre-oral pit. (From Korschelt and Heider, after Lankester and Willey.)

(*au.*) and olfactory pit appear, the latter as an ectodermal pit which com-municates with the neurocœle by the still open neuropore, (*np.*). The mouth (*m.*) attains a relatively immense size, still remaining on the left side.

Additional gill-slits arise behind the one already mentioned : they all make their appearance near the middle ventral line, and gradually shift over to the right side : at first they correspond with the myomeres, so that the segmenta-tion of the pharynx is part of the general metamerism of the body. Altogether fourteen clefts are produced in a single longitudinal series. Above, *i.e.*, dorsal to them, a second longitudinal series makes its appearance, containing eight clefts, so that at this stage there are two parallel rows of gill-slits on the right side of the body, and none on the left. But as growth goes on, the first or ventral series gradually travels over to the left side, producing a symmetrical arrangement, and at the same time the first slit and the last five of the first or definitely left series close up and disappear, so that the numbers are equalised on the two sides. At first each gill-slit is simple, but before long a fold grows down from its dorsal edge, and, extending ventrally, divides the single aperture into two : this fold is the secondary or tongue-lamella, the original bars of tissue between the undivided slits becoming the primary lamellæ.

While the development of the gill-slits is proceeding, the atrium is in course of formation. Paried longitudinal ridges, the *metapleural folds* (Fig. 51, *lf. rf.*, Fig. 52, *sf.*), appear on the ventral side of the body, behind the gill-slits, and gradually extend forwards, dorsal to the latter, their arrangement being very unsymmetrical in correspondence with that of the clefts themselves. On the inner face of each fold, *i.e.* the face which looks towards its fellow

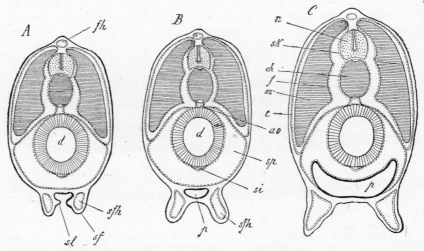

FIG. 52.—**Amphioxus lanceolatus.** Diagrammatic transverse sections of three larvæ to show the development of the atrium. *ao.* aorta ; *c.* dermis ; *d.* intestine ; *f.* fascia (layer of connective-tissue on inner surface of myomere) ; *fh.* cavity for dorsal fin-ray ; *m.* myomere ; *n.* neuron ; *p.* atrium ; *sf.* metapleural folds ; *sfh.* metapleural lymph-space ; *si.* sub-intestinal vein ; *sk.* sheath of notochord and neuron ; *sl.* sub-atrial ridge ; *sp.* cœlome. (From Korschelt and Heider, after Lankester and Willey.)

of the opposite side, a longitudinal, *sub-atrial ridge* (Fig. 52, *A*, *sl.*) appears, and the two sub-atrial ridges meeting and coalescing, a canal (*B*, *p.*) is formed immediately below the ventral body-wall. This canal is the commencement of the atrium : it is at first quite narrow, but gradually extends upwards on each side (*C*, *p.*) until it attains its full dimensions. It is open, at first, both in front and behind : the posterior opening remains as the atriopore : the anterior opening becomes gradually shifted forwards as the fusion of the sub-atrial ridges proceeds (Fig. 51, *B* and *C*), and is finally completely closed. In this way the gill-slits come to open, not directly on the exterior, but into a cavity formed by the union of paired ridges of the body-wall, and therefore lined by ectoderm.

The mouth gradually passes to the ventral surface, and undergoes a relative diminution in size : a fold of integument develops round it and forms the oral hood, which is probably to be looked upon as a stomodæum. The endostyle appears on the right of the pharynx (Fig. 50, *fl.*), and is at first rod-shaped, then V-shaped : ultimately the limbs of the V unite in the middle ventral line. The gill-slits increase in number and become more and more vertically elongated. The provisional caudal fin disappears. The gonads arise from the outer and ventral regions of the protovertebræ in the form of pouches, which gradually assume their permanent form.

Distribution.—The Branchiostomidæ are very widely distributed in tropical and warm-temperate seas. *Amphioxides* has only been obtained with the tow-net and is, seemingly, of permanently pelagic habit. It differs from Amphioxus in the absence of oral cirri and of an atrial cavity, the branchial slits opening directly on the exterior in an unpaired ventral row. No fully mature specimens have yet been found, but the larger specimens have a single row of gonads.

Distinctive Characters.—The Acrania may be defined as Euchorda in which the notochord extends to the anterior end of the snout, in advance of the central nervous system. There is no skull, and no trace of limbs. The ectoderm consists of a single layer of cells which may be ciliated. The pharynx is of immense size, perforated by very numerous gill-slits, and surrounded by an atrium. The liver is a hollow pouch of the intestine. There is no heart, and the blood is almost colourless. The nephridia remain distinct and open into the atrium. The brain is very imperfectly differentiated ; there are only two pairs of cerebral nerves ; and the dorsal and ventral spinal nerves do not unite. There are no paired eyes, but there is a median pigment-spot in the wall of the brain, and many others in the spinal cord ; an auditory organ is absent. The gonads are metamerically arranged and have no ducts. There is a typical invaginate gastrula, and the mesoderm arises in the form of metameric cœlomic pouches. The cœlome is an enterocœle.

Affinities.—Amphioxus has had a chequered zoological history. Its first discoverer placed it among the Gastropoda, considering it to be a slug. When its vertebrate character was made out, it was for a long time placed definitely among fishes, as the type of a distinct order of that class ; but, on further study, it became obvious that an animal without skull, brain, heart, auditory organs, paired eyes, or true kidneys, and with colourless blood and a pharynx surrounded by an atrium, must be as widely separated from the lowest fish as is the lowest fish from a bird or mammal.

There was still, however, no suspicion of any connection between Amphioxus and the Urochorda until the development of both was worked out, and it was shown that in many fundamental points, notably in the formation of the nervous system and the notochord, there was a close resemblance between the two. The likeness was further emphasised by the presence in both forms of an endostyle, an epipharyngeal groove (dorsal lamina) and peripharyngeal bands, and of an atrium, and by the homology of the gill-slits of Tunicates with those of *Amphioxus*. The Urochorda being obviously a highly specialised group with many organs degenerated, it was suggested that the peculiarities of *Amphioxus* might also be explained on the same lines. A still more recent suggestion [1] that *Amphioxus* is a modified and degenerate form of one of the Agnatha is interesting. According to this view the acquired specialisations are the multiplication of the gill-slits and myomeres, the asymmetry and the complicated larval history. The losses by degeneration are to be seen in the simplification of the brain (which has more the appearance of a degenerate structure than that of the beginning of a primitive chordate brain), of eyes, otic capsules, exoskeleton, and of generative ducts. Such losses are not impossible, as they can largely be paralleled in other vertebrata. The presence, on the other hand, of true nephridia with solenocytes, a structure otherwise unknown in the Chordata, is evidence of the persistence of a very primitive character.

The evidence as to the real position of this form is as yet insufficient, but investigations have tended to bring the Acrania nearer to the Craniate Vertebrata and to remove them further from the lower Chordata.

GENERAL INTRODUCTION TO CRANIATE FORMS

The group of the Craniata (Vertebrata) includes all those animals known as Fishes, Amphibians, Reptiles, Birds, and Mammals, or, in other words, Vertebrata having a skull, a highly complex brain, a heart of three or four chambers, and red blood-corpuscles.

In spite of the obvious and striking diversity of organisation obtaining among Craniata—between, for instance, a Lamprey, a Pigeon, and a Dog—there is a fundamental unity of plan running through the whole group, both as to the general arrangement of the various systems of organs and the structure of the organs themselves—far greater than in any of the principal invertebrate groups. The range of variation in the whole of the classes included in the division is, in fact, considerably less than in many single classes of Invertebrata—for instance, Hydrozoa or Crustacea. Hence, while the plan hitherto adopted of treating the group class by class will be followed, it will be found convenient to begin by devoting a considerable space to a preliminary account of the Craniata as a whole, since in this way much needless repetition will be avoided.

External Characters.—The body of Craniata (Fig. 53) is bilaterally symmetrical, elongated in an antero-posterior direction, and usually more or less cylindrical. It is divisible into three regions : the *head*, which contains the

[1] Gregory, W. K.: " The Transformation of Organic Designs : a Review of the Origin and Deployment of the Earlier Vertebrates," *Biological Reviews*, 1936. Cambridge.

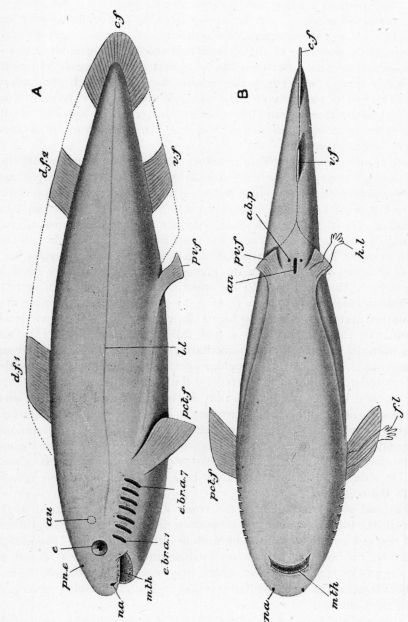

Fig. 53.—Lateral (A) and ventral (B) views of an ideal **Craniate**. *ab. p.* abdominal pore; *au.* position of auditory organ; *an.* anus; *c. f.* caudal fin; *d. f. 1,* first, and *d. f. 2,* second dorsal fin; *e.* paired eye; *e. br. a. 1,* first, and *e. br. a. 7,* seventh gill-cleft; *f. l.* fore-limbs; *h. l.* hind-limb; *l. l.* lateral line; *mth.* mouth; *na.* nasal aperture; *pct. f.* pectoral fin; *pn. e.* pineal sense-organ; *pv. f.* pelvic fin; *v. f.* ventral fin. The dotted line in *A* indicates a continuous median fin.

brain, the chief sensory organs, and the mouth and pharynx; the *trunk*, to which the cœlome is confined, and which contains the principal digestive and circulatory as well as the excretory and reproductive organs; and the *tail*, or region situated posteriorly to the cœlome and anus, and containing none of the more essential organs. Between the head and trunk there is frequently a narrow region or *neck*, into which the cœlome does not extend. In aquatic Vertebrates the tail is normally of great size, not marked off externally from the trunk, and is the chief organ of locomotion: in terrestrial forms it usually becomes greatly reduced in diameter, and has the appearance of a mere unpaired posterior appendage.

The *mouth* (*mth.*) is a transverse aperture placed at or near the anterior end of the head. Near it, sometimes dorsal, sometimes ventral in position, are the paired *nostrils* or *anterior nares* (*na.*)—or in Cyclostomi the single nostril —leading to the organs of smell. Farther back, on the sides of the head, are the large *paired eyes* (*e.*), and on the dorsal surface there is sometimes more or less indication of a vestigial *median* or *pineal sense-organ* (*pn. e.*), which may take the form of an eye. Posterior to the paired eyes are the *auditory organs* (*au.*), the position of which is indicated in the higher forms by an *auditory aperture*.

On the sides of the head, behind the mouth, are a series of openings, the *gill-slits* or *external branchial apertures* (*e. br. a. 1—7*): they are rarely more than seven in number and in air-breathing forms disappear more or less completely in the adult. In the higher Fishes a fold called the *operculum* (Fig. 206, *op.*) springs from the side of the head immediately in front of the first gill-slit and extends backwards, covering the branchial apertures. In the Aphetohyoidea (pp. 154–172) the operculum is supported by the mandibular arch.

On the ventral surface at the junction of the trunk and tail is the *anus* (*an.*). Distinct *urinary* and *genital apertures*, or a single *urino-genital aperture*, are sometimes found either in front of or behind the anus, but more commonly the urinary and genital ducts open into the termination of the enteric canal, or *cloaca*, so that there is only a single egestive opening, known as the *cloacal aperture*. On either side of this there may be a small *abdominal pore* (*ab. p.*) leading into the cœlome.

In Fishes and some Amphibians, the trunk and tail are produced in the middle dorsal line into a vertical fold or *median fin*, which is continued round the end of the tail and forwards in the middle line to the anus. Frequently this continuous fin becomes broken up into distinct *dorsal* (*d. f. 1* and *2*), *ventral* (*v. f.*), and *caudal* (*cd. f.*) *fins*, which may assume very various forms: in the higher classes all trace of median fins disappears (*cf.*, however, analogous structure in the Cetacea).

Fishes also possess *paired fins*. Immediately posterior to the last gill-slit is a more or less horizontal outgrowth, the *pectoral fin* (*pct. f.*), while a similar but smaller structure, the *pelvic fin* (*pv. f.*), arises at the side of the anus.

In all Craniata above Fishes, *i.e.* from Amphibia upwards, the paired fins are replaced by *fore-* and *hind-limbs* (*f.l.*, *h.l.*), each consisting of three divisions —*upper-arm*, *fore-arm*, and *hand* in the one case ; *thigh*, *shank*, and *foot* in the other. Both hand and foot normally terminate in five fingers or *digits*, and the *pentadactyle limb* thus formed is very characteristic of all the higher Vertebrata. The paired fins, or limbs, as the case may be, are the only lateral appendages possessed by Vertebrates.

Body-wall and Internal Cavities.—The body is covered externally by a *skin* consisting of two layers, an outer or epithelial layer, the *epidermis* (Fig. 54, *Ep.*), derived from the ectoderm of the embryo, and an inner or connective-tissue layer, the *dermis* (*Co*), of meso-dermal origin. The epidermis is always many-layered, the cells of the lower layers, forming the *stratum Malpighii*, being protoplasmic and capable of active multiplication, while those of the superficial layers often become flattened and horny, and constitute the *stratum corneum*. *Glands* are frequently present in the skin in the form of tubular or flask-shaped in-pushings of the epidermis or of isolated gland-cells (*B*).

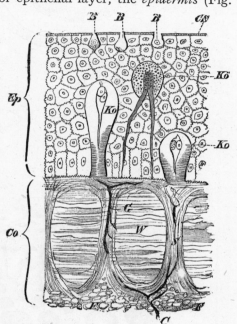

The skin may be naked, but is usually provided with protective structures of various kinds, such as scales, bony plates, feathers, or hair. Scales of the fishes are of different shapes, such as *cycloid*, *ctenoid* or *rhomboid*, but it is the structure rather than the shape that is of importance and of value in classification. There are three main kinds of scales in fishes : the *placoid*, the *cosmoid*, and the *ganoid*. The placoid scale (Fig. 55 (1)), with an ectodermal cap of enamel

FIG. 54.—Diagrammatic vertical section of the skin of a **Fish.** *B*, unicellular mucous glands ; *Co*, derm ; *CS*, cuticular margin ; *Ep.* epiderm ; *F*, fat ; *G*, blood-vessels ; *Ko*, goblet-cells ; *Kŏ*, granule-cells ; *S*, vertical, and *W*, horizontal bundles of connective-tissues. (From Wiedersheim's *Vertebrata*.)

and a body of dentine surrounding a pulp-chamber, has essentially the same composition as a tooth, and in the Chondrichthyes, in which group this scale is characteristic, there is a clear transition from the scales on the body to the teeth on the jaws. They lie superficially and, if lost, can be continually replaced.

The cosmoid scale (Fig. 55 (2)) lies deeper in the dermis, and consists of three layers : an outer one, known as the *cosmine* layer, which is formed of a cell-less substance somewhat like dentine with vascular spaces and fine radiating-tubules, and on the outer surface a thin layer of a hard glossy substance termed vitrodentine. The middle layer, the *vascular* layer, is formed of bone perforated by numerous anastomosing canals for the blood-vessels. The bottom layer, the *isopedine* layer, consists of several laminæ of bone lying parallel to one

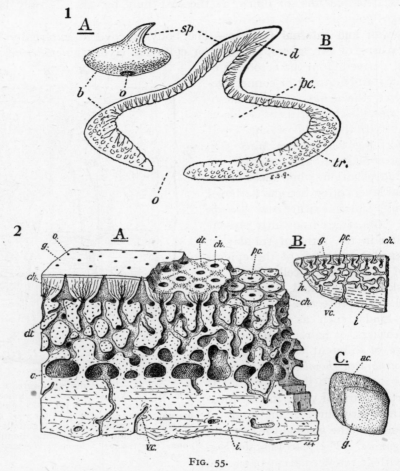

FIG. 55.

1. Placoid Scale. Median dorsal denticle scale of *Raja blanda*. *A*, left side view; *B*, section, enlarged; *b.* basal plate; *d.* dentinal tubules; *o.* opening of pulp cavity; *s.p.* projecting spine; *tr.* trabecular dentine. (After Goodrich.)

2. Cosmoid Scale of *Megalichthys hibberti*. *A*, piece of a thick transverse section enlarged; *B*, section through the hind edge, enlarged; *C*, outer view of a complete scale. *ac.* anterior region covered by next scale; *c.* large vascular cavity; *ch.* chamber of cosmine layer; *dt.* canaliculi of cosmine; *g.* thin outermost layer; *h.* irregular vascular canals; *i.* isopedine layer; *o.* opening of chamber of cosmine layer on surface; *pc.* pulp cavity from which canaliculi radiate; *vc.* vertical canal leading to vascular cavity. (After Goodrich.)

another, through which at intervals run canals for blood-vessels passing to the vascular layer. Cosmoid scales are not shed, and during growth expand by the addition of cosmine round the edge of the upper surface and by addition to the isopedine layers below. It appears that the vitrodentine covering of the scale can be resorbed and replaced at intervals during the life of the fish.[1] Cosmoid scales are found only in the Crossopterygians and in the Dipnoi, but in living forms of the last-named group much of the characteristic structure of the scale has been lost.

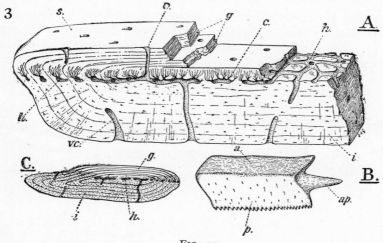

FIG. 55.

3. Ganoid Scale of *Eurynotus crenatus A*, diagrammatic and enlarged view of a piece of scale; *B*, outer view of a complete scale; *C*, transverse section of a scale. *a.* anterior covered region; *ap.* articulating process; *c.* fine canaliculi of cosmine layer; *g.* ganoine layer; *h.* system of horizontal canals; *i.* isopedine layer; *o.* opening of vertical canals on the outer surface; *p.* exposed posterior shiny part of the scale; *s.* outer surface; *vc.* vertical canal. (After Goodrich.)

The *ganoid* scale (Fig. 55 (3)) is composed of layers of cell-less *ganoine* on the upper surface which pass into layers of isopedine below. Between these two layers there are two more, an upper one resembling cosmine and a lower the vascular layers, but these are not universally present or may be much reduced. The growth of the ganoid scale differs from that of the cosmoid in that fresh layers are laid down on the top of the scale as well as on the underside. This type of scales and its derivatives is confined to the Actinopterygii.

Scales and bony plates occur in the higher vertebrata but their relation to those of the fishes is still obscure. In reptiles and birds the scales and feathers, and in mammals the hair, are epidermal in origin and are formed

[1] Westoll, T. S., " On the Structures of the Dermal Ethmoid Shield of Osteolepis." *Geol. Mag.* 73, No. 862. 1936.

of a horny substance termed *keratin* which is perhaps distantly allied to enamel. Details of the structure are given in the accounts of the respective classes.

Beneath the skin comes the *muscular layer*. This is always highly developed, and, in the lower Craniata, has the same general arrangement as in Amphioxus, *i.e.* consists of zigzag muscle-segments or *myomeres* (Fig. 56, *mym.*), separated from one another by partitions of connective-tissue, or *myocommas* (*myc.*), and formed of longitudinally disposed muscle-fibres. The myomeres are not placed at right angles to the long axis of the body, but are directed from the median vertical plane outwards and backwards, and are at the same time convex in front and concave behind, so as to have a cone-in-cone arrangement (Fig. 57, *C*). Each myomere, moreover, is divisible into a dorsal (*d. m.*) and a ventral (*v. m.*) portion. In the higher groups this segmental arrange-

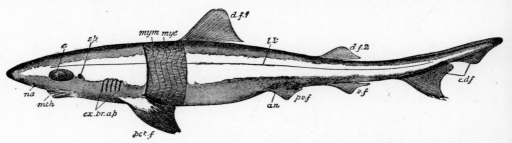

FIG. 56.—Side view of **Dogfish** (*Mustelus antarcticus*), with a strip of skin in the middle of the body removed to show the muscles. *an.* anus; *cf. d.* caudal fin; *d. f. 1, d. f. 2*, dorsal fins; *e.* eye; *ext. br. ap.* external branchial apertures; *l. l.* lateral line; *mth.* mouth; *myc.* myocommas; *mym.* myomeres; *n. a.* nasal aperture; *pct. f.* pectoral fin; *pv. f.* pelvic fin; *sp.* spiracle; *v. f.* ventral fin. (From Parker's *Biology*.)

ment, though present in the embryo, is lost in the adult, the myomeres becoming converted into more or less longitudinal bands having an extremely complex arrangement.

In the trunk, as shown by a section of that region, the muscles form a definite layer beneath the skin and enclosing the *cœlome* (Fig. 57, *A* and *C*, *cœl.*). The muscular layer, as in Amphioxus, is not of even diameter throughout, but is greatly thickened dorsally, so that the cœlome is, as it were, thrown towards the ventral side. Its dorsal portion, moreover, is excavated by a canal, the *neural* or *cerebro-spinal cavity* (*c. s. c.*), in which the central nervous system is contained, and the anterior portion of which is always dilated, as the *cranial cavity*, for the brain. Thus a transverse section of the trunk has the form of a double tube. In the head, neck, and tail (*B, D*), the cœlome is absent in the adult, and the muscles occupy practically the whole of the interval between the skin and the skeleton, presently to be referred to : in the tail, however, there is found a *hæmal canal* (*h. c.*) containing connective-tissue, and representing a virtual backward extension of the cœlome. The fins, or fore- and hind-limbs,

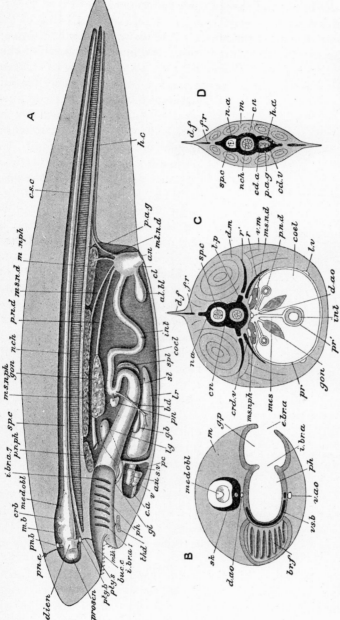

Fig. 57.—A, sagittal section of ideal **Craniate**; B, transverse section of the head; C, of the trunk; D, of the tail. *al. bl.* allantoic bladder; *an.* anus; *au.* auricle; *b. d.* bile-duct; *br. f.* branchial filaments; *buc. c.* buccal cavity; *c. a.* conus arteriosus; *cd. a.* caudal artery; *cd. v.* caudal vein; *cœl.* cœlome; *crd. v.* cardinal vein; *cn.* centrum; *crb.* cerebellum; *c. s. c.* cerebrospinal cavity; *d. ao.* dorsal aorta; *dien.* diencephalon; *d. f.* dorsal fin; *d. m.* dorsal muscles; *e. br. a.* external branchial aperture; *f. r.* fin-ray; *g. b.* gall-bladder; *gl.* glottis; *gon.* gonad; *g. p.* gill-pouch; *b. a.* hæmal arch; *h. c.* hæmal canal; *i. br. a.* internal branchial apertures; *int.* intestine; *lg.* lung; *lv.* liver; *l. v.* lateral vein; *m.* muscles; *m. b.* mid-brain; *med. obl.* medulla oblongata; *mes.* mesentery; *ms. n. d.* mesonephric duct; *ms. nph.* mesonephros; *mt.* metanephric duct; *mt. nph.* metanephros; *n. a.* neural arch; *nch.* notochord; *p. a. g.* post-anal gut; *pc.* pericardium; *ph.* pharynx; *pn.* pancreas; *pn. b.* pineal body; *p. n. d.* pronephric duct; *pn. e.* pineal sense-organ; *p. nph.* pronephros; *pr.* peritoneum, parietal layer, and *pr'.* visceral layer; *prosen.* prosencephalon; *pty. b.* pituitary body; *pty. s.* pituitary sac; *r.* sub-peritoneal rib; *r'.* intermuscular rib; *sk.* skull; *sp. c.* spinal cord; *spl.* spleen; *st.* stomach; *s. v.* sinus venosus; *thd.* thyroid; *t. p.* transverse process; *v.* ventricle; *v. ao.* ventral aorta; *v. m.* ventral muscles; *vs. b.* visceral bar.

are moved by longitudinal muscles derived from those of the trunk.   All the
voluntary or body-muscles of Craniata are of the striated kind.

The cœlome is lined by *peritoneum* (*C*, *pr.*), a membrane consisting of an
outer layer of connective-tissue, next the muscles, and an inner layer of cœlomic
epithelium bounding the cavity, and thus forming the innermost layer of the
body-wall.   In Fishes the cœlome is divided into two chambers, a large
abdominal cavity containing the chief viscera, and a small forwardly-placed
pericardial cavity (*A*, *pc.*) containing the heart, and lined by a detached portion of peritoneum known as the *pericardium*.   In Mammals there is a vertical muscular partition, the *diaphragm*, dividing the cœlome into an anterior chamber or *thorax*, containing the heart and lungs, and a posterior chamber or *abdomen* containing the remaining viscera.

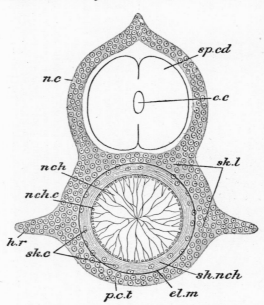

Fig. 58.—Semi-diagrammatic transverse section
of the vertebral column of a **Craniate embryo.**   *c. c.*
central canal; *el. m.* external elastic membrane;
h. r. hæmal ridges; *n. c.* neural tube; *nch.* notochord; *nch. c.* notochordal cells; *p. c. t.* perichordal
tube; *sh. nch.* sheath of notochord; *sk. c.* skeletogenous cells migrating into notochordal sheath; *sk. l.*
skeletogenous layer; *sp. cd.* spinal cord. (Modified
from Balfour and Gadow.)

Skeleton.—The hard parts or supporting structures of Craniata fall into two categories—the *exoskeleton* and the *endoskeleton*. The **exoskeleton** consists of bony or horny deposits in the skin, and may be either epidermal or dermal, or both, but is never, like the armour of an Arthropod or the shell of a Mollusc, cuticular.   The epidermal exoskeleton is always formed by the cornification or conversion into horn of epidermal cells, and may take the form of scales—as in Reptiles, feathers,

hairs, claws, nails, horns, and hoofs.   The dermal exoskeleton occurs in
the form of either bony or horn-like deposits in the derm, such as the
scales and dermal fin-rays of Fishes, and the bony armour of the Sturgeon,
Crocodile, or Armadillo.

The **endoskeleton,** or " skeleton " in the ordinary sense of the word, forms
one of the most complex portions of the body, and presents an immense range
of variation in the different classes and orders.   As in Amphioxus, the axis
of the entire skeletal system is formed by the *notochord* (Fig. 58, *nch.*), an
elastic rod made of peculiar vacuolated cells (Figs. 58, 59, *nch.*), resembling the

pith of plants, and covered by a laminated *sheath* (*sh. nch.*), with an *external elastic membrane* (*el. m.*) around it. The whole sheath is, in the Craniata, a cuticular product of the superficial notochordal cells (*nch. c.*), *i.e.* is developed as a secretion from their outer or free surfaces. The notochord lies in the middle line of the dorsal body-wall between the cerebro-spinal cavity above and the cœlome below : it is usually developed, as in the lower Chordata, from a median longitudinal outgrowth of the dorsal wall of the gut. Posteriorly it extends to the end of the tail, but in front it always stops short of the anterior end of the head, ending near the middle of the brain immediately behind a peculiar organ, the *pituitary body* (Fig. 57, *A*, *pty. b.*), which will be referred to again in treating of the digestive organs and of the nervous system. The extension of the nervous system in front of the notochord is one of the most striking differences between

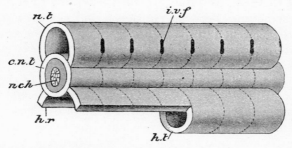

FIG. 59.—Diagram illustrating the segmentation of the vertebral column. *c. n. t.* perichordal tube ; *h. r.* hæmal ridge ; *h. t.* hæmal tube ; *i. v. f.* intervertebral foramen ; *n. t.* neural tube ; *nch.* notochord. The dotted lines indicate the segmentation into vertebræ.

the Craniata and Amphioxus, in which, it will be remembered, the notochord is prolonged to a considerable distance beyond the anterior end of the nerve-tube.

In the majority of Craniata the notochord is a purely embryonic structure, and all but the anterior end of it is replaced in the adult by the *vertebral column.* The cells of mesoderm surrounding the notochord become concentrated around the sheath and give rise to the *skeletogenous layer* (Fig. 58, *sk. l.*), some of the cells of which (*sk. c.*) may migrate through the elastic membrane into the sheath itself. In this way the notochord becomes surrounded by a cellular invest-ment which soon takes on the structure of cartilage, and may be called the *perichordal tube* (Fig. 58, *p. c. t.*, and Fig. 59, *c. n. t.*). The skeletogenous layer also grows upwards, and gives rise to an inverted tunnel of cartilage, the *neural tube* (*n. c., n. t.*), enclosing the cerebro-spinal cavity and connected below with the perichordal tube ; and to paired *hæmal ridges* (*h. r.*) of cartilage standing out from the sides of the perichordal tube into the muscles : in the region of the tail these unite below to enclose the *hæmal canal* (*h. c.*) already referred to. Actually, however, the vertebral column thus constituted is from the first more or less broken up into segments, and in the higher forms is replaced by a chain of bones called *vertebræ* which follow one another from before backwards, beginning a short distance behind the anterior end of the notochord and extending to the extremity of the tail.

A vertebra consists essentially of the following parts : (1) a *centrum* or *body* (Fig. 57, C, cn.) lying below the spinal canal in the position formerly occupied by the notochord and perichordal tube, and arising either in the skeletogenous layer proper, or in the notochordal sheath after its invasion by skeletogenous cells ; (2) a *neural arch* (n. a.) which springs from the dorsal surface of the centrum and encircles the spinal canal, representing a segment of the neural tube ; and (3) a pair of *transverse processes* (t. p.) which extend outward from the centrum among the muscles and represent segments of the hæmal ridges : to them are often attached *ribs* which extend downwards in the body-wall, sometimes between the dorsal and ventral muscles (r'.), sometimes immediately external to the peritoneum (r.). In the anterior part of the ventral body-wall a cartilaginous or bony *sternum* or breast-bone may be developed : in the Amphibia it is an independent structure ; in the higher classes it is formed by the fusion of some of the anterior ribs in the middle ventral line. In this way the anterior or thoracic region of the cœlome is enclosed in an articulated bony framework formed of the vertebral column above, the ribs at the sides, and the sternum below. The ribs under these circumstances become segmented each into two parts, a dorsal *vertebral rib*, articulating with a vertebra, and a ventral *sternal rib* with the sternum. In the tail there is frequently a *hæmal arch* (Fig. 57, D, h. a.) springing from the ventral aspect of the centrum and enclosing the hæmal canal. Thus the line of centra in the fully-formed vertebral column occupies the precise position of the notochord ; the neural arches encircle the spinal portion of the cerebro-spinal cavity ; the transverse processes, ribs, and sternum encircle the cœlome ; and the hæmal arches similarly surround the hæmal canal or vestigial cœlome of the tail. As we ascend the series of Craniata we find every gradation from the persistent notochord of the Cyclostomata, through the imperfectly differentiated vertebræ of Sharks and Rays, to the complete bony vertebral column of the higher forms.

The vertebræ are equal in number to the myomeres, but are arranged alternately with them, the fibrous partition between two myomeres abutting against the middle of a vertebra, so that each muscle-segment acts upon two adjacent vertebræ. Thus, the myomeres being metameric or segmental structures, the vertebræ are intersegmental.

In connection with the anterior end of the notochord, where no vertebræ are formed, there are developed certain elements of the *skull* or cephalic skeleton, a structure which is eminently characteristic of the whole craniate division, and to the possession of which it owes its name. The skull makes its first appearance in the embryo in the form of paired cartilaginous plates, the *para-*

chordals (Fig. 60, *pc.*), lying one on each side of the anterior end of the noto-chord (*nch.*), and thus continuing forward the line of vertebral centra. In front of the parachordals are developed a pair of curved cartilaginous rods, the *trabeculæ* (*tr.*) which underlie the anterior part of the brain, as the para-chordals underlie its posterior part : their hinder ends diverge so as to embrace the pituitary body (*pty.*) already referred to. Cartilaginous investments are also formed around the organs of the three higher senses : a pair of *olfactory capsules* round the organs of smell, one of *optic capsules* round the organs of sight, and one of *auditory capsules* (*au. c.*) round the organs of hearing. The optic capsule, which may be either cartilaginous or fibrous, remains free from the remaining elements of the skull in accordance with the mobility of the eye ; it constitutes, in fact, the *sclerotic* or outer coat of that organ. The olfactory capsules are usually formed in relation to the trabeculæ, and are continuous with those structures from an early stage. The auditory capsules in some cases arise as outgrowths of the parachordals, in others as independent cartilages, each of which, however, soon unites with the parachordal of its own side. As development goes on, the trabeculæ and parachordals become fused into a single *basal plate* (Fig. 61, *B, b. cr.*) underlying the brain : the skull-floor thus formed gives off vertical up-growths on each side which finally close

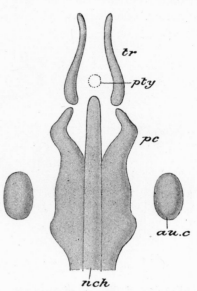

FIG. 60.—The elements of the cran-ium in an embryo **Salmon,** from above. *au. c.* auditory capsule ; *nch.* notochord ; *pc.* parachordal ; *pty.* position of pituit-ary body ; *tr.* trabecula. (From a model by Ziegler.)

in above to a greater or less extent, and so give rise to a more or less complete *cranium* or *brain-case* enclosing the brain and the organs of smell and hearing, and furnishing open cavities or *orbits* for the eyes.

In the continuous solid cranial box thus formed certain definite regions are to be distinguished : a posterior or *occipital region*, formed from the para-chordals, united or articulated with the anterior end of the vertebral column, and presenting a large aperture, the *foramen magnum* (Fig. 61, *B, for. mag.*), through which the spinal cord becomes continuous with the brain ; an *auditory region* formed by the two outstanding auditory capsules (*A, au. cp.*) ; and a *trabecular region*, including all the rest. The latter is again divisible into an *interorbital region*, between the orbits or eye-sockets ; an *olfactory region*, constituted by the olfactory capsules (*olf. cp.*), and by a median vertical plate,

the *mesethmoid* (*B, m. eth.*), which separates them from one another; and a *pre-nasal region* or *rostrum* (*r.*) extending forwards from the mesethmoid and forming a more or less well-marked anterior prolongation of the cranium. The cavity for the brain (*B*) extends from the foramen magnum behind to the olfactory region in front; its floor, formed from the basal plate of the embryo, is called the *basis cranii* (*b. cr.*): its roof is always incomplete, there being one or more apertures or *fontanelles* (*fon.*) closed only by membrane and due to the imperfect union above the side-walls.

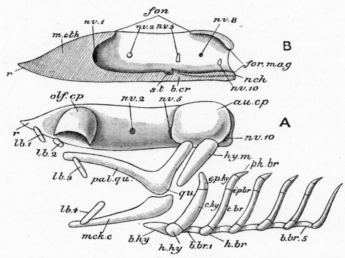

FIG. 61.—*A*, diagram of cartilaginous skull from the left side; *B*, cranium in sagittal section. *au. cp.* auditory capsule; *b. br. 1–5*, basi-branchials; *b. cr.* basis cranii; *b. hy.* basi-hyal; *c. br.* cerato-branchial; *o. hy.* cerato-hyal; *ep. br.* epi-branchial; *ep. hy.* epi-hyal; *fon.* fontanelle; *for. mag.* foramen magnum; *h. br.* hypo-branchial; *h. hy.* hypo-hyal; *hy. m.* hyomandibular; *lb. 1—4*, labial cartilages; *mck. c.* Meckel's cartilage; *m. eth.* mesethmoid; *nv. 1—10*, foramina for cerebral nerves; *olf. cp.* olfactory capsule; *pal. qu.* palato-quadrate; *ph. br.* pharyngo-branchial; *r.* rostrum; *s. t.* pituitary fossa or sella turcica.

In the walls of the brain-case are apertures or *foramina* for the passage outwards of the cerebral nerves (*vide* p. 101). The most important of these are the *olfactory foramina* (*nv. 1*) for the nerves of smell, situated at the anterior end of the cerebral cavity, one on each side of the mesethmoid; the *optic foramina* (*nv. 2*) for the nerves of sight, in the inter-orbital region; the *trige-minal foramina* (*nv. 5*) for the fifth nerves, just in front of the auditory capsule; the *auditory foramina* (*nv. 8*) for the nerves of hearing, in the inner wall of the auditory capsules; and the *vagus foramina* (*nv. 10*) for the tenth nerves, immediately posterior to the auditory capsules.

In addition to the elements of the brain-case—parachordals, trabeculæ, and auditory capsules—there enter into the composition of the skull another set of elements called *visceral bars*. These are cartilaginous rods formed in the walls of the pharynx between the gill-slits, and thus encircling the pharynx like a series of paired half-hoops (Fig. 61, *B, vs. b.*) The corresponding right and left bars become united with one another below by an unpaired cartilage (Fig. 61, *A, b. br.*), forming a *visceral arch*, and the unpaired ventral pieces may unite successive arches with one another in the middle ventral line, thus giving rise to a more or less basket-like *visceral skeleton*. It will be noticed that the visceral skeleton has a segmental arrangement, being formed of parts arranged in an antero-posterior series, whereas in the cranium there is no clear indication of segmentation. There is, however, no exact correspondence between the segments of the visceral skeleton and the metameres. The visceral arches vary in number from four to nine : the foremost of them is distinguished as the *mandibular arch*, and lies just behind the mouth ; the second is called the *hyoid arch*, and the rest *branchial arches*, from the fact that they support the gills in water-breathing forms.

In all Craniata except the Cyclostomes the mandibular arch becomes modified into structures called *jaws* for the support of the mouth. Each mandibular bar divides into a dorsal and a ventral portion called respectively the *palato-quadrate cartilage* (Fig. 61, *A, pal. qu.*) and *Meckel's cartilage* (*mck. c.*) : the palato-quadrates grow forwards along the upper or anterior margin of the mouth, and unite with one another in the middle line, forming an *upper jaw* : Meckel's cartilages similarly extend along the lower or posterior margin of the mouth and unite in the middle line, forming the *lower jaw*. The *quadrate* (*qu.*), or posterior end of the palato-quadrate, furnishes an articulation for the lower jaw, and often acquires a connection with the cranium, thus serving to suspend the jaws from the latter. Thus each jaw arises from the union of paired bars, the final result being two unpaired transverse structures, one lying in the anterior, the other in the posterior margin of the transversely elongated mouth, and moving in a vertical plane. The fundamental difference between the jaws of a Vertebrate and the structures called by the same name in an Arthropod or a Polychætous Worm will be obvious at once.

The hyoid bar usually becomes divided into two parts, a dorsal, the *hyomandibular* or *pharyngo-hyal* (*hy.m.*), and a ventral, the *hyoid cornu*, which is again divisible from above downwards into segments called respectively *epi-hyal* (*ep.hy.*), *cerato-hyal* (*c.hy.*), and *hypo-hyal* (*h.hy.*). The median ventral element of the arch, or *basi-hyal* (*b.hy.*), serves for the support of the tongue.

In the earliest fishes of all—*e.g.*, the Acanthodii (p. 154)—the jaws are attached by ligaments to the neurocranium and the hyoid arch, instead of being modified to support the upper and lower jaws, is as complete as are the posterior arches and the gill-slit lying in front of the hyoid arch, instead of being reduced to a spiracle which may even be closed and disappear, is fully functional as a complete gill. This type of jaw suspension may be termed *autodiastylic*.[1]

[1] de Beer and Moy-Thomas, *Trans. Royal Soc.*, B 514, 1935.

When the hyomandibular becomes attached to the hinge of the upper and lower jaws and supports them so that the attachment to the skull is lost, the suspension is termed *hyostylic*, and this is the method of attachment of the majority of fishes. In some early forms and in a few living fishes there is an attachment to the skull as well as to the hyomandibular, a condition known as *amphistylic*. It appears that in fishes the autodiastylic attachment is the most primitive, the amphistylic the next to be derived from it, and then the hyostylic as the most recent. It is probable that the latter condition has been arrived at independently in the Chondrichthyes and bony fishes.

Finally, the upper jaw, instead of merely lying against the skull and attached only by ligaments, as in the autodiastylic phase, may become definitely fused with it. This condition is termed *autosystylic*. Two groups of fishes have the jaws attached to the skull and no hyoid suspension—namely, the Dipnoi and Holocephali—but the condition is not the same in each case. The Holocephali have a complete hyoid arch which is free from the cranium, a condition which, according to different interpretations, may be an approach to the autodiastylic condition or a secondary modification such as is shown by the skates. To this kind of suspension the term *holostylic* [1] has been given. In the Dipnoi and all Tetrapods the hyoid arch becomes broken up and the hyomandibular attached to the skull, where it soon enters into the service of the ear region. This condition is usually termed *autostylic*. As this term, however, really covers more than one condition it is now divided into *autosystylic* and *holostylic*.

The branchial arches become divided transversely into dorsoventral segments called respectively *pharyngo-branchial* (*ph.br.*), *epi-branchial* (*ep.br.*), *cerato-branchial* (*c.br.*), and *hypo-branchial* (*h.br.*), and the visceral skeleton thus acquires the character of an articulated framework which allows of the dilatation of the pharynx during swallowing and of its more or less complete closure at other times.

In connection with, and always superficial to, the rostrum, olfactory capsules, and jaws, are frequently found *labial cartilages* (*lb. 1—4*), which sometimes attain considerable dimensions.

In certain Fishes, such as Elasmobranchs, the cartilages of the skull become more or less encrusted by a superficial granular deposit of lime-salts, giving rise, as in the vertebral column of these Fishes, to *calcified cartilage*; but in all the higher forms true ossification takes place, the cartilaginous skull becoming complicated, and to a greater or less extent replaced, by distinct *bones*. Of these there are two kinds, *replacing* or "*cartilage*"-*bones* and *investing* or "*membrane*"-*bones*. Replacing bones may begin by the deposition of patches of bony matter in the cartilage itself (*endochondral ossification*). As development proceeds, these may be replaced by ossification starting within the

[1] W. K. Gregory, *Biological Bulletin*, Vol. VII, no. 1, 1904, "The Relations of the Anterior Visceral Arches to the Chondrocranium."

perichondrium, or layer of connective-tissue surrounding the cartilage, and gradually invading the latter. More usually the bone is formed from the outset by the deposition of layers invading the cartilage from the perichondrium (or periosteum) inwards (*perichondral* or *periosteal ossification*). But in either case the bones in question are usually said to be *preformed in cartilage, i.e.* they replace originally cartilaginous parts. In the case of investing bones, centres of ossification also appear, in constant positions, in the fibrous tissue outside the cartilage : they may remain quite independent of the original cartilaginous skull and its replacing bones, so as to be readily removable by boiling or maceration ; or they may eventually become, as it were, grafted

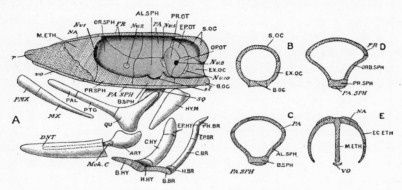

FIG. 62.—*A*, diagram of bony skull in sagittal section ; *B*, transverse section of occipital region ; *C*, of parietal region ; *D*, of frontal region ; *E*, of ethmoidal region. Cartilaginous parts are dotted ; replacing bones are marked in thick type, investing bones in italics. *Mck. C.* Meckel's cartilage ; *Nv. 1—10*, foramina for cerebral nerves ; *r.* rostrum ; *s. t.* sella turcica or pituitary fossa. Replacing bones—**AL.SPH.** alisphenoid ; **ART.** articular ; **B.BR.** basi-branchial ; **B.HY.** basi-hyal ; **B.OC.** basi-occipital ; **B.SPH.** basi-sphenoid ; **C.BR.** cerato-branchial ; **C.HY.** cerato-hyal ; **EC.ETH.** ecto-ethmoid ; **EP.BR.** epi-branchial ; **EP.HY.** epi-hyal ; **EY.OC.** ex-occipital ; **H.BR.** hypo-branchial ; **H.HY.** hypo-hyal ; **HY.M.** hyomandibular ; **M.ETH.** mesethmoid ; **OP.OT.** opisthotic ; **OR.SPH.** orbito-sphenoid ; **PAL.** palatine ; **PH.BR.** pharyngo-branchial ; **PR.OT.** pro-otic ; **PR.SPH.** pre-sphenoid ; **PTG.** pterygoid ; **QU.** quadrate ; **S.OC.** supra-occipital. Investing bones—*DNT.* dentary ; *F.R.* frontal ; *MX.* maxilla ; *NA.* nasal ; *PA.* parietal ; *PA.SPH.* para-sphenoid ; *P.MX.* premaxilla ; *SQ.* squamosal ; *VO., v.o.* vomer.

on to the cartilage; in which case all distinction between investing and replacing bones is lost in the adult. The investing bones are to be looked upon as portions of the exoskeleton which have retreated from the surface and acquired intimate relations with the endoskeleton.

The replacing bones have a very definite relation to the regions of the cartilaginous cranium. In the occipital region four bones are formed, surrounding the foramen magnum : a median ventral *basi-occipital* (Fig. 62, *A* and *B*, **B.OC.**), paired lateral *ex-occipitals* (**EX.OC.**), and a median dorsal *supra-occipital* (**S.OC.**). In each auditory capsule three ossifications commonly appear : a *pro-otic* (*A*, **PR.OT.**) in front, an *opisthotic* (**OP.OT.**) behind, and an *epi-otic* (**EP.OT.**) over the arch of the posterior semicircular canal of the ear

(*vide infra*).   In front of the basi-occipital a bone called the *basi-sphenoid*
(*A* and *C*, **B.SPH.**) is formed in the floor of the skull : it appears in the position
of the posterior ends of the trabeculæ, and bears on its upper or cranial surface
a depression, the *sella turcica* (*s.t.*), for the reception of the pituitary body.
Connected on either side with the basi-sphenoid are paired bones, the *ali-
sphenoids* (**AL.SPH.**), which help to furnish the side-walls of the interorbital
region.   The basi-sphenoid is continued forwards by another median bone, the
pre-sphenoid (*A* and *D*, **P.SPH.**) with which paired ossifications, the *orbito-
sphenoids* (**ORB.SPH.**) are connected and complete the side-walls of the inter-
orbital region.   The basi-occipital, basi-sphenoid, and pre-sphenoid together
form the basis cranii of the bony skull.   A vertical plate of bone, the *mesethmoid* (**M.ETH.**), appears in the posterior portion of the cartilage of the same
name, and the outer walls of the olfactory capsules may be ossified by paired
ecto-ethmoids (*E*, **EC.ETH.**).

So far, it will be seen, the cranial cavity has its hinder region alone roofed
over by bone, *viz.* by the supra-occipital : for the rest of it the replacing bones
furnish floor and side-walls only.   This deficiency is made good by two pairs
of investing bones, the *parietals* (*PA.*), formed immediately in front of the supra-
occipital and usually articulating below with the ali-sphenoids, and the *frontals*
(*FR.*), placed in front of the parietals, and often connected below with the
orbito-sphenoids.   A pair of *nasals* (*NA.*) are developed above the olfactory
capsules and immediately in advance of the frontals ; and below the base of
the skull two important investing bones make their appearance, the *vomer*
(*vo.*)—which may be double—in front, and the *para-sphenoid* (*PA.SPH.*)
behind.

The result of the peculiar arrangement of replacing and investing bones
just described is that the brain-case, in becoming ossified, acquires a kind of
secondary segmentation, being clearly divisible in the higher groups, and
especially in the Mammalia, into three quasi-segments.   These are the *occipital
segment* (*B*) formed by the basi-occipital below, the ex-occipitals at the sides,
and the supra-occipital above [1] ; the *parietal segment* (*C*), formed by the basi-
sphenoid below, the ali-sphenoids laterally, and the parietals above ; and the
frontal segment (*D*), constituted by the pre-sphenoid below, the orbito-sphenoids
on either side, and the frontals above.   It must be observed that this segmentation of the cranium is quite independent of the primary segmentation of the
head, which is determined by the presence of myomeres and by the relations
of the cerebral nerves.

The cranial bones have constant relations to the cerebral nerves.   The
olfactory nerves (*A*, *Nv. 1*) pass out one on either side of the mesethmoid, the
optic nerves (*Nv. 2*) through or immediately behind the orbito-sphenoids,

---

[1] With the occipital segment in many Fishes are amalgamated one or several of the most
anterior vertebræ.

the fifth nerves (*Nv. 5*) through or immediately behind the ali-sphenoids, and the tenth nerves (*Nv. 10*) through or immediately in front of the ex-occipitals.

It will be seen that a clear distinction can be drawn between the *primary cranium, chondrocranium* or *neurocranium* formed by the fusion of the para-chordals, auditory capsules, and trabeculæ, and consisting of an undivided mass of cartilage more or less replaced by bones, and the *secondary cranium* or *osteocranium*, modified by the super-addition of investing bones.

A similar distinction may be drawn between the *primary* and *secondary*

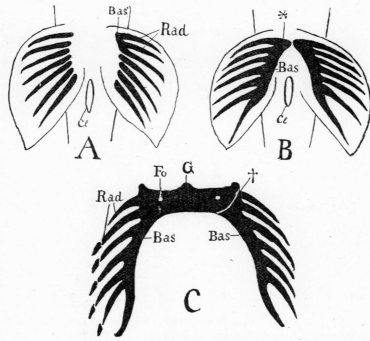

FIG. 63.—Diagram of three stages in the development of the pelvic fins. In *A*, the anterior pterygiophores on the right side (*Rad.*) have united to form a basal cartilage (*Bas.*); in *B* the basalia (*Bas.*) are fully formed and are uniting at * to form the pelvic girdle; in *C* the pelvic girdle (*G.*) is fully constituted, and at † has segmented from the basale on the right side. *Cl.* cloacal aperture. (From Wiedersheim's *Comparative Anatomy*.)

jaws. The *primary upper jaw*, or palato-quadrate, becomes ossified by three chief replacing bones on each side, the *palatine* (*A*, **PAL.**) in front, then the *pterygoid* (**PTG.**), and the *quadrate* (**QU.**) behind, the latter furnishing the articulation for the lower jaw or *mandible*. In the higher classes the primary upper jaw does not appear as a distinct cartilaginous structure, and the palatine and pterygoid are developed as investing bones. The *secondary upper jaw* is constituted by two pairs of investing bones, the *pre-maxilla* (*P.MX.*) and the *maxilla* (*MX.*), which in bony skulls furnish the actual anterior boundary of the mouth, the primary jaw becoming altogether shut out of the gape. The proximal end of the *primary lower jaw* ossifies to form a replacing bone, the *articular* (**ART.**), by which the mandible is hinged : the rest of it remains as a slender, unossified *Meckel's cartilage* (*Mck. C.*), which may disappear entirely in the adult. The *secondary lower jaw* is formed by a variable number of investing bones, the most important of which is the *dentary* (*DNT.*). In

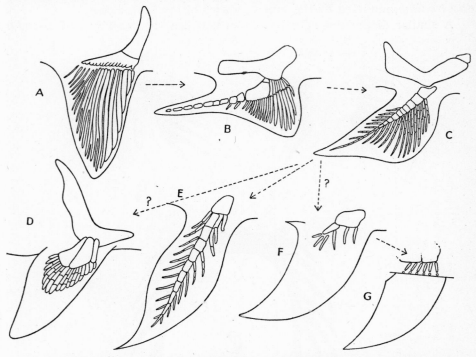

Fig. 64.—Right pectoral fins of A, **Cladoselache ;** B, **Cladodus ;** C, **Pleuracanthus ;** D, a " shark "; E, **Ceratodus ;** F, a primitive Actinopterygian ; G, a Teleost. The dotted lines suggest possible lines of *functional* evolution.

Mammalia the dentary forms the entire mandible, and articulates, not with the quadrate, but with a large investing bone formed external to the latter, and known as the *squamosal* (*SQ.*).

In the hyoid arch a replacing bone, the *hyo-mandibular* (**HY.M.**), appears in the cartilage of the same name, and ossifications are also formed in the various segments of the hyoid cornua (**EP.HY., C.HY., H.HY., B.HY.**) and of the branchial arches (**PH.BR., EP.BR., C.BR., H.BR., B.BR.**). In the air-breathing forms both hyoid and branchial arches undergo more or less complete atrophy, the whole gill-bearing apparatus becoming reduced mainly to a small *hyoid bone* serving for the support of the tongue.

The skeleton of the median fins is formed of a single row of cartilaginous rays or *pterygiophores* (Fig. 63, *C* and *D*, *f.r.*), lying in the median plane, and more numerous than the vertebræ. They may ossify, and may be supplemented by *dermal fin-rays*, of varying composition, developed in the derm towards the free margin of the fin. The latter are clearly exoskeletal structures.

Both pectoral and pelvic fins are supported by pterygiophores or *radialia* (Fig. 63, *Rad.*), the basal or proximal ends of which are articulated with stout cartilages, the *basalia* (*Bas.*), often replaced by bones, which serve to strengthen the fin at its point of union with the trunk.

The structure of the paired fins varies in different groups of fishes (Fig. 64). It is supposed that they arose from an originally continuous fold along each side of the body from which the fins became constricted. This view is to some extent supported by embryological evidence and by the condition of the paired fins of *Cladoselache*, which, being without a posterior notch, have the appearance of being the remains of a previously continuous fin. The rows of spines on each side of the Acanthodians (Fig. 125) and of the agnathous Anaspida (Fig. 99) are likewise suggestive of a continuous fold. When such a fin as that of *Cladoselache* (pleurorhachic type) became free from the body-wall, it would consist of an axis of basalia and a fringe of radialia on the preaxial side. When more radials appeared on the postaxial side, as in *Pleuracanthus*, the fin reached the condition known as the archipterygium (mesorhachic type). This type of fin is also found in the Crossopterygians and Dipnoans. In the majority of Chondryichthyes the fin has three basalia, termed the pro- meso- and meta-pterygium, respectively, and a number of radialia arranged around them. The fin of the Polypterini has a somewhat similar appearance, though probably of a different origin. The Actinopterygii show a further modification, the basalia being lost and the radials reduced to small ossicles which lie within the body-wall, and not in the fin web. Besides the basals and radials, the fins are all strengthened in the free part by fin-rays, which are of several kinds: horny, fibrous or modified scales.[1]

In all classes above Fishes the paired fins are, as we have seen, replaced by five-toed or *pentadactyle limbs*. These are supported by bones, probably to be looked upon as greatly modified pterygiophores, and obviously serially homologous in the fore- and hind-limbs. In the proximal division of each limb there is a single rod-like bone, the *humerus* (Fig. 65, **HU.**), or upper-arm-bone, in the fore-limb, the *femur* (Fig. 65, **FE.**) or thigh-bone, in the hind-limb. In the middle division there are two elongated bones, an anterior, the *radius* (**RA.**), and a posterior, the *ulna* (**UL.**), in the fore-limb; an anterior, the *tibia* (**TL**), and a posterior, the *fibula* (**FI.**), in the hind-limb. Next follow the bones of the hand and foot, which are again divisible into three sets: *carpals* or wrist-bones, *metacarpals* (**mtcp.**) or hand-bones, the *phalanges*

[1] See Goodrich. Vertebrata Craniata, 1909.

(ph.) or finger-bones, in the fore-limb; *tarsals* or ankle-bones, *metatarsals* (mtts.) or foot-bones, and *phalanges* (ph.) or toe-bones, in the hind-limb. The carpals and tarsals consist typically of three rows of small nodules of bone

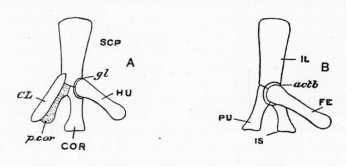

POSTAXIAL BORDER   PREAXIAL BORDER

Ulna ⎫
Fibula ⎭

Pisiform (Sesamoid)

Cuneiform ⎫
Calcaneum ⎭

Navicular (Centrale)-

Unciform ⎫
Cuboid ⎭

Magnum ⎫
Ectocuneiform ⎭

· Metatarsals·

{ Radius
{ Tibia

{ Lunar
{ Astragalus (in part)

{ Scaphoid
{ Astragalus

Centralia (1-3)

{ Trapezium
{ Entocuneiform

{ Trapezoid
{ Mesocuneiform

Metacarpals

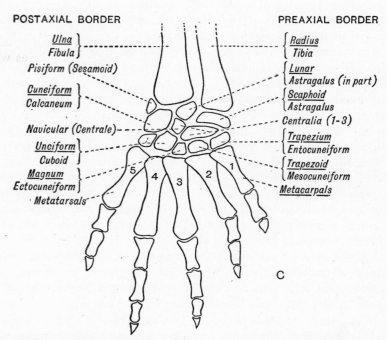

FIG. 65.—Diagrams of (A) the pectoral and (B) pelvic girdles and (C) generalised hand and foot of a Tetrapod. **actb.** acetabulum; *gl.* glenoid cavity; **p. cor.** pre-coracoid; **SCP.** scapula; **CL.** clavicle; **COR.** coracoid; **HU.** humerus; of shoulder blade. **FE.** femur; **IL.** ilium; **IS.** ischium; **PU.** pubis; of pelvic girdle. Bones of the fore limb are underlined.

or cartilage, the proximal row containing three, the middle two, and the distal five elements. The three proximal carpals are called respectively *radiale* (ra.), *intermedium* (int.), and *ulnare* (ul.), those of the middle row the first and second *centralia* (**cn. 1, cn. 2**), those of the third row the five *distalia* (**dst. 1–5**), the separate elements being distinguished by numbers, counting from the anterior or radial edge of the limb. In the tarsus the bones of the first row are known respectively as *tibiale* (**ti.**), *intermedium* (**int.**), and *fibulare* (**fi.**), those of the second row as *centralia* (**cn. 1, cn. 2**), and those of the third as *distalia* (**dst. 1–5**). The metacarpals (**mtcp. 1–5**) and metatarsals (**mtts. 1–5**) are five rod-like bones, one articulating with each distale : they are followed by the phalanges (**ph.**), of which each digit may have from one to five. The first digit of the fore-limb (Fig. 65, *I*) is distinguished as the *pollex* or thumb, that of the hind-limb (Fig. 65, *I*) as the *hallux* or great toe ; the fifth digit of each limb (*L*) is the *minimus*.

In connection with the paired appendages are formed supporting structures called the *limb-girdles* ; they occur in the portions of the trunk adjacent to the appendages and serve for the articulation of the latter. In the embryonic condition they are continuous with the basalia and are probably to be looked upon as ingrowths of the primitive fin-skeleton (Fig. 63). The *shoulder-girdle* or *pectoral arch* has primarily the form or paired bars, which may unite in the middle ventral line so as to form an inverted arch. Each bar—*i.e.* each half of the arch—furnishes a concave or convex *glenoid surface* (Fig. 65, *gl.*) for the articulation of the pectoral fin or fore-limb, and is thereby divided into two portions—a dorsal or *scapular region*, above the glenoid surface, and a ventral or *coracoid region* below it. The coracoid region is again divisible, in all classes above Fishes, into two portions : an anterior, the *pro-coracoid* (*p. cor.*), and a posterior, the *coracoid* proper. Each of these regions commonly ossifies—a replacing bone, the *scapula* (**SCP.**), appearing in the scapular region, another, the *coracoid* (**COR.**), in the coracoid region, while in relation with the pro-coracoid is formed a bone, the *clavicle* (*CL.*), largely or entirely developed independently of pre-existing cartilage.

The constitution of the *hip-girdle*, or *pelvic arch*, is very similar. It consists originally of paired bars, which may unite in the middle ventral line, and are divided by the *acetabulum* (Fig. 65, *actb.*), the articular surface for the pelvic fin or hind-limb, into a dorsal or *iliac region*, and a ventral or *pubo-ischial region*, the latter being again divisible, in all classes above Fishes, into an anterior portion, or *pubis*, and a posterior portion, or *ischium*. Each region is replaced in the higher forms by a bone, the pelvic girdle thus consisting of a dorsal *ilium* (**IL.**) serially homologous with the scapula, an antero-ventral *pubis* (**PU.**) with the pro-coracoid and clavicle, and a postero-ventral *ischium* (**IS.**) with the coracoid. The long bones of the limbs are divisible each into a *shaft*, and proximal and distal *extremities*. When ossification takes place the shaft is converted into a tubular bone, the cartilaginous axis of which is absorbed and replaced by a vascular fatty tissue called *marrow*. The extremities become simply calcified in the lower forms, but in the higher a distinct centre

of ossification may appear in each, forming the *epiphysis*, which finally becomes ankylosed to the shaft.

Digestive Organs.—The *enteric canal* is divisible into buccal cavity (Fig. 57, *A*, *buc. c.*), pharynx (*ph.*), gullet, stomach (*st.*), and intestine (*int.*), the latter often communicating with the exterior by a cloaca (*cl.*), which receives the urinary and genital ducts. The *buccal cavity* is developed from the stomodæum of the embryo : the proctodæum gives rise to a very small area in the neighbourhood of the anus, or, when a cloaca is present, to the external portion of the latter ; all the rest of the canal is formed from the mesenteron, and is therefore lined by an epithelium of endodermal origin. The *pharynx* communicates with the exterior, in Fishes and in the embryos of the higher forms, by the gill-slits (*i. br. a*, 1–7) ; it communicates with the stomach by the *gullet*. The *stomach* (*st.*) is usually bent upon itself in the form of a U ; the *intestine* (*int.*) is generally more or less convoluted ; hence the stomach and intestine are together considerably longer than the enclosing abdominal cavity. In the embryo the intestine is sometimes continued backwards into the hæmal canal by an extension called the *post-anal gut* (*p. a. g.*), which may perhaps indicate that the anus has shifted forwards in the course of evolution.

The epithelium of the buccal cavity is usually many-layered, like that of the skin, of which it is developmentally an in-turned portion ; the pharynx and gullet have also a laminated epithelium, but the rest of the canal is lined by a single layer of cells underlaid by a layer of connective-tissue, the deeper part of which is called the *sub-mucosa* ; epithelium and connective-tissue together constitute the *mucous membrane*. The mucous membrane of the stomach and sometimes of the intestine usually contains close-set tubular glands ; those of the stomach, the *gastric glands*, secrete *gastric juice*, which acts upon the proteid portions of the food only ; the secretion of the *intestinal glands* digests proteids, starch, and fats. Outside the mucous membrane are layers of *unstriped muscle*, usually an internal circular and an external longitudinal layer. Externally the intra-cœlomic portion of the canal is invested by peritoneum formed of a layer of connective-tissue next the gut and a single-layered cœlomic epithelium facing the body-cavity.

In connection with the enteric canal certain very characteristic structures are developed. In the mucous membrane of the mouth calcifications in most cases appear and form the *teeth*, which usually occur in a row along the ridge of each jaw, but may be developed on the roof of the mouth, on the tongue, and even in the pharynx. A tooth is usually formed of three tissues—*dentine, enamel*, and *cement*. The main bulk of the tooth is made up of dentine (Fig. 66, **A,** *ZB*), which occurs under three forms. *Hard dentine* consists of a matrix of animal matter strongly impregnated with lime-salts and permeated by delicate, more or less parallel, tubules containing organic fibrils. *Vaso-dentine* is permeated with blood-vessels, and consequently appears red and moist in the fresh condition. *Osteo-dentine* approaches bone in its structure and mode of development. The free surface of the tooth is usually capped by a layer of enamel (*ZS*), a dense substance, either structureless or presenting a delicate fibrillation, containing not more than 3 to 5 per cent. of animal matter, and being, therefore, the hardest tissue in the body. The cement (*ZC*) coats that portion of the tooth which is embedded in the tissues of the jaw, and sometimes forms a thin layer over the enamel; it has practically the structure of bone. At the inner end of the tooth there is frequently an aperture (*PH'*) leading into a cavity (*PH*) filled in the fresh condition by the *tooth-pulp*,

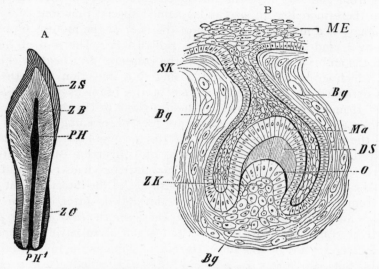

FIG. 66.—**A,** longitudinal section of a tooth, semi-diagrammatic. *PH*, pulp-cavity; *PH'*, opening of same; *ZB*, dentine; *ZC*, cement; *ZS*, enamel. **B,** longitudinal section of developing tooth. *Bg*, submucosa; *DS*, dentine; *Ma*, invaginated layer of enamel-organ; *ME*, epithelium of mouth; *O*, odontoblasts; *SK*, stalk of enamel-organ; *ZK*, tooth-papilla. (From Wiedersheim's *Vertebrata*.)

a sort of connective-tissue plug abundantly supplied with nerves and blood-vessels.

In the development of a tooth (Fig. 66, **B**) the deep layer of the buccal epithelium becomes invaginated and grows inwards into the sub-mucosa in the form of a narrow cord, the *enamel-organ* (*SK*). The distal end of this enlarges into a flask-like form, and the bottom of the flask becomes invaginated (*Ma*) by the growth of a conical process of the sub-mucosa, the *dental papilla* (*ZK*). Mesoderm cells accumulate on the free surface of the papilla and form a distinct layer of cells called *odontoblasts* (*O*). From these the dentine is formed in successive layers, which gradually accumulate between the layer of odontoblasts and the inner or invaginated layer of the enamel-organ. The lower, or proximal, part of the papilla remains uncalcified and forms the tooth-pulp. The enamel is formed by the deposition of successive layers of calcific matter from the inner or invaginated layer of the enamel-organ, the cement by the ossification of the tissue immediately surrounding the papilla. Thus the tooth is partly of ectodermal, partly of mesodermal origin.

In some Fishes the scales or elements of the dermal exoskeleton pass insensibly into the teeth over the ridges of the jaws, and agree with them in structure, so that there can be no doubt as to the homology of the two. Teeth are, in fact, to be looked upon as portions of the exoskeleton which have migrated from the skin into the buccal cavity, and even into the pharynx, and have there increased in size and assumed special functions.

The *tongue* is a muscular elevation of the floor of the mouth, supported by the basi-hyal, and usually more or less protrusible. The roof of the buccal cavity in the embryo sends off a pouch, the *pituitary diverticulum* (Fig. 57, *A*, *pty. s.*), which grows upwards, and, losing its connection with the mouth, becomes attached to the ventral surface of the brain as the *pituitary body* (*pty. b.*). It may correspond with the neural gland of Urochorda.

In terrestrial Craniata *buccal glands* are present, opening by ducts into the mouth : the most important of these are the racemose *salivary glands*, which secrete a digestive fluid—*saliva*, capable of converting starch into sugar. There are also two large and highly characteristic digestive glands in the abdominal cavity, both developed as outpushings of the intestine, but differing greatly from one another in their fully developed state, both in outward appearance and in histological structure : these are the *liver* and the *pancreas*.

The liver (Fig. 57, *A*, *lr.*) is a dark-red organ of relatively immense size : it not only secretes a digestive juice, the *bile*, which has the function of emulsifying fats, but also forms an amyloid substance called *glycogen* or animal starch, which, after being stored up in the liver-cells, is restored to the blood in the form of sugar. The liver is formed of a mass of polyhedral cells (Fig. 67, *l.*) with minute intercellular spaces which receive the bile secreted from the cells and from which it passes to the ducts (*b.*). The pancreas (Fig. 57, *A*, *pn.*) is a racemose gland, and secretes *pancreatic juice* which acts upon proteids, starch, and fats. The ducts of both glands usually open into the anterior end of the intestine : that of the liver (*b. d.*) generally gives off a blind offshoot ending in a capacious dilatation, the *gall-bladder* (*g. b.*) in which the bile is stored. We thus have one or more *hepatic ducts* conveying the bile from the liver and meeting with a *cystic duct* from the gall-bladder, while from the junction a *common bile-duct* leads into the intestine.

Another important and characteristic organ in the abdomen of Craniata is the *spleen* (*spl.*), a gland-like organ of variable size and shape, attached to the stomach by a fold of peritoneum, but having no duct. It is formed of a pulpy substance containing numerous red blood-corpuscles, many of them in process of disintegration : dispersed through the pulp are masses of leucocytes which multiply and pass into the veins.

Two other *ductless glands* are formed in connection with the enteric canal. The *thyroid* (*thd.*) is developed as an outpushing of the floor of the pharynx which becomes shut off, and forms, in the adult, a gland-like organ of considerable size. Its final position varies considerably in the different classes. It has been compared with the endostyle of Tunicata and of Amphioxus, which, as will be remembered, is an open groove on the ventral side of the pharynx. This view is supported by the condition of the parts in the larval Lamprey (see *Cyclostomata*).

The *thymus* is developed from the epithelium of the dorsal ends of the gill-clefts : in the adult it may take the form of a number of separate gland-like bodies lying above the gills, or may be situated in the neck or even in the thorax. The thymus and thyroid, by virtue of *internal secretions* which they produce, and which mingle with the blood, control and modify the physiological condition of various organs and tissues with which they have no immediate anatomical connection.

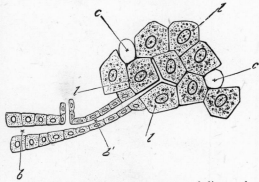

FIG. 67.—Diagram of structure of liver. *b.* a small branch of hepatic duct; *b'.* its ultimate termination in the intercellular spaces; *c.* blood-capillaries; *l.* liver-cells. (From Huxley's *Physiology*.)

The whole intra-abdominal portion of the enteric canal, as well as the liver, pancreas, spleen, and, indeed, all the abdominal viscera, are supported by folds of peritoneum, called by the general name of *mesentery* (Fig. 57, *C*, *mes.*) and having the usual relation to the parietal and visceral layers of the peritoneum.

Two kinds of **respiratory organs** are found in Craniata : water-breathing organs or *gills*, and air-breathing organs or *lungs*.

Gills arise as a series of paired pouches of the pharynx which extend outwards, or towards the surface of the body, and finally open on the exterior by the gill-slits already noticed. Each *gill-pouch* thus communicates with the pharynx by an *internal* (Fig. 68), with the outside water by an *external branchial aperture*, and is separated from its predecessor and from its successor in the series by stout fibrous partitions, the *interbranchial septa* (Fig. 68, *i. b. s.*). The mucous membrane forming the anterior and posterior walls of the pouches is raised up into a number of horizontal ridges, the *branchial filaments* (*br. f.*), which are abundantly supplied with blood. A current of water entering at the mouth passes into the pharynx, thence by the internal gill-slits into the gill-pouches, and finally makes its way out by the external gill-slits, bathing the branchial filaments as it goes. The exchange of carbonic acid for oxygen takes place in the blood-vessels of the branchial filaments, which are, there-fore, the actual organs of respiration. It will be noticed that the respiratory epithelium is endodermal, being derived from that of the pharynx, which, as we have seen, is a portion of the mesenteron.

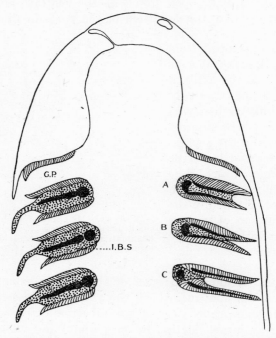

FIG. 68.—Diagrammatic horizontal section of the pharyngeal region of a **Craniate.** On the left are shown three gill pouches (*G.P.*) with fixed branchial filaments (the lamellar type) separ-ated by interbranchial septa (*I.B.S.*). On the right are three gills showing stages in the evolution of the filamentar type found in fishes other than the Chondrichthyes. A, *Ceratodus*; B, *Acipenser*; C, a Teleost. The nostril on the left side represents that of an Elasmobranch.

The skeletal supporting elements are in black.

As already mentioned, the walls of the pharynx are supported by the visceral arches, which surround it like a series of incomplete hoops, each half-arch or visceral bar being embedded in the inner or pharyngeal side of an interbranchial septum. Thus the visceral arches (*v. b.*) alternate with the gill-pouches, each being related to the posterior set of filaments of one pouch and the anterior set of the next. In the higher Fishes, such as the Trout or Cod, the interbranchial septa become reduced to narrow bars enclosing the visceral arches (right side of Fig. 68, *C*), with the result that a double set of free branchial filaments springs from each visceral bar and constitutes what is called a single *gill*. Thus an entire gill or *holobranch* (*hl. br.*) is the morphological equivalent of two half-gills—*hemibranchs* (*hm. br.*), or sets of branchial filaments belonging to the adjacent sides of two consecutive gill-pouches. On the other hand, a gill-pouch is equivalent to the posterior hemibranch of one gill and the anterior hemibranch of its immediate successor.

In some Amphibia water-breathing organs of a different kind are found.

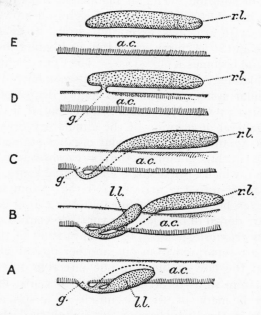

FIG. 69.—Diagrams illustrating the lung in fishes as seen from the left side. *A*, primitive symmetrical arrangement; *B*, **Polypterus**; *C*, **Ceratodus**; *D*, Physostomatous Teleost; *E*, Physoclistic Teleost; *a.c.* alimentary canal; *g.* glottis; *l.l.* left lung; *r.l.*, right lung. (From Goodrich after Kerr, J. G., *Zoology*, 1921.)

These are the *external gills* : they are developed as branched outgrowths of the body-wall in immediate relation with the gill-slits, and differ from the internal gills just described in having an ectodermal epithelium.

Lungs (Fig. 57, *A*, *lg.*) are found in all Craniata from the Dipnoi upwards. They are developed as a hollow outpushing from the ventral wall of the embryonic fore-gut or anterior part of the enteric canal ; this passes backwards and upwards, usually dividing into right and left divisions, and finally coming to lie in the dorsal region of the cœlome. The inner surface of the single or double lung thus formed is raised into a more or less complex network of ridges so as to increase the surface of blood exposed to the action of the air ; and, in the higher forms, the ridges, increasing in number and complexity, and uniting with one another across the lumen of the lung, convert it into a sponge-like structure.   The respiratory epithelium is, of course, endodermal.   Since the lungs are blind sacs, some contrivance is necessary for renewing the air contained in them : this is done either by a process analogous to swallowing or by the contraction and relaxation of the muscles of the trunk.

In " bony " Fishes there occurs, in the position occupied in air-breathers by the lungs, a structure called the **air-bladder** (Fig. 69), which contains gas, and serves as an organ of flotation.   The air bladder, like the lungs, from a primitive form of which it is derived, is developed as an outgrowth of the fore-gut. It arises, however, with very few exceptions, from the dorsal instead of the ventral side of the gut.   In many cases the air-bladder loses its connection with the pharynx and becomes a closed sac.   The Chondrichthyes never at any period had an air bladder.   Some teleosts have secondarily lost it.

The **blood-vascular system** attains a far higher degree of complexity than in any of the groups previously studied : its essential features will be best understood by a general description of the circulatory organs of Fishes.

The *heart* (Figs. 57 and 70) is a muscular organ contained in the pericardial cavity and composed of three chambers, the *sinus venosus* (*s. v.*), the *atrium* (*au.*), and the *ventricle* (*v.*), which form a single longitudinal series, the hindmost, the sinus venosus, opening into the atrium, and the atrium into the ventricle. They do not, however, lie in a straight line, but in a zigzag fashion, so that the sinus and atrium are dorsal in position, the ventricle ventral.   Usually a fourth chamber, the *conus arteriosus* (*c. art.*), is added in front of the ventricle.   The various chambers are separated from one another by valvular apertures (Fig. 71) which allow of the flow of blood in one direction only, *viz.* from behind forwards—that is, from sinus to atrium, atrium to ventricle, and ventricle to conus.   The heart is made of striped muscle of a special kind—the only involuntary muscle in the body having this histological character—which is particularly thick and strong in the ventricle.   It is lined internally by epithelium and covered externally by the visceral layer of the pericardium.

Springing from the ventricle, or from the conus when that chamber is present, and passing directly forwards in the middle line below the gills, is a large, thick-walled, elastic blood-vessel, the *ventral aorta* (Figs. 57, *B*, and 70, *v. ao.*).   At its origin, which may be dilated to form a *bulbus arteriosus*, are valves so disposed as to allow of the flow of blood in one direction only, *viz.* from the ventricle into the aorta.   It gives off on each side a series of half-hoop-like vessels, the *afferent branchial arteries* (*a. br. a.*), one to each gill. These vessels ramify extensively, and their ultimate branches open into a network of microscopic tubes or *capillaries* (Fig. 71, *G*), having walls formed of a single layer of epithelial cells, which permeate the connective-tissue layer of the branchial filaments, and have therefore nothing between them and the surrounding water but the epithelium of the filaments.   The blood, driven by

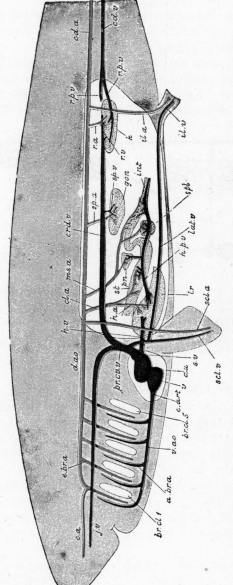

Fig. 70.—Diagram of the vascular system of a **Fish**. Vessels containing aërated blood red, those containing non-aërated blood blue. *a. br. a.* afferent branchial artery; *au.* atrium; *br. cl.* 1–2, branchial clefts; *c. a.* carotid artery; *c. art.* conus arteriosus; *cd. a.* caudal artery; *cd. v.* caudal vein; *cl. a.* cœliac artery; *crd. v.* cardinal vein; *d. ao.* dorsal aorta; *e. br. a.* efferent branchial artery; *gon.* gonad; *h. a.* hepatic artery; *h. p. v.* hepatic portal vein; *h. v.* hepatic vein; *il. a.* iliac artery; *il. v.* iliac vein; *int.* intestine; *j. v.* jugular vein; *k.* kidney; *lat. v.* lateral vein; *lr.* liver; *ms. a.* mesenteric artery; *pn.* pancreas; *pr. cv. v.* precaval vein; *r. a.* renal artery; *r. p. v.* renal portal vein; *r. v.* renal vein; *scl. a.* subclavian artery; *scl. v.* subclavian vein; *sp. a.* spermatic artery; *spl.* spleen; *sp. v.* spermatic vein; *st.* stomach; *s. v.* sinus venosus; *v.* ventricle; *v. ao.* ventral aorta. (From Parker's *Elementary Biology*.)

the contractions of the heart into the ventral aorta, is pumped into these respiratory capillaries, and there exchanges its superfluous carbonic acid for oxygen. It then passes from the capillaries into another set of vessels which join with one another, like the tributaries of a river, into larger and larger trunks, finally uniting in each gill, into an *efferent branchial artery* (*e. br. a.*). The efferent arteries of both sides pass upwards and discharge into a median longitudinal vessel, the *dorsal aorta* (*d. ao.*), situated immediately beneath the notochord or vertebral column. From this trunk, or from the efferent branchial arteries, numerous vessels, the *systemic arteries*, are given off to all parts of the

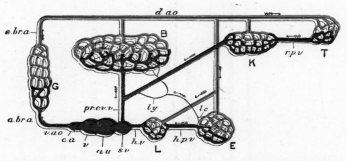

FIG. 71.—Diagram illustrating the course of the circulation in a **Fish.** Vessels containing aërated blood red, those containing non-aërated blood blue, lymphatics black. *B*, capillaries of the body generally ; *E*, of the enteric canal ; *G*, of the gills ; *K*, of the kidneys ; *L*, of the liver ; *T*, of the tail. *a. br. a.* afferent branchial arteries ; *au.* atrium ; *c. a.* conus arteriosus ; *d. ao.* dorsal aorta ; *e. br. a.* efferent branchial arteries ; *h. p. v.* hepatic portal vein ; *h. v.* hepatic vein ; *lc.* lacteals ; *ly.* lymphatics ; *pr. cv. v.* precaval veins ; *r. p. v.* renal portal veins ; *s. v.* sinus venosus ; *v.* ventricle ; *v. ao.* ventral aorta. The arrows show the direction of the current. (From Parker's *Elementary Biology.*)

body, the most important being the *carotid arteries* (Fig. 70, *c. a.*) to the head, the *subclavian* (*scl. a.*) to the pectoral fins, the *cœliac* (*cl. a.*) and *mesenteric* (*ms. a.*) to the stomach, intestine, liver, spleen, and pancreas, the *renal* (*r. a.*) to the kidneys, the *spermatic* (*sp. a.*) or *ovarian* to the gonads, and the *iliac* (*il. a.*) to the pelvic fins. After giving off the last the aorta is continued as the *caudal artery* (*cd. a.*) to the end of the tail.

With the exception of the capillaries, all the vessels described in the preceding paragraph, including the dorsal and ventral aortæ, are *arteries*. They are firm, elastic tubes, do not collapse when empty, usually contain but little blood in the dead animal, and serve to carry the blood from the heart to the body generally.

The systemic arteries branch and branch again into smaller and smaller trunks, and finally pour their blood into a capillary network (Fig. 71, *B, K,* and *T*) with which all the tissues of the body, except epithelium and cartilage, are permeated. In these *systemic capillaries* the blood parts with its oxygen and nutrient constituents to the tissues, and receives from them the various products of destructive metabolism—carbonic acid, water, and nitrogenous waste. The systemic, like the respiratory, capillaries are microscopic, and their walls are formed of a single layer of epithelial cells.

We saw that the respiratory capillaries are in connection with two sets of vessels, afferent and efferent. The same applies to the systemic capillaries, with the important difference that their efferent vessels are not arteries, but thin-walled, non-elastic, collapsible tubes called *veins*. They receive the impure blood from the capillaries, and unite into larger and larger trunks, finally opening into one or other of the great veins, presently to be described, by which the blood is returned to the heart. As a general rule the vein of any part of the body runs parallel to its artery, from which it is at once distinguished by its wider calibre, by its dark colour—due to the contained bluish-purple blood seen through its thin walls, by being gorged with blood after death, by the complete collapse of its walls when empty, and by its usually containing valves. In some cases the veins become dilated into spacious cavities called *sinuses* ; but sinuses without proper walls, such as occur in many Invertebrates, are never found in the Craniata.

The veins from the head join to form large, paired *jugular veins* (Fig. 70, *j. v.*) which pass backwards, one on each side of the head, and are joined by the *cardinal veins* (*crd. v.*) coming from the trunk, each jugular uniting with the corresponding cardinal to form a large *precaval vein* (*pr. cv. v.*) which passes directly downwards and enters the sinus venosus. The blood from the tail returns by a *caudal vein* (*cd. v.*), lying immediately below the caudal artery in the hæmal canal of the caudal vertebræ (Fig. 57, *D*). On reaching the cœlome the caudal vein forks horizontally, and the two branches either become directly continuous with the cardinals or pass one to each kidney under the name of the *renal portal veins* (Fig. 70, *r. p. v.*). In the kidneys they break up into capillaries (Fig. 71, *K*), their blood mingling with that brought by the renal arteries and being finally discharged into the cardinals by the *renal veins* (Fig. 70, *r. v.*). Thus the blood from the tail may either return directly to the heart in the normal manner or may go by way of the capillaries of the kidneys. In the latter case there is said to be a *renal portal system*, the essential characteristic of which is that the kidney has a double blood-supply, one of pure blood from the renal artery, and one of impure blood from the renal portal vein ; in other words, it has two afferent vessels, an artery and a vein, and the latter is further distinguished by the fact that it both begins and ends in capillaries instead of beginning in capillaries and ending in a vein of higher order.

The blood from the gonads is returned to the cardinals by veins called *spermatic* (*sp. v.*) in the male, *ovarian* in the female. That from the paired fins takes, in what appears to be the most typical case, a somewhat curious course. On each side of the body there is a *lateral vein* (*lat. v.*), running in the body-wall

and following the course of the embryonic ridge between the pectoral and pelvic fins. It receives, anteriorly, a *subclavian vein* (*scl. v.*) from the pectoral fin, and posteriorly an *iliac vein* (*il. v.*) from the pelvic fin, and in front pours its blood into the precaval.

The veins from the stomach, intestine, spleen, and pancreas join to form a large *hepatic portal vein* (*h. p. v.*), which passes to the liver and there breaks up into capillaries, its blood mingling with that brought to the liver by the *hepatic artery* (*h. a.*), a branch of the cœliac. Thus the liver has a double blood-supply, receiving oxygenated blood by the hepatic artery, and non-oxygenated but food-laden blood by the hepatic portal vein (Fig. 71 *L*). In this way we have a *hepatic portal system* resembling the renal portal system both in the double blood-supply, and in the fact that the afferent vein terminates, as it originates, in capillaries. After circulating through the liver the blood is poured, by *hepatic veins* (*h. v.*), into the sinus venosus. The hepatic, unlike the renal portal system, is of universal occurrence in the Craniata.

In the embryo there is a *sub-intestinal vein*, corresponding with that of Amphioxus, and lying beneath the intestine and the post-anal gut. Its posterior portion becomes the caudal vein of the adult, its anterior portion one of the factors of the hepatic portal vein.

To sum up :—The circulatory organs of the branchiate Craniata consist of (*a*) a muscular organ of propulsion, the *heart*, provided with valves and driving the blood into (*b*) a set of thick-walled elastic, afferent vessels, the *arteries*, from which it passes into (*c*) a network of microscopic vessels or *capillaries* which permeate the tissues, supplying them with oxygen and nutrient matters and receiving from them carbonic acid and other waste products : from the capillary network the blood is carried off by (*d*) the *veins*, thin-walled, non-elastic tubes by which it is returned to the heart. Thus the general scheme of the circulation is simple : the arteries spring from the heart, or from arteries of a higher order, and end in capillaries ; the veins begin in capillaries and end in vessels of a higher order or in the heart. Actually, however, the system is complicated (*a*) by the interposition of the gills in the course of the outgoing current, as a result of which we have arteries serving as both afferent and efferent vessels of the respiratory capillaries, the efferent arteries taking their origin in those capillaries after the manner of veins ; and (*b*) by the interposition of two important blood-purifying organs, the liver and the kidney, in the course of the returning current, as a result of which we have veins acting as both afferent and efferent vessels of the hepatic and renal capillaries, the afferent vessels of both organs ending in capillaries after the fashion of arteries.

In the embryos of the higher, or air-breathing, Craniata, the circulatory organs agree in essentials with the above description, the most important difference being that, as no gills are present, the branches of the ventral aorta do not break up into capillaries, but pass directly into the dorsal aorta, forming the *aortic arches* (Fig. 72, *Ab*.). With the appearance of the lungs, however, a very fundamental change occurs in the blood-system. The last aortic arch of each side gives off a *pulmonary artery* (Fig. 73, *Ap*.) to the corresponding lung, and the blood, after circulating through the capillaries of that organ, is returned by a *pulmonary vein (lr*.), not into an ordinary systemic vein of higher order, but into the heart directly: there it enters the left side of the auricle, in which a vertical partition is developed, separating a *left auricle (A[1])*, which receives the aërated

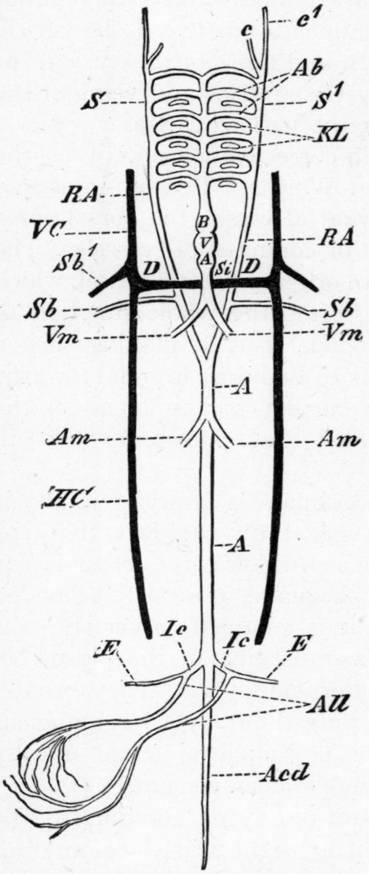

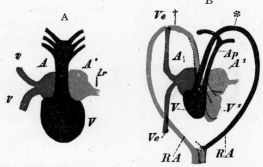

FIG. 73.—Diagram of the heart **A**, in an **Amphibian**; **B**, in a **Crocodile**. *A*, right auricle; *A[1]*. left auricle; *Ap*. pulmonary artery; *lr*. pulmonary vein; *RA*. aortic arches; *V*. ventricle; *V[1]*. left ventricle; *v, v*. and *Ve, Ve*. pre- and post-cavals. (From Wiedersheim's *Vertebrata*.)

FIG. 72.—Diagram of the vascular system in the embryo of an **air-breathing Craniate**. *A*. dorsal aorta and auricle; *Ab*. aortic arches; *Acd*. caudal artery; *All*. allantoic arteries; *Am*. vitelline arteries; *B*, ventral aorta; *c, c'*. carotid arteries; *D*. precaval veins; *Ic, E*. iliac arteries; *HC*. cardinal veins; *KL*. gill-clefts; *RA, S, S[1]*. roots of dorsal aorta; *Sb*, subclavian arteries; *Sb[1]*. subclavian veins; *V*. ventricle; *VC*. jugular vein; *Vm*. vitelline veins. (From Wiedersheim's *Vertebrata*.)

blood from the lungs, from a *right auricle (A)*, into which is poured the impure blood of the sinus venosus. Lastly, in Crocodiles, Birds, and Mammals (**B**) the ventricle also becomes divided into right and left chambers, and we get a four-chambered heart, having right and left auricles and right and left ventricles: at the same time the conus arteriosus and sinus venosus cease to exist as distinct chambers. The left auricle receives aërated blood from the lungs and passes it into the left ventricle, whence it is propelled through the system: the right auricle receives impure blood from the system, and passes it into the right ventricle to be pumped into the lungs for aëration. Thus the four-chambered heart of the higher Vertebrata is quite a different thing from that of a Fish : in the latter the four chambers—sinus venosus, atrium, ventricle, and conus arteriosus—form a single longitudinal series, whereas in a Mammal, for instance, the four chambers constitute practic- ally a double heart, there being no direct communication between the auricle and ventricle of the right side, or *respiratory heart*, and those of the left side, or *systemic heart*. The modifications undergone by the arteries and veins in the higher Vertebrata will be best considered under the various classes.

It will be noticed that there is a sort of rough correspondence between the blood-vessels of Craniata and those of the higher Worms. The sub-intestinal vein, heart, and ventral aorta together form a ventral vessel, the dorsal aorta a dorsal vessel, and the aortic arches transverse or commissural vessels. The heart might thus be looked upon as a portion of an original ventral vessel, which has acquired strongly muscular walls, and performs the whole function of propelling the blood. But in making such a comparison it has to be borne in mind that the direction of the current of the blood in the Craniata is exactly the opposite of that in the Annulata.

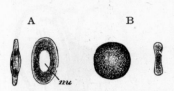

A   B

FIG. 74.—Surface and edge views of red blood-corpuscles of Frog (*A*) and Man (*B*). *nu.* nucleus. (From Parker's *Biology*.)

The *blood* of Craniata is always red, and is specially distinguished by the fact that the hæmoglobin to which it owes its colour is not dissolved in the plasma as in most red-blooded Invertebrates, but is confined to certain cells called *red blood-corpuscles* (Fig. 74), which occur floating in the plasma in addition to, and in far greater numbers than, the leucocytes. They usually have the form of flat oval discs (*A*), the centre bulged out by a large nucleus (*nu.*), but in Mammals (*B*) they are bi-concave, non-nucleated, and usually circular. The red corpuscles do not perform amœboid movements.

The colour of the blood varies with the amount of oxygen taken up by the hæmoglobin. When thoroughly aërated it is of a bright scarlet colour, but assumes a bluish-purple hue after giving up its oxygen to the tissues. Owing to the fact that oxygenated blood is usually found in arteries, it is often spoken of as *arterial* blood, while the non-oxygenated, purple blood, being usually found in veins, is called *venous*. But it must not be forgotten that an artery, *e.g.*, the ventral aorta or the pulmonary artery, may contain venous blood, and a vein, *e.g.*, the pulmonary vein, arterial blood. The distinction between the two classes of vessels does not depend upon their contents, but upon their relation to the heart and the capillaries.

In addition to the blood-vessels the circulatory system of Craniata contains *lymph-vessels* or **lymphatics** (Fig. 75, *ly.*). In most of the tissues there is a network of *lymph-capillaries*, interwoven with, but quite independent of, the blood-capillaries. From this network lymphatic vessels pass off, and finally discharge their contents into one or other of the veins. Many of the lower

Craniata possess spacious *lymph-sinuses* surrounding the blood-vessels; and there are communications between the lymphatics and the cœlome by means of minute apertures or *stomata*. The lymphatics contain a fluid called *lymph*, which is to all intents and purposes blood *minus* its red corpuscles. The lymph-plasma consists of the drainage from the tissues : it makes its way into the lymph capillaries, and thence into the lymphatics, which are all efferent vessels, conveying the fluid from the capillaries to the veins. Leucocytes are added to the plasma in bodies, called *lymphatic glands*, which occur in the course of the vessels. Valves may be present to prevent any flow of lymph

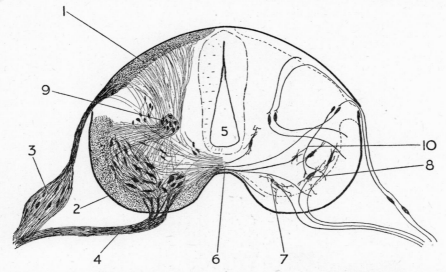

Fig. 75.—Diagrammatical cross section of spinal cord. *1*, posterior funiculus; *2*, antero-lateral funiculus; *3*, spinal ganglion of dorsal (sensory) root; *4*, ventral (motor) root; *5*, central canal; *6*, anterior commissure; *7*, ventral motor cells; *8*, ventral motor cells; *9*, lateral nucleus; *10*, connector fibres.

towards the capillaries, and in some cases the flow of the fluid is assisted by *lymph-hearts*, muscular dilatations in the course of certain of the vessels. The lymphatics of the intestine have an important function in the absorption of fats, and are known as *lacteals* (*lc.*).

The NERVOUS SYSTEM attains in the higher vertebrates a structural complexity and functional co-ordination which are quite without parallel in the rest of the animal kingdom. As in other Chordata, it arises from a *dorsal medullary groove* ; the two edges of the groove fuse, forming a tube beneath them. This ectodermal tube sinks from the epidermis, becoming the longitudinal nerve-cord ; its cavity is the *neurocœle* or characteristic axial canal.

So far the agreement with the lower Chordata is complete, but a fundamental advance is seen in the fact that at an early period—before the closure of the medullary groove—the anterior end of the longitudinal cord undergoes a marked dilation and forms the rudiment of the *brain*, the rest becoming the *spinal cord*. Moreover, as growth goes on, a space appears in the mesoderm immediately surrounding the nervous system, and forms the *neural* or *cerebro-spinal cavity* already referred to (Fig. 57, *c.s.c.*), so that the longitudinal cord, instead of being solidly imbedded in mesoderm, lies in a well-marked and often spacious tube enclosed by the neural arches of the vertebræ, and in front by the *cranium* (Fig. 57, *B-D*).

The spinal cord (Fig. 76) is a thick-walled cylinder, continuous in front with the brain. It is traversed from end to end by the neurocœle, here a

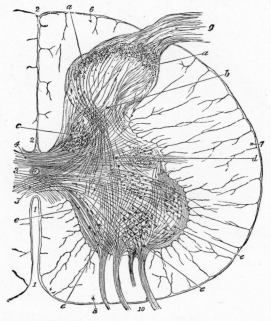

FIG. 76.—Transverse section of spinal cord. *1*, ventral fissure; *2*, dorsal fissure; *3*, central canal; *4, 5*, bridges connecting grey matter of right and left sides; *6, 7, 8*, white matter; *9*, dorsal root of spinal nerve; *10*, ventral root. *a, b.* dorsal horn of grey matter; *c,* Clarke's column; *e.* ventral horn. (From Huxley's *Physiology*.)

narrow *central canal* lined by a ciliated epithelium derived from the superficial layer of in-turned ectodermal cells. The cord is made up of two kinds of tissue. Surrounding the central canal, and having a λ- or X-shaped transverse section, is the *grey matter*; it contains the nerve-cell nuclei and the *synapses* by which the nerve-impulses are passed on from one nerve-cell to the next. Superficial to the grey is the *white matter*, in which lie medullated nerve-fibres running longitudinally, and so connecting various levels of the cord. Besides the conducting cells, the nerve-cord contains innumerable processes of supporting cells.

From the sides of the cord the *spinal nerves* are given off; one nerve is given off to each somite, so that normally they arise in pairs. Each nerve runs out by two *roots*, a *dorsal* and a *ventral*. Each root arises from one of the horns of the grey matter, and the two mingle to form the *trunk* of the nerve, which emerges from the spinal canal usually between the arches of adjacent vertebræ. Nerve-cells of the dorsal root conduct to the cord *somatic sensory* impulses from the skin and segmented mesoderm, and *viscero-sensory* impulses from the unsegmented (lateral plate) mesoderm and from the derivatives of the endoderm. Impulses are interrupted on the dorsal root .by a synapse in the *dorsal ganglion*. The ventral root similarly is made up of visceral and somatic components, but it carries *motor* tracts from the cord : there is no ganglion. Although the ventral root never carries sensory fibres, the dorsal root may carry motor fibres. The *visceral motor* component separates from the trunk, near the origin of the latter, from two roots, and enters a *sympathetic ganglion* ; these ganglia are connected by paired longitudinal *sympathetic trunks*, which lie on each side of the aorta in the dorsal wall of the cœlom. The post-ganglionic fibres may pass directly out from the ganglion to their terminations, or run some way along the sympathetic trunk first. The visceral motor system runs to the viscera, blood-vessels, etc., with the viscero-sensory system : the two together are termed the sympathetic system ; the viscero-motor alone is termed the *autonomic system*. The *somatic motor* fibres run directly to their terminations, instead of passing on the impulses to another nerve-cell at a synapse in a ganglion, as do the other components.

As already mentioned, the anterior end of the embryonic nervous system undergoes, at a very early period, a marked dilation, and becomes distinguished as the *brain* (Fig. 77). Constrictions appear in the dilated part and divide it into three bulb-like swellings or vesicles, the *fore-brain* (*A, f.b.*), *mid-brain* (*m.b.*) and *hind-brain* (*h.b.*). The fore-brain then becomes divided into a *telencephalon* anteriorly and a *diencephalon* posteriorly ; the mid-brain is unaltered, and is termed the *mesencephalon* ; a commissure on the anterior dorsal area of the hind-brain, the *cerebellum*, becomes so enlarged as to form virtually another division of the brain in most vertebrates, and the remainder of the hind-brain is termed the *myelencephalon* or *medulla oblongata*. Additional constrictions appear in the medulla oblongata, giving it a segmented appearance ; but they disappear as development proceeds, and, whatever may be their significance, they have nothing to do with the main divisions of the adult organ. The original cavity of the brain becomes correspondingly divided into communicating chambers or *ventricles*.

The chief divisions are the first, third, and fourth ventricles, which are respectively in the telencephalon, diencephalon, and medulla.

In some Fishes the brain consists throughout life of these five divisions only, but in most cases the prosencephalon grows out into paired lobes, the right and left *cerebral hemispheres* (*I-L, c.h.*), each containing a cavity, the *lateral ventricle*, which communicates with the third ventricle (3) by a narrow

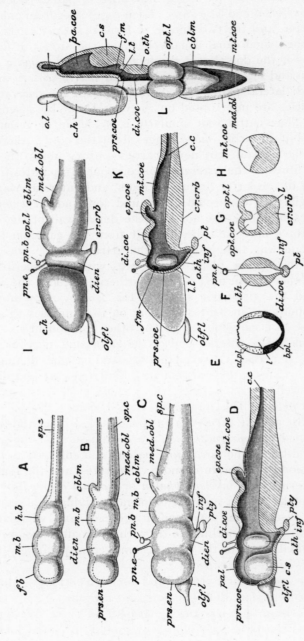

Fig. 77.—Diagrams of the **Craniate brain**. *A*, first stage, side view, the cavity indicated by a dotted line; *B*, second stage; *C*, side view of fully-formed brain with undivided prosencephalon; *D*, the same in sagittal section; *E*, transverse section of prosencephalon; *F*, of diencephalon; *G*, of mesencephalon; *H*, of medulla oblongata; *I*, side view of brain with cerebral hemispheres; *K*, sagittal section of the same; *L*, dorsal view, the cavities exposed on the right side; *Al.pl.* alar, or dorsolateral wall; *B.-pl.* basal or ventro-lateral wall; *cblm.* cerebellum; *c. c.* central canal; *cr. crb.* crura cerebri; *c. h.* cerebral hemispheres; *c. s.* corpora striata; *di. cœ.* third ventricle; *dien.* diencephalon; *ep. cœ.* cerebellar ventricle; *f. b.* fore-brain; *f. m.* foramen of Monro; *h. b.* hind-brain; *inf.* infundibulum; *l.* iter; *l. t.* lamina terminalis; *m. b.* mid-brain; *m. cœ.* mesocele; *med. obl.* medulla oblongata; *mt. cœ.* fourth ventricle; *olf. l.* olfactory lobe; *opt. cœ.* optic ventricle; *opt. l.* optic lobes; *o. th.* optic thalami; *pa. cœ.* lateral or first ventricle; *pal.* pallium; *pn. b.* pineal body (epiphysis); *pn. e.* pineal eye (parietal organ); *prs. cœ.* prosocele; *prs. en.* telencephalon; *pt. pty.* pituitary body; *rh. cœ.* rhinoceles; *sp. c.* spinal cord.

passage, the *foramen of Monro* (*f. m.*). Moreover, each hemisphere gives off a forward prolongation, the *olfactory bulb*. In the embryo of some forms there is a median *unpaired olfactory bulb*, like that of Amphioxus. The part of the cerebral hemisphere with which the olfactory bulb is immediately related is the *olfactory lobe* (*olf. l.*).

The brain undergoes further complications by the unequal thickening of its walls. In the medulla oblongata the floor becomes greatly thickened (*D, H, K*), while the roof remains thin, consisting of a single layer of epithelial cells, assuming the character therefore of a purely non-nervous epithelial layer (*ependyme*). In the cerebellum the thickening takes place to such an extent that the epicœle is usually obliterated altogether. In the mid-brain the ventral wall is thickened in the form of two longitudinal bands, the *crura cerebri* (*cr. crb.*), the dorsal wall in the form of paired oval swellings, the *optic lobes* (*opt. l.*) : extensions of the neurocœle into the latter form the *optic ventricles* (*G, opt. v.*) : the median portion of the mid-brain ventricle is then called the *iter* (*l.*) or *aqueduct of Sylvius*. In the diencephalon the sides become thickened, forming paired masses, the *optic thalami* (*D, F, o. th.*), the roof remains for the most part in the condition of a thin membrane (*ependyme*) composed of a single layer of cells, but part of it gives rise to a very peculiar adjunct of the brain, the *pineal apparatus*. This originates as an outgrowth, which consists typically of two narrow diverticula, one in front of the other, the anterior being the *parietal organ*, the posterior the *pineal organ or epiphysis* : these two parts may be developed independently, or the latter may originate by outgrowth from the former. The parietal organ in the Lampreys and some Reptiles develops an eye-like organ, the *pineal eye* (*pn. e.*) at its extremity, but is vestigal or absent in most other Vertebrates. The epiphysis is eye-like (*parapineal eye*) only in Lampreys ; in other Vertebrates it is represented by a gland-like structure, the *pineal body* (*pn. b.*), connected by a hollow or solid stalk with the roof of the diencephalon. The term *paraphysis* is applied to a non-nervous outgrowth of the roof of the fore-brain developed in front of the epiphysis in the hinder region of the prosencephalon. The floor of the diencephalon grows downwards into a funnel-like prolongation, the *infundibulum* (*inf.*) : with this the pituitary diverticulum of the pharynx (p. 84) comes into relation, and there is formed, partly from the dilated end of the diverticulum, partly from the extremity of the infundibulum, a gland-like structure, the *pituitary body* or *hypophysis* (*pt.*), always situated immediately in front of the anterior extremity of the notochord and between the diverging posterior ends of the trabeculæ. The hypophysis in higher Craniates appears to be of the nature of a ductless, internally secreting gland. In lower Craniata it consists of two distinct glandular parts, the one (*saccus vasculosus*) situated more dorsally and formed as an outgrowth of the infundibulum, the other (*hypophysis proper*) ventral and arising from the pharyngeal diverticulum.

The telencephalon grows forward above the *lamina terminalis*, which lies at the front end of the diencephalon and is the true anterior termination of the nerve-cord. Typically the telencephalon begins as a tube with thick lateral walls of nervous tissue and thin dorsal and ventral non-nervous walls (Fig. 77a 1.). In most vertebrates the bulging out of the growing lateral walls enlarges the cavity of the ventricle, leaving a narrow membranous area dorsally and ventrally, which is soon largely obscured by transverse commissures (Fig. 77a 2). During the further expansion of the telencephalon, there is a fusion of the inturned dorsal and ventral edges of each lateral wall, thus forming two cerebral hemispheres out of the unpaired end-brain vesicle (Fig. 77a 3).

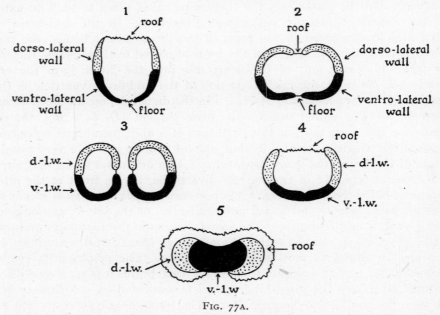

FIG. 77A.

But in some fishes, especially teleosts, the dorsal part of the lateral wall, the pallium, grows outwards and downwards over the thickened ventral lateral wall (Fig. 77a 4). In the teleosts this is carried so far that it forms a solid mass lying over the ventral part of the lateral wall. The roof of the ventricle is now formed by a huge expansion of the dorsal non-nervous wall uniting the medial edges of the pallium * (Fig. 77a 5).

In the preceding description the brain has been described as if its parts were in one horizontal plane ; but, as a matter of fact, at a very early period of development the anterior part becomes bent down over the end of the noto-

* It has also been held that the non-nervous roof of teleosts is developed by a degeneration of a part or the whole of the pallium ; the teleost brain and the typical brain differ so greatly that it is difficult to determine such questions of homology, but the investigators who have studied the fore-brain tracts have generally agreed that the teleost pallium is everted dorsally, while the typical pallium is introverted dorsally.

chord, so that the whole organ assumes a retort-shape, the axis of the fore-brain being strongly inclined to that of the hind-brain. The bend is known as the *cerebral flexure* : it is really permanent, but, as the hemispheres grow forward parallel to the hind-brain and the floor of the mid- and hind-brain thickens, it becomes obscure, and is not noticeable in the adult.

The brain, like the spinal cord, is composed of grey and white matter, but the grey matter either forms a thin superficial layer or *cortex*, as in the hemispheres and cerebellum, or occurs as ganglionic masses surrounded by white matter.

The whole cerebro-spinal cavity is lined with a tough membrane, the *dura mater*, and both brain and spinal cord are covered by a more delicate investment, the *pia mater* : the space between the two contains a serous fluid. In the higher forms there is a delicate *arachnoid membrane* outside the pia, and in many cases the regions of the pia in immediate contact with the thin epithelial roofs of the diencephalon and medulla become greatly thickened and very vascular, forming in each case what is known as a *choroid plexus*.

From the brain are given off the cranial or cerebral nerves. They are referred to as Nerves I—XII, as if they were a single series. This nomenclature is convenient, but has only a topographic basis.

The majority of cranial nerves are each related to a particular myotome, and in primitive and embryonic forms are segmentally arranged. They contain components each having a functional unity. These segmental cranial nerves therefore develop in a manner essentially similar to the spinal nerves. But there are other cranial nerves which probably are not related to particular myotomes.

The specialisation in the front end of vertebrates has made it difficult to recognise the primitive arrangement of cranial nerves. They are obscured by the growth, dorsally, of the brain and organs of special sense, and by the growth, ventrally, of the jaws and other visceral arches. It is important to remember that the segmentation of this visceral region is secondary, and therefore does not necessarily correspond to the fundamental segmentation of the head-somites.

A typical segmental cranial nerve contains the following components :—

dorsal root :

somatic sensory	from skin and muscle.
viscero-sensory	from endodermal surfaces, visceral muscle, etc.
special viscero-sensory	from organs of taste.
viscero-motor	to blood-vessels, visceral muscle, etc.
special viscero-motor	to jaw and visceral arch musculature which has become striped and voluntary.

ventral root :

somatic motor	to cranial somites.

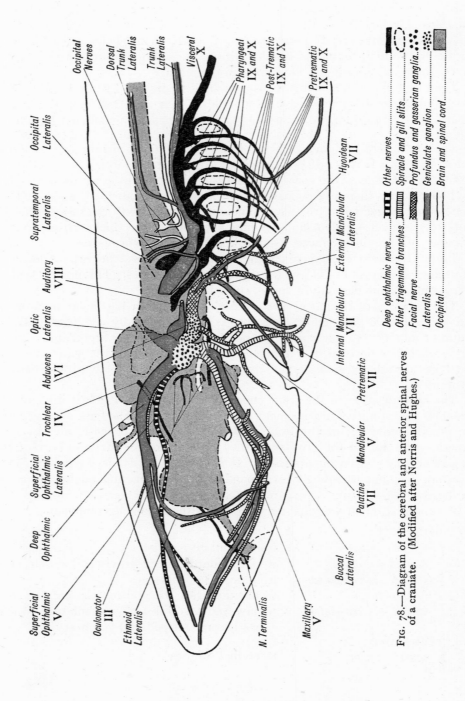

FIG. 78.—Diagram of the cerebral and anterior spinal nerves of a craniate. (Modified after Norris and Hughes.)

The confining of the viscero-motor component to the dorsal root is parallel to the condition in all somites of Amphioxus, and may well be primitive.

The nerves supplying the *acoustico-lateral* system are usually included in tables of cranial nerve components as the *special somatic sensory* component; this is a controversial matter, which is discussed below.

The origin from the brain, the peripheral termination, and function of the cranial nerves will now be described, beginning anteriorly (Fig. 78). The acoustico-lateral system will be dealt with separately.

The Olfactory Nerve (I).—A special sensory system running from the olfactory epithelium of the olfactory sac on each side, as a number of groups of fibres, the *fila olfactoria*, to the olfactory bulb. The olfactory tract is not a nerve, but a hollow outgrowth from the brain.

In the nose of many air-breathing vertebrates, a special region of the olfactory sac is developed as the *vomero-nasal organ*, or *organ of Jacobson*; it is innervated by a special branch of the olfactory nerve, for which in some forms there is a special development of the olfactory bulb.

The nervus terminalis conveys sensory impulses from the skin and blood-vessels in the region medial to the olfactory bulbs. Its fibres run into the end-brain, and can be traced a long way posteriorly within the brain.

The Optic Nerve (II).—This is not a true nerve, but a hollow outgrowth of the wall of the first primary vesicle from the chiasma in the ventral region of the diencephalon just in front of the infundibulum. Its nerve-cells run from the retina into the brain.

The Oculomotor Nerve (III).—A motor nerve arising in the floor of the mid-brain to supply the *inferior oblique* and the *inferior, internal,* and *superior rectus* muscles of the eye. With this nerve run some visceral motor fibres through the *ciliary ganglion* which innervate the muscles of the ciliary process and iris forming the mechanism for accommodation of the lens and contraction of the pupil.

The Trochlear or Pathetic Nerve (IV).—A motor nerve arising from the floor of the mid-brain behind the oculomotor to supply the *superior oblique* muscle of the eye.

The Trigeminal Nerve (V).—This large nerve arises from the side either of the medulla or of the pons in close contact not only with the roots of the seventh nerve, but also with some large tracts of the acoustico-lateralis system. It is therefore difficult to dissociate the parts of this complex without examining microscopic sections.

The fifth nerve, soon after leaving the brain, enters the *trigeminal* or *Gasserian* ganglion. There are three main branches of the true trigeminal nerve, of which two are somatic sensory in function and the third is both sensory and motor. Above the origin of the true trigeminal nerve, the *profundus nerve* runs out from the *profundus ganglion;* it is frequently included in descriptions of the trigeminal nerve, as the *ramus ophthalmicus profundus.* It has two branches : one runs forward over the eye and is somatic sensory ; the other joins the oculomotor nerve.

The trigeminal proper sends one branch above the eye, the *ramus ophthalmicus superficialis ;* it sends one branch below the eye, the *ramus maxillaris.* The third main branch runs to the lower jaw as the *mandibular* branch. It has somatic sensory and viscero-motor fibres : the latter may be termed the *masticator* nerve.

The Abducent Nerve (VI).—A purely motor nerve arising from a column of cells in line with the nuclei of the oculomotor and trochlear nerves. It supplies the *external rectus* muscle and, in some forms, the *retractor bulbæ.*

The Facial Nerve (VII).—This is the first of the branchial nerves. The rami of each branchial nerve follow very similar courses. In Cyclostomes, each nerve has a branch to the dorsal skin area, a branch to the pharynx, and a branch to a gill-arch : these have, respectively, somatic sensory, viscero-sensory, and combined somatic and viscero-sensory and viscero-motor components.

In Gnathostomes, the somatic sensory components, and with them the dorsal branch, are reduced or absent ; on the other hand, each nerve sends a new branch, the pre-trematic, to the gill-arch next in front. Typically, there is now a pharyngeal, one or more pre-trematics, and one or more post-trematics. All three divisions carry viscero-sensory fibres, but there is also a viscero-motor component in the post-trematic.

The facial nerve arises from the *geniculate* ganglion. Its pharyngeal branch, the *palatine,* runs above the palato-quadrate bar. The pre-trematic, or *pre-spiracular,* supplies the lower jaw in fishes, but appears to be reduced in tetrapods.

The post-trematic, or hyomandibular, is in two main parts. An anterior branch (interior mandibular of fishes, inferior mandibular of amphibia and reptiles) also supplies the lower jaw : it is this branch which is usually believed to have become the *chorda tympani* of mammals.

The posterior post-trematic (*hyoidean* or *jugular* nerve) carries the viscero-motor component.

In mammals the facial nerve is mainly motor in function, serving the muscles of the hyoid arch, the platysma, and muscles of facial expression. The sensory part consists of the *chorda tympani,* containing fibres to the anterior two-thirds of the tongue and secretory fibres to the salivary glands of the mucous membrane of the snout. In the higher mammals the gustatory area and the territory supplied by the sensory roots of the facial nerve have been considerably reduced, so that, as compared with a fish, the sensory function is smaller in extent than the motor.

The Auditory Nerve (VIII).—This is held to be a part of the acoustico-lateral system.

The Glossopharyngeal Nerve (IX).—This nerve runs out under the auditory capsule from a ganglion which is distinct in lower forms, but closely apposed to that of the tenth in higher groups. Peripherally it is a typical branchial nerve. Except in Elasmobranchs, it is usually connected to the seventh nerve by an anastomosis of viscero-sensory fibres (*Jacobson's anastomosis*).

The Vagus or Pneumogastric Nerve (X).—A very large nerve arising from the medulla by several roots. From it are given off nerves to the remaining gills, each nerve dividing into three branches which behave just like those of the ninth nerve. The nerve then continues down the body as the visceral branch to the œsophagus, stomach, heart, and swim-bladder or lung.

The Spinal Accessory (XI).—This is part a of the vagus in fishes, but becomes a separate nerve in higher forms. In mammals its anterior or vagal portion supplies the muscles of the larynx (the recurrent laryngeal nerve), and its posterior or spinal part runs to the muscles of the neck.

The Hypoglossal Nerve (XII).—This nerve arises from the ventral aspect of the medulla in the manner of a ventral motor root of a spinal nerve. It is purely motor in function, and supplies the muscles of the tongue and occasionally certain neck-muscles. In the amphibia its place is taken by the most anterior root of the second cervical, the first cervical being suppressed. In the higher mammals the nerve arises by two or more rootlets from the ventral side of the posterior portion of the medulla, and supplies the muscles of the tongue. It is formed by the fusion of roots from three or more precervical segments.

We may now consider the relation between the nerves and the somites.

Examination of primitive types has shown to which somite each segmental cranial nerve belongs, and has demonstrated that each head-somite has primitively a separate nerve-supply of all four components. This can be seen from the table on next page.

As the table suggests, it is extremely probable that the oculomotor, trochlear, and abducent hypoglossal nerves are the ventral roots to the first, second, and third somites respectively, and that the profundus, trigeminal, facial, and glosso-pharyngeal are the dorsal roots from the first, second, third, and fourth somites.

In Petromyzon, the dorsal and ventral roots of somites immediately following the fifth are almost normally developed. The hypoglossal is formed in Petromyzon by a peripheral anastomosis of the somatic motor roots of the somites above the posterior end of the branchial region. The vagus, however, still supplies the visceral components to all the gill-openings behind the first.

The segmental system in the head is obscured in vertebrates more advanced than selachians, because each component tends to be especially developed in one or two roots and to disappear in the rest. Thus the somatic sensory component of the trigeminal comes to supply the skin of most of the head, and to be correspondingly reduced in other cranial nerves.

TABLE SHOWING THE RELATION BETWEEN SEGMENTAL NERVES AND SOMITES OF THE HEAD

NERVE.	SOMITE to which the nerve runs.	PETROMYZON.	SELACHIAN.
III Oculomotor	First	— s.m.	v.m. s.m.
Vi Profundus	First	s.s. —	s.s. v.s.
IV Trochlear	Second	s.m.	s.m.
The rest of V Trigeminal	Second	s.s. — v.m.	s.s. — v.m.
VI Abducent	Third	s.m.	s.m.
VII Facial	Third	s.s. v.s. v.m.	— v.s. v.m.

These nerves are pre-otic in position; the remainder, behind the ear region, are post-otic.

—	Fourth	—	(fourth somite disappears)
IX Glossopharyngeal	Fourth	s.s. v.s. v.m.	(s.s. in a few cases) v.s. v.m.
First ventral spinal root	Fourth and Fifth	s.m.	(fifth somite disappears)
X Vagus	Fifth	s.s. v.s. v.m.	(s.s. in a few cases) v.s. v.s.
2nd ventral spinal root of Cyclostomes : hypoglossal of Gnathostomes	Sixth	s.m.	—
	Sixth and several subsequent somites	s.m.	s.m.

s.s., v.s., v.m., s.m., indicate the presence of somatic sensory, viscero-sensory, viscero-motor, and somatic motor components, respectively. The table is a statement of the results of work by J. B. Johnston, Norris and Hughes, and J. Z. Young among more recent investigators.

The two special visceral components are developed from normal visceral components in some segments and therefore are not specially mentioned in the table.

See Johnston, J. B., *Morph. Jahrb.*, vol. 34, 1905, pp. 149–203; Norris, H. W., and Hughes, Sally B., *Journ. Comp. Neurol.*, vol. 31, 1920, pp. 293–404; Young, J. Z., *Q. J. Micr. Sci.*, 1931, pp. 491–536: 1933, pp. 571–624.

Some special points can now be considered.

J. Z. Young has pointed out that the viscero-motor component only runs out with the ventral root in cases where the dorsal and ventral roots coalesce peripherally—that is, in the first cranial somite and in the spinal roots of Gnathostomes. Where the roots remain separate, as in somites after the first in the vertebrate head, the viscero-motor component runs out with the dorsal root. This condition is found in all somites of Amphioxus, and is probably primitive, as has been said.

The number of segments which compose a vertebrate " head," and include the cranial nerves, is not the same throughout. It varies from four in the Cyclostomes to nine in some Elasmobranchs, six in modern Amphibia, and eight in Reptiles, Birds, and Mammals. Since modern Amphibia have only ten intracranial nerves, while some fossil forms had twelve, it is possible that the head of modern Amphibia has been secondarily reduced.

If the dorsal roots of the head are held to be primitively intersegmental—which seems to be the condition in the trunk—then the nervus terminalis might be considered the dorsal root in front of the first somite. The other dorsal roots would then belong to the intersegment behind the somite to which they run.

THE ACOUSTICO–LATERAL SYSTEM.—This consists of the lateral-line, vestibular, and auditory nerves; the two latter are believed to be special developments of the lateral-line system.

The lateralis nerves are confined to the Agnatha, the fishes, and water-living Amphibia. They arise from two roots, one above the seventh nerve, and the other above the ninth and tenth nerves. Outside the brain they enter distinct lateralis ganglia.

Peripherally, they are closely associated with some branch of the somatic sensory system, where there is one available. Stensiö has shown, in the fossil Cyclostome *Cephalaspis*, that the lateralis nerves only joined segmental components some distance from the central nervous system.

In the embryo it is found that the *placodes* which give rise to the lateralis nerves differ in position from those giving rise to all other sensory components. It is stated, however, that the lateralis placodes are at first segmental in position.

It seems therefore reasonable to consider the lateralis system as a special somatic sensory component of the head; but it remains doubtful whether this component develops in relation to the somites, or is primitively separate from the segmental cranial nerves.

If the lateralis system is regarded as segmental, the superficial ophthalmic and buccal branches are considered an extension from the seventh nerve. All other lateralis branches are held to be components of the segmental nerves which they accompany from the brain (see Fig. 79).

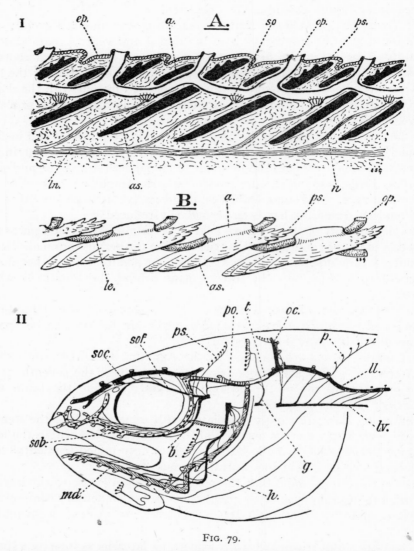

FIG. 79.

I. Diagrams showing the relation of the lateral-line canal to the scales on the body of *Perca fluviatilis*. *A*, longitudinal section ; *B*, scales and canal seen in side view. *a*. bridge of scale covering the canal ; *a.s.* anterior region of scale ; *ep*. epidermis ; *l.c.* lateral-line canal ; *l.n.* lateral-line nerve ; *n*. nerve to sense organ ; *op*. external opening of canal ; *p.s.* posterior edge of scale ; *s.o.* sense organ in canal.

II. Diagram of the head of *Amia calva* showing the system of lateral-line canals and their nerve supply (from Allis). *b*. buccal branch of facial nerve ; *g*. dorsal branch of glossopharyngeal ; *h*. hyomandibular branch of facial ; *ll*. lateral-line of trunk ; *l.v.* lateral-line of vagus ; *md*. mandibular canal ; *o.c.* occipital canal ; *p*. pit organs on body ; *po*. postorbital canal ; *ps*. pit organs on the head. *sob*. sub-orbital canal ; *s.o.f.* superior ophthalmic branch of facial. *t*. temporal canal.

Sympathetic System of the Head.—In Petromyzon a longitudinal sympathetic cord connects the seventh and tenth visceral sensory components; it then runs back above the branchial region. In Selachians there is no such longitudinal connection. In some Teleosts there is a direct connection between both visceral components of each cranial segment; it runs to all dorsal roots and to the oculomotor nerve. In Tetrapods also the cranial sympathetic nerves become linked up, but not in so direct a fashion. Presumably the longitudinal connections have been achieved independently in the three cases.

III

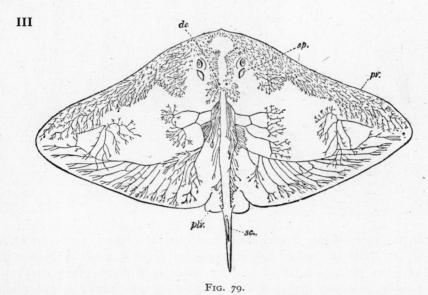

FIG. 79.

III. Dorsal view of *Pteroplatæa valenciennii*, showing the great development of the lateral line organs in this species. *de.* endolymphatic openings; *pv.* pectoral fin; *plv.* pelvic fin; *sc.* spine; *sp.* spiracle. (From Goodrich, *Vertebrata Craniata*, 1909.)

Sensory Organs.—The whole surface of the body forms an organ of touch, but special tactile organs are more or less widely distributed. *End-buds* consist of ovoidal groups of sensory cells supplied by a special nerve: *touch-cells* (Fig. 80, *A*) are nerve-cells occurring in the dermis at the termination of a sensory nerve: *touch-corpuscles* (*B*) are formed of an ovoidal mass of connective-tissue containing a ramified nerve, the terminal branches of which end in touch-cells: *Pacinian corpuscles* (*C*) consist of a terminal nerve-branch surrounded by a complex laminated sheath. Touch-corpuscles and Pacinian bodies are found only in the higher forms.

In Fishes, characteristic sense-organs are present, known as the *neuromast-organs* or *organs of the lateral-line*. Extending along the sides of the trunk and tail is a longitudinal streak, due to the presence either of an open groove or of a tube sunk in the epidermis, and continued on to the head in the form of branching grooves or canals (Fig. 79). These organs, and also certain

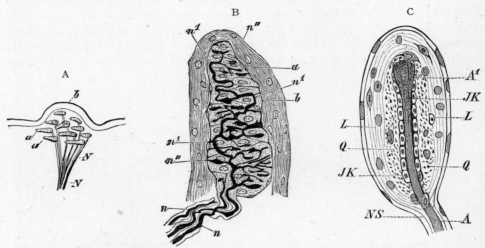

FIG. 80.—**A,** tactile spot from skin of **Frog.** *a.* touch-cells; *b.* epidermis; *N*, nerve. **B,** tactile corpuscle from dermal papilla of **human** hand. *a.* connective-tissue investment; *b.* touch-cells; *n, n', n'', n'''*, nerve. **C,** Pacinian corpuscle from back of **Duck.** *A, A¹.* neuraxis; *JK.* central knob and surrounding cells; *L, Q.* investing layers; *NS,* medullary sheath of nerve-fibre. (From Wiedersheim's *Vertebrata*.)

others in the form of pits or of unbranched canals, are lined with epithelium, some of the cells of which are arranged in groups, the *neuromasts*, and have the form characteristic of sensory cells produced at their free ends into hair-like processes : they are innervated by the lateral nerve, and in

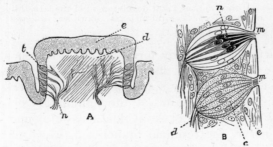

FIG. 81.—*A*, vertical section of one of the papillæ of the tongue of a **Mammal.** *d.* sub-mucosa; *e.* epithelium; *n.* nerve-fibres; *t.* taste-buds. *B,* two taste-buds. *c.* covering cells shown in lower bud; *d.* sub-mucosa; *e.* epithelium of tongue; *m.* sensory processes; *n.* internal sensory cells shown in upper bud. (From Foster and Shore's *Physiology*.)

the head, by the seventh and sometimes also the ninth nerve. At their first appearance in the embryo the organs of the lateral line are distinct, segmentally-arranged patches of sensory epithelium in intimate connection with the ganglia of the third, fifth, seventh, ninth, and tenth nerves. Cutaneous sense-organs of the lateral-line system, having at first a metameric arrangement, also occur in the aquatic Amphibia.

The function of the neuromast-organs has been shown to be to enable the animal to detect vibrations in the water of too low a frequency to form a sound capable of perception by the ear.

The sense of **taste** has for its special organs taste-buds (Fig. 81), similar in general character to the end-buds in the skin, and composed of groups of narrow rod-shaped cells. In Fishes these are widely distributed in the mouth and branchial cavities, also on the outer surface of the head, and in some Fishes over almost the whole surface of the body. In higher Craniates they

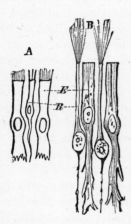

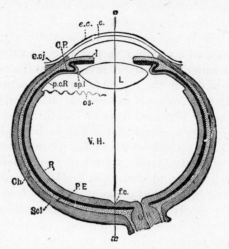

FIG. 82.—Epithelial cells of olfactory mucous membrane. *A*, of **Lamprey**; *B*, of **Salamander**. *E.* interstitial cells; *R.* olfactory cells. (From Wiedersheim's *Vertebrata.*)

FIG. 83.—Diagrammatic horizontal section of the eye of **Man**. *c.* cornea; *Ch.* choroid (dotted); *C. P.* ciliary processes; *e. c.* epithelium of cornea; *e. cj.* conjunctiva; *f.o.* yellow spot; *I.* iris; *L.* lens; *O. N.* optic nerve; *os.* ora serrata; *o—x.* optic axis; *p. c. R.* anterior non-visual portion of retina; *P. E.* pigmented epithelium (black); *R.* retina; *sp. l.* suspensory ligament; *Scl.* sclerotic; *V. H.* vitreous chamber. (From Foster and Shore's *Physiology.*)

are chiefly confined to the epithelium of the tongue and soft palate, and are supplied mainly by branches of the glossopharyngeal.

The **olfactory organ** is typically a sac-like invagination of the skin of the snout, anterior to the mouth, and communicating with the exterior by an aperture, the *external nostril*. It is paired in all Craniata, except Cyclostomes, in which there is a single olfactory sac, supplied, however, by paired olfactory nerves. The sac is lined by the olfactory mucous membrane or *Schneiderian membrane*, the epithelium of which contains peculiar, elongated sensory cells (Fig. 82), their free ends often produced into hair-like processes. In the Dipnoi and all higher groups the posterior end of each sac communicates with

the cavity of the mouth by an aperture called the *posterior nostril*, and an analogous communication occurs in the case of the unpaired organ of the Hags (*vide* p. 142).

In many air-breathing Vertebrates there is formed an offshoot from the olfactory organ, which, becoming separated, forms a distinct sac lined with olfactory epithelium and opening into the mouth. This is *Jacobson's organ* : it is supplied by the olfactory and trigeminal nerves.

The **paired eye** is a more or less globular structure, lying in the orbit, and covered externally by a thick coat of cartilage or of dense fibrous tissue, the optic capsule or *sclerotic* (Fig. 83, *Scl.*). On the outer or exposed portion of the eye the sclerotic is replaced by a transparent membrane, the *cornea* (*c.*), formed of a peculiar variety of connective-tissue, and covered on both its outer and inner faces by a layer of epithelium. The whole external coat of the eye has thus the character of an opaque spherical case—the sclerotic, having a circular hole cut in one side of it and fitted with a transparent window, the cornea. The curvature of the cornea is not the same as that of the sclerotic ; the former is almost flat in Fishes, but bulges outwards in terrestrial Vertebrates.

Lining the sclerotic is the second coat of the eye—the *choroid* (*ch.*)—formed of connective-tissue abundantly supplied with blood-vessels. At the junction of sclerotic and cornea, it becomes continuous with a circular membrane (*I*), placed behind but at some distance from the cornea, and called the *iris*. This latter is strongly pigmented, the colour of the pigment varying greatly in different species, and giving, as seen through the transparent cornea, the characteristic colour of the eye. The iris is perforated in the centre by a circular or slit-like aperture, the *pupil*, which, in the entire eye, appears like a black spot in the middle of the coloured portion. Except in Fishes, the pupil can be enlarged by the action of a set of radiating unstriped muscle-fibres contained in the iris, and contracted by a set of circular fibres ; and the anterior or outer portion of the choroid, where it joins the iris, is thrown into radiating folds, the *ciliary processes* (*C. P.*), containing unstriped muscular fibres, the *ciliary muscle*.

Lining the choroid and forming the innermost coat of the eye is a delicate semi-transparent membrane, the *retina* (*R.*), covered on its outer or choroidal surface with a layer of black pigment (*P. E.*). It extends as far as the outer ends of the ciliary processes, where it appears to end in a wavy line, the *ora serrata* (*o. s.*) : actually, however, it is continued as a very delicate membrane (*p. c. R.*) over the ciliary processes and the posterior face of the iris. The optic nerve (*O. N.*) pierces the sclerotic and choroid and becomes continuous with the retina, its fibres spreading over the inner surface of the latter. Microscopic examination shows that these fibres, which form the innermost layer of the retina (Fig. 84, *o. n.*), turn outwards and become connected with a layer of nerve-cells (*n. c.*). External to these come other layers of nerve-cells and granules, supported by a framework of delicate fibres, and finally, forming the outer surface of the retina proper, a layer of bodies which correspond to modified sensory cells and are called, from their shape, the *rods* and *cones* (*r*.). These are placed perpendicularly to the surface of the retina, and their outer ends are imbedded in a single layer of hexagonal *pigment-cells*, loaded with granules of the black pigment already referred to.

Immediately behind and in close contact with the iris is the transparent biconvex *lens* (Fig. 83, *L*.), formed of concentric layers of fibres, each derived

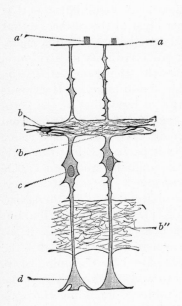
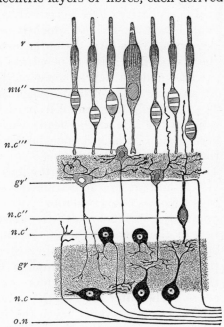

FIG. 84.—Diagram of the retina, the supporting structures to the left, the nervous and epithelial elements to the right. *a—d*, fibrous supporting structures; *gr. gr′.* granular layers; *n.c., n.c′., n.c″., n.c‴.* nerve-cells; *nu.* nuclear layer of rods and cones; *o. n.* fibres of optic nerve; *r.* rods and cones. (From Wiedersheim's *Vertebrata*, after Stöhr.)

from a single cell. The lens is enclosed in a delicate *capsule*, attached by a *suspensory ligament* (*sp. l.*) to the ciliary processes. The suspensory ligament exerts a pull upon the elastic lens so as to render it less convex than when left to itself; when the ciliary muscles contract they draw the suspensory ligament towards the iris, relaxing the ligament and allowing the lens to assume, more or less completely, its normal curvature. It is in this way that the accommodation of the eye to near and distant objects is effected.

The space between the cornea in front and the iris and lens behind is called the *aqueous chamber* of the eye, and is filled by a watery fluid—the *aqueous humour*. The main cavity of the eye, bounded in front by the lens and the ciliary processes and for the rest of its extent by the retina, is called the *vitreous chamber* (*V. H.*), and is filled by a gelatinous substance, the *vitreous humour*.

The cornea, aqueous humour, lens, and vitreous humour together constitute the dioptric apparatus of the eye, and serve to focus the rays of light from external objects on the retina. The iris is the diaphragm by which the amount of light entering the eye is regulated. The percipient portion or actual organ of sight is the retina, or, more strictly, the layer of rods and cones. The great peculiarity of the vertebrate eye, as compared with that of a Cephalopod (Vol. I, Section IX), to which it bears a close superficial resemblance, is that the sensory cells form the outer instead of the inner layer of the retina, so that the rays of light have to penetrate the remaining layers before affecting them.

The mode of development of the eye is as characteristic as its structure. At an early stage of development a hollow outgrowth—the *optic vesicle* (Fig. 85, *A, opt. v.*)—is given off from each side of the fore-brain (*dien.*). It extends towards the side of the head, where it meets with an inpushing of the ectoderm (*inv. l.*) which deepens and forms a pouch, and finally, separating from the ectoderm, a closed sac (*B, l.*) with a very small cavity and thick walls. This sac is the rudiment of the lens : as it enlarges it pushes against the optic vesicle, and causes it to become invaginated (*B*) ; the single-layered optic vesicle thus becomes converted into a two-layered *optic cup* (*opt. c., opt. c'.*), its cavity, originally continuous with the diacœle, becoming obliterated. The invagination of the vesicle to form the cup does not take place symmetrically, but obliquely from the external (posterior) and ventral aspect of the vesicle, so that the optic cup is incomplete along one side where there is a cleft—the *choroid fissure*—afterwards more or less completely closed by the union of its edges. The outer layer of the optic cup becomes the pigmentary layer of the retina : from its inner layer the rest of that membrane, including the rods and cones, is formed. The stalk of the optic cup occupies, in the embryonic eye, the place of the optic nerve, but the actual fibres of the nerve are formed as backward growths from the nerve-cells of the retina to the brain.

During the formation of the lens, mesoderm grows in between the pouch from which it arises and the external ectoderm ; from this the main substance of the cornea and its inner or posterior epithelium are formed, the adjacent ectoderm becoming the external epithelium. Mesoderm also makes its way into the optic cup, through the choroid fissure, and becomes the vitreous humour. Lastly, the mesoderm immediately surrounding the optic cup is differentiated to form the choroid, the iris, and the sclerotic.

Thus the paired eye of Vertebrates has a threefold origin : the sclerotic, choroid, iris, vitreous, and the greater part of the cornea are mesodermal : the lens and external epithelium of the cornea are derived from the ectoderm of the head : the retina and optic nerve are developed from a hollow pouch of the brain, and are, therefore, in their ultimate origin, ectodermal. The sensory cells of the retina—the rods and cones, although not directly formed from the external ectoderm, as in Invertebrates, are ultimately traceable into the superficial layer of ectoderm, since they are developed from the inner layer of the optic vesicle, which is a prolongation of the inner layer of the brain, and the latter is continuous before the closure of the medullary groove with the ectoderm covering the general surface of the body.

The eye-ball is moved by six muscles (Fig. 86). Four of these arise from the inner wall of the orbit, and pass, diverging as they go, to their insertion round the equator of the eye. One of them is dorsal in position, and is called

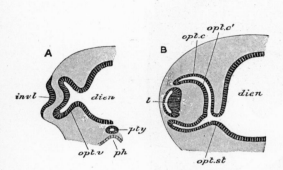

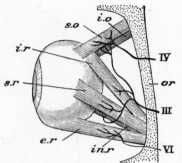

FIG. 85.—Early (*A*) and later (*B*) stages in the development of the eye of a **Craniate**. *dien*. diencephalon; *inv. l.* invagination of ectoderm to form lens; *l.* lens; *opt. c.* outer, and *opt. c'*. inner layer of optic cup; *opt. st.* optic stalk; *opt. v.* optic vesicle; *ph.* pharynx; *pty.* pituitary body. (Altered from Marshall.)

FIG. 86.—Muscles and nerves of the eye of a **Skate** (semi-diagrammatic). *III*. oculomotor nerve; *IV*. trochlear; *VI*. abducent. *e. r.* posterior rectus; *i. o.* inferior oblique; *in. r.* inferior rectus; *i. r.* anterior rectus; *or*. wall of orbit; *s. o.* superior oblique; *s. r.* superior rectus.

the *superior rectus* (*s. r.*), a second ventral the *inferior rectus* (*in. r.*), a third anterior, the *anterior* or *internal rectus* (*i. r.*), and a fourth posterior, the *posterior* or *external rectus* (*e. r.*). The usual names (internal and external) of the two last-named muscles originate from their position in Man, where, owing to the eye looking forwards instead of outwards, its anterior surface becomes internal, its posterior surface external. The two remaining muscles usually arise from the anterior region of the orbit, and are inserted respectively into the dorsal and ventral surface of the eye-ball. They are the *superior* (*s. o.*) and *inferior oblique* (*i. o.*) muscles.

The *median* or *pineal eye* (Fig. 87) is formed, in certain cases, from the distal end of the parietal organ already mentioned. It has the form of a rounded capsule, the outer or anterior portion of the wall of which is a lens (*l.*) formed of elongated cells, while its posterior portion has the character of a retina (*M. r.*). The latter has a layer of nerve-fibres on its outer and one of rod-like visual elements (*r*.) on its inner surface : it thus agrees with the usual types of invertebrate retina, and not with that of the paired eye.

The **organ of hearing,** like that of sight, presents quite peculiar features. It arises in the embryo as a paired invagination of the ectoderm in the region of the hind-brain, a shallow depression being formed which deepens and becomes flask-shaped, and finally, as a rule, loses its connection with the external ectoderm, forming a closed sac surrounded by mesoderm. At first simple, it soon becomes divided by a constriction into dorsal and ventral compartments.

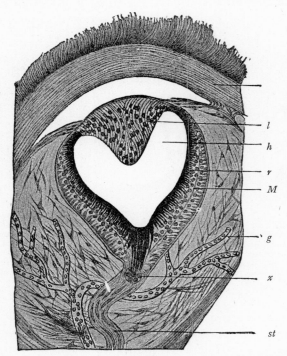

FIG. 87.—Section of the pineal eye of **Sphenodon.** *g*. blood-vessel ; *h*. cavity of eye, filled with fluid ; *k*. connective-tissue capsule ; *l*. lens ; *M*. molecular layer of retina ; *r*. layer of rods and cones ; *st*. nerve ; *x*. cells in nerve. (From Wiedersheim's *Vertebrata*, after Baldwin Spencer.)

The dorsal compartment is differentiated into an irregular chamber, the *utriculus* (Fig. 88, *u*.), and usually, three tubes, the *semicircular canals*. Of these two, the *anterior* (*ca*.) and *posterior* (*cp*.) *canals*, are vertical in position and have their adjacent limbs united, so that the two canals have only three openings between them into the utriculus : the third or *external canal* (*ce*.) is horizontal, and opens into the utriculus at either end. Each canal is dilated at one of its ends into an *ampulla* (*aa*., *ae*., *ap*.), placed anteriorly in the anterior and external canals, posteriorly in the posterior canal.

The ventral compartment of the auditory sac is called the *sacculus* (*s.*) : it gives off posteriorly a blind pouch, the *cochlea* (*l.*), which attains considerable dimensions in the higher classes ; while from its inner face is given off a narrow tube, the *endolymphatic duct* (*de.*), which either ends blindly or opens on the dorsal surface of the head. The utricle and saccule are sometimes imperfectly differentiated, and are then spoken of together as the *membranous vestibule.*

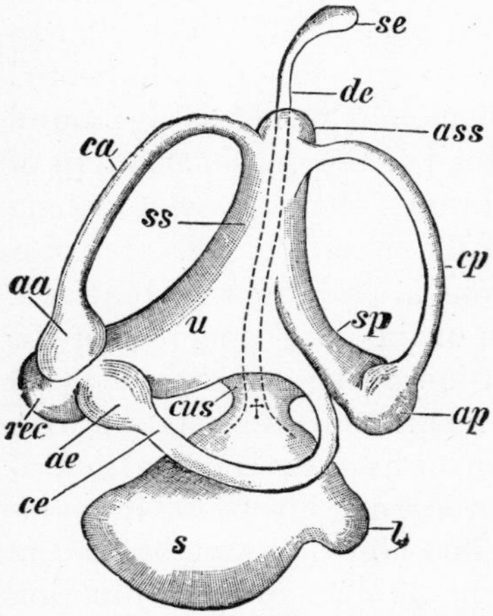

Patches of sensory cells (Fig. 89, *ae.*)—elongated cells produced into hair-like processes (*a. h.*)—occur in the ampulla and in the utricle and saccule : they are known as *maculæ acusticæ* and *cristæ acusticæ* (*c. r.*),

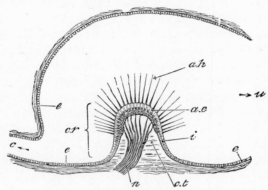

FIG. 88.—External view of organ of hearing of **Craniata** (semi-diagrammatic). *aa.* ampulla of anterior canal ; *ae.* of horizontal canal ; *ap.* of posterior canal ; *ass.* apex of superior utricular sinus ; *ca.* anterior, *ce.* horizontal, *cp.* posterior semi-circular canal ; *cus.* canal uniting sacculus with utriculus ; *de.* endolymphatic duct ; *l.* cochlea ; *rec.* utricular recess ; *s.* sacculus ; *se.* endolymphatic sac ; *sp.* posterior utricular sinus ; *ss.* superior utricular sinus ; *u.* utriculus. (From Wiedersheim's *Vertebrata.*)

FIG. 89.—Longitudinal section through an ampulla. *a. e.* auditory epithelium ; *a. h.* auditory hairs ; *c.* part of semi-circular canal ; *cr.* crista acustica ; *ct.* connective-tissue ; *e, i.* epithelium ; *n.* nerve ; *u.* junction with utriculus. (From Foster and Shore's *Physiology.*)

and to them the fibres of the auditory nerve (*n.*) are distributed. A fluid, the *endolymph*, fills the whole of the auditory organ or *membranous labyrinth*, and in it are formed *otoliths* of varying size and number. There is every reason for thinking that the labyrinth, like the otocysts or statocysts in the lower animals, functions as an *organ of equilibration* as well as of hearing.

As the membranous labyrinth develops in the embryo, it becomes surrounded and enclosed by the auditory capsule, the cartilage of which adapts itself to the form of the labyrinth, presenting a large excavation for the utricle and saccule and tunnel-like passages for the canals. The auditory organ does not, however, fit tightly into this system of cavities, but between it and the cartilage is a space, filled by a fluid called *perilymph*, which acts as a buffer to the delicate organ floating in it.

The early history of the auditory apparatus in the embryo shows that it belongs to the same series of structures as the lateral-line system, of which it may be regarded as a highly specialised part.

The parts so far mentioned constitute the *inner ear*, and this is all the auditory apparatus that fishes possess (except for such accessory apparatus as the *Weberian ossicles* found in certain teleosts (see page 280)). The change from water to land when the first tetrapoda arose was profound, and affected the whole organism in many directions, among them that of hearing. Sound vibrations had to be conveyed through the air instead of the denser medium of water. The first new acquisition was a membrane, the *ear-drum*, which enclosed a space, the *middle ear*, lying external to the inner ear. To transmit the sound-waves impinging on the ear-drum some apparatus was required, and this was effected by a transference of function of the upper member of the hyoid arch. No longer required in jaw suspension owing to the acquired autostyly (or autosystyly), the hyo-mandibular element came into relation with the inner ear at its medial end, and with the ear-drum at its outer end, and henceforth is known as the *columella auris* (amphibia, reptiles, and birds) and in mammals as the *stapes* (see Figs. 295, 640). The final, and highest, stage of hearing is reached by the mammals when two more elements change their function and are drawn into the middle ear. This time it is from the upper and lower jaws that the bones are obtained. Owing to the hinge of the jaws now being supplied by the articulation of the dentary to the squamosal, the *quadrate* and *articular* are set free, and become modified and drawn into the middle ear as the *incus* and *malleus*, respectively, to form with the stapes a chain of three bones, the *auditory ossicles* (see Fig. 640). The passage from the ear-drum to the exterior is known as the *outer ear*.

There is now complete evidence both palæontological and embryological, to show a continuous evolutionary change in the ear region from fish to mammal.

Urinogenital Organs.—In all Craniata there is so close a connection between the organs of renal excretion and those of reproduction that the two systems are conveniently considered together as the urinogenital organs.

Speaking generally, the excretory organ consists of three parts, all paired and situated along the dorsal wall of the cœlome ; the *fore-kidney* or *pronephros* (Fig. 91, *A, p. nph.*), the *mid-kidney* or *mesonephros* (*ms. nph.*), and the *hind-kidney* or *metanephros* (*mt. nph.*). Each of these is provided with a duct, the *pro-* (*pn. d.*), *meso-* (*m. sn. d.*), or *meta-nephric* (*mt. n. d.*) duct, which opens into the cloaca. The gonads (*gon.*) lie in the cœlome suspended to its dorsal wall by a fold of peritoneum : in some cases their products are discharged into the cœlome and make their exit by genital pores, but more usually the pronephric duct in the female assumes the functions of an oviduct and the mesonephric duct in the male those of a spermiduct (*cf.* p. 120). The pronephros is almost always functionless in the adult, and usually disappears altogether. The mesonephros is generally the functional kidney in the lower Craniata, in which, as a rule, no metanephros is developed, and the meso-nephric duct, in addition to carrying the seminal fluid of the male, acts as a ureter. In the higher forms the mesonephros atrophies, and the metanephros is the functional kidney, the metanephric duct becoming the true ureter.

The *kidney*—meso- or meta-nephros—of the adult is a massive gland of a deep red colour made up of convoluted *urinary tubules* (Fig. 90), separated from one another by connective-tissue containing an abundant supply of blood-vessels. The tubules are lined by a single layer of glandular epithelial cells (*B*, *C*), and each ends blindly in a globular dilatation, the *Malpighian capsule* (*A*, *gl.*), lined with squamous epithelium. In many of the lower Craniata, a

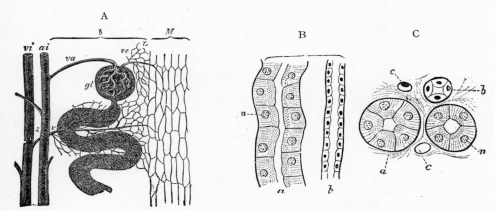

FIG. 90.—*A*, part of a urinary tubule with blood-vessels. *ai.* artery; *gl.* Malpighian capsule containing glomerulus; *v.* veinlet returning blood from capillary network (to the right) to vein *vi.*; *va.* afferent vessel of glomerulus; *ve.* efferent vessel. *B*, longitudinal, and *C*, transverse sections of urinary tubules. *a.* secreting part of tubules; *b.* conducting part of tubules; *c.* capillaries; *n.* nuclei. (From Foster and Shore's *Physiology*.)

branch goes off from the tubule, near the Malpighian capsule, and, passing to the ventral surface of the kidney, ends in a ciliated funnel-like body (Fig. 91 A, *nst.*), resembling the nephrostome of a worm, and, like it, opening into the cœlome. At their opposite ends the tubules join with one another, and finally discharge into the ureter.

The renal arteries branch extensively in the kidney, and give off to each Malpighian capsule a minute *afferent artery* (Fig. 90, *A*, *va.*) : this pushes the wall of the capsule before it, and breaks up into a bunch of looped capillaries, called the *glomerulus*, suspended in the interior of the capsule. The blood is carried off from the glomerulus by an *efferent vessel* (*ve.*), which joins the general capillary system of the kidneys, forming a network over the urinary tubules : finally, the blood is returned from this network to the renal vein. The watery constituents of the urine are separated from the blood in traversing the glomerulus, and, flowing down the tubule, take up and dissolve the remaining constituents—urea, uric acid, etc.—which are secreted by the cells of the tubules.

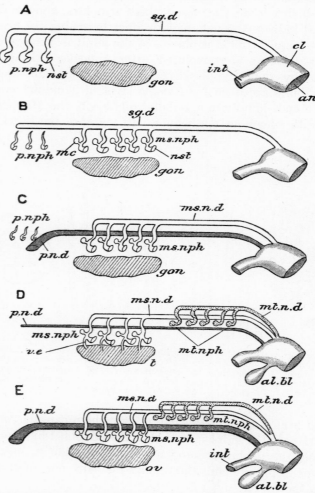

FIG. 91.—Diagram illustrating the development of the urinogenital organs of **Craniata.** *A,* development of pronephros and pronephric duct; *B,* atrophy of pronephros, development of mesonephros; *C,* differentiation of pro- and mesonephric ducts; *D,* development of metanephros; male type; *E,* female type. *al. bl.* allantoic bladder; *an.* anus; *cl.* cloaca; *gon.* gonad; *int.* intestine; *m. c.* Malpighian capsule; *ms. n. d.* mesonephric duct; *ms. nph.* mesonephros; *mt. n. d.* metanephric duct; *mt. nph.* metanephros; *nst.* nephrostome; *ov.* ovary; *p. n. d.* and *sg. d.* pronephric duct; *p. nph.* pronephros; *t.* testis; *v. e.* vasa efferentia.

The development of the kidney reveals a resemblance to the cœlomoducts of Annulata which would hardly be suspected from its adult structure. The pronephros (Fig. 91, *A, p. nph.*) originates as a small number of coiled tubes formed from mesoderm in the body-wall at the anterior end of the cœlome ; they are arranged metamerically, and each opens into the cœlome by a ciliated funnel (*nst.*).   Obviously such tubes are cœlomoducts : their chief peculiarity is that their outer ends do not open directly on the exterior, but into a longitudinal tube, the *pronephric* or *segmental duct* (*sg. d.*), which passes backwards, and discharges into the cloaca.   It seems probable that this arrangement is to be explained by supposing that the cœlomoducts originally opened externally into a longitudinal groove, which, by the apposition of its edges, was converted into a tube.   All the tubules of the pronephros open, by their ciliated funnels, into the narrow anterior end of the cœlome, into which projects a branch of the aorta ending a single large glomerulus.

The pronephros soon degenerates, its tubules losing their connection with the pronephic duct (*B*), but in the meantime fresh tubules appear in the segments posterior to the pronephros, and together constitute the mesonephros or *Wolffian body* (*B, ms. nph.*), from which the permanent kidney is formed in most of the lower Craniata.   The mesonephric tubules open at one end into the pronephric duct (*sg. d.*), at the other by ciliated funnels (*nst.*), into the cœlome ; a short distance from the funnel each gives off a blind pouch, which dilates at the end and forms a Malpighian capsule (*m. c.*), and a branch from the aorta entering it gives rise to a glomerulus.

In some forms the pronephric duct now becomes divided by a longitudinal partition into two tubes : one retains its connection with the mesonephros and is known as the mesonephic or *Wolffian duct* (*C, ms. n. d.*) : the other has no connection with the tubules, but opens into the cœlome in the region of the vanishing pronephros, and is called the *Müllerian duct* (*p. n. d.*).   In some Craniata the Müllerian appears quite independently of the Wolffian duct : the latter is then simply the pronephric duct after the union with it of the mesonephric tubules.

In the higher Vertebrata, from Reptiles to Mammals, a diverticulum (*D, E, mt. n. d.*) is given off from the posterior end of the Wolffian duct, which grows forwards and becomes connected with the hindmost tubules.   In this way is formed a *metanephros* (*mt. nph.*), which forms the permanent kidney and a metanephric duct (*mt. n. d.*), which gives rise to the ureter.   The Wolffian body ceases to discharge a renal function, and becomes a purely vestigial organ.

In many Fishes there is a dilatation of the mesonephric duct, the *urinary bladder*, which serves as a receptacle for the urine.   In the higher Craniata the ventral wall of the cloaca sends off a pouch, the *allantoic bladder* (*al. bl.*), which serves the same purpose, although morphologically an entirely different structure.

The *gonads* (*gon.*) are developed as ridges growing from the dorsal wall of the cœlome and covered by cœlomic epithelium, from the cells of which, as in so many of the lower animals, the ova and sperms are derived.   The testis consists of crypts or tubules, lined with epithelium, and usually discharging their

products through delicate *vasa efferentia* (*D, v. e.*) into the Wolffian duct, but in some groups into the cœlome. The sperms are always motile. The ovary is formed of a basis of connective-tissue or *stroma*, covered by epithelium, certain of the cells of which become enlarged to form ova. In the majority of cases the ova are discharged from the surface of the ovary into the cœlome and thus into the open ends of the Müllerian ducts (*E, p. n. d.*), which thus function simply as oviducts, having no connection in the adult with the urinary system. In some groups the ova, like the sperms, are shed into the cœlome and escape by the genital pores, and in many bony Fishes the ovary is a hollow organ, as in Arthropoda, discharging its ova into an internal cavity, whence they are carried off by a duct continuous with the gonad.

A few Craniata are normally hermaphrodite, but the vast majority are diœcious, hermaphroditism occurring, however, occasionally as an abnormality.

In close topographical relation with the urinogenital organs are found certain " ductless glands," the *adrenals* or *inter-* and *supra-renal bodies*. They are developed partly from ridges of the dorsal wall of the cœlome—*i.e.*, from mesoderm, partly from the sympathetic ganglia. There may be numerous adrenals segmentally arranged, or a single pair. Like other ductless glands the adrenals produce an *internal secretion*, which mingles with the blood and produces physiological effects on other parts.

Development.—The ova of Craniata are usually telolecithal, but the amount of food-yolk varies within wide limits. When it is small in quantity, cleavage is complete but usually unequal, when abundant, incomplete and discoidal. In the latter case the embryo proper is formed, as in Cephalopods, from a comparatively small portion of the zygote, the rest giving rise to a large yolk-sac and, in the higher forms, to other embryonic membranes.

There is never a typical invaginated gastrula, as in Amphioxus, but in some of the lower Craniata a gastrula stage is formed by a combination of inpushing and overgrowth : details will be given in the sections on the various groups. In the higher forms the gastrula stage is much modified and obscured.

The mode of development of the mesoderm and of the cœlome differs strikingly from the process we are familiar with in Amphioxus. At an early stage the mesoderm is found in the form of paired longitudinal bands (Fig. 92, *A, msd.*) lying one on each side of the middle line, where they are separated from one another by the medullary groove (*md. gr.*) and the notochord (*nch.*), and completely filling the space between the ectoderm and the endoderm. Each mesoderm-band becomes differentiated into a dorsal portion, the *vertebral plate*, bounding the nervous system and notochord, and a ventral portion, the *lateral plate*, surrounding the mesenteron. The vertebral plate undergoes metameric segmentation, becoming divided into a row of squarish masses, *somites* or *mesodermal segments* (*B, pr. v.*) ; the lateral plate splits into two layers, a somatic (*som.*), adherent to the ectoderm, a splanchnic (*spl.*), to the endoderm. The space between the two is the cœlome (*cœl.*), which is thus a *schizocœle*, or cavity hollowed out of the mesoderm, and is, except in the head-region in the Lampreys (p. 147), at no stage in communication with the mesenteron, as are some of the cœlomic pouches of Amphioxus. The dorsal portion of the cœlome assumes the character of a series of paired diverticula of the main ventral part, each situated in the interior of a somite ; but such an arrangement is temporary, and these somitic cavities early disappear. From the dorsal portions of the somites the myomeres are formed, from their medial portions the sclerotomes which give rise to the vertebræ.

The development of the principal organs has been described in general

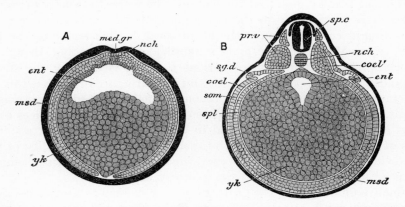

FIG. 92.—Transverse section of earlier (*A*) and later (*B*) embryos of **Frog.** *cœl.* cœlome ; *cœl'.* prolongation of cœlome into protovertebra ; *ent.* mesenteron ; *med. gr.* medullary groove ; *msd.* mesoderm ; *nch.* notochord ; *pr. v.* protovertebra ; *sg. d.* segmental duct ; *som.* somatic layer of mesoderm ; *sp. c.* spinal cord ; *spl.* splanchnic layer of mesoderm ; *yk.* yolk-cells. (After Marshall.)

terms, in the preceding account of the organs themselves : it will be convenient to defer further consideration of this subject until we come to deal with the development of the various types of Craniata, and with the embryological characteristics of the classes and sub-classes.

Metamerism.—A tendency, more or less strongly marked, to a serial repetition of parts is to be observed in a number of different systems of organs. Instances of this have already been pointed out in the skeleton, and the muscular, nervous, and excretory systems. This phenomenon seems to lead to the conclusion that the structure of the Craniata can be understood only when they are regarded as metamerically-segmented animals. The phase of metamerism presented by the Craniata is, however, widely different from that which prevails in the segmented Invertebrates. In the latter the segmentation is usually quite distinctly pronounced externally, and it may involve a metameric division extending to the cœlome as well as to the various systems of internal organs. In the Craniata, on the other hand, segmentation is never visible on the exterior, and in the adult condition the cœlome never shares in the division. Even in the case of the organs which present metameric characters, the metamerism often appears indefinite and uncertain : thus, as already pointed out, the segmentation of the spinal column, which in the adult is the most pronounced of all, does not coincide with the segmentation of the muscular and nervous system. Yet when we take the phenomena of embryonic development into account, it becomes sufficiently clear that in the Craniata we have to do with animals possessing a metameric segmentation of the same general type as that possessed by Amphioxus, and that the apparent anomalies are due to processes of secondary modification.

It is in the trunk region that the metamerism is most strongly pronounced and that more particularly in the lower groups. In the head there is great specialisation in co-ordination with the presence in this region of the brain, the chief organs of special sense, and the mouth and jaws ; so that, though there are indications of metamerism of various parts, it is only by the study of development that it is possible to interpret the structure of the head in terms of a metameric segmentation which becomes much modified and disguised in the adult animal. When the development is followed out, it becomes evident that, as in the Arthropoda, the head in Craniata is formed as a result of a process of fusion between a number of metameres, the individuality of which is quite evident in early stages, more particularly among lower forms, being most pronounced in the region behind the auditory capsules.

Distinctive Characters.—The Craniata may be defined as Euchorda in which the notochord is not continued to the end of the snout, but stops short beneath the fore-brain, some distance from its anterior end. A skull is always present, and there are usually paired limbs. The ectoderm is many-layered and is never ciliated in the adult, and only rarely in the larva. The pharynx is of moderate dimensions, and is perforated by not more than seven pairs of gill-slits (except in some Cyclostomes). The gill-pouches do not open into an atrium. The liver is large, massive, and not obviously tubular. There is a muscular, chambered heart, and the blood contains red corpuscles. The renal tubules unite to form large paired kidneys and open into ducts which discharge into or near the posterior end of the intestine. The brain is complex, and there are at least ten pairs of cerebral nerves : the spinal nerves are, except in Cyclostomes, formed by the union of dorsal and ventral roots. Paired eyes of great complexity, derived in part from the brain, are present ; and there is a pair of auditory organs. There is typically a single pair of gonads, and the reproductive products are usually discharged by ducts derived from the renal system. There is never a typical invaginate gastrula, and the mesoderm arises in the form of paired longitudinal bands which subsequently become segmented. The cœlome is nearly always developed as a schizocœle.

SUB-PHYLUM IV—AGNATHA.

Formerly certain groups of Palæozoic fishes and fish-like animals, whose position was at that time uncertain, were classed together as the " Ostraco-dermi." This " class " was subdivided into three orders, the *Osteostraci* (or *Cephalaspidomorphi*), *Heterostraci* (or *Pteraspidomorphi*) and the *Antiarchi* (or *Pterichthyomorphi*).

Recent work has done much to establish a truer zoological position for these three groups with the result that the Antiarchi are now placed with the Gnathostomata and the Osteostraci and Heterostraci, together with the living Cyclostomes, are joined in a single sub-phylum the Agnatha.

The Agnatha, whose name is taken from their chief characteristic, the absence of true jaws, form a section morphologically equivalent to all the rest of the vertebrata from fish to man, though in apparent extent a much smaller one. It must, however, be remembered that we may perhaps know only a small proportion of the forms that have existed. Members of the group appear first in the Silurian period, and continued to expand throughout the Devonian, when they attainéd their maximum development. From that time to the present day nothing is known of the group, but there can be no doubt that the living cyclostomes are rightly classed as members of the Agnatha whose post-Devonian ancestors have not been discovered.

The group may be classified as follows *:—

SUB-PHYLUM AGNATHA.

CLASS CEPHALASPIDOMORPHI.

Sub-classes OSTEOSTRACI.
ANASPIDA.

CLASS PTERASPIDOMORPHI.

Sub-classes HETEROSTRACI.
CŒLOLEPIDA.

* This classification is conservative and to some extent non-committal as to the relation-ship of some of the component groups. Attention may be drawn to an alternative scheme as follows :—

Branch AGNATHI.
Class OSTRACODERMI (Cyclostomata).
Sub-class PTERASPIDOMORPHI.
Orders *Heterostraci.*
Palæospondyloidea.
Myxinoidea.
Sub-class CEPHALASPIDOMORPHI.
Orders *Osteostraci.*
Anaspida.
Petromyzontia.

This classification expresses the opinion that there has been a division between the two sub-classes from as remote a time as the Devonian period. It is based on certain notable differences in the anatomy of the two groups. The Pteraspidomorphi have the rostral part of the head

CLASS CYCLOSTOMI.

Sub-classes Petromyzontia.
Myxinoidea.

CLASS CEPHALASPIDOMORPHI.

Sub-class Osteostraci.
Families **Cephalaspidæ.**
Tremataspidæ.

These are forms with a single naso-hypophysial opening placed far back on the head. The head region is expanded and flattened, and is protected by a hard, bony carapace often highly ornamented with tubercles and spines, and produced on each side into a backwardly directed " horn " which leaves a bay, or *pectoral sinus*, between itself and the trunk. The body is protected by rows of scales in which true bone-cells are present. The tail is heterocercal, with a well-developed lobe and a dorsal fin is present.

In **Cephalaspis** (Figs. 93, 96), the most completely known genus, there is a pair of lobed appendages arising from the pectoral sinus on each side. Of the internal anatomy a good deal is known. The brain, with its ten pairs of cranial nerves, is closely comparable with that of the living Cyclostomes, but, in addition, there is a well-developed system of nerves arising in the acustico-lateralis region of the brain, from which five pairs of stout nerves run to depressions on the upper surface of the head-shield. By analogy with such modern forms as the Torpedos, it has been thought that these nerves and

---

formed by the ethmoidal region of the cranium, and the naso-hypophysial opening lies near the mouth on the ventral side of the head (see Fig. 117). In the Cephalaspidomorphi the rostral part of the head is formed by the growth of the upper lip so great in its development that the naso-hypophysial opening, which in the young Petromyzon lies in the normal position (Fig. 110) is pushed on to the top of the head to some distance behind the rostrum. The extinct groups, as far as can be seen, seem to fall into one or the other of these two categories. This classification has received considerable but not unanimous support. There are certain criticisms which will have to be met before it is completely acceptable (see E. S. Goodrich, *Proc. Linn. Soc.*, 1929–30, pp. 45–49).

A third classification is as follows (see E. I. White, *Phil. Trans. Roy. Soc.*, B, 527, 1935) :—

Group AGNATHA.
    Class and Order HETEROSTRACI.
        Family **Palæspidæ.**
            Cyathaspidæ.
            Pteraspidæ.
            Drepanaspidæ.
    Order ANASPIDA.
    Order OSTEOSTRACI.
    Order CYCLOSTOMATA.
        Sub-orders *Palæospondyloidea.*†
            Hyperartii (Petromyzontia).
            Hyperotreti (Myxinoidea).

This classification is essentially the same as is adopted here, except that by not using the divisions Cephalaspidomorphi and Pteraspidomorphi, no emphasis is laid on the presumed relationship between the Anaspida and the Osteostraci, nor on the considerable differences between these two groups and the Heterostraci.

† It will be noticed that *Palæospondylus* still appears in these two classifications. It has recently been shown to be a gnathostome (see page 170 post).

depressions formed a kind of electric organs[1] (Fig. 94). If so, it is interesting to see how early in the history of the vertebrata so advanced a specialisation

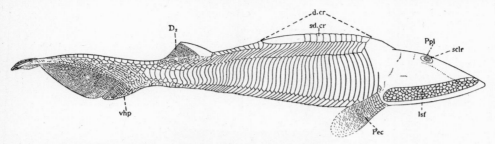

FIG. 93.—**Hemicyclaspis murchisoni.** $D.^2$ dorsal fin; *d.cr.* dorsal crest of trunk; *sd.cr.* dorsal scutes; *Ppl.* pineal plates; *sclr.* sclezotic ring; *lsf.* lateral " electric field "; *Pec.* pectoral fin; *vhp.* ventral axis of caudal fin. (After Stensiö.)

can be evolved. The eyes are placed close together on the top of the cephalic shield, with the pineal opening between them and the naso-hypophysial opening

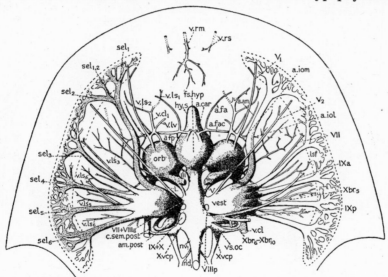

FIG. 94.—**Kiaeraspis auchenaspidoides.** A cast of the cranial cavity, the orbits, the labyrinth cavities and of certain canals. *sel.* 1–6. nerves of the electric fields. V., VII., IX., X., cranial nerves. For further details *see* Stensiö, " The Downtonian Vertebrates." (After Stensiö.)

just in front. The mouth is ventral, and is followed on each side by ten pairs of gill pouches (Fig. 95), of which the first two are related to the opthalmicus

[1] There is, however, some difficulty in accepting this view. The electric organs of such a fish as the *Torpedo* are formed from specialised muscles which are not innervated by the acustico-lateralis system but by branches from the seventh and tenth nerves. It is, moreover, not easy to see how muscles could be situated in depressions outside the bony carapace.

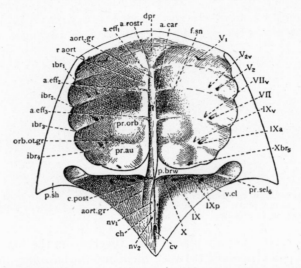

FIG. 95.—**Cephalaspis.** Diagram of the endocranium from the ventral aspect. Showing the position of the gills. (After Stensiö.)

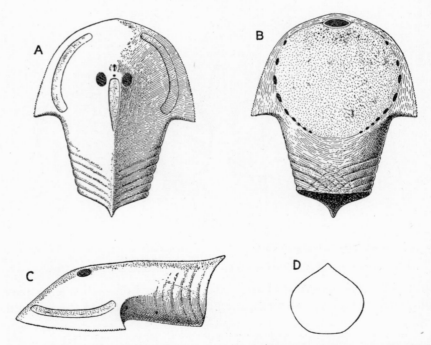

FIG. 96.—**Kiaeraspis auchenaspidoides.** *A*, cephalic shield in dorsal, *B*, in ventral view. *C*, in lateral view. *D*, transverse section through " neck " region. (After Stensiö.)

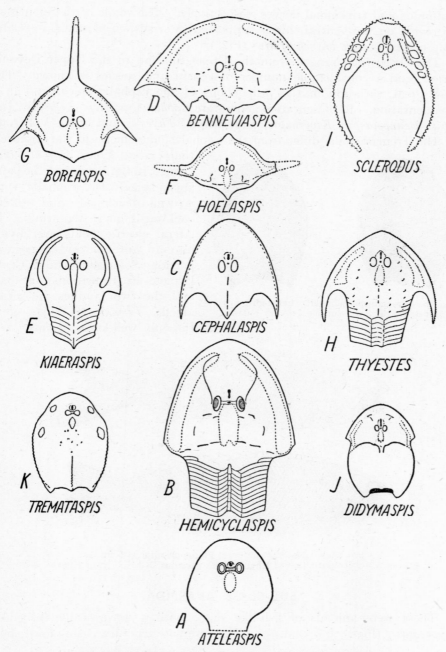

FIG. 97.—Head shields of various Cephalaspids. (After Gregory.)

profundus and trigeminal nerves, respectively. The whole of the mouth and
gill region on the ventral side is supported by a system of small, tesselated,
bony plates, the *oro-branchial area* (Fig. 96).

The Osteostraci ranged from the Upper Silurian to the Upper Devonian
period, and a considerable number of genera and species is known. They
show great variation in the proportions of the cephalic shield and in its
ornamentation. Representative genera are *Cephalaspis, Hemicyclaspis, Atele-
aspis, Benneviaspis, Kiaeraspis, Didymaspis, Thyestes* and others [1] (Fig. 97).

The Tremataspidæ differ from the Cephalaspidæ chiefly in the absence of

FIG. 98.—**Tremataspis schmidti.** Left figure upper,
right figure the lower surface. (After Patten.)

the pectoral sinus, and, in consequence, in the absence of the paired
appendages. The cephalic shield
is well developed, and extends
backwards on to the trunk. The
lateral electric fields are divided
into an anterior and a posterior
portion. Some genera of the Cephalaspidæ are transitional in shape,
and the two families are clearly
allied. *Tremataspis* (Fig. 98) is
the only well-known genus.

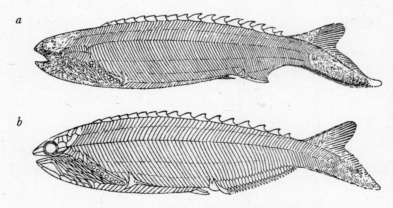

FIG. 99 *a*.—Reconstruction of **Pterolepis nitidus,** Kiær.
FIG. 99 *b*.—Reconstruction of **Rhyncholepis parvulus**, Kiær. (After Kiær.)

SUB-CLASS ANASPIDA.

These were animals of fish-like shape with a downwardly turned tail
(*hypocercal*) (Figs. 99 *a* and *b*). The internal structure is unknown, but a

[1] For which see Stensiö. "The Downtonian and Devonian Vertebrates of Spitzbergen.
Part I. Cephalaspidae."

highly developed dermal skeleton is present. The scales on the head are small and show a complicated arrangement which differs in pattern in different genera. The scales on the trunk are arranged in lateral and ventral series, which, with a set of tall lateral scales, show great resemblance to the condition found in the Cephalaspidæ, as does also the method of their articulation. There are no paired appendages, unless a pair of pectoral spines be taken to represent them. There is a series of ridge spines along the back, and an anal spine below. The eyes are lateral, and the pineal and naso-hypophysial openings are placed on the top of the head in relatively the same position as in the Cephalaspidæ. A series of gill openings, varying in number in the different genera, are placed in front of the pectoral spine.

There are several families, all, with one exception, *Euphanerops* (a Devonian genus), confined to the Silurian period.

Examples are *Lasanius, Birkenia, Pharyngolepis, Pterolepis* (Fig. 99 *a*) *Rhyncholepis* (Fig. 99 *b*).

CLASS PTERASPIDOMORPHI.

The Pteraspidomorphi are forms with a broad depressed head protected by a carapace of exoskeletal plates. The eyes are widely separated, and lateral in position. There are no fins on the body, either paired or unpaired. The tail behind the carapace is laterally compressed and downwardly turned (*hypocercal*), and is covered with scales having the same composition as the plates of the carapace. The sub-class may be divided into two orders : the Heterostraci, containing four closely allied families, and a group, the Cœlolepida, whose position in the class is still a matter of doubt.

The Pteraspidomorphi differ from the Cephalaspidomorphi in several essential points. The nostrils, when known, are paired instead of single. The plates and scales are without bone-cells, and the plates are formed of three layers, of which the outer one is composed of a substance allied to dentine. The gill-pouches unite into a single exhalent pore placed rather far back on the sides of the carapace. Paired appendages are absent.

The four families which form the Heterostraci—*i.e.*, the Paleaspidæ, Cyathaspidæ, Pteraspidæ (Fig. 100) and Drepanaspidæ (Fig. 101)—are distinguished from one another by the number of plates in the carapace. The Paleaspidæ have an undivided upper shield, the Cyathaspidæ have the upper surface of the carapace divided into four plates, the Pteraspidæ into nine and the Drepanaspidæ into twelve.

A description of *Pteraspis rostrata*, a species of the best-known genus, will serve for all the remainder. The carapace is somewhat elongated and rectangular in section. The dorsal surface is composed of nine plates, of which three, the *rostral, pineal,* and large *dorsal,* are unpaired. The remaining six

plates form three pairs : the *orbital* in which lie the eye sockets ; the *branchial*, with the gill opening at the posterior border, and just behind these the *cornual* plates. In the adult all these plates are bound together by a fusion of their inner laminæ. On the ventral surface a large unpaired plate covers

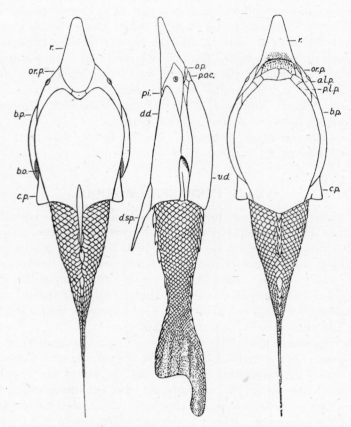

FIG. 100.—Restoration of **Pteraspis rostrata** dorsal (left hand figure) lateral and ventral views. *a.l.p.* anterior lateral plate ; *b.p.* branchial plate ; *c.p.* cornual plate ; *d.d.* dorsal disc ; *d.sp.* dorsal spine ; *l.o.p.* lateral oral plate ; *o.p.* oral plate ; *or.p.* orbital plate ; *pi.* pineal plate ; *p.l.p.* posterior lateral plate ; *p. o.p.* post-oral plate ; *r.* rostrum ; *v.d.* ventral disc. (After E. I. White.)

most of the area except for a number of small oral plates round the lower border of the mouth, and immediately behind these three pairs of small plates the *post-oral* and the anterior and posterior *laterals*. The trunk is covered with a series of ridge-scales along the upper and lower surface. From impressions of the internal surface of the upper carapace it seems clear that there were seven pairs of gill pouches, and an X-like impression just behind the pineal opening has been interpreted as evidence of two semicircular canals on each side.

The second division of the Pteraspidomorphi, the Cœlolepida, shows so little resemblance to the Heterostraci that some authorities question their right to be included in the group, and even their status as Agnatha. There are three genera included in the division : *Thelodus, Lanarkia,* and *Cœlolepis,* which all appear as flattened impressions (Fig. 102), with a broad head-region followed

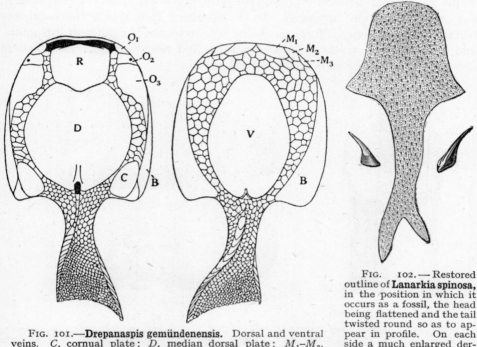

FIG. 101.—**Drepanaspis gemündenensis.** Dorsal and ventral veins. *C,* cornual plate; *D,* median dorsal plate; *M₁–M₃,* ventral oral plates; *O₁–O₃,* ocular plates; *R,* rostral plate; *V,* ventral plate; *B,* branchial plate. (From Stensiö, after Kiær.)

FIG. 102. — Restored outline of **Lanarkia spinosa,** in the position in which it occurs as a fossil, the head being flattened and the tail twisted round so as to appear in profile. On each side a much enlarged dermal denticle is shown. (From the *Cambridge Natural History,* after Traquair.)

by a heterocercal tail. There is no armour beyond scales which bear each a spine. These have been likened to the placoid scale of the Chondrichthyes, but the homology is very doubtful. The eyes are placed far apart, and there is in *Thelodus* an indication of a gill apparatus which is consistent with that of the Pteraspids, but otherwise all other structures are unknown, and the true relationship of this group must for the present remain *sub judice.*

CLASS CYCLOSTOMATA.

The Cyclostomata, or Lampreys and Hags, are eel-like animals, distinguished from all other living Craniata by the possession of a suctorial mouth devoid of functional jaws, by the single olfactory organ, and by the absence of lateral appendages, or paired fins.

1. EXAMPLE OF THE CLASS.—THE LAMPREY (*Petromyzon*).

Three species of Lamprey are common in the Northern Hemisphere : the Sea-lamprey (*P. marinus*), which attains a length of a metre ; the Lampern, or common fresh-water Lamprey (*P. fluviatilis*), which may reach a length of about 90 cm. ; and the Sandpride, or lesser fresh-water Lamprey (*P. planeri*), not exceeding 45 cm. in length. In the Southern Hemisphere the Lampreys belong to two genera : *Mordacia*, found on the coasts of Chili and Tasmania, and *Geotria*, in the rivers of Chili, Australia, and New Zealand. Both genera differ from *Petromyzon* in minor details only.

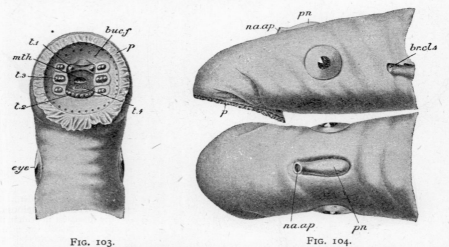

FIG. 103. FIG. 104.

FIGS. 103–4.—**Petromyzon fluviatilis.** Ventral (Fig. 103), lateral and dorsal (Fig. 104) views of the head. *br. cl. 1*, first gill-cleft ; *buc. f.* buccal funnel ; *eye*, eye ; *mth.* mouth ; *na. ap.* nasal aperture ; *p.* papillæ ; *pn.* pineal area ; *t 1. t 2. t 3.* teeth of buccal funnel ; *t 4.* teeth of tongue. (After W. K. Parker.)

External Characters.—The head and trunk (Fig. 104) are nearly cylindrical, the tail-region compressed or flattened from side to side. At the anterior end, and directed downwards, is a large, basin-like depression, the *buccal funnel* (*buc. f.*), surrounded with papillæ (*p*) and beset internally with yellow, *horny teeth* (*t 1—t 3*). At the bottom of the funnel projects a prominence, the so-called " tongue " (*t 4*), also bearing horny teeth, and having immediately above it the narrow *mouth* (*mth.*). On the dorsal surface of the head is the single median *nostril* (*na. ap.*), and immediately behind it a transparent area of skin (*pn.*) indicates the position of the pineal organ. The paired eyes have no eyelids, but are covered by a transparent area of skin. The gill-slits (*br. cl. 1*) are seven pairs of small apertures on the sides of the head, the first a little

behind the eyes.   On the ventral surface, marking the junction between trunk
and tail, is the very small *anus* (Fig. 113, *a*), lying in a slight depression, and
having immediately behind it a small papilla pierced at its extremity by the
urinogenital aperture (*z*.).   There is no trace of paired appendages, and the only
organs of locomotion are the unpaired fins.   Two dorsal fins of approximately
equal dimensions, separated by a notch, and a caudal fin are present, the
second dorsal being continuous with the caudal.

Lampreys prey upon Fishes, attaching themselves to the bodies of the latter
by the sucker-like mouth, and rasping off their flesh with the armed tongue.
They are often found holding on to stones by the buccal funnel, and under
these circumstances perform regular respiratory movements, the branchial
region expanding and contracting like the thorax of a Mammal.   The reason

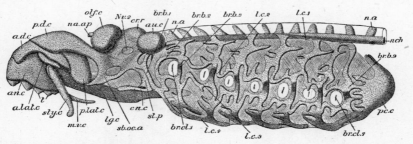

Fig. 105.—**Petromyzon marinus.**   Skull, with branchial basket and anterior part of vertebral
column.   The cartilaginous parts are dotted.   *a. d. c.* anterior dorsal cartilage ; *a. lat. c.* anterior
lateral cartilage ; *an. c.* annular cartilage ; *au. c.* auditory capsule ; *br. b. 1—7*, vertical bars of
branchial basket ; *br. cl. 1—7*, external branchial clefts ; *cn. c.* cornual cartilage ; *cr. r.* cranial
roof ; *l. c. 1—4*, longitudinal bars of branchial basket ; *lg. c.* lingual cartilage ; *m. v. c.* median
ventral cartilage ; *n. a.* neural arch ; *na. ap.* nasal aperture ; *nch.* notochord ; *Nv. 2*, foramen for
optic nerve ; *olf. c.* olfactory capsule ; *pc. c.* pericardial cartilage ; *p. d. c.* posterior dorsal cartilage ;
p. lat. c. posterior lateral cartilage ; *sb. oc. a.* subocular arch ; *st. p.* styloid process ; *sty. c.* styliform cartilage ; *t.* teeth.   (After W. K. Parker.)

of this is that when the animal is adhering by the mouth the respiratory current
cannot take its usual course—entering at the mouth and leaving by the gill-
slits—but is pumped by muscular action both into and out of the branchial
apertures.

The *skin* is soft and slimy, mottled greenish-brown in *P. marinus*, bluish
above and silvery on the sides in the fresh-water species.   The epiderm contains
unicellular glands, the secretion of which gives its slimy character to the skin.
The segmental sense-organs take the form of a *lateral line* which is superficial,
not enclosed in a canal, and of minute pits on the head.   There is no trace of
exoskeleton.

Skeleton.—The *axial skeleton* of the trunk is very simple.   There is a
persistent notochord (Fig. 105, *nch.*) with a tough sheath composed of an
inner fibrous and an outer elastic layer.   Attached to the sides of the notochord are little vertical rods of cartilage (*n.a.*), arranged segmentally, bounding

the spinal canal on each side, and corresponding to rudimentary neural and interneural arches : in the caudal region these fuse into a single plate perforated by foramina for the spinal nerves and sending off processes to the base of

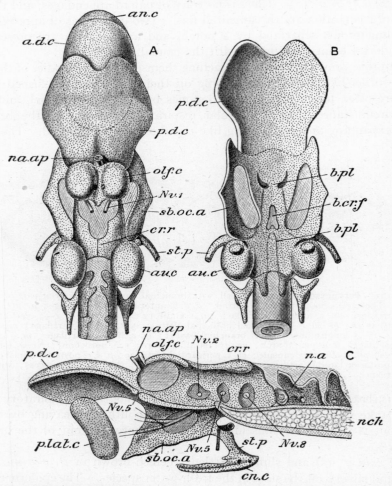

FIG. 106.—**Petromyzon marinus.** Dorsal (*A*), ventral (*B*), and sectional (*C*) views of skull. The cartilaginous parts are dotted. *a. d. c.* anterior dorsal cartilage ; *an. c.* annular cartilage ; *au. c.* auditory capsule ; *b. cr. f.* basicranial fontanelle ; *b. pl.* basal plate ; *cn. c.* cornual cartilage ; *cr. r.* cranial roof ; *n. a.* neural arch ; *na. ap.* nasal aperture ; *nch.* notochord ; *Nv. 1*, olfactory nerve ; *Nv. 2, 5,* and *8,* foramina for the optic, trigeminal, and auditory nerves ; *Nv. 5′*, fifth nerve ; *olf. c.* olfactory capsule ; *p. d. c.* posterior dorsal cartilage ; *p. lat. c.* posterior lateral cartilage ; *sb. oc. a.* sub-ocular arch ; *st. p.* styloid process. (After W. K. Parker.)

the fin. For the rest of its extent the spinal canal is enclosed only by tough, pigmented connective-tissue. Slender rods of cartilage support the median fins.

The *cranium* also exhibits a very primitive type of structure. Its floor is formed by a *basal plate* (Fig. 106, *b. pl.*), made by the union of the para-chordals and trabeculæ, and surrounding posteriorly the fore-end of the notochord. Immediately in front of the termination of the notochord is a large aperture, the *basi-cranial fontanelle* (*b. cr. f.*), due to the non-union of the posterior ends of the trabeculæ; through it passes the pituitary pouch, presently to be referred to (Fig. 109), on its way from the olfactory sac to the ventral surface of the notochord. Lateral walls extend upwards from each side of the basal plate, but the roof of the cranium is formed by membrane except at one point, where a narrow transverse bar (*cr. r.*) extends across be-tween the side-walls and furnishes a rudimentary roof. United with the posterior end of the basal plate and forming the end of the neurocranium are the *auditory capsules* (*au. c.*), and the side-walls are pierced with apertures for the cerebral nerves (*Nv. 2, Nv. 5, Nv. 8*).

So far the skull is thoroughly typical, though in an extremely simple or embryonic condition; the remaining parts of it differ a good deal from the ordinary structure as described in the preceding section, and are in many cases very difficult of interpretation.

The *olfactory capsule* (*olf. c.*) is an unpaired concavo-convex plate which supports the posterior wall of the olfactory sac and is pierced by paired apertures for the olfactory nerves. It is unique in being united to the cranium by fibrous tissue only.

Extending outwards and downwards from each side of the basal plate is an inverted arch of cartilage, called the *sub-ocular arch* (Figs. 105 and 106, *sb. oc. a.*) from the fact that it affords a support to the eye. From its posterior end a slender *styloid process* (*st. p.*) passes directly downwards and is connected at its lower end with a small *cornual cartilage* (*cn. c.*). Perhaps the sub-ocular arch answers to the palato-quadrate or primary upper jaw, the styloid and cornual cartilages to the main part of the hyoid arch. In close relation with the angle of the sub-ocular arch is an upwardly directed plate, the *posterior lateral cartilage* (*p. lat. c.*).

Connected with the anterior end of the basal plate is the large bilobed *posterior dorsal cartilage* (*p. d. c.*); it appears to be formed from the united anterior ends of the trabeculæ. Below and projecting in front of it is the *anterior dorsal cartilage* (*a. d. c.*), which is probably homologous with the upper labial cartilage of some Fishes and Amphibians (see below). Also belonging to the series of labial cartilages are the paired *anterior lateral cartilages* (*a. l. c.*) and the great ring-shaped *annular cartilage* (*an. c.*) which supports the edge of the buccal funnel.

The " tongue " is supported by a long unpaired *lingual cartilage* (Fig. 105, *lg. c.*), which may answer to the united Meckel's cartilages or ventral portion of the mandibular arch of other Craniata (see p. 78); it is tipped in front by a small median and a pair of still smaller lateral cartilages. Below it is a slender T-shaped *median ventral cartilage* (*m. v. c.*), which may possibly be the median ventral element of the mandibular arch. Lastly, attached to each side of the annular cartilage and passing backwards and downwards are a pair of tapering, rod-like *styliform cartilages* (*sty. c.*).

The visceral skeleton also differs in a remarkable manner from the ordinary Craniate type, and is only doubtfully related to it. It consists of a *branchial basket*, formed, on each side, of nine irregularly curved vertical bars of cartilage (Fig. 105, *br. b. 1—9*), the first placed almost immediately posterior to the styloid cartilage, the second immediately in front of the first gill-cleft, the remaining seven just behind the seven gill-clefts. These bars are united together by four longitudinal rods (*lc. 1—4*), of which one lies alongside the notochord and is connected in front with the cranium, two others are placed respectively above and below the gill-clefts, while the fourth is situated close to the middle ventral line and is partly fused with its fellow of the opposite side. The posterior vertical bar is connected with a cup-like cartilage (*pc. c.*), which supports the posterior and lateral walls of the pericardium. The whole branchial basket lies external to the gill-pouches and branchial arteries, not, like typical visceral arches, in the walls of the pharynx.

The median fins are supported by the delicate cartilaginous rods already referred to, which are more numerous than the myomeres, and lie parallel to one another in the substance of the fin, extending downwards to the fibrous neural tube.

The structure of the cartilage is peculiar and varies in different parts; it has very little matrix.

The **muscles** of the trunk and tail are arranged in myomeres which take a zigzag course. In the branchial region they are divided into dorsal and ventral bands, which pass respectively above and below the gill-slits; but in the trunk there is no division into dorsal and ventral parts. A great mass of radiating muscle is inserted into the buccal funnel, and the " tongue " has an extremely complex musculature which derives its nerve-supply from the trigeminal.

Digestive Organs.—The *teeth* are laminated horny cones : beneath them lie mesodermal papillæ covered with ectoderm which bear a superficial resemblance to the germs of true calcified teeth. When worn out they are succeeded by others developed at their bases. The mouth leads into a *buccal cavity* (Fig. 107, *m.*) formed from the stomodæum of the embryo, and communicating behind with two tubes placed one above the other : the dorsal of these is the gullet (*œs.*), the ventral the *respiratory tube* (*r. t.,* see below) : guarding the entrance to the latter is a curtain-like fold, the *velum* (*vl.*). The gullet bends over the pericardium and enters the intestine (*int.*) by a valvular aperture. The *intestine* passes without convolutions to the anus ; its anterior end is slightly dilated, and is the only representative of a stomach : its posterior end is widened to form the *rectum* (Fig. 113, *r.*). The whole of the intestine is

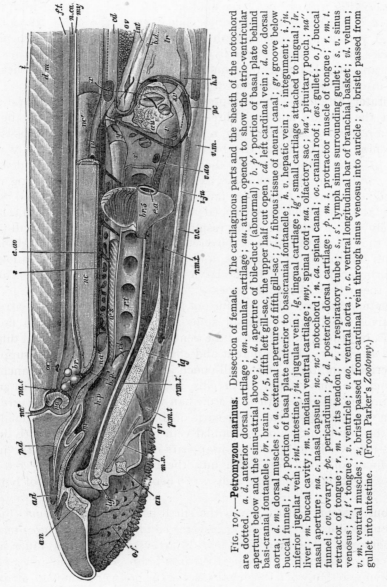

Fig. 107.—**Petromyzon marinus.** Dissection of female. The cartilaginous parts and the sheath of the notochord are dotted. *a. d.* anterior dorsal cartilage ; *an.* annular cartilage ; *au.* atrium, opened to show the atrio-ventricular aperture below and the sinu-atrial above ; *b. d.* aperture of bile-duct (abnormal) ; *b. p'.* portion of basal plate behind basi-cranial fontanelle ; *br.* brain ; *br. 5,* fifth left gill-sac, the upper half cut open ; *cd.* left cardinal vein ; *d. ao.* dorsal aorta ; *d. m.* dorsal muscles ; *e. a.* external aperture of fifth gill-sac ; *f. t.* fibrous tissue of neural canal ; *gr.* groove below buccal funnel ; *h. p.* portion of basal plate anterior to basicranial fontanelle ; *h. v.* hepatic vein ; *i.* integument ; *i. ju.* inferior jugular vein ; *int.* intestine ; *ju.* jugular vein ; *lg.* lingual cartilage ; *lg'.* small cartilage attached to lingual ; *lv.* liver ; *m.* buccal cavity ; *m. v.* median ventral cartilage ; *my.* spinal cord ; *na.* olfactory sac ; *na'.* pituitary pouch ; *na''.* nasal aperture ; *na. c.* nasal capsule ; *nc.,* notochord ; *n. ca.* spinal canal ; *oc.* cranial roof ; *œs.* gullet ; *o. f.* buccal funnel ; *ov.* ovary ; *pc.* pericardium ; *p. d.* posterior dorsal cartilage ; *p. m. t.* protractor muscle of tongue ; *r. m. t.* retractor of tongue ; *v. m. t'.* its tendon ; *v. t.* respiratory tube ; *s., s'.* lymph sinus surrounding gullet ; *s. v.* sinus venosus ; *t., t'.* tongue ; *v.* ventricle ; *v. ao.* ventral aorta ; *v. c.* ventral longitudinal bar of branchial basket ; *vl.* velum ; *v. m.* ventral muscles ; *x,* bristle passed from cardinal vein through sinus venosus into auricle ; *y.* bristle passed from gullet into intestine. (From Parker's *Zootomy*.)

formed from the mesenteron of the embryo, and the blastopore becomes the anus, there being no proctodæum. The lumen of the intestine is crescentric, owing to the presence of a *typhlosole* (Fig. 112, *int.*), which takes a somewhat spiral course and is hence known as the *spiral valve*. There is no continuous mesentery, but a number of narrow supporting bands.

The *liver* (Fig. 107, *lr*.) is a large bilobed organ, and is peculiar from the fact that there is neither gall-bladder nor bile-duct in the adult, except as an individual variation, although both are present in the larva. There are a few follicles on the surface of the liver, which may represent a *pancreas* : the *spleen* is absent. Paired glands imbedded in the muscles of the head, and opening into the mouth, are known as " *salivary glands*."

Respiratory Organs.—The Lampreys differ from all other Vertebrata in the fact that the gills do not open directly into the enteric canal in the adult, but into a *respiratory tube* (Fig. 107, *r. t*.) lying below the gullet. This is a wide tube opening in front into the buccal cavity, and ending blindly a short distance in front of the heart : in the larva it communicates behind with the intestine, and is, in fact, the pharynx, the gullet of the adult being not yet developed ; but at the time of metamorphosis it loses its connection with the intestine, and the gullet is developed as a forward extension of the latter—an entirely new formation. The respiratory organs are typical gill-pouches (*br. 5*) : they have the form of biconvex lenses, with numerous gill-lamellæ developed on the inner surfaces, and are separated from one another by wide interbranchial septa. In the larva an additional cleft has been found in front of the first of the adult series.

Circulatory System.—The atrium (*au*.) lies to the left of the ventricle (*v*.) and receives blood from a small sinus venosus (*s.v*.). There is no conus arteriosus, but the proximal end of the ventral aorta presents a slight dilatation or *bulbus arteriosus*. Both afferent and efferent branchial arteries supply each the posterior hemibranch of one gill-pouch and the anterior hemibranch of the next : they are thus related to the gills, not to the gill-pouches. In addition to the paired jugulars (*ju*.) there is a median ventral *inferior jugular vein* (*i. ju*.) returning the blood from the lower parts of the head. There is no renal-portal system, the two branches of the caudal vein being continued directly into the cardinals (*cd*.). The left precaval disappears in the adult, so that the jugulars and cardinals of both sides open into the right precaval. The red blood-corpuscles are circular, nucleated discs. There is a large system of lymphatic sinuses.

Nervous System.—In the brain the small size of the *cerebellum* (Fig. 108, *crb*.) is remarkable : it is a mere transverse band roofing over the anterior end of the metacœle. The *optic lobes* (*opt. l*.) are very imperfectly differentiated, and the central region of the roof of the mid-brain is formed merely of a layer of epithelium, so that when the membranes of the brain are removed, an aperture is left which is covered in the entire organ by a vascular thickening of the pia, or *choroid plexus* (*ch. pl. 2*). On the dorsal border of the lateral wall of the diencephalon are the two *ganglia habenulæ*, the right (*r. gn. hb*.) much larger than the left (*l. gn. hb.*) : they are connected with the pineal apparatus. Below the diencephalon is a small flattened pituitary body (Fig. 109, *pty. b.*). In front of the diencephalon are paired bean-like masses, each consisting of a small posterior portion, the *olfactory lobe* (*crb. h.*), and a larger anterior portion, the *olfactory bulb* (*olf. l.*). The diacœle communicates in front with a small proso-

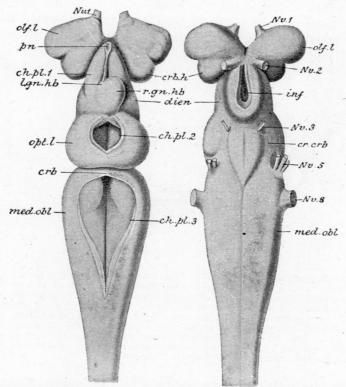

FIG. 108.—**Petromyzon marinus.** Dorsal (*A*) and ventral (*B*) views of brain. *ch. pl. 1*, anterior choroid plexus forming roof of prosencephalon and diencephalon; *ch. pl. 2*, aperture in roof of mid-brain exposed by removal of middle choroid plexus; *ch. pl. 3*, metacœle exposed by removal of posterior choroid plexus; *crb.* cerebellum; *crb. h.* olfactory lobes; *cr. crb.* crura cerebri; *dien.* diencephalon; *inf.* infundibulum; *l. gn. hb.* left ganglion habenulæ; *med. obl.* medulla oblongata; *Nv. 1*, olfactory, *Nv. 2*, optic, *Nv. 3*, oculo- motor, *Nv. 5*, trigeminal, and *Nv. 8*, auditory nerves; *olf. l.* olfactory bulbs; *opt. l.* optic lobes; *pn.* pineal eye; *r. gn. hb.* right ganglion habenulæ. (After Ahlborn.)

cœle or common fore-ventricle, which is roofed over by a choroid plexus (*ch. pl. 1*), and from which a transverse passage goes off on each side and divides into two branches, a rhinocœle going directly forwards into the olfactory bulb, and a paracœle backwards into the olfactory lobe.

The *pineal apparatus* consists of two vesicles placed in a vertical series: the dorsal-most of these is the vestigial *pineal eye* (Fig. 109, *pn. e.*) : it has

a pigmented retina, a flat and imperfectly formed lens, and is connected with the right ganglion habenulæ. The lower vesicle (*parapineal organ, pn.*), of the same nature as the upper but more imperfectly developed, is in connection with the small left ganglion habenulæ. The pineal eye is not an organ capable, like the paired eyes, of forming definite images of objects, but probably is capable of distinguishing differences in the intensity of the light. The optic nerves differ from those of most of the higher classes in the fact that the *chiasma* is not visible externally—the intercrossing of the fibres taking place beneath the surface.

The *spinal cord* (Figs. 107 and 112, *my.*) is flattened and band-like. The

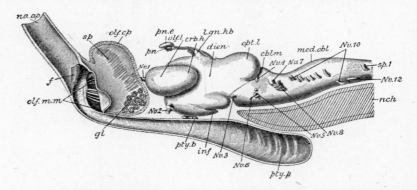

FIG. 109.—**Petromyzon.** Side view of brain with olfactory and pituitary sacs, in section. *cblm.* cerebellum; *crb. h.* olfactory lobe; *dien.* diencephalon; *f.* fold in nasal tube; *gl.* nasal glands; *inf.* infundibulum; *l. gn. hb.* left ganglion habenulæ; *med. obl.* medulla oblongata; *na. ap.* nostril; *nch.* notochord; *Nv. 1,* olfactory nerve; *Nv. 2,* optic; *Nv. 3,* oculomotor; *Nv. 4,* trochlear; *Nv. 5,* trigeminal; *Nv. 6,* abducent; *Nv. 7,* facial; *Nv. 8,* auditory; *Nv. 10,* vagus; *Nv. 12,* hypoglossal; *olf. cp.* olfactory capsule; *olf. l.* olfactory bulb; *olf. m. m.* olfactory mucous membrane; *opt. l.* optic lobe; *pn.* parapineal organ; *pn. e.* pineal eye; *pty. b.* pituitary body; *pty. p.* pituitary pouch; *sp.* median septum of olfactory sac; *sp. 1,* dorsal root of first spinal nerve. (Combined from figures by Ahlborn and Kaenische.)

dorsal roots of the spinal nerves alternate with the ventral roots, and do not unite with them to form a trunk: the dorsal roots are opposite the myo-commas, the ventral opposite the myomeres. A sympathetic is represented. The hypoglossal is the first spinal nerve.

Sensory Organs.—The external nostril (Fig. 107, *na''*, Fig. 109, *na. ap.*) leads by a short passage into a rounded *olfactory sac* (Fig. 107, *na.*, Fig. 109) placed just in front of the brain and having its posterior wall raised into ridges covered by the olfactory mucous membrane (Fig. 109, *olf. m. m.*). From the bottom of the sac is given off a large *pituitary pouch* (Fig. 107, *na'.*, Fig. 109, *pty. p.*) which extends downwards and backwards, between the brain and the skull-floor, passes through the basicranial fontanelle, and ends blindly below the anterior end of the notochord.

The relations between the olfactory sac, the pituitary pouch, and the pituitary body are very remarkable. In the embryo, before the stomodæum (Fig. 110, *A*, *stdm.*) communicates with the mesenteron, two unpaired ectodermal invaginations appear in front of the mouth. The foremost of these is the rudiment of the olfactory sac (*olf. s.*). The other, which is situated between the olfactory sac and the mouth, is the pituitary sac (*pty. s.*), which in this case opens just outside the stomodæum instead of within it as in other Craniata : its inner or blind end extends to the ventral surface of the fore-brain and termin-

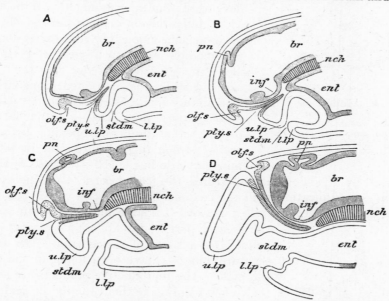

Fig. 110.—**Petromyzon.** Diagrams of four stages in the development of the olfactory and pituitary sacs. *br.* brain ; *ent.* mesenteron ; *inf.* infundibulum ; *l. lp.* lower lip ; *nch.* notochord ; *olf. s.* olfactory sac ; *pn.* pineal body ; *pty. s.* pituitary sac ; *stdm.* stomodæum ; *u. lp.* upper lip. (Altered from Dohrn.)

ates just below the infundibulum (*inf.*). As development goes on, the olfactory and pituitary invaginations become sunk in a common pit (*B*), which, by the growth of the immense upper lip (*up. l.*), is gradually shifted to the top of the head (*C*, *D*), the process being accompanied by elongation of the pituitary sac, into which the olfactory sac opens posteriorly. Where the pituitary sac comes in contact with the infundibulum it gives off numerous small follicles which become separated off and give rise to the pituitary body (Fig. 109, *pty. b.*). Thus the entire nasal passage of the Lamprey, including its blind pouch, is a persistent pituitary sac into which the single olfactory organ opens. Moreover, owing to the extraordinary displacement undergone during development, the pituitary sac perforates the skull-floor from above instead of from below, as in all other Craniata.

The auditory organ (Fig. 111) is remarkable for having only two semicircular canals, corresponding to the anterior (*a.s.c.*) and posterior (*p.s.c.*) of the typical organ.

Organs of taste are present on the wall of the pharynx between the gill-sacs, and neuromast- or lateral line-organs are present on the head and trunk.

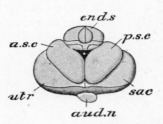

FIG. 111.—Auditory sac of **Petromyzon**. *a.s.c.* anterior semicircular canal; *aud.n.* auditory nerve; *end. s.* endolymphatic sac; *p.s.c.* posterior canal; *sac.* sacculus; *utr.* utriculus. (After Retzius.)

Urinogenital Organs.—The *kidneys* (Figs. 112 and 113, *k*) are long strap-shaped bodies developed from the mesonephros of the embryo. The tubules have no nephrostomes. Each kidney is attached along one edge to the dorsal wall of the body-cavity by a sheet of peritoneum; along the other or free edge runs the "*ureter*" (*ur.*), which is the undivided pronephric duct. The ureters open posteriorly into a small *urinogenital sinus* (Fig. 113, *u.g.s.*), placed just behind the rectum, and opening, by a *urinogenital papilla* (*u.g.p.*), into a pit in which the anus (*a.*) also lies. The side-walls of the sinus are pierced by a pair of small apertures, the *genital pores* (*y.*), which place its cavity in communication with the cœlome.

The *gonad* (Fig. 107, *ov.*, Fig. 112, *ts.*) is a large unpaired organ occupying the greater part of the abdominal cavity and suspended by a sheet of peritoneum. The sexes are separate, but ova have been found in the testis of the male. The reproductive products are shed into the cœlome and make their way by the genital pores into the urinogenital sinus, and so to the surrounding water, where impregnation takes place.

Development.—The egg is telolecithal, having a

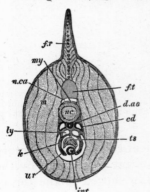

FIG. 112.—**Petromyzon marinus.** Transverse section of trunk. *cd.* cardinal veins; *d. ao.* dorsal aorta; *f. r.* fin-rays; *f. t.* fibrous tissue of spinal canal; *int.* intestine, the line pointing to the spiral valve; *k.* kidneys; *ly.* subvertebral lymph-sinus; *m.* body-muscles; *my.* spinal cord; *nc.* notochord; *n. ca.* spinal canal; *ts.* testis; *ur.* ureter. (From Parker's *Zootomy*.)

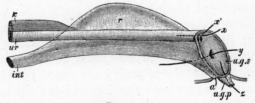

FIG. 113.—**Petromyzon marinus.** The urinogenital sinus with posterior end of intestine and part of left kidney. *a.* anus; *int.* intestine; *k.* left-kidney; *r.* rectum; *u.g.p.* urinogenital papilla; *u.g.s.* urinogenital sinus; *ur.* left urinary duct; *x, x',* apertures of ureters into urinogenital sinus; *y,* bristle passed into right genital pore; *z,* bristle passed from urinogenital aperture into sinus. (From Parker's *Zootomy*.)

considerable accumulation of yolk in one hemisphere ; in correspondence with this, cleavage is complete but unequal, the morula consisting of an upper hemisphere of small cells or micromeres (Fig. 114, *mi. m.*), free from yolk, and of a lower hemisphere of large cells or macromeres (*mg. m.*) containing much yolk. In the blastula stage (*D*) the segmentation-cavity or blastocœle (*blcl.*) is situated nearer to the upper than to the lower pole. A transverse semilunar groove appears which is bounded by a prominent rim towards the future dorsal and anterior side : this is the blastopore (*blp.*). The macromeres become gradually enclosed by the micromeres as a result of a process which is partly invagination, partly epiboly. During this process the segmentation cavity becomes

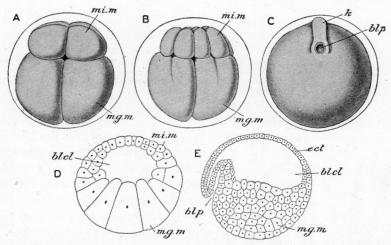

FIG. 114.—**Petromyzon.** *A* and *B*, two stages in segmentation ; *C*, early embryo from the posterior aspect ; *D*, section of blastula stage ; *E*, section of gastrula stage. *blp.* blastopore ; *blcl.* blastocœle or segmentation-cavity ; *k.* keel ; *mg. m.* macromeres ; *mi. m.* micromeres. (After Shipley and Kupffer.)

displaced by the archenteron. The dorsal and ventral walls of the latter, unlike those of the archenteron of Amphioxus, differ widely from one another, the ventral wall being composed of a thick mass of yolk-cells (macromeres), while the roof is comparatively thin and consists of two or three layers of rounded cells. The lumen is a narrow, dorso-ventrally compressed cleft. When the process of gastrulation is completed, the blastopore takes up a position at the postero-dorsal end. The development of the central nervous system differs widely from the corresponding process in Amphioxus, and is only approached among the Craniata by the Bony Fishes. The dorsal surface becomes flattened along a narrow longitudinal area, and along this a groove appears, which stops short just in front of the blastopore. The area along which the groove runs soon becomes raised up above the general

surface so as to form a narrow longitudinal elevation. Sections of this stage
show that the ectoderm has developed a thickening along the course of the
longitudinal groove, and this comes to grow downwards towards the archenteron

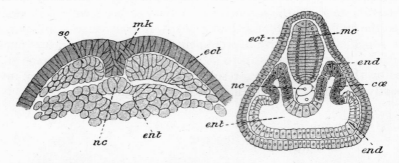

Fig. 115.—**Petromyzon.** Sections of embryos. *A*, transverse section of the trunk-region.
B, transverse section of the head-region. *cœ*. cœlomic sacs; *ect.* ectoderm; *end.* endoderm; *ent.*
enteric cavity; *so.* mesoderm-strand; *m.c.*, *mk.* medullary cord and medullary keel; *nc.* notochord. (From O. Hertwig; *A*, after Goette, *B*, after Kupffer.)

as a solid longitudinal *medullary keel* (Fig. 114, *C*, *k*; Fig. 114, *A*, *mg*.). This
is the rudiment of the central nervous system. Subsequently the keel becomes

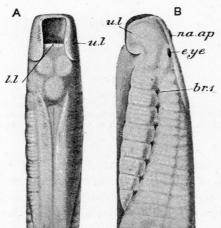

Fig. 116.—**Petromyzon fluviatilis.** Head
of larva. *A*, from beneath; *B*, from the
side. *br. 1*, first branchial aperture; *eye*,
eye; *l. l.* lower lip; *na. ap.* nostril; *u. l.*
upper lip. (After W. K. Parker.)

separated off from the surface ectoderm,
and lies below it as a solid cord. It is
only at a considerably later period that a
lumen appears in this cord, and gives rise
to the ventricles of the brain and the
central canal of the spinal cord. During
the formation of the medullary keel the
rudiment of the notochord is developed
from the underlying endoderm very much
as in Amphioxus (p. 54). On each side of
the medullary cord and notochord is a
group of cells arranged as a longitudinal
strand—the mesoderm plates. In the
head-region (Fig. 115, *B*) a number of
diverticula from the archenteron—*cœlomic diverticula*—are given off into these
strands: in the trunk region (*A*) these
are absent. The inner portion of the
mesoderm on each side becomes divided
up into a series of mesodermal somites, the lateral part remaining undivided
and forming the lateral plate. In this restriction of somite-formation to the
part of the mesoderm immediately adjacent to the middle line, the Lamprey

differs from Amphioxus and resembles all the rest of the Craniata. The blastopore does not close up, but is converted into the anus, so that there is no proctodæum. The dorsal lip of the blastopore, very prominent from the first, becomes produced to give rise to the rudiment of the tail region. The mouth is developed later than the anus by the formation of a stomodæal invagination.

The young is hatched as a peculiar larval form called *Ammocœtes* (Fig. 116), which differs from the adult in several respects. The median fin is continuous. There is a semicircular, hood-shaped upper lip (*u. l.*) instead of the suctorial buccal funnel of the adult, and teeth are absent. The buccal cavity is separated from the pharynx by a velum. A ciliated peripharyngeal groove encircles the pharynx in front and is continued backwards on the ventral side as a median groove opening behind into the thyroid gland, which is thus proved to be a special development of a structure corresponding to the endostyle of Amphioxus (p. 43) and the Tunicata. The eyes are rudimentary and hidden beneath the skin ; the brain is of far greater proportional size than in the adult ; and, as already mentioned, the gill-pouches open into the pharynx in the normal manner.

2. Distinctive Characters and Classification.

The Cyclostomata are Craniata in which the mouth lies at the bottom of a sucker-like buccal funnel, or in a depression edged with tentacles, and there are no jaws. Horny teeth are borne on the interior of the buccal funnel and on the large " tongue." Paired fins are absent. There is no exoskeleton ; the skin is glandular. The vertebral column consists of a persistent notochord with a fibrous neural tube, in which rudimentary neural arches may be developed. The skull is largely or wholly roofed by membrane, and there is an extensive development of labial cartilages. The segments of the post-auditory region of the head are more distinct than in the rest of the Craniata. The enteric canal is straight, and there is no cloaca. The respiratory organs are six to fourteen pairs of gill-pouches. There is no conus arteriosus and no renal portal system. There are large olfactory lobes, which may be either hollow or solid ; the cerebellum is very small. The olfactory organ is single and median, but is supplied by paired olfactory nerves ; it opens into a large persistent pituitary sac which perforates the basis cranii from above. The auditory organ has one or two semicircular canals. The kidney is a mesonephros, the ureter a pronephric duct. The gonad is unpaired, and there are no gonoducts, the genital products making their exit by genital pores.

The Class is divided into two Orders.

Order I.—Petromyzontes.

Cyclostomata in which there is a well-developed dorsal fin and a complete branchial basket ; the pituitary sac terminates posteriorly in a blind pouch ;

the gills open into a respiratory tube below the gullet. This order includes the Lampreys, which belong to the genera *Petromyzon*, *Mordacia*, *Geotria*, *Ichthyomyzon*, etc.

ORDER 2.—MYXINOIDEI.

Cyclostomata in which the dorsal fin is absent or feebly developed; the branchial basket is reduced; the pituitary sac opens posteriorly into the mouth; the gills open into the pharynx in the normal manner.

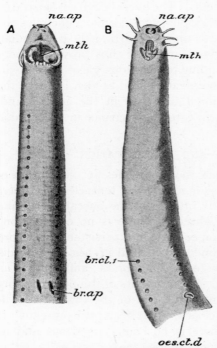

FIG. 117.—Head of **Myxine glutinosa** (*A*) and of **Eptatretus cirratus** (*B*), from beneath. *br. ap.* branchial aperture; *br. cl. 1*, first branchial cleft; *mth.* mouth; *na. ap.* nasal aperture; *œs. ct. d.* œsophageo-cutaneous duct. The smaller openings in *A* are those of the mucus-glands. (After W. K. Parker.)

This order includes the Hags or Slime-eels, belonging to the genera *Myxine*, *Paramyxine*, and *Eptatretus* (*Bdellostoma*).

3. COMPARISON OF THE MYXINOIDS WITH THE LAMPREY.

The organisation of the Lampreys is so uniform that all that will be necessary in the present section is to indicate the principal points in which the Hags differ from them.

Myxine is about the size of a freshwater Lamprey—*i.e.*, some forty-five cm. long: *Eptatretus* is fully a metre in length. Both are remarkable for the immense quantities of slime they are capable of exuding from the general surface and from the segmentally arranged mucus-glands of the skin. It is said that two specimens of *Myxine* thrown into a bucket of water are capable of gelatinising the whole with their secretion. The slime-glands of *Myxine* contain peculiar " thread-cells " containing a much-coiled thread which unwinds either before or after the discharge of the cell from the gland.

Myxine approaches most nearly to the condition of an internal parasite of any Vertebrate; it is said to attach itself to living Fishes and gradually to bore its way into the cœlome, devouring the flesh as it goes.

There is no true buccal funnel: the space on which the mouth opens is edged with tentacles (Fig. 117) supported by cartilages; there is a single median tooth above the oral aperture, and two rows of smaller teeth on the tongue.

The papillæ beneath the cone-like horny teeth bear a still closer superficial resemblance to rudiments (or vestiges) of true calcified teeth than is the case in the Lamprey; but it appears that no odontoblasts and no calcified substance of any kind are formed in connection with them. A velum separates the buccal cavity from the pharynx. The nostril (*na. ap.*) is a large unpaired aperture situated in the dorsal margin of the buccal space, and is continued into a passage, the pituitary sac, which opens into the pharynx by an aperture which appears in late embryonic life. *Myxine* commonly lives nearly buried in mud, and the respiratory current passes through this passage to the gills.

The only fin is a narrow caudal surrounding the end of the tail. The respiratory organs present striking differences in the two genera. In *Eptatretus* there are in different species six to fourteen very small external branchial apertures (*br. cl. 1*) on each side, each of which communicates by a short tube with one of the gill-pouches, which is again connected with the pharynx by another tube. Behind and close to the last gill-slit, on the left side, is an aperture leading into a tube, the *œsophageo-cutaneous duct* (*œs. ct. d.*), which opens directly into the pharynx. In *Myxine* (Fig. 117, *A*) the tubes leading outwards from the gill-pouches all unite together before opening on the exterior, so that there is only a single external branchial aperture (*br. ap.*) on each side; into the left common tube (*c. br. t.*) the œsophageo-cutaneous duct (*œs. ct. d.*) opens. In both genera the internal branchial apertures communicate directly with the pharynx; there is no respiratory tube.

The neural canal is over-arched merely by fibrous tissue (Fig. 118, *n.t.*); there is no trace of neural arches in the trunk, but in the posterior part of the caudal region both neural canal and notochord are enclosed in a continuous cartilaginous plate. Similarly the roof of the skull is entirely membranous. The nasal passage (*na. t.*) is strengthened by rings of cartilage, and the buccal tentacles are supported by rods of the same tissue. Behind the styloid cartilage or hyoid bar (*st. p.*) is a rod connected below with the subocular arch; it probably represents the first branchial bar. The " tongue " is supported by an immense cartilage (*m. v. c.*), in part corresponding to the lingual cartilage of the Lamprey. The branchial basket is rudimentary, being represented only by certain small irregular cartilages, such as one in the walls of the œsophageo-cutaneous duct, and, in *Myxine* (Fig. 118, *br. b.*), one on the right side supporting the common external gill-tube.

The myotomes of one side alternate with those of the other.

The intestine is very wide. The liver consists of two separate portions, the ducts of which open separately into the gall-bladder. A pancreas-like gland is present in both *Myxine* and *Eptatretus*. The brain differs considerably from that of the Lamprey, especially in the larger olfactory lobes and the reduced ventricles, and smaller mid-brain. The dorsal and ventral roots of the

spinal nerves unite instead of remaining separate. The eyes are vestigial and
sunk beneath the skin, and the auditory organ (Fig. 119) has only single semi-

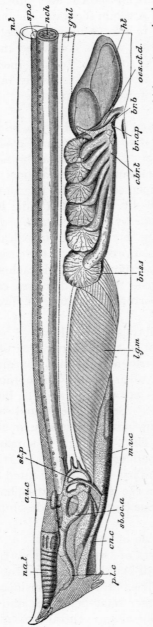

FIG. 118.—Dissection of **Myxine glutinosa** from the left side. *au. c.* auditory capsule; *br. ap.* left branchial aperture; *br. b.* rudiment of branchial basket; *br. s. I,* first gill-sac; *c. br. t.* common branchial tube; *cn. c.* cornual cartilage; *gul.* gullet; *ht.* heart; *lg. m.* lingual muscles; *m. v. c.* median ventral cartilage; *na. t.* nasal tube; *nch.* notochord; *n. t.* neural tube; *œs. ct. d.* œsophageo-cutaneous duct; *p.l. c.* posterior lateral cartilage; *sb. oc. a.* subocular arch; *sp. c.* spinal cord; *st. p.* styloid process. (After W. K. Parker and modified from Burn.)

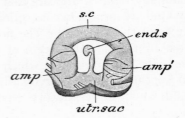

FIG. 119.—Auditory organ of **Myxine.** *amp.*, *amp'.* ampullæ; *end. s.* endolymphatic sac; *s. c.* semicircular canal; *utr. sac.* utri-culo-sacculus. (After Retzius.)

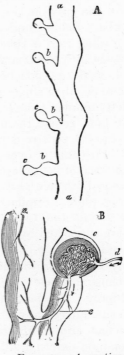

FIG. 120.—*A*, portion of kidney of **Eptatretus.** *B*, segment of same, highly magnified. *a*, ureter; *b*, urinary tubule; *c*, Malpighian capsule; *d*, afferent artery; *e*, efferent artery. (From Gegenbaur's *Comparative Anatomy*.)

circular canal, which, having an ampulla at each end, probably represents both
anterior and posterior canals.

Eptatretus has a persistent pronephros in the form of a paired irregularly
ovoidal body situated just above the heart and consisting of a large number of
tubules richly branched peripherally : the nephrostomes open into the pericardium.   The tubules do not communicate with the pronephric duct in
Myxine, but end blindly : in *Eptatretus* they open into an incomplete longitudinal duct, which does not communicate with the permanent kidney-duct.
The functional kidney is the mesonephros, and is specially interesting from the
fact that in Myxinoids it retains in the adult its primitive segmental arrangement.   The " ureter " (pronephric duct, Fig. 120, *A*) sends off in each segment
a coiled tubule (*b*) with a single Malpighian capsule (*c*), into which a branch
from the aorta (*d*) enters and forms a glomerulus.

Myxine is hermaphrodite, the anterior part of the gonad being ovary, the
posterior testis : in some the ovary is mature and the testis rudimentary, in
others the opposite condition holds good, so that, while hermaphrodite, each
individual is either predominantly female or predominantly male.   The eggs
of both genera are of great proportional size, and those of *Myxine* are enclosed,
when laid in a horny, shell bearing numerous hooked processes at each pole ;
by means of these the eggs are entangled together, and probably also attached
to seaweed.

In *Eptatretus stouti*, the only Myxinoid of which the development is known,
the eggs are elongated and cylindrical, and contain a large quantity of food-
yolk.   The segmentation is meroblastic, being confined to a germinal disc
situated at one end of the elongated egg.   The blastoderm thus formed extends
gradually over the suface of the yolk, which it only completely encloses at a
late stage, when the gill-clefts are all formed.   *Eptatretus* differs from *Petromyzon* and resembles the majority of the Craniata in the mode of development
of the central nervous system, which is formed, not from a solid ectodermal
keel, but from an open medullary groove the lips of which bend inwards and
unite to form a medullary canal.

The geographical distribution of the class is interesting from the fact that
each order contains some genera which are mainly northern, others which
are exclusively southern.   *Petromyzon* is found on the coasts and in the rivers
of Europe, North America, Japan, and West Africa ; it is therefore mainly
Holarctic.   *Ichthyomyzon* is found in the Mississippi, St. Lawrence and
Hudson's Bay drainage systems, *Mordacia* in Tasmania and Chili, *Geotria* in
the rivers of Chili, Australia, and New Zealand.   *Myxine* occurs in the North
Atlantic and on the Pacific Coast of South America ; *Paramyxine* in the Pacific ;
Epiatretus on the coasts of South Africa, New Zealand, and Chili.

SUB-PHYLUM V—GNATHOSTOMATA.

The sub-phylum Gnathostomata includes all vertebrate animals with upper and lower jaws, and comprises a wide range of animals, from fish to the various tetrapod classes, which have in turn been derived from a fish ancestor.

An entirely satisfactory classification of fishes is not easy to construct, because of the incompleteness of several parts of the fossil record, and the consequent lack of connecting links. Complete agreement as to their arrangement, therefore, has not been reached, and the student will meet with a considerable choice of classifications.

The view, however, has steadily been gaining ground that within the old group of " *Pisces* "—fishes, that is, in the widest sense—there are certain fundamental divisions which are of great antiquity, and which have little to do with one another beyond the possession of a possible but unknown common ancestor at a very remote, and equally unknown, period.

The old classification, therefore, of the Gnathostomata into the five classes— Pisces, Amphibia, Reptilia, Aves, and Mammalia—becomes modified by the division of the fishes into four classes as follows :—

Class APHETOHYOIDEA

Sub-classes ACANTHODII
ARTHRODIRA
ANTIARCHI (PTERICHTHYOMORPHI)
PETALICHTHYIDA (ANARTHRODIRA)
RHENANIDA
PALÆOSPONDYLIA

Class CHONDRICHTHYES (SELACHII. ELASMOBRANCHII)

Sub-classes PLEUROPTERYGII (CLADOSELACHII)
ICHTHYOTOMI
EUSELACHII
HOLOCEPHALI

Class ACTINOPTERYGII

Sub-classes PALÆOPTERYGII
NEOPTERYGII

Class CHOANICHTHYES [1]

Sub-classes CROSSOPTERYGII (RHIPIDISTIA and ACTINISTIA).
DIPNEUSTI (DIPNOI)

---

[1] The Choanichthyes and the Tetrapoda together make up a class, the Choanata, but one which is so unwieldy as to require a division into separate parts, each of which has to be termed a " class."

As compared with the tetrapoda, these four classes have certain characters in common. They have organs of respiration and of locomotion adapted for an aquatic mode of life. The chief, and in the majority the only, organs of respiration are the gills, which are in the form of a series of vascular processes attached to the septa of the branchial arches and persisting throughout life.[1]

The organs of locomotion are the paired pectoral and pelvic fins and the unpaired dorsal, anal, and caudal fins. These fins are all supported by fin-rays of dermal origin, in addition to the endoskeletal supports, and these fin-rays are diagnostic, as in no other animals in which fin-like structures may be present are fin-rays ever to be found. A dermal exoskeleton is typically present, and only on occasions is secondarily lost. In the endoskeleton the notochord is usually to some extent replaced by vertebræ, either of bone or cartilage. There is a well-developed skull and a system of visceral arches, of which the first pair form [2] the upper and lower jaws, the latter movably articulating with the skull, and both normally bearing teeth (page 73). There is no middle ear (page 118) and no allantoic bladder, the latter being a structure which arises for the first time in the amphibia. These two negative characters are therefore also diagnostic.

There are other characters found in one or other of the four classes which, though highly characteristic when they occur, cannot be called diagnostic, and it is the unequal distribution of these characters that makes the division of fishes into four classes desirable. A swim-bladder, for instance, is normally present, though it may be secondarily lost, in all fishes except the Chondrichthyes, which never at any time possessed this structure.[3] The nasal capsules open by inhalent and exhalent apertures. These may be only partly separate, as in the Chondrichthyes, or may be completely separate, as in the Actinopterygii, where they are both dorsal in position. In the Choanichthyes one pair is external, the other internal in the mouth, a character from which the group takes its name. The condition of the circulatory system, the structure of the brain, the urogenital organs, fins, and scales all yield characters which help to diagnose the four sub-classes.

The kidney is a mesonephros with an occasional persistence of a few pronephric tubules. As in all gnathostomes, there are three semicircular canals in the ear.

---

[1] This is a diagnostic character. Gill slits occur in the embryos of all vertebrates, but only in fishes do they function in the adult. The external gills found in some fishes and amphibia are not homologous structures.

[2] Actually the second pair, primitively there was a premandibular arch which is represented in the Agnatha.

[3] In the Aphetohyoidea and other extinct groups this structure, as also the condition of most other of the soft parts, can only be surmised.

CLASS APHETOHYOIDEA.

In this class are now collected together a number of orders which show a wide range of adaptive radiation, and in some instances an appearance so un-fishlike that their zoological position has been one of uncertainty. Some have been thought to be Agnatha, some as being allied to the Dipnoi, and some to the Chondrichthyes. Although there is still a body of opinion that considers the elasmobranch relationship to be fairly close, it can now be shown, or made very probable, that all the orders here included in the Aphetohyoidea are united in having at least one character of fundamental importance in which they differ from all other Gnathostomes, and that is the possession of a complete hyoid gill-slit and, in consequence, a type of jaw suspension (see page 73) that is more primitive than in any other class of Gnathostome.[1] There are a number of other characters which suggest an ultimate common ancestor for all the orders, one which is probably most nearly approached by the Acanthodii.

The sub-classes comprising the Aphetohyoidea are the :—

> Acanthodii,
> Arthrodira,
> Antiarchi,
> Petalichthyida,
> Rhenanida,
> Palæospondylia

Sub-Class Acanthodii.

This order contains the oldest known Gnathostomes. Appearing first in the Upper Silurian, it reached its maximum development during the Lower Devonian, at a time when other classes of fishes were only just beginning to evolve, and persisted until its extinction in the Lower Permian.

Acanthodians are fish-like organisms, usually with elongated fusiform bodies, which, in the final stages of evolution, became almost eel-like. The snout is blunt, the mouth terminal, and the eyes are large and forwardly placed. The tail is heterocercal, the fins are supported each by a strong anterior spine. There are primitively two dorsal fins (reduced to one in the later forms) and one anal fin. Between the pairs of pectoral and pelvic fins is an intermediate series of pairs of fins which increase in size as they proceed backwards. Primitively this series is more numerous, consisting of as many as five pairs, which suggests a derivation from an originally continuous fin-fold, but later the series becomes reduced to one small pair, and finally to none. A pectoral girdle (Fig. 121) is present, consisting of a scapular and coracoid

---

[1] See Watson, *Phil. Trans. Royal Soc.*, " The Acanthodian Fishes," 1937.

part, to which the spine of the fin is affixed. The pectoral fin shows traces of basal elements, as does also the dorsal fin. The peripheral part of the fin is supported by ceratotrichia.

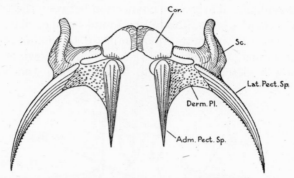

FIG. 121.—**Diplacanthus.** Pectoral girdle. *Adm.Pect.Sp.* median pectoral spine; *Cor.* coracoid; *Sc.* scapula; *Derm.Pl.* dermal plate; *Lat.Pect.Sp.* lateral pectoral spine. (After Watson.)

Externally the body is covered with scales of highly characteristic appearance, being rhomboid in shape, and ornamented with striæ, and so small as to

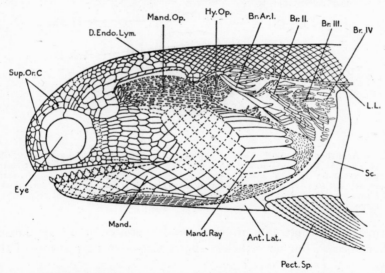

FIG. 122.—**Climatius reticulatus.** *Ant.Lat.* antero-lateral dermal bone of the shoulder-girdle; *Br.Ar.* 1–4. dermal elements of the branchial arches and their opercula; *D. Endo.Lym.* foramen of *Ductus endolymphaticus*; *Eye*, orbit; *Hy.Op.* hyoid operculum; *L.L.* lateral line; *Mand.* mandible; *Mand.Op.* dorsal part of mandibular operculum; *Mand.Ray*, lower part of mandibular operculum; *Pect.Sp.* pectoral spine; *Sc.* scapula; *Sup.Or.C.* supra-orbital canal. (After Watson.)

appear almost granular. On the head (Fig. 122) they are rather larger, and are arranged in a definite pattern. In section they can be seen to be made up of layers of bone substance in a manner comparable to a ganoid scale. Teeth are usually absent, but, when present, seem to be derived from modified scales, and to be replaceable as in the elasmobranchs, which is more probably a primitive feature than evidence of any close connection between the two classes.

As a rule, specimens of Acanthodii are found crushed flat, and not sufficiently well preserved to do more than indicate the external features, but specimens of the genus *Acanthodes* (*A. bronni*) are known sufficiently well preserved to allow a description of the neurocranium and visceral arches.

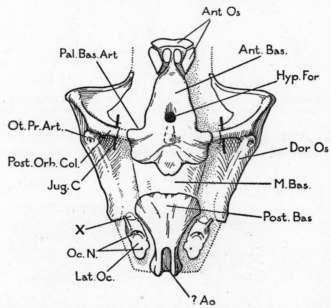

FIG. 123.—**Acanthodes.** Skull, Ventral aspect. *Ant. Bas.* anterior basal; *Ant. Os.* anterior ossicles; *? Ao.* groove for dorsal aorta; *Dor. Os.* dorsal bone; *Hyp. For.* hypophysial foramen; *Jug. C.* jugular canal; *Lat. Oc.* lateral occipital; *M. Bas.* middle basal; *Oc. N.* foramina for occipital nerves; *Ot. Pr. Art.* articulation for the otic process; *Pal. Bas. Art.* articulation for the palatobasal process; *Post. Bas.* posterior basal; *Post. Orb. Col.* post-orbital column; *X.* notch for vagus nerve. (After Watson.)

This form is somewhat late in time, and therefore more specialised than the earlier species, but nevertheless shows the essential features of the order and class.

The neurocranium (Figs. 123, 124) jaws and branchial arches (Fig. 124) are largely cartilaginous, but ossified in parts by a layer of external perichondrial bone, a primitive type of ossification such as occurs also in some of the Agnatha. The ossifications of the neurocranium are not easy to reconcile with those of other Gnathostomes. They consist of paired lateral dorsal plates which may fuse, an anterior middle and posterior ventral plates, and in front five small ossicles, one unpaired, supporting the rostrum. A pair of lateral occipital ossicles, one lying on each side of the posterior ventral plate, but at a higher level, completes the list. . The jaws consist of a stout palato-quadrate bar for the upper and the mandible for the lower portion. The interesting and important point about these elements is that each ossifies from two centres, two

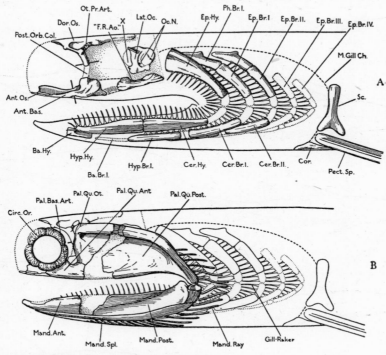

FIG. 124.—**Acanthodes**, sp.   Heads reconstructed :
    A. With the mandible and palato-quadrate removed.
    B. Complete except for the removal of the scales.

Ant.Bas. anterior basal ; *Ant.Oss.* anterior ossification in the basis cranii ; *Ba.Br.I.* basibranchial ; *Cer.Br.I.–II.* cerato-branchials ; *Cer.Hy.* ceratohyal ; *Circ.Or.* circum-orbital bones ; *Cor.* coracoid ; *Dor.Os.* dorsal bone of neurocranium ; *Ep.Br.* epibranchials 1–4 ; *F.R.Ao.* foramen for aorta ; *Hyp.Br.* & *Hy.* hypobranchial and hypohyal ; *Lat.Oc.* lateral ossification in neurocranium ; *M.Gill.Ch.* margin of gill chamber ; *Mand.Ant.* anterior ossification of Meckel's cartilage ; *Mand.Post.* posterior ossification of Meckel's cartilage ; *Mand.Ray.* ray of the mandibular operculum ; *Mand.Spl.* mandibular splint ; *Oc.N.* foramina for occipital nerve ; *Oc.Pr.Art.* articular facet for otic process ; *Pal.Bas.Art.* palato-basal articulation ; *Pal.Qu.Ant.* anterior bone of palato-quadrate cartilage ; *Pal.Qu.Post.* posterior bone of palato-quadrate cartilage ; *Pect. Sp.* spine of pectoral fin ; *Sc.* scapula ; *X,* vagus foramen.   (After Watson.)

for the upper and two for the lower, so that the jaws are formed from four pieces, exactly as are the hyoid and subsequent gill-arches, evidence that the jaws are themselves modified gill-arches. Later in life a special ossification occurs in the otic process.   The hyoid arch is complete, and takes no part in the jaw suspension, and is supplied throughout its length with gill-rakers, which is sufficient proof that there was a complete hyoid gill-slit. In earlier forms a small operculum is present on each gill-arch, and a rather larger one on the jaws. In the latter forms the mandibular operculum gradually extends back.

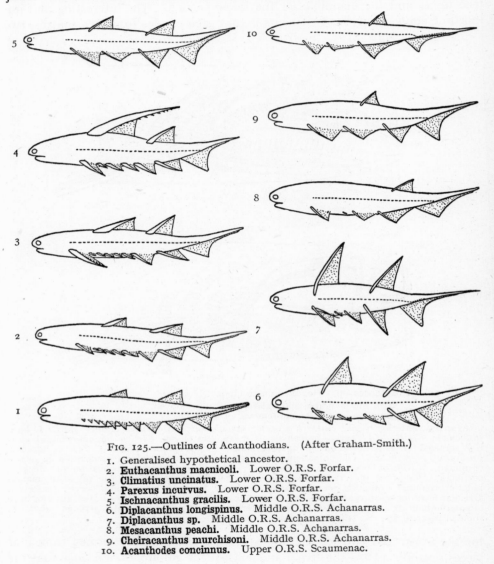

FIG. 125.—Outlines of Acanthodians. (After Graham-Smith.)

1. Generalised hypothetical ancestor.
2. **Euthacanthus macnicoli.** Lower O.R.S. Forfar.
3. **Climatius uncinatus.** Lower O.R.S. Forfar.
4. **Parexus incurvus.** Lower O.R.S. Forfar.
5. **Ischnacanthus gracilis.** Lower O.R.S. Forfar.
6. **Diplacanthus longispinus.** Middle O.R.S. Achanarras.
7. **Diplacanthus sp.** Middle O.R.S. Achanarras.
8. **Mesacanthus peachi.** Middle O.R.S. Achanarras.
9. **Cheiracanthus murchisoni.** Middle O.R.S. Achanarras.
10. **Acanthodes concinnus.** Upper O.R.S. Scaumenac.

at first to cover the lower part of the gills, and finally to take over the whole function of covering them, so as to produce an operculum comparable in extent and external appearance with that of the later bony fishes.

The Acanthodians (Fig. 125) may be classified into four families : the Diplacanthidæ, with two dorsal fins and the ventral fin spines well marked (*Diplacanthus, Parexus, Climatius*) ; the Acanthodidæ, with a single dorsal fin and a tendency to the reduction of the ventral fin spines (*Acanthodes, Cheiracanthus, Mesacanthus*) ; the Ischnacanthidæ, with two dorsal fins and simplified ventral fins and well-developed teeth (*Ischnacanthus*) ; the Gyracanthidæ (*Gyracanthus*) are probably Acanthodians, but are as yet insufficiently known.

Sub-class Arthrodira.

In external appearance the Arthrodira seem, at first sight, to be very different from the Acanthodii. The head is always protected by bony plates united to form a strong cranial roof, which is articulated by means of sockets to a pair of condyles on an equally strong bony cuirass covering the anterior parts of the body. These plates are usually ornamented by tubercles. The remaining free part of the body, when known, tapers to a whip-like tail, and is either naked or, in some, covered with scales. A dorsal fin is commonly present, and a pair of fins on the ventral side must be regarded as representing the pelvics. Free pectoral fins do not occur, but are represented by an immovable spine on each side, which gradually becomes reduced almost to extinction. The presence of an operculum covering branchial arches can be inferred. The vertebral column, when known, has a widely open notochord, well-developed neural and hæmal arches, but no centra or ribs. Jaws and teeth, the latter rather soon worn down, have been seen in some forms, and may be presumed to have normally been present throughout the group.

Arthrodires, which are not known to occur outside the Devonian period, may be classified as follows :

Acanthaspidomorphi :   Monaspidæ.
                            Mediaspidæ.
                            Polyaspidæ.
                            Ptyctodontidæ.
Coccosteomorphi :   Coccosteidæ.
                            Homosteidæ.
                            Mylostomidæ.

The Acanthaspidomorphi are the more primitive, and, except for some Upper Devonian Ptyctodonts, ranged from the Lower to the Middle Devonian. The Monaspidæ (Fig. 126) have a head and carapace with the plates firmly united and the sutures hardly visible externally. In the Mediaspidæ the sutures are still firm, but more noticeable, while in the Polyaspidæ and Ptyctodonidæ they became so loosely united that specimens are never found

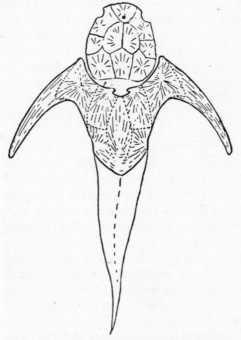

FIG. 126.—**Jækelaspis decipiens.** (After Heintz.)

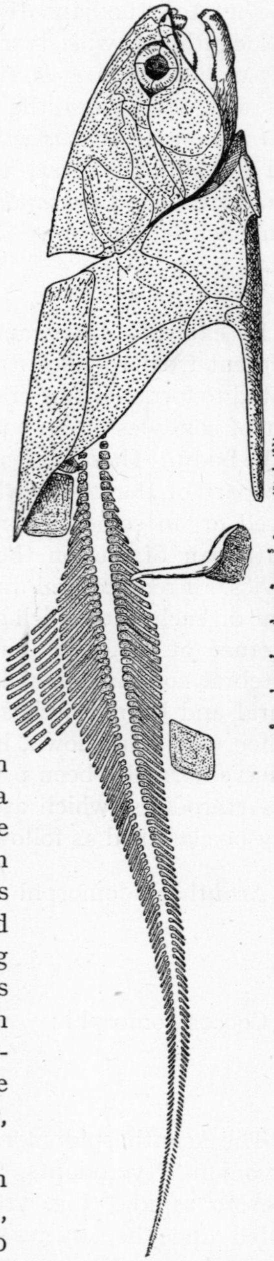

FIG. 127.—**Coccosteus decipiens.** (After Heintz.)

preserved entire, an instance of the gradual reduction of armour. The dermal armour over the trunk has a considerable backward extension, and is noticeable for the long hollow spine on each side projecting from the ventro-lateral part of the shoulder-girdle. This structure is comparable with the fin-spine and shoulder-girdle of such a form as *Climatius* among the Acanthodians. The arrangement of the plates on the head and body bear a close comparison with those found in the Coccosteomorphi. Some representative genera of the Acanthaspidomorphi are *Jækelaspis, Monaspis, Acanthaspis, Pholidosteus, Phlyctænaspis, Lunaspis,* etc.[1]

The Coccosteomorphi are fishes ranging from medium to a very large size, some of them—*e.g., Dinichthys*—having reached a length of not less than 30 feet. The most completely known form, *Coccosteus* (*e.g., C. decipiens*) (Fig. 127),

[1] See Heintz in list of literature at end of volume.

may be taken as typical of the rest. The head and carapace (Fig. 127, 128, 129) are stout, and occupy about a third of the total body length. The body was

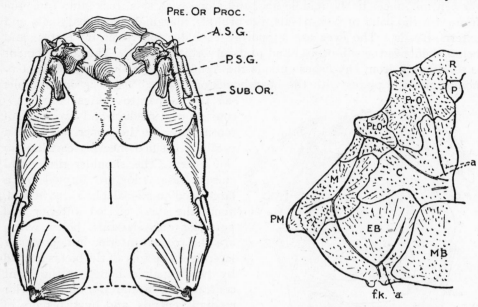

FIG. 128a.—**Coccosteus decipiens.** Restoration of palatal view. *A.S.G.*, *P.S.G.* anterior and posterior tooth-plates; *Pre.Or.Proc.* preorbital process; *Sub. Or.* sub-orbital bone. (After Watson.)

FIG. 128b.—**Coccosteus decipiens.** Head plates of the left side. *R.* rostral plate; *P.* pineal plate; *Pro.*, *Pto.* pre- and postorbitals; *Pm.* post-median; *C.* central; *M.* marginal; *MB.* median basal; *E.B.* exterobasal; *a.* lateral line canals. (After Heintz.)

apparently naked, and ended in a whip-like tail. A dorsal fin and a pair of pelvic fins and a curious " anal " plate are the only appendages, except for a

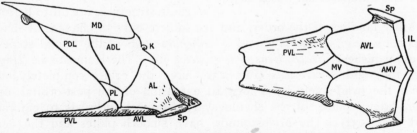

FIG. 129.—**Coccosteus decipiens.** Shoulder girdle in side and ventral view. *Sp.* spine; *IL.* infero-lateral; *K.* articular process for head. Other letters as in Fig. 131. (After Heintz.)

reduced spine on each side representing the pectoral appendage. The vertebral column is as that described above as typical of the Arthrodires in general. The head (Figs. 128a, b) is covered along the mid-dorsal line by three unpaired

M

plates, a rostral in front followed by a pineal, both small, and by a large median plate at the back of the skull.   All other plates are paired.   Of them one pair, the centrals, meet in the middle line, and along each side, reckoning from the front, are the pairs of post-nasals, pre-orbitals, marginals, post-marginals and externo-basals.   The eyes are supported each by four sclerotic plates, and below them are the sub-orbital and post-sub-orbital plates.   This arrangement is so different from any fishes outside the Aphetohyoidea that any attempt to homologise the plates with the head-bones of "bony" fishes is unworkable.

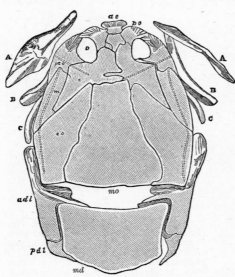

FIG. 130.—**Homosteus milleri.** *A. B*, uncertain elements probably displaced gnathals; *C.* antero-lateral, somewhat displaced; *ae.* rostral; *o.* orbit; other letters as in Fig. 131. (After Traquair, from Smith Woodward.)

The jaw apparatus (Figs. 127, 128) consists of a median and two pairs of tooth-plates in the upper jaw, and a partially ossified meckels cartilage in the lower.   The shoulder-girdle and cuirass (Fig. 129) are formed by a large median dorsal plate above and, along the sides, paired anterior and posterior dorso-laterals, below which are the paired anterior and posterior laterals.   The floor of the box is formed by two unpaired bones in the front central part, the anterior and posterior median ventrals, and by two pairs of larger plates, the anterior and posterior ventro-laterals.   The front part of this base is braced together by a transverse pair of rod-like bones, the intero-laterals, between whose outer ends and the anterior laterals is fixed the small pectoral spine on each side. These structures are all to be found in the other families of the order, and are subject only to changes of shape and proportion—*e.g.*, *Dinichthys* and *Titanichthys* (where the lateral spines have almost vanished), *Brachydirus*, *Pachyosteus*, etc.   The Homosteidæ (*Homosteus* (Fig. 130) and *Heterosteus* (Fig. 131) have the orbits completely enclosed within the head-shield by a forward extension of the post-orbital, and the antero-lateral plates of the shoulder-girdle project forwards to embrace the head (Fig. 131).   The Mylostomidæ have smooth plates and the dentition arranged as crushing plates.

Sub-Class Antiarchi (Pterichthyomorphi).

Like the Arthrodira, the Antiarchi are provided with a strong armour over the head and shoulders, but with a somewhat different arrangement of the plates, and with a different method of articulation of the head to the body the sockets being in this case on the cuirass and the articulating processes on the head. The pectoral appendages are of a much more elaborate structure.

Pterichthyodes (*Pterichthys*) (Fig. 132) may be taken as the type of the sole family, the Asterolepidæ, the genera differing only in relatively unimportant details. The eyes are placed close together on the top of the head, a modification which is no doubt responsible for a rearrangement of the plates. Between the

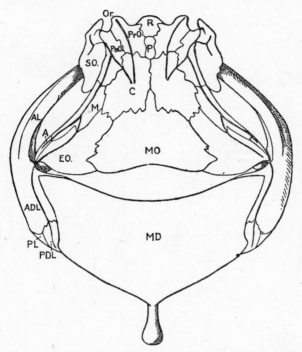

FIG. 131.—**Heterosteus.** *A.* angular; *ADL.* antero-dorso-lateral; *AL.* anterior lateral; *C.* central; *EO.* exoccipital (extero-basal); *M.* marginal; *MD.* median dorsal; *P.* pineal; *PDL.* posterior dorso-lateral; *PL.* posterior lateral; *Pt.O.* post-orbital; *Pr.O.* pre-orbital; *R.* rostral; *SO.* sub-orbital. (After Heintz.)

eyes lies a pineal plate, which is unattached to the neighbouring bones, and it is probable that there is another small prepineal plate just in front. The eyes are protected each by a saucer-like bone, which may be a series of fused sclerotics. This bone is found lying directly over the eye, so as, apparently, to prevent any sight. Probably in life the eyes projected somewhat after the fashion of the living goby *Periophthalmus*, and these plates could be turned aside. The other head-plates are for the most part firmly united. There is a single premedian plate in front extending back to the orbit, and behind the orbit are the unpaired post-median and nuchal plates. At the sides are a large opercular and a smaller sufflaminal plate, both free along their outer borders. These overlie a space in the shoulder region, and together form the gill-chamber. On the inner side of the sufflaminal plate on each side is a lateral plate whose inner border articulates with the nuchal, and which carries a shelf-like projection fitting into a socket on one of the shoulder-plates to allow of some movement of the head. The cuirass is formed by a large median dorsal and a posterior dorsal

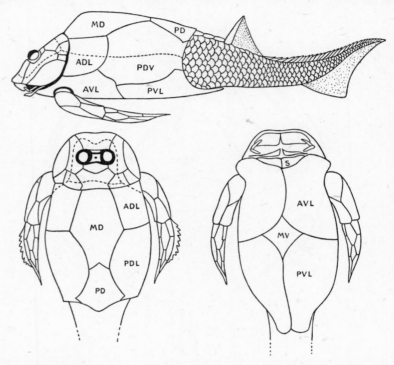

FIG. 132.—**Pterichthyodes.** Upper figure in side view. Left-hand figure in dorsal, right-hand figure in ventral view. *ADL.* antero-dorsolateral; *AVL.* antero-ventrolateral; *MD.* median dorsal; *MV.* median ventral; *PD.* posterior dorsal; *PDL.* posterior dorsolateral; *PVL.* posterior ventrolateral; *S.* semilunar plate.

plate, both unpaired. Along the sides are the anterior and posterior dorsolaterals. The floor is made up anteriorly by a pair of anterior ventro-lateral plates, which enclose between them a pair of small semilunar plates, and posteriorly by a pair of posterior ventrals. Between these pairs lies an unpaired median ventral. The anterior ventro-lateral plate have at their sides an excavation to hold the condylar head of the " arms " or pectoral appendages. These are highly developed, and are the leading characteristic of the order. They are formed of a number of plates, closely united except for a flexible joint dividing them into a proximal and distal section. The arms were hollow, and provided with internal muscles, nerves and arteries. The jaw apparatus consists of a pair of large superognathals which bear a notch at the side, into which is fitted a small elongated element, and this in turn articulates with a third. The system therefore corresponds to some degree with that of *Coccosteus*. The lower jaws, except for being rather more weakly developed, are exactly like those of *Coccosteus*.

The trunk is protected by well-developed scales and terminates in a heterocercal tail with a ventral web. A single dorsal fin is present supported by an anterior spine, and a series of fulcral scales runs along the upper border of the body from the fin to the tail. In this genus there are no pelvic fins.

Another well-known genus is *Bothriolepis* (Fig. 133), which had a naked body, an extra plate on the head and a pair of fleshy protuberances at the ventro-

FIG. 133.—**Bothriolepis.** (After Patten.)

lateral border of the cuirass which are supposed to represent a pair of pelvic fins. *Remigolepis* lacks the median joint to the pectoral fins. *Microbrachius* and *Asterolepis*, *Ceraspis* and *Ceratolepis* are other recorded genera, and differ only in small particulars. The whole sub-class is very compact, and was confined to the Devonian period.

Sub-Class Petalichthyida (Anarthrodira).

The Petalichthyida depart somewhat from the plan of *Coccosteus* and the other Arthrodires. In the first place, the ball-and-socket joint between the head and body does not exist, the pattern of the head plating (Fig. 134) is somewhat different, and the pectoral and pelvic fins are constructed on a very different plan. On the other hand, the facts that the neurocranium (very well known in *Macropetalichthys*) (Fig. 135) so much resembles that of an Acanthaspid, and that the hyoid arch took no part in the suspension of the jaws, are evidence that the order is rightly placed in the class of Aphetohyoidea. Certain characters have caused some authorities [1] to look upon these fishes as allied to the Elasmobranchs. The paired fins in particular have been cited as evidence, and the structure of the shoulder-girdle, the tribasal pectoral fin (Fig. 137), and the *Cladoselache*-like pelvic fin are undoubtedly points of resemblance. The

[1] See especially Stensiö no. 47 and Heintz no. 35 in the Appendix on Literature.

shoulder-girdle, however, is equally like the primary girdle of such Acanthodians as *Climatius* or *Diplacanthus*, and the tribasal pectoral fin is paralleled,
except for the absence of a spine, by that of *Acanthodes*. Moreover, a tribasal
fin at this period is too advanced in structure to lead to the more simple but
later fin of the earliest known elasmobranchs, such as *Cladoselache*. The

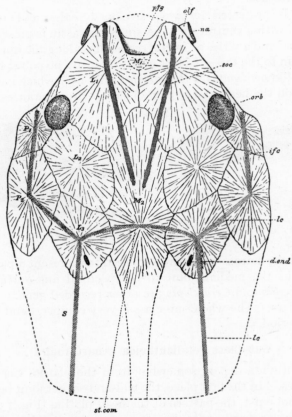

FIG. 134.—**Epipetalichthys wildungensis.** Dorsal head-plates. *L. 1–3.* lateral plates; *M. 1–2.*
central plates; *P. 1–2.* external plates; *S.* position of posterior plates; *d. end.* Ductus endolymphaticus; *ifc.* infraorbital sensory canal; *lc.* lateral line on head; *Na.* nasal opening; *olf.*
olfactory capsule; *orb.* orbit; *pfg.* anterior vacuity; *st. com.* commissure of sensory canal;
soc. supra-orbital sensory canal. (After Stensiö.)

pelvic fin certainly resembles that of *Cladoselache*, but is of a type that is found
equally in the early sturgeons and Palæoniscids, and is too generalised and
primitive to be of much value as evidence of any particular affinity. Other
elasmobranch characters, such as the ventral position of the mouth and the
flattening of the neurocranium, may be accounted for as the result of adaptation
to a bottom living life. The different arrangement of the head-plates from the

general arthrodire pattern is not so great as appears at first sight, the chief difference being along the mid-dorsal line, which might be put down as the result of a secondary fusion.

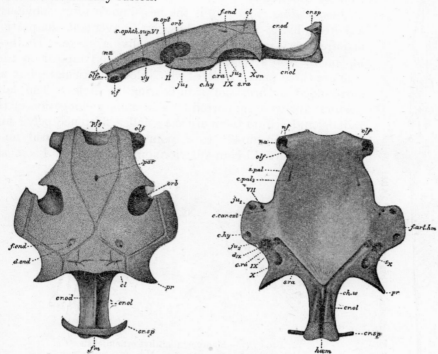

FIG. 135.—**Macropetalichthys rapheidolabis.** Neurocranium in side (upper figure), dorsal (left-hand figure) and ventral (right-hand figure) views. *a. opt.* optic artery; *c. car. ext.* external carotid; *c. hy.* hyoid vein; *c. opth. sup. .V.* ? opthalmic ramus of Vth nerve; *ch. w.* groove for notochord; *c. pal.₃* palatine branch of VIIth nerve; *c.ra.* aorta; *cl.* dorsal branch of Xth nerve; *cr. od.* dorsal occipital crest; *cr. ol.* lateral occipital crest; *cr. sp.* cranio-spinal process; *d. IX.* dorsal branch of IXth nerve; *d. end.* ductus endolymphaticus; *f. art. hm.* ? facet for hyomandi-bular; *f. end.* endolymphatic fossa; *f. m.* foramen magnum; *hæm.* hæmal groove; *ju.* mandi-bular vein; *n. l.* lateralis nerve; *n. a.* nasal opening; *n.f.* nasal fontanelle; *olf.* nasal capsule; *orb.* orbit; *par.* pineal opening; *pfg.* anterior vacuity; *pr.* postero-lateral process of occipital region; *s. pal.* palatine ramus of VIIth nerve; *s. ra.* root of aorta; *s.x₂.* external opening for Xth nerve. (After Stensiö.)

In this sub-class are placed the genera *Macropetalichthys* (Fig. 136) a Middle Devonian form, *Stensiöella* (Fig. 138) of the Lower Devonian, *Epipetalichthys* of the Upper Devonian and perhaps *Cratoselache* of the Lower Carboniferous.

Sub-Class Rhenanidi.

This order comprises only two families : the Asterosteidæ (*Gemuendina*, a Lower Devonian and *Asterosteus*, a Middle Devonian form) and the Jagorinidæ (with a sole genus *Jagorina* in the Upper Devonian). In these fishes the cranial bones are not greatly developed, and become progressively less so during the Devonian Period, so that in *Jagorina* they are reduced merely to bony tubercles.

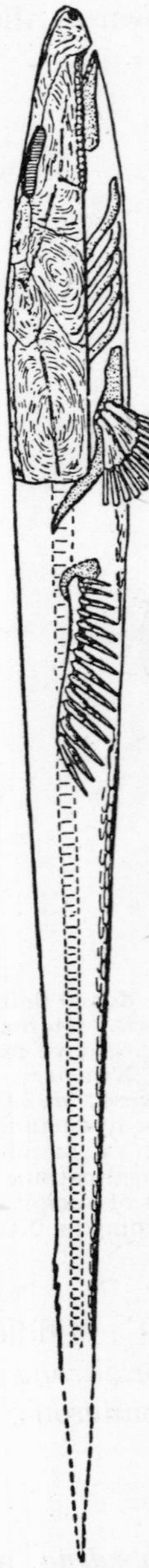

Gemuendina (Fig. 139) is the best-known form; obviously a bottom-living animal it has, by convergent adaptation, acquired very much the shape of a living skate. The head has on the top a central plate of bone, and ranged on each side are three pairs of plates which do not articulate, but are surrounded by areas of skin-bearing tubercles. The large pectoral fins were supported by a secondary elongation of the radials, and behind them are the smaller, flattened pelvic fins. The body then tapers to a pointed tail. A dorsal fin is present supported by an anterior spine much as in *Acanthodes*

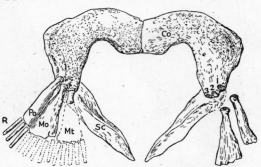

FIG. 137.—**Macropetalichthys pruemiensis.** *Co.* coracoid; *S.* scapula; *Po.*, *Mo.*, *Mt.* pro-, meso- and metapterygia; *R.* radials. (After Broili.)

or *Pterichthyodes*. Behind this fin is a row of dorsal spines, and there is a row of similar spines on each side which start from a point just behind the pelvic fins and run to join the dorsal row at the end of the tail. The pectoral girdle (Fig. 140) is comparable with that of a Ptyctodont, but lacks the lateral spine.

It will be seen from the foregoing account that, while fuller details are still required in several directions, there is sufficient evidence to warrant the bringing together of these fishes into a class separate from other fishes. There is a general similarity in the external skeleton of the Arthrodira, Antiarchi, and Petalichthyida, and the Rhenanida can be related to the latter order as relations with a reduced armature. The presence of gills supported on branchial arches and covered by an operculum can be demonstrated in some instances, and from them the presence

FIG. 136.—Macropetalichthys prumiensis. (After Broili.)

of gills of a similar type can be reasonably inferred in the others. The jaws, when known, show no signs of any hyoid suspension, from which the aphetohyoid condition with its complete hyoid gill slit naturally follows.

The Acanthodii, although they have undergone an adaptive radiation of

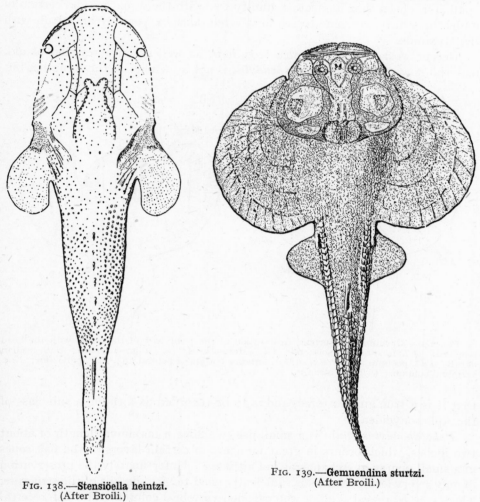

FIG. 138.—Stensiöella heintzi.
(After Broili.)

FIG. 139.—Gemuendina sturtzi.
(After Broili.)

their own, give, in the basal facts of their anatomy, a reasonable picture of an ancestral form from which the other highly specialised orders could have evolved.

Sub-Class Palæospondylia.

Palæospondylus gunni, the sole representative of this sub-class, occurs only in two restricted areas of the Mid-Devonian of Caithness in Scotland.

From the time of its first discovery by Traquair in 1890 it has been the subject of much speculation, and has in turn been considered either as the larva of a dipnoan fish, of *Coccosteus*, or of an amphibian; as a fish of Chrondichthyan affinity, and even as a teleost. Until quite recently the general consensus of opinion has been that its nearest affinity was with the Agnatha, and certain of its features have led some to see in it a relationship, possibly ancestral, with the Myxinidæ.

Recent work by Moy-Thomas [1] on new, as well as on a revision of old, material now shows that *Palæospondylus* is not a member of the Agnatha, but

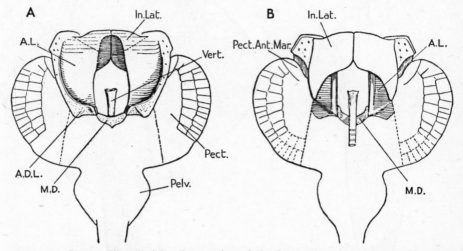

FIG. 140.—**Guemundina sturtzi.** Restoration of the front part of the body, with the head removed. *A.D.L.* antero-dorsolateral; *A.L.* antero-lateral; *In. Lat.* inter-lateral; *M.D.* median dorsal; *Pect.* pectoral fin; *Pect.Ant.Mar.* anterior margin of petoral fin; *Pelv.* pelvic fin; *Vert.* vertebral column. (After Watson.)

that it is a true gnathostome, and is to be regarded as forming a sub-class of the Aphetohyoidea.

Palæospondylus gunni is a small fish, reaching a maximum length of about two inches, which occurs in great numbers in certain layers of the flagstones of a small quarry at Achanarras in Caithness. Unfortunately the preservation of only a very few specimens is sufficiently good to yield details of the structure. There is a depressed skull, a well-calcified vertebral column and a heterocercal tail. The fin-rays of the ventral lobe of the tail are longer than those of the dorsal, and the lower radials are two-jointed and the second row bifurcated (Fig. 141*a*). Paired fins were present, and traces of pectoral and pelvic girdles have been observed. In the vertebral column the neural arches are low in

[1] Dr. Moy-Thomas' description is not yet published (March 1939). I am indebted to him for information as well as for the two figures.—C. F-C.

front, but gradually lengthen into neural spines as the tail region is approached. Ventrally there are short hæmal ribs which posteriorly become hæmal spines. The vertebral centra are stout and ring-shaped. The neurocranium (Fig. 141b), with its ring of tentacles in front, is complicated, and the interpretation of

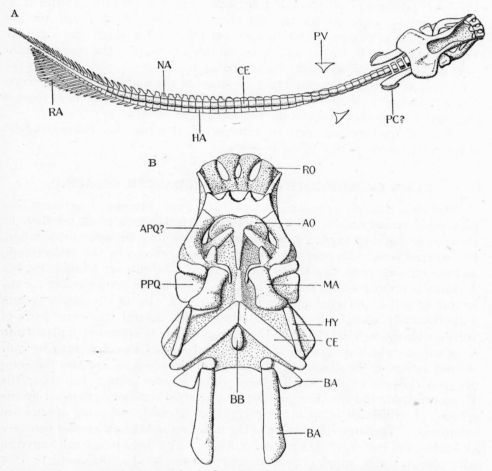

FIG. 141.—*Palæospondylus gunni*. A. Complete animal. The head and anterior vertebræ in dorsal view, the posterior vertebræ and tail in lateral view. *CE.* centrum; *HA.* hæmal arch; *NA.* neural arch; *PC?.* pectoral girdle; *PV.* pelvic girdle; *RA.* radials.

B. Head in ventral view. *AD.* anterior median palatine; *APQ.* anterior part of palatoquadrate; *BA.* branchial arch; *BB.* basibranchial; *CE.* ceratohyal; *Hy.* hyomandibular; *MA.* mandible; *PPQ.* posterior part of palatoquadrate. (After Moy-Thomas.)

some of its structures presents some difficulties. At first sight it gives the impression of a larval condition, but against this view is the fact that much of it is calcified, and that the vertebral column is fully calcified even in the smallest specimens. It is dorso-ventrally compressed, complete and fully

calcified as regards its ventral surface and sides, but lacks a roof where no calcification has taken place. The auditory capsules are large, and form the end of the neurocranium. The upper jaws (Fig. 141, *APQ, PPQ*) are formed by a pair of elements, an anterior and posterior palatoquadrate, on each side. The lower jaws are represented by a single pair which end bluntly (*MA*). If, as seems possible, there was an anterior uncalcified piece on each side, the jaw apparatus would be comparable to that found in the Acanthodii (*see* Fig. 124). The hyoid arch (*HY, CE*) is complete, and takes no part in the support of the jaws which is also an aphetohyoidean character.

A pair of ventral elements lying posterior to the auditory capsules represent a branchial arch, and a small element lying outside the second of these is considered to represent part of the pectoral girdle.

If these structures are correctly interpreted, it seems that *Palæospondylus* is correctly placed in the Aphetohyoidea.

CLASS CHONDRICHTHYES (ELASMOBRANCHII SELACHII).

This class comprises the living sharks, rays, and chimæras, together with a number of extinct orders. The characters of the class as a whole are that the skeleton is entirely cartilaginous, in which there may be some calcification, but no true bone. An operculum is not present, except in the Holocephali, and the gill-slits open directly to the exterior. The gills are laminar (p. 85). A cloaca is present whose external opening serves as a common outlet for the rectum as well as the renal and reproductive ducts. In the circulatory system a rhythmically contractile conus arteriosus with several transverse rows of valves is always well developed. The venous system is expanded in places into large sinuses which do not occur in other fishes, and therefore may be considered as one of the diagnostic characters of the class, as are also the complicated claspers in the male (absent only in one extinct sub-class, the Pleuropterygii), and the large and highly organised egg-cases produced by the female. Fertilisation is, with few exceptions, internal, and many species are viviparous. The large spiral valve in the intestine and the abdominal pores are characteristic, but occur in some other fishes. The body is normally covered with placoid scales, which in practice may be considered as diagnostic.[1]

Chondrichthyes appear for the first time towards the end of the Devonian period, and the more modern types not until the Carboniferous, so that the class as a whole appears somewhat later than the other three classes, all of which appear during the Middle Devonian or earlier.

---

[1] Small denticles indistinguishable histologically from placoid scales have been found in some other fishes—*e.g.*, *Lepidosteus* and in the Siluroids or " Catfishes ". An explanation of the occurrence of such scales in addition to the ordinary kind in these actinopterygians presents some difficulties, and there is as yet not enough evidence to show whether they are persistent or new structures.

Sub-Class Pleuropterygii (Cladoselachii).

Extinct, shark-like Chondrichthyes with a fusiform body, heterocercal tail with a large lower lobe, and horizontal keel-like fin on each side of the caudal peduncle. In this pair of lateral expansions, which stand out at right angles to the body, there are basal elements, but apparently no radials. The structure is not known in any other fish, and is not easy to homologise. No anal fin has been described, and appears to be absent, and it has been suggested that these keel fins represent a doubled anal fin. The mouth is subterminal and without any pronounced rostrum. The body is covered with small denticles, whose minute structure is as yet unknown. The teeth are typically selachian, and consist of a long, thin, pointed main cusp with smaller lateral cusps fixed on a broad base. The jaw suspension was amphistylic, and the notochord unconstricted. The absence of claspers in the male is a feature unique in the Chondrichthyes, and may be regarded as a very primitive character.

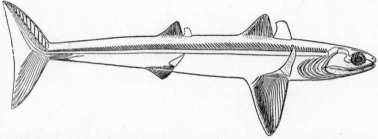

FIG. 142.—**Cladoselache fyleri.** The dorsal spine as found in its natural position. The neuro-cranium and jaws are from specimens in the Cleveland Museum of Natural History. (Modified by J. E. Harris after Dean.)

The pectoral and pelvic fins show a very wide basal attachment to the body, and were without the anterior and posterior constriction from the body-wall, which is usual in the paired fins of almost all fishes. The skeleton of the fins consists of parallel cartilages of simple structure. These features, together with what is known of the rest of the anatomy, suggest that the sub-class represents the most primitive selachians as yet known.

Cladoselache fyleri (Fig. 142),[1] from the Upper Devonian, is the best-known form, and *Cladodus* and *Symmorium* are related forms ranging from the Upper Devonian to the Upper Carboniferous.

It is possible, although complete proof is still lacking, that the Pleuropterygii represent part of the ancestral stock from which the other Chondrichthyes have radiated. Excluding the somewhat specialised Ichthyotomi mentioned below, there seems, broadly speaking, to have been two main radiations. One of these, composed of the Bradyodonti and Edestidæ, eventually gave

[1] Harris, J. E. (" Scientific Publications of the Cleveland Museum," VIII, no. 1, 1938), shows the presence of a dorsal spine.

rise to the Holocephali, while the other produced the Ctenacanthidæ and Hybodontidæ which are on the line of the modern sharks and rays.

The Bradyodont sharks are for the most part known only by their dentition. They are characterised by having only a small number of teeth in use at a time, and also by the small number of series of teeth in succession. They are composed of tubular dentine similar to that of the teeth of the Holocephali. There are four families : the Cochliodontidæ, Petalodontidæ, Psammodontidæ, and Copodontidæ, which differ from one another in the shape and arrangement of the teeth. The number of described genera and species of Bradyodonts, which range from the Upper Devonian to the Permian, shows that this group was an important one during palæozoic times.

The Edestidæ, lower Carboniferous and Permian fishes, are specialised forms, in which the teeth on the symphysis of the jaws were enlarged and fused into a coil which either fell away at intervals or persisted throughout life as an " ammonite "-like spiral.

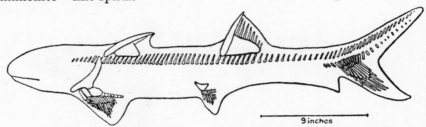

9 inches

FIG. 143.—**Ctenacanthus costellatus.**   (Restoration of fish after Moy-Thomas.)

The Ctenacanthidæ (Fig. 143), which are found from the Upper Devonian to the Permian, were advanced from the Pleuropterygii in the greater development of the spines to the dorsal fins, in the paired fins being a little, but not much, advanced beyond the condition found in *Cladoselache*. The Hybodonts likewise had spines to the dorsal fins and several series of teeth in function at once.

Sub-Class Ichthyotomi (Pleuracanthodii).

These are extinct Chondrichthyes in which the pectoral fin has acquired the form of an " archipterygium," an elongated axis, that is to say, extending out from the body and bearing pre- and post-axial rays. The post-axial rays are fewer in number than the pre-axial, which may be a primitive feature. The only satisfactorily known species is *Pleuracanthus decheni* (Fig. 144), which occurs from the Carboniferous to the Permian. It is clearly in many respects a specialised form. The long body, with its slender diphycercal tail, a continuous fin fold along the back, the anal fin with its unusual fore and aft duplication and direct suspension from the hæmal arches, and the long, movable spine on the head, all point to a considerable degree of specialisation. Scales have not been

observed, and are thought to have been absent.
the male is a typically chondrichthyan feature.
the Ichthyotomi are presumed to have branched
terygian stock, but to have given rise to no
successors.

The presence of claspers in
Like other Chondrichthyes,
off from the early Pleurop-

Sub-Class Euselachii.

The living and extinct orders of this sub-class,
which occur from the Mesozoic periods onward,
are distinguished, in addition to the general
characters of the class, by having numerous
teeth developed in continual succession, and by
the pectoral fins having three basal pieces (the
pro-, *meso-*, and *meta-pterygium*), from which a
number of pre-axial radials spread out.[1]

The sub-class is divided into two orders, the
Pleurotremata (sharks) and the Hypotremata
(rays), chiefly on the position of the gill-slits
which are lateral in the first group and ventral
in the second. That the division is a fairly
natural one is upheld by the following additional
differences. In the Pleurotremata the anterior
margin of the pectoral fin is free from the body,
the pectoral radials are simple and of few
segments, and, as a rule, only the anterior ones
reach the free edge of the fin ; the two halves
of the pectoral arch are well separated above.
In the Hypotremata, on the other hand, the
pectoral fin is joined to the side of the body
or to the head, the pectoral radials are numerous,
multi-segmented, bifurcated at the ends, and all of
them reach the free edge of the fin. The halves
of the pectoral girdle either fuse with one
another or else both fuse to the vertebral column.
There is a further difference, in that the skull
of the Pleurotremata is without cartilages
attached to the olfactory capsules, and the
pterygo-quadrate has a process articulating
with, or attached by ligament to, the cranium.

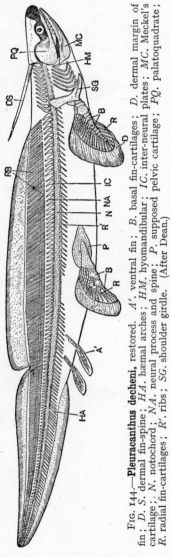

FIG. 144.—**Pleuracanthus decheni**, restored. *A'*. ventral fin ; *B*. basal fin-cartilages ; *D*. dermal margin of fin ; *D. S.* dermal fin-spine ; *H.A.* haemal arches ; *HM*. hyomandibular ; *IC*. inter-neural plates ; *MC*. Meckel's cartilage ; *N*. notochord ; *N.A.* neural process and spine ; *P*. supposed pelvic cartilage ; *PQ*. palatoquadrate ; *R*. radial fin-cartilages ; *R'*. ribs ; *SG*. shoulder girdle. (After Dean.)

In the skull of the Hypotremata there are paired preorbital cartilages
attached to the olfactory capsules, which are often very well developed, and

---

[1] In the Hybodonts and in early stages of some Euselachii there are traces of reduced postaxial radials.

the pterygo-quadrate has no articulating process to the skull. Finally, in the Pleurotremata the hyomandibular and ceratohyal both bear cartilaginous rays, and both take part in supporting the first gill. The ceratohyal is a single cartilage, and is attached to the lower end of the hyomandibular. In the Hypotremata the hyomandibular lacks rays, and so takes no part in the support of the gill, and the ceratohyal is segmented and attached to the hyomandibular either high up or not at all.

FIG. 145.—**Chlamydoselachus auguineus.** (From the *Cambridge Natural History*, after Günther.)

The Pleurotremata can be divided into three sub-orders chiefly on the number of dorsal fins, on the presence or absence of spines on these fins and on the presence or absence of an anal fin. These sub-orders are the Notidanoidea, Galeoidea, and Squaloidea.

The Notidanoidea include the most primitive of living sharks—*i. e.*, *Chlamydoselachus* (*Notidanus*) (Fig. 145)—the Frilled shark; *Heptranchias* and *Hexanchus*, and are characterised by the simple vertebral column with its

FIG. 146.—**Porbeagle Shark** (*Lamna cornubica*). (From Dean's *Fishes*.)

unconstricted notochord, the sub-terminal mouth, single spineless dorsal fin, and the presence of more than five gill-slits.

In the Galeoidea there are two dorsal fins without spines, an anal fin, and five gill-slits. The four families are the Odontaspidæ—*i. e.*, *Odontaspis* (the " Sand shark ") and *Scapanorhynchus* (*Mitsukurina*), (the " Goblin shark "). The Lamnidæ with numerous genera such as *Lamna* (the " Mackerel sharks "), *Carcharodon* (" Man eaters "), *Cetorhinus* (" Basking shark "), *Isurus* (*Lamna*) " Porbeagle ") (Fig. 146), and *Alopias* (the " Thresher ") ; the Orectolobidæ

(the " Carpet " and " Tiger " sharks), *Orectolobus* and *Stegostoma* ; the Scylior-
hinidæ ; *Scyliorhinus* (the " Dogfishes "), and lastly the Carcharinidæ, with
Carcharinus (the " Blue " sharks), *Galeus* (" Topes "), *Mustelus* (the " Nurse
hounds ") and *Sphyrna* (the " Hammerheads ").

The Squaloidea have two dorsal fins, each with an anterior spine, and an
anal fin which may at times be absent. In this order are placed the Hetero-
dontidæ (the " Port Jackson sharks "), Squatinidæ, *Squatina* (the " Angel
or Monk fish "), the Squalidæ, *Squalus* (the " Spiny dogfishes "), the Pristio-
phoridæ (the " Saw sharks ") and others.

The Hypotremata are divided into two orders : the Narcobatoidea or
" Electric rays," and the Batoidea, which include all other skates and rays
such as the Rhinobatidæ (the " Guitar fishes "), the Pristidæ (the " Sawfishes "),
Myliobatidæ (" Eagle rays "), Raiidæ (true " Skates and Rays "), etc.

FIG. 147.—Dogfish (**Brachælurus modestus**). Lateral view. (After Waite.)

EXAMPLE OF THE SUB-CLASS : A DOGFISH (*Scyliorhinus
canicula* or *Brachælurus modestus*).

General External Features.—The general shape of the body (Fig. 147) may
be roughly described as fusiform ; at the anterior or head-end it is broader and
depressed ; posteriorly it tapers gradually and is compressed from side to side.
The head terminates anteriorly in a short, blunt snout. The tail is narrow and
bent upwards towards the extremity. The colour is grey with brown markings,
or dark brown above, lighter underneath. The entire surface is covered closely
with very minute hard *placoid scales* or *dermal teeth*, rather larger on the upper
surface than on the lower. These are pointed, with the points directed somewhat backwards, so that the surface appears rougher when the hand is passed
over it forwards than when it is passed in the opposite direction. When
examined closely each scale is found to be a minute spine situated on a broader
base. The spine consists of dentine covered with a layer of enamel ; the base
is composed of bone-like substance, and the whole scale has thus the same
essential structure as a tooth. Along each side of the head and body runs a
faint depressed longitudinal line or slight narrow groove—the *lateral line*,
marking the position of the *lateral line canal*, which contains integumentary
sense-organs.

As in Fishes in general, two sets of fins are to be recognised—the *unpaired* or *median* fins, and the *paired* or *lateral*. These are all flap-like outgrowths, running vertically and longitudinally in the case of the median fins, nearly horizontally in the case of the lateral : they are flexible, but stiffish, particularly towards the base, owing to the presence of a supporting framework of cartilage. Of the median fins two—the *dorsal*—are situated, as the name indicates, on the dorsal surface : they are of triangular shape ; the anterior, which is the larger, is situated at about the middle of the length of the body, the other a little further back. The *caudal fin* fringes the tail : it consists of a narrower dorsal portion and a broader ventral, continuous with one another round the extremity of the tail, the latter divided by a notch into a larger, anterior, and a smaller, posterior lobe. The tail is *heterocercal, i.e.* the posterior extremity of the spinal column is bent upwards and lies in the dorsal portion of the caudal fin. The *ventral* or so-called *anal* fin is situated on the ventral surface, in *Scyliorhinus*, opposite the interval between the anterior and posterior dorsals, in *Hemiscyllium* behind the latter ; it resembles the latter in size and shape.

Of the *lateral fins* there are two pairs, the pectoral and the pelvic. The *pectoral* are situated at the sides of the body, just behind the head. The *pelvic*, which are the smaller, are placed on the ventral surface, close together, about the middle of the body. In the males the bases of the pelvic fins are united together in the middle line, and each has connected with it a *clasper* or *copulatory organ*. The latter is a stiff rod, on the inner and dorsal aspect of which is a groove leading forwards into a pouch-like depression in the base of the fin.

The *mouth*—a transverse, somewhat crescentic opening—is situated on the ventral surface of the head, near its anterior end. In front and behind it is bounded by the upper and lower jaws, each bearing several rows of teeth with sharp points directed backwards. The nostrils are situated one in front of each angle of the mouth, with which each is connected by a wide groove—the *nasobuccal grove*. In *Brachælurus* the outer edge of the groove is prolonged into a narrow subcylindrical appendage—the *barbel*. A small rounded aperture, the *spiracle*—placed just behind the eye—leads into the large pharynx. Five pairs of slits running vertically on each side of the neck—the *branchial slits*—also lead internally into the pharynx. A large median opening on the ventral surface at the root of the tail, between the pelvic fins, is the opening leading into the cloaca, or chamber forming the common outlet for the intestine and the renal and reproductive organs. A pair of small depressions, the *abdominal pores*, situated behind the cloacal opening, lead into narrow passages opening into the abdominal cavity.

The **skeleton** is composed entirely of cartilage, with, in certain places, depositions of calcareous salts. As in vertebrates in general, we distinguish two sets of elements in the skeleton—the axial set and the appendicular, the former comprising the skull and spinal column, the latter the limbs and their arches.

The *spinal column* is distinguishable into two regions—the region of the trunk and the region of the tail. In the trunk-region each vertebra (Fig. 148, *A* and *B*) consists of a centrum (*c*), neural arch (*n.a.*), and transverse processes (*tr.pr*). In the caudal region there are no transverse processes, but *inferior* or *hæmal arches* (C, D, *h.a.*) take their place. The centra of all the vertebræ are deeply biconcave or *amphicœlous*, having deep conical concavities on their anterior and posterior surfaces. Through the series of centra runs the noto-

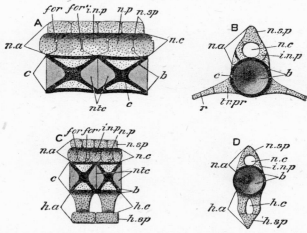

Fig. 148.—Portions of the vertebral column of **Scyliorhinus canicula.** *A* and *B*, from the trunk; *C* and *D*, from the middle of the tail; *A* and *C*, two vertebræ in longitudinal section; *B* and *D*, single vertebræ viewed from one end. *b*, calcified portion of centrum; *c*. centrum; *for*. foramen for dorsal, and *for'*. for ventral root of spinal nerve; *h. a.* hæmal arch (basi-ventral); *h. c.* hæmal canal; *h. sp.* hæmal spine; *i.n. p.* intercalary piece (interdorsal, or interneural plate); *n. a.* neural arch; *n. c.* neural canal; *n. p.* neural plate (basi-dorsal); *n. sp.* neural spine; *ntc.* intervertebral substance (remains of notochord); *r.* proximal portion of rib; *tr. pr.* transverse process (basal stump). (From Parker's *Practical Zoology.*)

chord (*ntc.*), greatly constricted in the centrum itself, and dilated in the large spaces formed by the apposition of the amphicœlous centra of adjoining vertebræ, where it forms a pulpy mass. The concave anterior and posterior surfaces of the centra are covered by a dense calcified layer, and in *Brachælurus* eight radiating lamellæ of calcified tissue run longitudinally through the substance of the centrum itself. The centra, unlike those of the higher forms, are developed as chondrifications of the sheath of the notochord into which cells of the skeletogenous layer have migrated (p. 68). On the dorsal side of the row of centra the spinal column is represented by the series of neural arches which support the walls of the spinal canal. Owing to the presence of a series of intercalary cartilages the neural arches appear to be twice as numerous as the centra. Each neural arch consists on each side of a process, the *neural process*, given off from the centrum, and of a small cartilage, the *neural plate* (*basidorsal*), which becomes completely fused with the neural process in the adult. Between successive neural plates, the width of each of which is only about half the length of the centrum, is interposed a series of plates of very similar shape, the *interdorsal* or *interneural plates*. Small median cartilages, the *neural spines*, fit in between both neural and interneural plates of opposite sides and form keystones completing the arches.

The transverse processes are very short : connected with each of them is a rudimentary cartilaginous *rib* (*r.*) about half an inch in length.

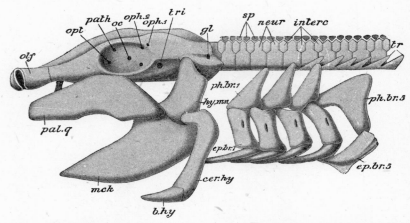

FIG. 149.—**Brachælurus,** lateral view of skull with visceral arches and anterior part of spinal column ; the branchial rays are not represented. The skull and hyoid arch are somewhat drawn downwards, so that the hyoid and first branchial arch are not exactly in their natural relations ; *cer.hy.* ceratohyal ; *ep. br. 1, ep. br. 5,* first and fifth epibranchials ; *gl.* aperture for glossopharyngeal nerve ; *b. hy.* basihyal ; *hy.mn.* hyomandibular ; *interc.* intercalary (interdorsal) plates ; *mck.* Meckel's cartilage ; *neur.* neural processes ; *olf.* olfactory capsule ; *oc.* foramen for oculomotor ; *oph. 1,* foramen for ophthalmic division of facial nerve ; *oph. 2,* foramen for ophthalmic division of trigeminal ; *opt.* optic foramen ; *pal.q.* palatoquadrate ; *path.* foramen for 4th nerve ; *ph.br. 1* and *ph.br. 5,* first and fifth pharyngobranchial ; *sp.* neural spines ; *tr.* transverse processes and ribs ; *tri.* foramen for trigeminal nerve.

The *cranium* (Fig. 149) is a cartilaginous case, the wall of which is continuous throughout, and not composed, like the skulls of higher vertebrates, of a number of distinct bony elements fitting in together. At the anterior end is a *rostrum*, consisting in *Scyliorhinus* of three cartilaginous rods converging as they extend forwards and lateral ones meeting anteriorly. At the sides of the base of this are the *olfactory capsules* (*olf.*)—thin rounded cartilaginous sacs opening widely below, the cavities of the two capsules being separated from one another by a thin septum. The part of the roof of the cranial cavity behind and between the olfactory capsules is formed not of cartilage, but of a tough fibrous membrane, and the space thus filled in is termed the *anterior fontanelle* : in contact with the lower surface of the membrane is the pineal body, to be afterwards mentioned in the account of the brain. Each side-wall of this part of the skull presents a deep concavity—the *orbit*—over which is a ridge-like prominence, the *supra-orbital crest*, terminating anteriorly and posteriorly in obscure processes termed respectively the *pre-orbital* and *post-orbital processes*. Below the orbit is a longitudinal *infra-orbital* ridge.

Behind the orbit is the *auditory region* of the skull—a mass of cartilage in which the parts of the membranous labyrinth of the internal ear are embedded. On the upper surface of this posterior portion of the skull are two small apertures situated in a mesial depression. These are the openings of the *aqueductûs vestibuli* (*endolymphatic ducts*), leading into the vestibule of the membranous labyrinth. Behind this again is the *occipital region*, forming the posterior boundary of the cranial cavity, and having in the middle a large rounded aperture—the *foramen magnum*—through which the spinal cord, contained in the neural canal and protected by the neural arches of the vertebræ, becomes continuous with the brain, lodged in the cranial cavity. Below this, on either side is an articular surface—the *occipital condyle*—for articulation with the spinal column, and between the two condyles is a concavity, like that of the vertebral centra, containing notochordal tissue.

A number of smaller apertures, or *foramina*, chiefly for the passage of nerves, perforate the wall of the skull. Behind and to the outer side of the anterior fontanelle are apertures (*oph. 2, 1*) through which the ophthalmic branches of the fifth and seventh nerves leave the skull. Piercing the inner wall of the orbit are foramina through which the optic or second pair of cerebral nerves (*opt.*), the oculomotor (*oc.*), or third, the pathetic, or fourth (*path.*), the trigeminal, or fifth (*tri.*), the abducent, or sixth, and the facial, or seventh, gain an exit from the interior of the cranial cavity. Just behind the auditory region is the foramen for the glossopharyngeal (*gl.*), and in the posterior wall of the skull, near the foramen magnum, is the foramen for the vagus.

In close connection with the cranium are a number of cartilages composing the *visceral arches* (Figs. 149 and 150). These are incomplete hoops of cartilage, mostly segmented, which lie in the sides and floor of the mouth-cavity or pharynx. The first of these forms the upper and lower jaws. The upper jaw, or *palatoquadrate* (*pal. q.*), consists of two stout rods of cartilage firmly bound together in the middle line and bearing the upper series of teeth. The lower jaw, or *Meckel's cartilage* (*mck.*), likewise consists of two stout tooth-bearing cartilaginous rods firmly united together in the middle line, the union being termed the *symphysis*. At their outer ends the upper and lower jaws articulate with one another by a movable joint. In front the upper jaw is connected by a ligament with the base of the skull.

Immediately behind the lower jaw is the *hyoid arch*. This consists of two cartilages on each side, and a mesial one below. The uppermost cartilage is

the *hyomandibular* (*hy. mn.*) : this articulates by its proximal end with a distinct articular facet on the auditory region of the skull : distally it is connected by ligamentous fibres with the outer ends of the palatoquadrate and Meckel's cartilage. The lower lateral cartilage is the *ceratohyal* (*cer. hy.*). Both the hyomandibular and ceratohyal bear a number of slender cartilaginous rods— the branchial rays of the hyoid arch. The mesial element, or *basihyal* (*b.hy.*), lies in the floor of the pharynx. Behind the hyoid arch follow the *branchial arches*, which are five in number. Each branchial arch, with exceptions to

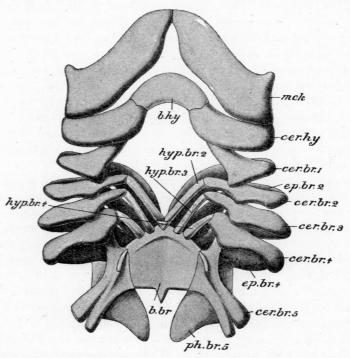

Fig. 150.—**Brachælurus,** ventral view of the visceral arches. Letters as in preceding figure. In addition—*b.br.* basibranchial plate ; *cer.br.* ceratobranchials ; *hyp.br.* hypobranchials.

be presently noted, consists of four cartilages. The uppermost of these— *pharyngobranchial* (*ph. br. 1–ph. br. 5*)—lie in the dorsal wall of the pharynx, not far from the spinal column ; the pharyngobranchials of the last two arches are fused together. The next in order—the *epibranchials* (*ep. br.*)—with the exception of those of the last arch, bear a number of slender cartilaginous rods—the *branchial rays*—which support the walls of the gill-sacs ; and the next—the *ceratobranchials* (*cer. br.*)—are, with the same exception, similarly provided. The *hypobranchials* (*hyp. br.*), which succeed these, are absent in the case of the first and fifth arches. In the middle line on the floor of the pharyngeal cavity is a mesial cartilage—the *basibranchial* (Fig. 150, *b, br.*)—which is connected with the ventral ends of the third, fourth, and fifth arches. A series of slender curved rods—the *extrabranchials*—lie superficial to the branchial arches, along the borders of the corresponding external branchial clefts.

Two pairs of delicate *labial* cartilages are present at the sides of the mouth, and a couple at the margins of the openings of the olfactory capsules.

The skeleton of all the fins—paired and unpaired—presents a considerable degree of uniformity. The main part of the expanse of the fin is supported by a series of flattened semented rods, the *pterygiophores* or cartilaginous fin-rays, which lie in close apposition : in the case of the dorsal fins these may be partly calcified. At the outer ends of these are one or more rows of polygonal plates of cartilage. On each side of the rays and polygonal cartilages are a number of slender "horny" rays or *ceratotrichia* of dermal origin.[1] In the smaller median fins there may be an elongated rod of cartilage constituting the skeleton, or cartilage may be entirely absent. In the pectoral fin (Fig. 151) the fin-rays are supported on three *basal carti-lages* articulating with the *pectoral arch*. The latter (*pect.*) is a strong hoop of cartilage incomplete dorsally, situated immediately behind the last of the branchial arches. It consists of a dorsal, or scapular, and a ventral, or *coracoid* portion, the coracoid portions of opposite

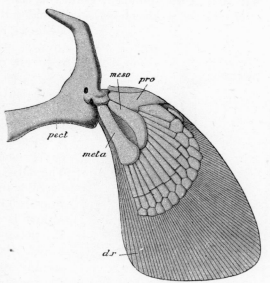

FIG. 151.— **Brachælurus**, pectoral arch and fin. *d. r.* dermal horny rays ; *meso.* mesoterygium ; *meta.* metapterygium ; *pect.* pectoral arch ; *pro.* proptery-gium.

sides being completely continuous across the middle line, while the scapular are separated by a wide gap in which the spinal column lies. Between the two portions are the three articular surfaces for the three basal cartilages. The coracoid portions are produced forwards in the middle line into a flattened process supporting the floor of the pericardial cavity in which the heart is lodged. The three basal cartilages of the fin are named, respectively, the anterior, *propterygium* (*pro.*), the middle, *mesopterygium* (*meso.*), and the posterior, *metapterygium* (*meta.*). Of these the first is the smallest and the last

---

[1] Though, on account of their appearance and horn-like consistency, these structures are commonly referred to as horny, they do not consist of true horn (which is always epidermal in origin), but of a substance called *elastin*, characteristic of elastic connective-tissue fibres.

the largest : the first bears only one large ray ; the other two bear twelve or more rays, differently arranged in the two genera.

The *pelvic fin* (Fig. 152) has only a single basal cartilage (*meta.*) articulating with the *pelvic arch*, with which also one or two of the fin-rays articulate directly. The pelvic arch (*pelv.*) is a nearly straight bar of cartilage which runs transversely across the ventral surface of the body, just in front of the cloacal opening.

Alimentary Canal (Fig. 153).—The mouth leads into a very wide cavity, the *pharynx*, into which open at the sides the internal apertures of the branchial clefts and of the spiracle. From this runs backwards a short wide tube—the *œsophagus* (*œs.*)—which passes behind into the stomach. The *stomach* is a

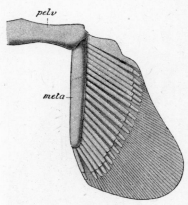

FIG. 152.—**Brachælurus,** pelvic arch and pelvic fin. *meta.* meta- pterygium ; *pelv.* pelvic arch.

U-shaped organ, with a long left limb continuous with the œsophagus, and a short right one passing into the intestine. At the *pylorus* (*pyl.*)—the point where the stomach passes into the intestine—is a slight constriction, followed by a thickening. The *intestine* consists of two parts—*small intestine* or *duodenum* and *large intestine*. The former is very short, only an inch or two in length. The latter is longer and very wide ; it is divisible into two portions—the *colon* (*col.*) in front and the *rectum* (*rect.*) behind. The former is very wide and is characterised by the presence in its interior of a *spiral valve,* a fold of the mucous membrane which runs spirally round its interior, and both retards the too rapid passage of the food and affords a more extensive surface for absorption. The rectum differs from the colon in being narrower and in the absence of the spiral valve ; it opens behind into the cloaca.

There is a large *liver* (*liv.*) consisting of two elongated lobes. A rounded sac —the *gall-bladder* (*g. bl.*)—lies embedded in the left lobe at its anterior end. The duct of the liver—the *bile-duct* (*b.dct.*)—runs from the liver to the intestine. Proximally it is connected with the gall-bladder, and by branch-ducts with the right and left lobes of the liver. It opens near the commencement of the colon.

The *pancreas* (*pancr.*) is a light-coloured compressed gland consisting of two main lobes with a broad connecting isthmus, lying in the angle between the right-hand limb of the stomach and the small intestine. Its duct enters the wall of the small intestine and runs in it for about half an inch, opening eventually at the point where the small intestine passes into the colon.

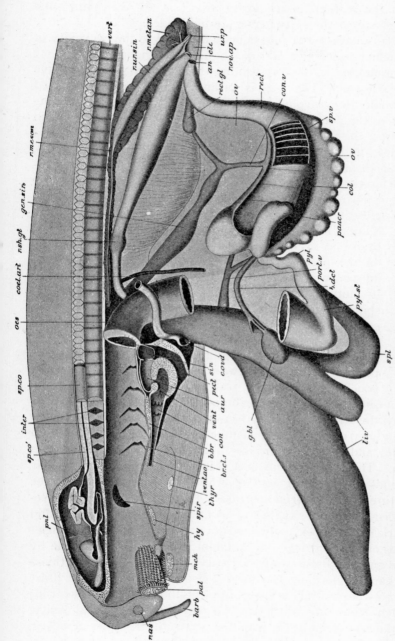

FIG. 153.—**Brachaelurus**, lateral dissection. The left side of the body-wall has been removed so as to bring into view the various parts of the digestive, renal, and reproductive systems. The left oviduct and kidney have been removed; the cloaca has been opened. The head is represented in median vertical section. The chambers of the heart have been removed. *an.* opening of rectum into cloaca; *aur.* atrium; *barb.* barbule; *b. br.* basi-branchial plate; *b. dct.* bile-duct; *br. cl.* internal branchial clefts; *clo.* cloaca; *cœl. art.* cœliac artery (cut short); *col.* colon; *con.* conus arteriosus; *con. v.* connecting vein between the genital (ovarian) sinus and the hepatic portal system; *c. ovd.* common cœlomic aperture of oviducts; *g. bl.* gall-bladder; *gen. sin.* genital sinus; *hy.* basi-branchial; *inter.* intervertebral substance; *liv.* liver; *mck.* Meckel's cartilage; *nas.* nasal cartilage; *œs.* œsophagus; *ov.* ovary; *pal.* palato-quadrate; *pancr.* pancreas; *pect.* pectoral arch; *pnl.* stalk of pineal body; *port. v.* hepatic portal vein; *pyl.* pylorus; *pyl. st.* pyloric portion of stomach; *rect.* rectum; *rect. gl.* rectal gland; *r. meson.* right kidney; *r. melan.* posterior portion of kidney; *r. ov. ap.* aperture of right oviduct into cloaca; *r. sh. gl.* right shell-gland; *r. ur. sin.* right urinary sinus; *sin.* sinus venosus; *sp. co.* spinal cord; *sp. co'.* anterior part of spinal cord in median vertical section; *spir.* spiracle; *spl.* spleen; *sp. v.* spiral valve; *thyr.* thyroid; *ur. p.* urinary papilla; *vent. ao.* ventral aorta; *vert.* centra of vertebræ.

Connected with the rectum on its dorsal aspect is an oval gland—the *rectal gland* (*rect. gl.*)—about three-quarters of an inch in length.

The *spleen* (*spl.*) is a dark-red or purple body attached to the convexity of the U-shaped stomach and sending a narrow lobe along the right-hand limb.

The **organs of respiration** in the Dog-fish are the *gills*, situated in the five *gill-pouches*. Each gill-pouch (Fig. 154) is an antero-posteriorly compressed cavity opening internally into the pharynx and externally by the corresponding gill-slit. The walls of the pouches are supported by the branchial and hyoid arches with their rays, the first pouch being situated between the hyoid and first branchial arches, the last between the fourth and fifth branchial arches. On the anterior and posterior walls of the pouches are the *gills*, each hemibranch consisting of a series of close-set parallel folds or plaits of highly vascular mucous membrane. Separating adjoining gill-pouches, and supporting the gills, is a series of broad *interbranchial septa*, each containing the corresponding branchial arch with its connected branchial rays. The most anterior hemibranch is borne on the posterior surface of the hyoid arch. The last gill-pouch differs from the rest in having gill-plaits on its anterior wall only. On the anterior wall of the spiracle is a vestigial gill—the *pseudobranch* or *spiracular gill*—in the form of a few slight ridges.

FIG. 154.—**Brachæ-lurus.** Branchial sac exposed from the outside.

Blood-system.—The *heart* is situated in the pericardial cavity, on the ventral aspect of the body, in front of the pectoral arch, and between the two series of branchial pouches. The dorsal wall of the pericardial cavity is supported by the basibranchial cartilage. Placing it in communication with the abdominal cavity is a canal—the *pericardio-peritonial canal*. The heart (Fig. 155) consists of four chambers—*sinus venosus* (*sin.*), *atrium* (*aur.*), *ventricle* (*vent.*), and *conus arteriosus* (*con.*), through which the blood passes in the order given. The *sinus venosus* is a thin-walled, transverse, tubular chamber, into the ends of which the great veins open. It communicates with the atrium by an aperture, the *sinu-atrial* aperture. The *atrium* is a large, three-cornered, thin-walled chamber, situated in front of the sinus venosus and dorsal to the ventricle. Its apex is directed forwards, and its lateral angles project at the sides of the ventricle : it communicates with the ventricle by a slit-like aperture guarded by a two-lipped valve. The *ventricle* is a thick-walled, globular chamber, forming the most conspicuous part of the heart when looked at from the ventral surface. From it the *conus arteriosus* runs forwards as a median stout tube to the anterior end of the pericardial cavity, where it gives off the *ventral aorta*. It contains two transverse rows of valves, anterior and posterior, the former consisting of three, the latter of three or four. The *ventral aorta* (Fig. 155) gives origin to a series of paired *afferent branchial* *arteries* (*af. br.*), one for each branchial pouch. In *Scyliorhinus* the two most posterior arise close together near the beginning of the ventral aorta, the third pair a little further forwards. The ventral aorta then runs forwards a little distance and bifurcates to form the two *innominate* arteries, right and left, each of which in turn bifurcates to form the first and second afferent vessels (*af. br.*¹, *af. br.*²) of its side. In *Brachælurus* (Fig. 156 A, B) the arrangement is somewhat different.

From the gills the blood passes by means of the *efferent branchial arteries*. These efferent vessels (Fig. 155, *ef. br.*) form a series of loops, one running around the margin of each of the first four internal branchial clefts : a single vessel runs along the anterior border of the fifth branchial cleft and opens into

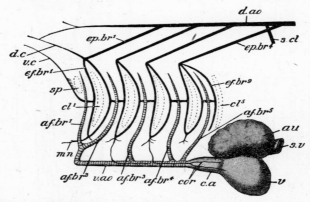

FIG. 155.—The heart and branchial arteries of **Scyliorhinus**, from the side. *af. br.*¹—⁵, afferent branchial arteries ; *au.* atrium ; *c.a.* conus arteriosus ; *cl.* ¹—⁵, branchial clefts ; *cor.* coronary artery ; *d. ao.* dorsal aorta ; *d. c.* dorsal carotid artery ; *ef. br.*¹—⁹, efferent branchial arteries ; *ep. br.*¹—⁴, epibranchial arteries ; *mn.* mandibular artery ; *sp.* spiracle ; *s.cl.* subclavian artery ; *s. v.* sinus venosus ; *v.* ventricle ; *v. ao.* ventral aorta ; *v. c.* ventral carotid artery. (From Parker's *Practical Zoology.*)

the fourth loop. The four main efferent branchial vessels (*epibranchials*, *ep. br.*) run inwards and backwards from the loops under cover of the mucous membrane of the roof of the pharynx to unite in a large median trunk—the *dorsal aorta* (*d. ao.*). A *dorsal carotid artery* (*d. c.*) *is* given off from the first efferent branchial. A branch (*hyoidean*) given off from the same efferent vessel supplies the pseudobranch, and the blood from the latter is taken up by the *ventral carotid* (*v. c.*). Both carotids run forwards to supply the head.

The *dorsal aorta* (Fig. 155, *d. ao.*) runs backwards throughout the length of the body-cavity, giving off numerous branches, and is continued as the *caudal artery*, which runs in the canal enclosed by the inferior arches of the caudal vertebræ. The first pair of branches are the *subclavians* (*s. cl.*), for the supply of the pectoral fins ; these are given off between the third and fourth pairs of epibranchial arteries. The next large branch is the unpaired *cœliac*

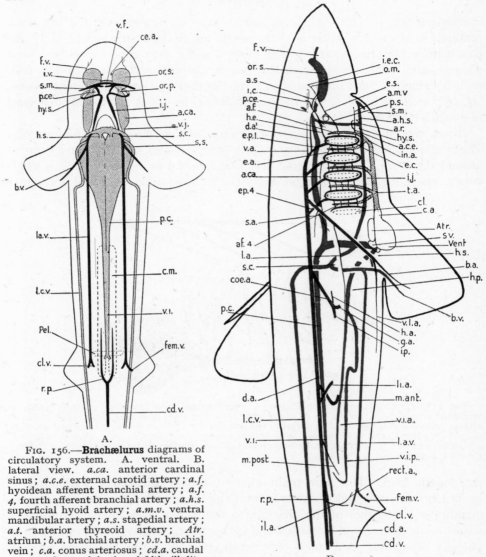

A.

FIG. 156.—**Brachælurus** diagrams of
circulatory system. A. ventral. B.
lateral view. *a.ca.* anterior cardinal
sinus; *a.c.e.* external carotid artery; *a.f.*
hyoidean afferent branchial artery; *a.f.
4,* fourth afferent branchial artery; *a.h.s.*
superficial hyoid artery; *a.m.v.* ventral
mandibular artery; *a.s.* stapedial artery;
a.t. anterior thyreoid artery; *Atr.*
atrium; *b.a.* brachial artery; *b.v.* brachial
vein; *c.a.* conus arteriosus; *cd.a.* caudal
artery; *cd.v.* caudal vein; *cl.* fifth gill slit;

B.

cl.v. cloacal vein; *cœ.a.* cœliac artery; *d.a.* dorsal aorta; *d.a.* paired dorsal aorta; *e.a.* anastomosis between efferent collector loops; *e.c.* efferent collector loop; *ep. 1-4,* first and fourth epibranchial arteries; *e.s.* spiracular epibranchial artery; *fem.v.* femoral vein; *f.v.* anterior facial
vein; *g.a.* gastric artery; *h.a.* hepatic artery; *h.e.* hyoidean epibranchial artery; *h.p.* hepatic
portal vein; *h.s.* hepatic sinus; *hy.s.* hyoidean sinus; *i.c.* internal carotid artery; *i.e.c.* intracranial branch of the spiracular epibranchial artery; *i.j.* inferior jugular sinus; *il.a.* iliac artery;
in.a. innominate artery; *i.p.* intestino-pyloric artery; *l.a.* lateral artery; *l.a.v.* lateral abdominal
vein; *l.c.v.* superior lateral cutaneous vein; *li.a.* lienogastric artery; *m.ant.* anterior mesenteric
artery; *m.post.* posterior mesenteric artery; *o.m.* great ophthalmic artery; *or.s.* orbital sinus;
p.c. posterior cardinal sinus; *p.ce.* posterior cerebral vein; *p.s.* afferent spiracular artery; *r.p.*
renal portal vein; *rect.a.* rectal artery; *s.a.* subclavian artery; *s.c.* subclavian vein; *s.m.* sub-
mental sinus; *s.v.* sinus venosus; *t.a.* truncus arteriosus (ventral aorta); *v.a.* vertebral artery;
Vent. Ventricle; *v.i.* interrenal portion of posterior cardinal sinus; *v.i.a.* anterior intestinal vein;
v.i.p. posterior intestinal vein; *v.l.a.* ventro lateral artery. (After O'Donoghue.)

(Fig. 153, *cœl.*) : this runs in the mesentery and divides into branches for the supply of the stomach and liver, the first part of the intestine, and the pancreas. The *anterior mesenteric* artery, also median, supplies the rest of the intestine and gives off branches to the reproductive organs. The *lienogastric* supplies part of the stomach, the spleen, and part of the pancreas. The *posterior mesenteric* is a small vessel mainly supplying the rectal gland. Small *renal* arteries carry a small quantity of arterial blood to the kidneys, and a pair of *iliac* arteries, likewise of small size, pass to the pelvic fins. In addition to these a number of small arteries, the *parietal*, supplying the wall of the body, are given off throughout the length of the aorta.

The *veins* are very thin-walled, and the larger trunks are remarkable for their dilated character, from which they have obtained the name of *sinuses*, though they are true vessels and not sinuses in the sense in which the word is used in dealing with the Invertebrates.

The venous blood is brought back from the head by a pair of *jugular* or *anterior cardinal sinuses* (Fig. 156, *a. ca.*), and from the trunk by a pair of *posterior cardinal sinuses* (*p. c.*). At the level of the sinus venosus the anterior and posterior cardinals of each side unite to form a short, nearly transverse sinus, the *precaval, sinus* or *ductus Cuvieri*, which is continued into the lateral extremity of the sinus venosus. Into the precaval sinus, about its middle, opens an *inferior jugular sinus* (*v. j.*) which brings back the blood from the floor of the mouth and about the branchial region of the ventral surface. The two posterior cardinal sinuses extend backwards throughout the length of the body-cavity ; in front they are enormously dilated, behind they lie between the kidneys. Anteriorly each receives the corresponding *subclavian vein* bringing the blood from the pectoral fin and adjacent parts of the body-wall. The *lateral vein* (*la. v.*), instead of joining with the subclavian, opens separately into the precaval. The *genital sinus* discharges into the posterior cardinal sinus.

There are two *portal* systems of veins, the *renal* (*r. p.*) and the *hepatic portal* (*h. p.*), by which the kidneys and liver, respectively, are supplied with venous blood. The *caudal vein*, which brings back the blood from the tail, running, along with the caudal artery through the inferior arches of the vertebræ, divides on entering the abdominal cavity into right and left *renal portal* veins, which end in a number of afferent renal veins supplying the kidneys.

The *hepatic portal* vein (*h. p.*) is formed by the confluence of veins derived from the intestine, stomach, pancreas, and spleen, and runs forwards to enter the liver a little to the right of the middle line. In *Brachælurus* a large branch connects the genital sinus with the intestinal tributaries of the hepatic portal system : the blood from the liver enters the sinus venosus by two *hepatic sinuses* placed close together.

Nervous System.—The fore-brain consists of a rounded smooth *prosencephalon*
(Fig. 157, *V.H.*) divided into two lateral parts by a very shallow median
longitudinal groove.　From its antero-lateral region each half gives off a thick

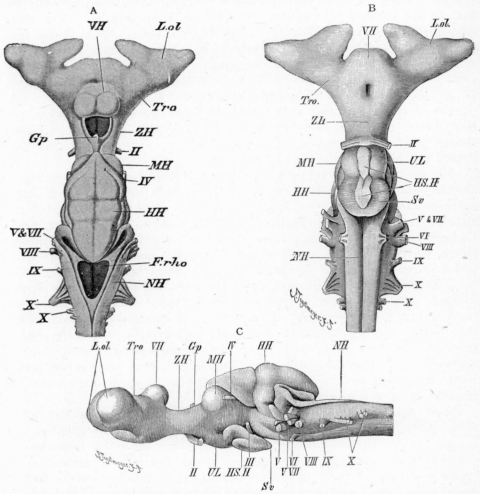

Fig. 157.—Brain of **Scyliorhinus canicula.** **A,** dorsal view; **B,** ventral view; **C,** lateral view.
F. rho. fossa rhomboidalis (fourth ventricle); *Gp,* epiphysis; *HH,* cerebellum; *HS. H,* hypophysis; *L. ol.* olfactory bulb; *MH,* mid-brain; *NH,* medulla oblongata; *Sv,* saccus vasculosus;
Tro, olfactory peduncle; *UL,* lobi inferiores; *VH,* prosencephalon; *ZH,* diencephalon; *II,* optic
nerves; *III,* oculomotor; *IV,* pathetic; *V,* trigeminal; *VI,* abducent; *VII,* facial; *VIII,*
auditory; *IX,* glossopharyngeal; *X,* vagus.　(From Wiedersheim's *Comp. Anatomy.*)

cord, which dilates into a large mass of nerve-matter, the *olfactory bulb* (*L. ol.*),
closely applied to the posterior surface of the corresponding olfactory capsule.
The diencephalon (*ZH*) is comparatively small; its roof is very thin, while the

lateral walls are composed of two thickish masses—the *optic thalami*. Attached to the roof is a slender tube, the *epiphysis cerebri* or *pineal organ* (*Gp.*), which runs forwards and terminates in a slightly dilated extremity fixed to the membranous part of the roof of the skull. Projecting downwards from its floor are two rounded bodies, the *lobi inferiores* (*UL*), which are dilated portions of the *infundibulum*. Behind these give off a thin-walled vascular out-growth—the *saccus vasculosus* (*Sv.*). Attached to the infundibulum and extending backwards from it is a thin-walled sac—the *pituitary body* or *hypophysis cerebri* (*HS*), having on its ventral surface a median tubular body attached at its posterior end to the floor of the skull. In front of the infundibulum, and also on the lower surface of the diencephalon, is the *optic chiasma*, formed by the decussation of the fibres of the two optic nerves. The mid-brain (*MH*) consists of a pair of oval *optic lobes* dorsally, and ventrally of a band of longitudinal nerve-fibres corresponding to the *crura cerebri* of the higher vertebrate brain. The cerebellum (*HH*) is elongated in the antero-posterior direction, its anterior portion overlapping the optic lobes, and its posterior the medulla oblongata. Its surface is marked with a few fine grooves. The medulla oblongata (*NH*), broad in front, narrows posteriorly to pass into the spinal cord. The *fourth ventricle* or *fossa rhomboidalis* (*F. rho.*) is a shallow space on the dorsal aspect of the medulla oblongata covered over only by a thin vascular membrane, the *choroid plexis*: it is wide in front and gradually narrows posteriorly. At the sides of the anterior part of the fourth ventricle are a pair of folded ear-shaped lobes, the *corpora restiformia*.

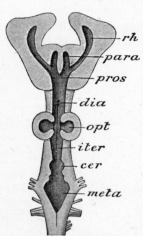

FIG. 158.—**Hemiscyllium.** The brain viewed from the dorsal side, the roofs of the various ventricles removed so as to show the relations of the cavities (semi-diagrammatic). *cer.* dilatation from which the epicœle is given off; *dia.* diacœle, pointing to the opening leading into the infundibulum; *iter.* iter or mesocœle; *meta.* metacœle; *opt.* optocœle; *para.* paracœle; *pros.* prosocœle; *rh.* rhinocœle.

The fourth ventricle or *metacœle* (Fig. 158, *meta.*) is continuous behind with the central canal of the spinal cord. It gives off an epicœle above, and in front is continuous with a narrow passage, the *iter* or *mesocœle* (*iter.*) which opens anteriorly into a wider space, the *diacœle* or *third ventricle* (*dia.*), occupying the interior of the diencephalon. From this opens in front a median *prosocœle*, which gives off a pair of *paracœles* (*para.*) extending into the two lateral portions of the prosencephalon.

From the anterior enlargements of the olfactory bulbs already mentioned spring numerous fibres which constitute the first pair of cerebral nerves and enter the olfactory capsules. Between the two olfactory lobes two small

nerves, the *terminal* or *pre-olfactory*, arise from the prosencephalon : they are the nerves of ordinary sensation for the interior of the olfactory sacs.   From the optic chiasma the two nerves (Figs. 151, 159, 160, *II*) run outwards through the optic foramina into the orbits, each perforating the sclerotic of the corresponding eye and terminating in the retina.   The third, fourth, and sixth pairs of nerves have the general origin and distribution which have already been described as universal in the Craniata (p. 103).

The *trigeminal* (Figs. 157, 160, 162, *V*) arises in close relation to the facial.

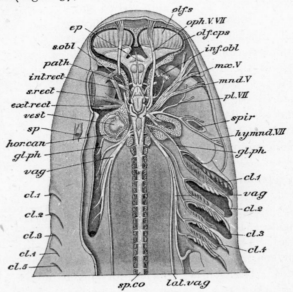

FIG. 159.—**Scyliorhinus stellaris.** Dissection of the brain and spinal nerves from the dorsal surface.   The right eye has been removed.   The cut surfaces of the cartilaginous skull and spinal column are dotted.   The buccal branch of the facial is not represented.   *cl.1—cl.5*, branchial clefts ; *ep.* epiphysis ; *ex. rect.* posterior rectus muscle of the eye-ball ; *gl.ph.* glossopharyngeal ; *hor. can.* horizontal semicircular canal ; *hy.mnd. VII.* hyomandibular portion of the facial ; *inf. obl.* inferior oblique muscle ; *int. rect.* anterior rectus muscle ; *lat. vag.* lateral branch of vagus ; *mx. V.* maxillary division of the trigeminal ; *olf. cps.* olfactory capsule ; *olf. s.* olfactory sac ; *oph. V. VII.* superficial ophthalmic branches of trigeminal and facial ; *path.* fourth nerve ; *pl. VII.* palatine branch of facial ; *sp. co.* spinal cord ; *sp.* and *spir.* spiracle ; *s. rect.* superior rectus muscle ; *s. olb.* superior oblique ; *vag.* vagus ; *vest.* vestibule.   (From Marshall and Hurst.)

As it passes into the orbit it swells into a ganglion—the *Gasserian*.   Its chief branches are three in number.   The first given off is the *superficial ophthalmic* (Fig. 159, *oph. V* ; Fig. 160, *V op.*), which runs forwards through the orbit above the origin of the recti muscles, and in very close relation with the ophthalmic branch of the facial.   Anteriorly it breaks up into branches distributed to the integument of the dorsal surface of the snout.[1]   The main

---

[1] In most Chondrichthyes a nerve of considerable size—the *ophthalmicus profundus* (Fig. 78) —arises from the dorsal and anterior part of the Gasserian ganglion, and is usually regarded as a branch of the trigeminal.   It runs forwards over the posterior rectus muscle and under the

trunk of the nerve then runs forwards and outwards across the floor of the orbit, and divides into two branches, the *maxillary* and *mandibular*, or second and third divisions of the trigeminal. The former (*mx. V*) supplies the skin of the ventral surface of the snout, the latter (*mnd. V*) the skin and muscles of the lower jaw.

Of the branches of the facial, the *ophthalmic* runs through the orbit in close relation to the superficial ophthalmic branch of the trigeminal, and is distributed to the lateral line and ampullary canals of the snout region ; the *buccal* runs forwards in intimate relation with the maxillary division of the trigeminal, and breaks up into branches which are distributed to the sensory canals and

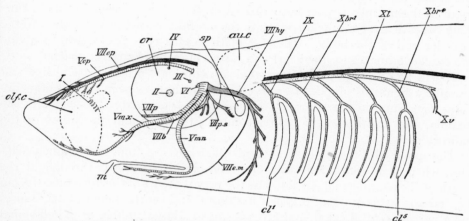

Fig. 160.—Semi-diagrammatic figure of the cerebral nerves of **Scyliorhinus canicula** dissected from the left side. The nerves supplying integumentary sense-organs are shown in black. *au.c.* auditory capsule ; *cl.*¹—⁵, branchial clefts ; *m.* mouth ; *olf. c.* olfactory capsule ; *or.* orbit ; *sp.* spiracle. *I—X*, cerebral nerves. *Vop.* ophthalmic, *Vmx.* maxillary, and *Vmn.* mandibular, divisions of the trigeminal ; *VIIop.* ophthalmic, *VIIp.* palatine, *VIIb.* buccal, *VIIps.* prespiracular, *VIIe.m.* external mandibular, and *VIIhy.* hyomandibular branches of the facial ; *Xl.* lateral, *Xbr.*¹—⁴, branchial, and *Xv.* visceral branches of the vagus. (From Parker's *Practical Zoology*.)

ampullæ of the region of the snout ; the *palatine* (*pl. VII, VIIp.*) passes to the roof of the mouth ; the main body of the nerve—*hyomandibular* nerve (*hy.mnd. VII, VIIhy.*)—then runs outwards close to the edge of the hyomandibular cartilage and behind the spiracle, eventually becoming distributed to the muscles between the spiracle and the first branchial cleft ; a small external mandibular branch (*VII e.m.*) comes off from it and goes to the lateral line and ampullary canals of the lower jaw.

The *eighth* or *auditory* nerve passes directly into the internal ear, and breaks

---

superior rectus, and perforates the pre-orbital process to end in the integument of the snout. Among other branches it gives off ciliary branches to the iris : these are joined by the ciliary branches of the oculomotor. Anophthalmicus profundus is not present in *Scyliorhinus* in the adult condition.

up into branches for the supply of its various parts. The *glossopharyngeal* (*gl. ph., IX*) perforates the posterior part of the auditory region of the skull, and, after it reaches the exterior, passes to the first branchial cleft, where it bifurcates, one branch going to the anterior, and the other to the posterior wall of the cleft. The last nerve of the series—the *pneumogastric* or *vagus* (*vag., X*)—is a large nerve which emerges from the skull by an aperture situated between the auditory region and the foramen magnum. It first gives off a series of four *branchial* branches, each of which bifurcates to supply the anterior and posterior borders of the last four branchial clefts. The *lateralis* nerve (*lat. vag., X.l.*) is frequently referred to as a branch of the vagus since it runs in intimate connection with the trunk of that nerve for some distance, but it has a distinct origin in the medulla : after becoming separated from the vagus trunk it runs along beneath the peritoneum opposite the lateral line, which it supplies, to the posterior end of the body. The rest of the vagus runs backwards to divide into *cardiac* branches for the heart and *gastric* branches for the stomach.

It will be observed that the system of neuromast organs (lateral line and ampullary organs) is supplied by nerve-fibres which pass out in various branches of the facial and in the lateralis : all these fibres originate in a centre in the medulla, the *acustico-lateral centre*, common to them and the fibres of the auditory nerve.

The spinal cord is a cylindrical cord which extends from the foramen magnum, where it is continuous with the hind-brain, backwards throughout the length of the neural canal, enclosed by the neural arches of the vertebræ. As in the Craniata in general (see p. 96), it has dorsal and ventral longitudinal fissures and a narrow central canal, and gives origin to a large number of paired spinal nerves, each arising from it by two roots.

Organs of Special Sense.—The *olfactory organs* are rounded chambers enclosed by the cartilage of the olfactory capsules of the skull, and opening on the exterior by the nostrils on the ventral surface of the head. The interior has its lining membrane raised up into a number of close-set ridges running out from a median septum. The fibres of the olfactory nerves terminate in cells of the epithelium covering the surface of these ridges.

The *eye* has the general structure already described as characterising the Craniata in general (p. 112). The sclerotic is cartilaginous, the choroid has a shining metallic internal layer or *tapetum cellulosum*, and the lens is spherical. There are the usual eye-muscles, the two *obliques* situated anteriorly, the four *recti* posteriorly, not embracing the optic nerve. The eyelids are represented by stiff folds.

The ear consists only of the *membranous labyrinth* (Fig. 88), equivalent to the internal ear of higher Craniata, the middle and outer ear being absent. The membranous labyrinth consists of the *vestibule* and three *semicircular canals*. The former, which is divided into two parts by a constriction, communicates by a narrow passage—the *endolymphatic duct* or *aqueductûs vestibuli*—with the exterior, in the position already mentioned. Of the three semi-circular canals, the anterior and posterior are vertical and the external horizontal, as in Craniata in general. Each has an ampulla, that of the anterior and external canals situated at their anterior ends, and that of the posterior canal, which is the largest of the three and forms an almost complete circle, at its posterior end. In the fluid (*endolymph*) in the interior of the vestibule are suspended, in a mass of gelatinous connective-tissue, numerous minute calcareous particles or *otoliths*, giving it a milky character.

The *sensory canals* of the integument running along the lateral line and over the head contain special nerve-endings (*neuromasts*), and doubtless function as organs of some special sense (see p. 109). The same probably holds good of a number of unbranched canals (*ampullary canals*) arranged in groups situated on the anterior portion of the trunk and on the head, and being particularly numerous in the neighbourhood of the snout. These are dilated internally into vesicles, the *ampullæ*, provided with special nerve-endings.

Urinogenital Organs.—In the female there is a single ovary (Figs. 153, 161, *ov.*), an elongated soft, lobulated body, lying a little to the right of the middle line of the abdominal cavity, attached by a fold of peritoneum, the *mesovarium*. On its surface are rounded elevations or *follicles* of various sizes, each containing an ovum of a bright yellow colour. There are two oviducts (Müllerian ducts) entirely unconnected with the ovaries. Each oviduct (Figs. 153 and 161, *ovd.*) is a greatly elongated tube extending throughout the entire length of the abdominal cavity. In front the two unite behind the pericardium to open into the abdominal cavity by a wide median aperture (*ovd¹.*). At about the point of junction of the middle and anterior thirds is a swelling marking the position of the *shell-gland* (*sh. gl.*). The posterior part dilates to form a wide uterine chamber, and in *Scyliorhinus* the two unite to open into the cloaca by a common aperture situated just behind the opening of the rectum, while in *Brachælurus* they remain distinct and have separate cloacal openings. Each kidney consists of two parts, anterior and posterior. The former (Fig. 153, *r. meson*, Fig. 161, *k¹*) is a long narrow ribbon of soft reddish substance, which runs along throughout a great part of the body-cavity at the side of the vertebral column, covered by the peritoneum. The posterior portion (*r. metan*, *k*) is a compact, lobulated, dark red body, lying at the side of the cloaca, continuous with the anterior portion; like the latter, it is covered over by the peritoneum. Both portions have their ducts. Those of the anterior are narrow tubes, which run over its ventral surface and become dilated behind to form a pair of elongated chambers, the *urinary sinuses* (Fig. 162, *ur. sin.*), uniting behind into a median sinus (*med. ur. sin.*), opening into the cloaca by a median aperture situated on a papilla, the *urinary papilla*. The ducts of the posterior portion, which are usually from four to six in number, open into the urinary sinuses.

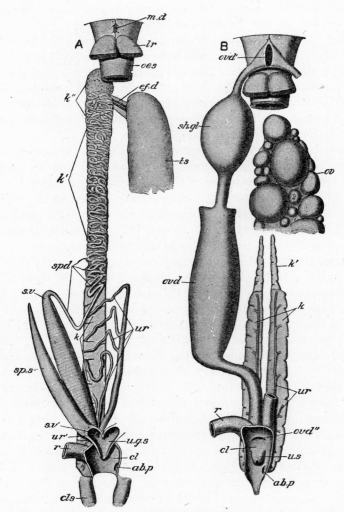

FIG. 161.—The urinogenital organs of **Scyliorhinus canicula** from the ventral side. *A*, male and *B*, female. Only the anterior end of the gonad is represented in each figure, and except that in *B* both kidneys are shown, the organs of the right side only are drawn. In *A* the seminal vesicle and sperm-sac are dissected away from the kidneys and displaced outwards, and the ureters inwards. *ab. p.* depression into which the abdominal pore opens; *cl.* cloaca; *cls.* clasper; *ef. d.* efferent ducts of spermary; *k.* kidney; *k'. k".* anterior non-renal portion of the kidney, forming in the male the so-called " Leydig's gland," which, together with the coiled spermiduct, constitutes the epididymis; *lr.* anterior portion of liver; *m. d.* vestigial Müllerian duct in the male; *œs.* gullet; *ov.* ovary; *ovd.* oviduct; *ovd'.* its cœlomic aperture; *ovd".* the common aperture of the oviducts into the cloaca; *r.* rectum; *sh. gl.* shell-gland; *spd.* spermiduct; *sp. s.* sperm-sac; *s. v.* seminal vesicle; *s. v'.* its aperture into the urinogenital sinus; *ts.* spermary (testis); *u.g. s.* urinogenital sinus; *ur.* posterior mesonephric ducts; *ur'.* their apertures into the urinogenital sinus; *u. s.* urinary sinus. (From Parker's *Practical Zoology*.)

In the male (Fig. 161, *A*) there are two elongated, soft, lobulated *testes*, each attached to the wall of the abdominal cavity by a fold of peritoneum—the *mesorchium*. From each testis anteriorly, a small number of efferent ducts (*ef.d*) pass to the anterior end of a long, narrow, strap-shaped body, which corresponds to the vestigial anterior portion of the kidney in the female. This is the *epididymis*; the duct, *spermiduct* or *vas deferens*, runs along the entire length of the non-renal part of the kidney, or " *Leydig's gland*," and, where it leaves the latter posteriorly, becomes a wide tube, which opens into the

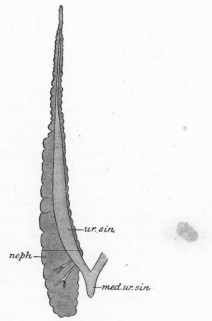

FIG. 162.—**Brachælurus.** Right kidney and urinary sinus of female, *med. ur. sinus*, median urinary sinus ; *neph.* kidney ; *ur. sinus*, right urinary sinus.

FIG. 163.—**Dogfish**, egg-case. (After Dean.)

urinogenital sinus (*u.g. s.*), a median chamber projecting into the cloaca. Posteriorly the spermiduct dilates to form a wide thin-walled sac, the *vesicula seminalis*. Closely applied to the latter is a thin-walled elongated sac, the *sperm-sac*. Anteriorly the sperm-sac narrows to a blind extremity ; posteriorly the right and left sperm-sacs combine to form the urinogenital sinus. The posterior part of the kidney has the same character as in the female ; its ducts, usually five in number on each side, upon into the urinogenital sinus, some of the most anterior first uniting to form a common tube. The sinus has a median aperture into the general cavity of the cloaca situated on the summit of a prominent *urinogenital papilla*. The oviducts (Müllerian ducts) of the female are represented in the male by vestiges of their anterior portions (*m.d.*). The entire kidney is sometimes regarded as a mesonephros, but the posterior portion, developed entirely behind the portion which, in the male, takes part in forming the epididymis, and having its own ducts, is sometimes looked upon as foreshadowing the metanephros of the higher Vertebrates.

The ripe ovum, rupturing the wall of its follicle, escapes into the abdominal cavity, whence it reaches the interior of one of the oviducts; there it is fertilised by sperms received from the male in the act of copulation, and then becomes enclosed in a chitinoid case or shell (Fig. 163) secreted by the shell-gland.

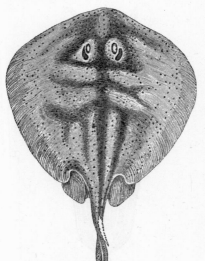

FIG. 164.—**Sting-Ray** (*Urolophus cruciatus*). (After Günther.)

GENERAL ORGANISATION.

External characters.—In general shape most Sharks (Fig. 146) are somewhat fusiform and slightly compressed laterally. In the Rays (Fig. 164), on the other hand, there is great dorso-ventral compression. The head is in many cases produced forwards into a long rostrum, which is of immense length and bordered with triangular teeth in the Saw Shark (*Pristiophorus*) and Saw-fish (*Pristis*). In the Hammerhead Shark (*Sphyrna* or *Zygæna*) the anterior part of the head is elongated transversely.

There are well-developed median and paired fins. The caudal fin is large, and, as a rule, strongly heterocercal in the Sharks and shark-like Rays, reduced in most of the latter group. The dorsal and anal fins are large in the Sharks, the former completely divided into two: in the Rays the dorsal fin is usually small, and the anal absent. The paired fins differ widely in the two groups. In the Sharks both pairs are well developed, the pectoral being the larger. In the Rays the pectoral fins are extremely large, very much larger than the pelvic, fringing the greater part of the length of the flattened body, and becoming prolonged forwards on either side and even in front of the head, so that the animal presents the appearance of a broad fleshy leaf.

In all recent Chondrichthyes the male has, connected with the pelvic fins, a pair of grooved appendages—the *claspers* or *myxopterygia*—which subserve copulation.

The mouth is situated on the ventral surface of the head, usually a considerable distance from the anterior extremity. In front of each angle of the mouth on the ventral surface is the opening of one of the olfactory sacs, each of which is frequently connected by a groove—the naso-buccal groove—with the mouth-cavity. Behind the mouth, on the dorsal surface in the Rays, and at the side in the Sharks, is the spiracle. Along each side of the neck in the Sharks, and on the ventral surface in the Rays, there is a row of slit-like apertures—the branchial slits or branchial clefts. These are usually five in number on each side; but in *Hexanchus* and *Chlamydoselachus* there are six, and in *Heptranchias* seven. In *Chlamydoselachus* (Fig. 145) a fold comparable to a rudimentary operculum extends back over the first branchial cleft, and is continuous across the middle line ventrally; in the remainder of the sub-class no such structure is represented. A large cloacal opening is situated just in front of the root of the tail, and in most members of the sub-class a pair of small openings placed close to it—the *abdominal pores*—lead into the abdominal cavity.

When the **integument** develops any hard parts as is the case in the majority of the Chondrichthyes, they take the form, not of regular scales, as in most other fishes, but of numerous hard bodies (Fig. 165) which vary greatly in shape, are usually extremely minute, but are in some cases developed, in certain parts of the surface, into prominent tubercles or spines. When these hard bodies are, as is commonly the case, small and set closely together in the skin, they give the surface very much the character of a fine file; and the skin so beset, known as " shagreen," was formerly used for various polishing purposes in the arts. This is the *placoid* form of exoskeleton, to which reference has been already made (page 63). Each of the hard bodies has the same structure as a tooth, being composed of

FIG. 165.—Dermal denticles of **Centrophorus calceus,** slightly magnified. (From Gegenbaur's *Comparative Anatomy*.)

dentine, capped with an enamel-like layer, and supported on a base of a substance somewhat resembling the bony cement or *crusta petrosa* of the tooth.

The **skeleton** is composed of cartilage, with, in many cases, deposition of calcareous matter in special places—notably in the jaws and the vertebral column. The entire spinal column may be nearly completely cartilaginous (*Hexanchus* and *Heptranchias*), but usually the centra are strengthened by radiating or concentric lamellæ of calcified tissue; or they may be completely calcified. They are deeply amphicœlous, the remains of the notochord persisting in the large inter-central spaces. *Intercalary pieces* (Fig. 166, *Ic.*)

are interposed between both superior and inferior arches. In the Rays (Fig. 167) the anterior part of the spinal column becomes converted into a continuous solid cartilaginous and calcified mass—the *anterior vertebral plate* (*a. v. p.*). As in fishes in general, two regions are distinguishable in the spinal column—the *precaudal* and the *caudal*, the latter being characterised by the possession of inferior or hæmal arches. In the precaudal region short ribs may be developed, but these are sometimes rudimentary or entirely absent. In the Sharks pterygiophores, sometimes jointed, fused at their bases with the hæmal spines, support the ventral lobe of the caudal fin, and the dorsal lobe of the same fin is supported by a series of pterygiophores resembling produced neural spines, but only secondarily related to the spinal column, and sometimes also divided by joints. The dorsal and ventral fins are sometimes supported by similar pterygiophores; but in many cases the cartilaginous supports of these fins consist, in whole or in part, of expanded plates of cartilage. The marginal portions of the unpaired fins beyond the limits of the endoskeleton are supported by dermal fibre-like structures (*ceratotrichia*) composed of elastin.

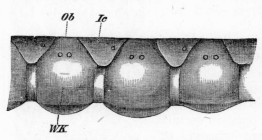

FIG. 166.—Portion of the spinal column of **Scymnorhinus.** *Ic.* intercalary cartilages; *Ob.* neural arches; *WK*, centra. (From Wiedersheim's *Vertebrata.*)

The **skull** is an undivided mass of cartilage, hardened, in many cases, by deposition of calcareous matter, but not containing any true bony tissue. It consists of a cartilaginous case for the protection of the brain and the organs of special sense. The structure of this cartilaginous brain-case as it occurs in the Dog-fish has already been described. The main differences observable in the different families are connected with the size and form of the rostrum. In the Rays the lower lip of the foramen magnum is deeply excavated for the reception of a short process, the so-called *odontoid process*, which projects forwards from the anterior vertebral plate, and on either side of this is an articular surface—the *occipital condyle*—for articulation with corresponding surfaces on that plate. In the Sharks the skull is not so definitely marked off from the spinal column. The apertures of the aqueductûs vestibuli in the Rays are not situated in a median depression such as is observable in the Dog-fish and in all the Sharks. The articular surface in the auditory region for the hyomandibular is sometimes borne on a projecting process, sometimes on the general level of the lateral surface. Sometimes in the Rays there is a smaller articulation behind for the first branchial arch.

The upper and lower jaws—the *palatoquadrate* and *Meckel's cartilage*—are connected with the skull through the intermediation of a *hyomandibular* cartilage (Fig. 149, *hy.mn.*; Fig. 167, *h. m.*). The skull is thus of the hyostylic type as regards the mode of suspension of the jaws. In the Sharks the palatoquadrate has a process (absent in the Rays) for articulation with the base of the skull in the pre-orbital region. In *Hexanchus* and *Heptranchias*

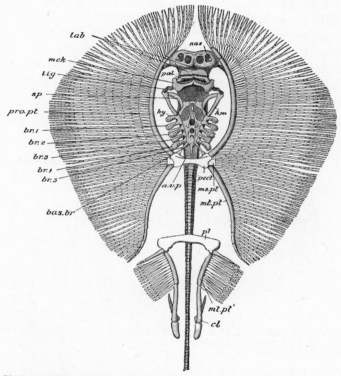

FIG. 167.—Skeleton of **Sting-Ray** (*Urolophus*), ventral view. *a. v. p.* anterior vertebral plate; *bas.br.* basibranchial plate; *br.1—br.5* branchial arches. (The branchial rays are not represented, the round dots indicating their articulations with the arches.) *cl.* skeleton of clasper; *h.m.* hyomandibular; *hy.* hyoid arch; *lab.* labial cartilage; *lig.* ligament connecting the hyomandibular with the palatoquadrate and Meckel's cartilage; *mck.* Meckel's cartilage; *ms.pt.* mesopterygium, and *mt.pt.* metapterygium of pectoral fin; *mt.pt'.* metapterygium of pelvic fin; *nas.* nasal cartilage; *pal.* palatoquadrate; *pect.* pectoral arch; *pl.* pelvic arch; *pro.pt.* propterygium; *sp.* spiracular cartilage.

(Fig. 168) there is in addition to this a prominent post-orbital process of the palatoquadrate for articulation with the post-orbital region of the skull (*amphistylic* arrangement). *Cestracion* is also in a sense amphistylic; the palatoquadrate is firmly united with the skull, articulating with a groove on the base, and the hyomandibular takes only a small share in the suspension of the jaws. At the sides of the mouth in all Chondrichthyes is a series of *labial cartilages*, usually two pairs above and one pair below. Attached to

the hyomandibular is a thin plate of the cartilage—the *spiracular* (Fig. 167, *sp.*)—which supports the anterior wall of the spiracle.

The hyoid arch proper is in most of the Chondrichthyes connected at its dorsal end with the hyomandibular—sometimes at its distal extremity, sometimes near its articulation with the skull; but in some Rays it is not so related, but articulates separately and independently with the skull behind the hyomandibular, and in the genera *Hypnarce* and *Trygonorhina* it articulates with the dorsal portion of the first branchial arch. In the Sharks the hyoid is usually relatively massive; in the Rays it is smaller, and in most cases closely resembles the branchial arches, and bears similar cartilaginous *rays*; a larger or smaller median element, or basihyal, is present in all cases.

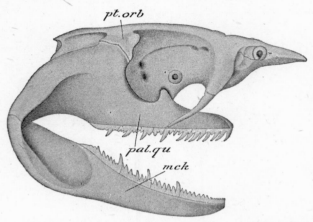

Fig. 168.—Lateral view of the skull of **Heptranchias.** *mck.* Meckel's cartilage; *pal.qu.* palatoquadrate; *pt. orb.* post-orbital process of the cranium, with which the palatoquadrate articulates. (After Gegenbaur.)

There are always five pairs of *branchial arches* except in *Hexanchus* and *Chlamydoselachus*, which have six, and *Heptranchias*, in which there are seven. Their dorsal ends are free in the Sharks, articulated with the anterior vertebral plate of the spinal column in most Rays. Externally they bear a series of slender cartilaginous *branchial rays*. The median ventral elements of the branchial arches are usually more or less reduced, and in some cases are represented by a single *basi-branchial* plate (Fig. 150 *bas. br.*). In the Rays the fifth branchial arch articulates with the pectoral arch, a connection which is absent in the Sharks. A series of slender cartilages, probably modified branchial rays—the *extra-branchial cartilages*—absent as such in some Dog-fishes and Rays, support the branchial apertures.

The pectoral arch (Figs. 151, 167, *pect.*) consists of a single cartilage, with, however, in most of the Sharks, a mesial flexible portion by which it is divided into right and left halves. Each lateral half consists of a dorsal *scapular* and a ventral *coracoid* part, the two being separated by the articular surfaces for the basal cartilages of the fin. In the Rays, but not in the Sharks, the dorsal ends of the pectoral arch are connected with the spinal column (anterior vertebral plate) by a distinct articulation, the portion of the arch on which the articular surface is situated sometimes forming an independent cartilage (*supra-scapula*).

The *basal pterygiophores* of the pectoral fin are typically three, *pro-*, *meso-*, and *meta-pterygium* (Figs. 151 and 167), but there are sometimes four, and the number may be reduced to two. The pro- and meta-pterygia are divided in the Rays (Fig. 167) into several segments, and the former articulates, through the intermediation of a cartilage termed the *antorbital*, with the olfactory region of the skull.

The *pelvic arch* (*pl.*) is usually, like the pectoral, a single cartilage, but in some exceptional cases it consists of two lateral portions. In some cases a median *epipubic process* projects forwards from the pelvic arch, and frequently there is on each side a *prepubic* process. A lateral *iliac* process, which becomes highly developed in the Holocephali, is sometimes represented, and may attain considerable dimensions. The pelvic fin has usually two basal cartilages, representing the pro- and meta-pterygia, but the former is often absent. In the male special cartilages attached to the metapterygia support the claspers. With the basal cartilages of both pectoral and pelvic fins are connected a number of jointed cartilaginous fin-rays supporting the expanse of the fin.

The arrangement of the **muscles** is simple. The trunk-muscles are divided into a pair of dorsal and a pair of ventral divisions, each composed of many myomeres with intercalated myocommata (Fig. 56, p. 66), following a metameric arrangement. The ventral part, where it forms the muscles of the wall of the abdominal cavity, is composed externally of obliquely running fibres, and represents one of the two *oblique* muscles of the abdomen of higher forms. Mesially this passes into a median band of longitudinally running fibres corresponding to a primitive *rectus*. The muscles of the limbs are distinguishable into two main sets—those inserted into the limb-arch and those inserted into the free part of the appendage. The latter, according to their insertion, act as elevators, depressors, or adductors. A series of circular muscles passes between the cartilages of the visceral arches and, when they contract, have the effect of contracting the pharynx and constricting the apertures. A set of muscles pass between the various arches and act so as to approximate them; and a broad sheet of longitudinal fibres divided into myomeres extends forwards from the shoulder-girdle to the visceral arches.

Electric organs—organs in which electricity is formed and stored up, to be discharged at the will of the Fish—occur in several Chondrichthyes. They are best developed in the Electric Rays and (*Hypnarce* and *Torpedo*, Fig. 169), in which they form a pair of large masses running through the entire thickness of the body, between the head and the margin of the pectoral fin. A network of strands of fibrous tissue forms the support for a number of vertical prisms, each divided by transverse partitions into a large number of compartments or cells. Numerous nerve-fibres pass to the various parts of the organ. These are derived mainly from four nerves, which originate from an *electric lobe* of the medulla oblongata, with a branch from the trigeminal. By means of the electric shocks which they are able to administer at will to animals in their immediate neighbourhood, the Torpedoes are able to ward off the attacks of enemies and to kill or paralyse their prey. In the other Rays in which the electric organs are developed they are comparatively small organs situated at the sides of the root of the tail. In all cases the cells are formed from metamorphosed muscular fibres.

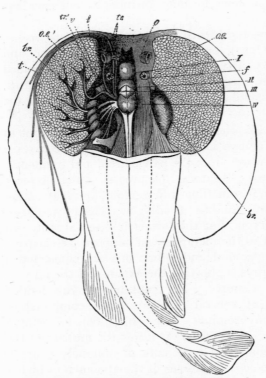

FIG. 169.—A **Torpedo** with the electric organs dissected out. On the right the surface only of the electric organ (*O.E.*) is shown, on the left the nerves passing to the organ are shown. The roof of the skull is removed to bring the brain into view. *br.* gills; *f.* spiracle; *o.* eyes; *tr.* trigeminal; *tr'.* its electric branch; *v.* vagus; *I*, fore-brain; *II*, midbrain; *III*, cerebellum; *IV*, electric lobe. (From Gegenbaur.)

Luminous organs by the agency of which a phosphorescent light is produced occur on the surface of a few oceanic elasmobranchs.

Digestive System.—*Teeth* are developed on the palatoquadrate and on Meckel's cartilage. They are arranged in several parallel rows, and are developed from a groove within the margin of the jaw, successive rows coming to the front, and, as they are worn out, falling off and being replaced by others. In the Sharks the teeth are usually large, and may be long, narrow, and pointed, or triangular with serrated edges, or made up of several sharp cusps; in the Rays, however, the teeth are more or less obtuse, sometimes, as in the Eagle-Rays, forming a continuous pavement of smooth plates covered with enamel, adapted to crushing food consisting of such objects as shell-fish and the like. The Sharks have a prominent tongue supported by the median basihyal; this is entirely or almost entirely absent in the Rays. The various divisions of the alimentary canal are similar in all the members of the class to what has already been described in the case of the Dogfish. A spiral valve is always present in the large intestine, though its arrangement varies considerably in the different families. In some cases (*e.g. Carcharinus*) the fold is not a spiral one, but, attached by one edge in a nearly longitudinal line to the intestinal wall, is rolled up in the shape of a scroll. A pair of pyloric cæca occur in *Somniosus*. Appended dorsally to the rectum is a median glandular cæcum, the *rectal gland*. The rectum always terminates in a *cloaca*, into which the urinary and genital ducts also lead. There is always a voluminous liver and a well-developed pancreas.

A *thyroid* lies in the middle line behind the lower jaw. A representative of the *thymus* lies on either side, a little below the upper angles of the branchial clefts.

The **respiratory organs** of the Chondrichthyes always have the general structure and arrangement already described in the case of the Dogfish. In the Rays the water for respiration is taken in mainly through the spiracles; in the Sharks through the mouth.

In addition to the gills supported on the hyoid and branchial arches there is also in the Notidanidæ a gill on the anterior side of the spiracular cleft—the *spiracular gill*—represented in many others by a *rete mirabile* or network of blood-vessels (*pseudobranch*). In *Cetorhinus* (the Basking Shark) there is a series of slender rods, the *gill-rakers*, which impede the passage outwards through the branchial clefts of the small animals on which those Sharks feed.

Blood-system.—The *heart* has, in all essential respects, the same structure throughout the group. The conus arteriosus is always contractile, and contains several rows of valves. The general course of the circulation is the same in all (see p. 186), with some variation in the precise arrangement of the vessels. In some of the Rays the ventral aorta and the roots of the afferent vessels are partly enclosed in the cartilage of the basi-branchial plate.

The **brain** attains a much higher stage of development than in the Cyclostomata. The fore-brain greatly exceeds the other divisions in size. In *Scymnorhinus* there are two widely-separated parencephalic lobes or *cerebral hemispheres* containing large lateral ventricles. In other genera there is at most, as in the Dogfish, a median depression of greater or less depth, indicating a division into two lateral portions. In *Scyliorhinus*, as already pointed out, there is a median prosocœle which gives rise anteriorly to two lateral ventricles, or paracœles, and the same holds good of *Squatina* and *Squalus*. In most Rays there is only a very small prosocœle without anterior prolongations; in *Myliobatis* this is absent. The olfactory bulbs are of great size, in some cases with short and thick, in others longer and narrower, stalks. In *Scyliorhinus*, *Squatina*, and *Squalus*, as well as in *Scymnorhinus*, they contain ventricles (*rhinocœles*) continuous with the paracœles; in the Rays they are solid.

The *diencephalon* is of moderate extent. On its lower aspect are a pair of rounded *lobi inferiores*, which are of the nature of dilatations of the *infundibulum*, and a *saccus vasculosus*, which is a diverticulum of the infundibulum; directly below the saccus vasculosus lies the *hypophysis*. The *epiphysis* is long and narrow.

In the hind-brain the *cerebellum* is relatively greatly elongated and overlaps the optic lobes and sometimes also the diencephalon in front, while behind it extends over the anterior part of the *medulla oblongata*. It usually contains a cerebellar ventricle or *epicœle*. The medulla is elongated in the Sharks, shorter and more triangular in the Rays. The Electric Rays are characterised by the presence of the *electric lobes*, rounded elevations of the floor of the fourth ventricle.

Organs of Sense.—Integumentary sense-organs (*neuromasts*, p. 109) are highly developed in the *Chondrichthyes*. They are supplied, as already mentioned, by branches of the nerves of what is known as the *lateral system*, comprising, in addition to the lateralis, nerves in relation with the facial and sometimes the glossopharyngeal. These integumentary sense-organs occur in the interior of a continuous system of closed tubes, the *sensory tubes*, more rarely of open grooves. The chief canals of this system are a *lateral-line canal*, running along the middle of each side of the body, which is continuous with certain canals in the head : these communicate with the exterior at intervals by small pores. In addition to the canals of the lateral-line system there are a number of isolated canals, the *ampullary canals*, with neuromasts contained in terminal enlargements or *ampullæ*; these, which are peculiar to the *Chondrichthyes*, are most numerous about the snout region. Of similar essential character are the *vesicles of Savi* which occur in the Electric Rays.

The *olfactory organs* are a pair of cavities opening on the lower surface of the head, a little distance in front of the mouth, and enclosed by the cartilaginous olfactory capsules of the skull. Their inner surface is raised up into a number of ridges on which the fibres of the olfactory nerves are distributed. The *eye* has a cartilaginous sclerotic, and is in most cases attached to the inner wall of the orbit by means of a cartilaginous stalk. There appears to be no mechanism providing for accommodation. A fold of the conjunctiva resembling the *nictitating membrane*, or third eyelid of higher Vertebrates, occurs in some Sharks. The *ear* consists of the membranous vestibule, which is partly divided into two (utriculus and sacculus), from which arise the three semicircular canals with their ampullæ, and also the *aqueductûs vestibuli* or *endolymphatic duct*—which opens to the exterior on the dorsal surface of the head. In the Rays the semicircular canals form almost complete circles and open separately into the vestibule by narrow ducts.

Urinogenital Organs.—The *kidneys*, as already noticed in the account given of the Dogfish, differ somewhat in their relations in the two sexes. In the male the anterior portion persists in the epididymis, and its duct becomes the spermiduct, while the posterior portion, which is the functional kidney, has a duct or ducts of its own. In the female there is no direct connection between the reproductive and renal organs; the anterior portion of the kidney may be functional, and its duct persists, opening along with those of the posterior portion. In the male the urinary ducts open into a median chamber—the *urinogenital sinus*—which extends into the cloaca, and receives also the spermiducts: it communicates with the general cavity of the cloaca by a median opening situated on a papilla—the *urinogenital* papilla. In the female there is a median *urinary sinus*, into which the urinary ducts open, or the latter may open separately into the cloaca.

Save in certain exceptional cases (*e.g. Scyliorhinus*), there are two ovaries, varying considerably in form, but always characterised towards the breeding season by the great size of the follicles enclosing the mature ova. The oviducts (Müllerian ducts) are quite separate from the ovaries. The right and left oviducts come into close relationship anteriorly, being united in the middle on the ventral surface of the œsophagus, where each opens by a wide orifice into the abdominal cavity, or both open by a single median aperture. The following part of the oviduct is very narrow; at one point it exhibits a thickening, due to the presence in its walls of the follicles of the *shell-gland*. Behind this is a dilated portion which acts as a *uterus*, and this communicates with the cloaca through a wide *vagina*. A considerable number of the Chondrichthyes are viviparous, and in these the inner surface of the uterus is beset with numerous vascular villi, while the shell-gland is small or vestigial.

The testes are oval or elongate: the convoluted epididymis is connected with the anterior end by efferent ducts, and from it arises the vas deferens. The latter is dilated near its opening into the urinogenital sinus to form an ovoid sac—the *vesicula seminalis*. A *sperm-sac* is sometimes present, opening close to the aperture of the vas deferens. The Müllerian ducts are vestigial in the male.

Impregnation is internal in all the Chondrichthyes with the possible exception of *Somniosus* (the Greenland Shark), the claspers acting as intromittent organs by whose agency the semen is transmitted into the interior of the oviducts.

In all the Chondrichthyes the ova are very large, consisting of a large mass of yolk-spherules held together by means of a network of protoplasmic threads, with, on one side, a disc of protoplasm—the *germinal disc*. The process of maturation is similar to that observable in holoblastic ova ; one polar body is thrown off in the ovary, the other apparently at impregnation. The ripe ovum ruptures the wall of the enclosing follicle and so passes into the abdominal cavity to enter one of the oviducts through the wide abdominal opening. Impregnation takes place in the oviduct, and the impregnated ovum in the oviparous forms becomes surrounded by a layer of semi-fluid albumen and enclosed in a shell of keratin secreted by the shell-gland. The shell varies in shape somewhat in the different groups : most commonly, as in many Dogfishes (Fig. 163), it is four-cornered, with twisted filamentous

appendages at the angles, by means of which it becomes attached to sea-weeds and the like. In the Skates the filaments are absent. In the Port Jackson Sharks (*Heterodontus*, Fig. 170) it is an ovoid body, the wall of which presents a broad, spiral flange. The young Shark or Ray goes through its development enclosed in the shell, until it is fully formed, when it escapes by rupturing the latter. In the viviparous forms the ovum undergoes its development in the uterus, in which in most cases it lies free —except in some Mustelidæ and Carcharinidæ, in which there is a close connection between the yolk-sac of the embryo and the wall of the uterus, folds of the former interdigitating with folds of the latter, and nourishment being thus conveyed from the vascular system of the mother to that of the fœtus by diffusion. In some of the viviparous forms a distinct though very delicate shell, sometimes having rudiments of the filaments, is formed, and is thrown off

FIG. 170.—Egg-case of **Heterodontus galeatus.** (After Waite.)

in the uterus. In the genera *Rhinobatus* and *Trygonorhina*, which are both viviparous, each shell encloses not one egg, but three or four. *Somniosus* is said to differ from all the rest of the Chondrichthyes in having the ova fertilised after they have been deposited, as well as in the small size of the ova.

Development.—Cleavage is meroblastic,[1] being confined to the germinal disc, which, before dividing, exhibits amœboid movements. While cleavage is going on in the germinal disc there appears a number of nuclei, the heads of accessory sperms, in the substance of the yolk. When cleavage is complete, the blastoderm appears as a lens-shaped disc, thicker at one end— the embryonic end. A segmentation-cavity appears early beneath the blastoderm.

[1] Except in one species of Cestracion.

An in-folding (Fig. 171) now begins at the posterior edge of the thickened embryonic blastoderm, which here becomes continuous with the cells of the lower layer. The cavity (*al*), at first very small, formed below this in-folding is the rudiment of the *archenteron*, and the cells lining this cavity above, which

FIG. 171.—Longitudinal section through the blastoderm of a **Pristiurus** embryo before the medullary groove has become formed, showing the beginning of the process of in-folding or invagination. *al*. archenteron; *ep*. ectoderm; *er*. embryonic rim; *m*. mesoderm. (After Balfour.)

form a definite layer, partly derived from the in-folded blastoderm, partly from the cells of the lower layer, are the beginning of the definite *endoderm*. The edge of the in-folding, entitled the *embryonic rim*, is obviously the equivalent of the dorsal lip of the blastopore in Amphioxus. The endoderm and its underlying cavity soon grow forwards towards the segmentation-cavity. Under the latter appears a floor of lower-layer cells, but the cavity soon becomes obliterated as the archenteron develops.

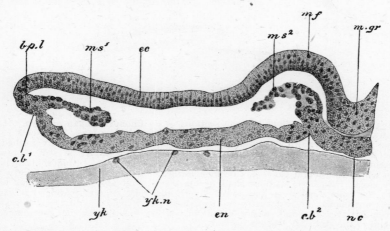

FIG. 172.—**Pristiurus,** transverse section of blastoderm, showing the formation of the mesoderm. *bp. l.* dorsal lip of blastopore; *c. b.*[1] external cœlomic bay; *c. b.*[2] internal cœlomic bay; *ec*. ectoderm; *en*. endoderm; *m. f.* medullary fold; *m. gr.* medullary groove; *ms.*[1] external rudiment of mesoderm; *ms.*[2] internal rudiment of mesoderm; *nc*. notochord; *yk*. yolk; *yk. n.* yolk nuclei. (From O. Hertwig, after Rabl.)

After the formation of the embryonic rim a shield-like *embryonic area* is distinguishable in front of it, with two folds bounding a groove—the *medullary groove*. The mesoderm becomes established at about the same time. It is formed from two separate and distinct sources (Fig. 172). Along the edge of the embryonic rim appears a horizontal groove-like depression: this—the *external cœlomic bay* (*c. b.*[1])—marks the line of origin of the *peripheral* part of the mesoderm ($m. s.^1$), which grows inwards from it as a plate of cells between the ectoderm and the endoderm. The *central* part of the embryonal mesoderm ($m. s.^2$) is developed from the endoderm at a point immediately external to the rudiment of the notochord : here also a slight groove—the *internal cœlomic bay* ($c. b.^2$)—is distinguishable, and from this a plate of mesoderm cells grows outwards. Eventually the peripheral and central plates of mesoderm come into contact and coalesce to form a continuous sheet on

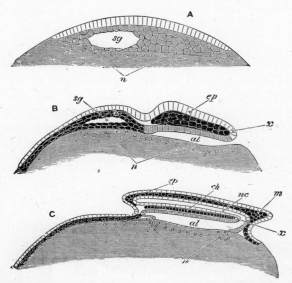

FIG. 173.—Diagrammatic longitudinal sections of an **Chondrichthyan embryo.** *A*, section of the young blastoderm with segmentation-cavity enclosed in the lower layer cells ; *B*, older blastoderm with embryo in which endoderm and mesoderm are distinctly formed, and in which the alimentary slit has appeared. The segmentation-cavity is still represented as being present, though by this stage it has in reality disappeared. *C*, older blastoderm with embryo in which the neural canal has become formed and is continuous posteriorly with the alimentary canal. *Ectoderm* without shading ; *mesoderm* and also *notochord* black with clear outlines to the cells ; *endoderm* and lower layer cells with simple shading. *al.* alimentary cavity ; *ch.* notochord ; *ep.* ectoderm ; *m.* mesoderm ; *n.* nuclei of yolk ; *nc.* neurocœle ; *sg.* segmentation-cavity ; *x.* point where ectoderm and endoderm become continuous at the posterior end of the embryo. (From Balfour.)

each side of the middle line. Though the mesodermal rudiments, peripheral and central, contain no cavities, the grooves (*cœlomic bays*) from which their development takes its origin may represent the cavities of the cœlomic sacs of Amphioxus.

As the blastoderm extends over the yolk, its posterior edge assumes the form of two prominent *caudal swellings* (Fig. 174, *cd.*). The medullary groove meanwhile deepens, and its edges grow over so as to form a canal (Fig. 173, *C* ; Fig. 175). The union takes place first in the middle, the anterior and posterior parts (Fig. 175, *neur.*) remaining open for a while. When the posterior part closes, it does so in such a way that it encloses the blastopore, and there is thus formed a temporary passage of communication between the medullary canal and the archenteron—the *neurenteric passage.*

The ectoderm gives rise, as in Vertebrates in general, not only to the epidermis and the central nervous system, but also to the peripheral nervous system, the lining membrane of the olfactory sacs, the lens of the eye, and the lining membrane of the auditory labyrinth of the mouth, and of the outer portions of the cloaca and gill-clefts.

The notochord (Fig. 173 *C, ch.*) is developed as a cord of cells derived from the dorsal lip of the blastopore.

Each lateral sheet of mesoderm, soon after its formation by the coalescence

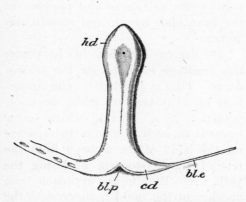

FIG. 174.—Embryo of **Scyliorhinus canicula** with the tail-swellings well marked and the medullary groove just beginning. *bl. e.* edge of blastoderm; *bl. p.* blastopore; *cd.* caudal swellings; *hd.* head. (After Sedgwick.)

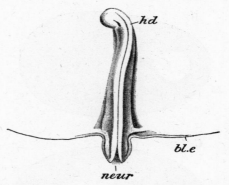

FIG. 175.—Embryo of a **Ray** with the medullary groove closed except at the hind end. The notched embryonic part of the blastoderm has grown faster than the rest and come to project over the surface of the yolk. *bl. e.* edge of blastoderm; *hd.* head; *neur.* unenclosed part of the neurocœle. (After Sedgwick.)

of the peripheral and central rudiments, becomes divided by the development of a horizontally directed cleft-like space in its interior. The inner part of each sheet then separates from the outer by the formation of a longitudinal fissure. The former, which is known as the *vertebral plate*, becomes divided by transverse fissures into a number of squarish masses, the *mesodermal somites.* The outer part forms a broad plate, the *lateral plate.* The lateral plate consists of two layers, a dorsal or *somatic,* and a ventral or *splanchnic,* and the cavity between them is the beginning of the cœlome. The somites send off cells round the notochord to form the bodies of the vertebræ, the remainder of the somites giving rise to the muscles of the voluntary system. An isthmus of mesoderm cells (*nephrotome*), which still connects each protovertebra with the lateral plate and contains a prolongation of the cavity, gives rise to the pronephric duct and tubules. The lateral plates eventually unite ventrally,

and their cavities coalesce to form the body-cavity. The parts derived from the mesoderm are the system of voluntary muscles, the dermis, the inter-muscular connective-tissue, the endo-skeleton, the muscular and connective-tissue layers of the alimentary canal, the vascular system, and the generative organs. The segmentation of the mesoderm extends into the head where the somites give rise to the extrinsic eye muscles. On the formation of the gill-clefts, a series of visceral muscle plates appear, the cells of which give rise to the cartilages and muscles of the branchial, hyoid, and mandibular arches.

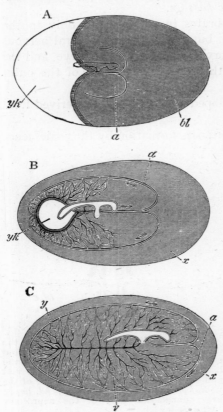

FIG. 176.—Three views of the developing egg of a **Chondrichthyan**, showing the embryo, the blastoderm, and the vessels of the yolk-sac. The shaded part (*bl.*) is the blastoderm, the white part the uncovered yolk. *A*, young stage with the embryo still attached at the edge of the blastoderm; *B*, older stage with the yolk not quite enclosed by the blastoderm; *C*, stage after the complete closure of the yolk. *a.* arterial trunks of yolk-sac; *bl.* blastoderm; *v.* venous trunks of yolk-sac; *y.* point of closure of the yolk-blastopore; *x*, portion of the blastoderm outside the arterial sinus terminalis. (From Balfour.)

By degrees the body of the young fish becomes moulded on the blastoderm. This is effected by the formation of a system of folds, anterior, posterior, and lateral, which grow inwards in such a way as to separate off the body of the embryo from the rest of the blastoderm enclosing the yolk. As the folds approach one another in the middle, underneath the embryo, they come to form a constriction connecting the body of the embryo with the yolk enclosed in the extra-embryonic part of the blastoderm. The process may be imitated if we pinch off a portion of a ball of clay, leaving only a narrow neck connecting the pinched-off portion with the rest. The body of the embryo is thus gradually folded off from the *yolk-sac* and comes to be connected with it only by a narrow neck or yolk-stalk (Fig. 176). The head and tail of the young Fish soon undergo differentiation and a series of perforations at the sides of the neck (Fig. 177) form the branchial clefts and spiracle. A number of very delicate filaments (Figs. 177, 178) grow out from these apertures and become greatly elongated; these are the provisional gills, which atrophy as the development approaches completion, their bases alone persisting to give rise to the permanent gills. The great development of these gill-filaments in the embryos of some viviparous forms suggests that, in addition to their respiratory functions, they may also serve as organs for the absorption of nutrient fluids secreted by the villi of the uterine wall.[1] The fins, both paired and unpaired, appear as longitudinal ridges of the ectoderm enclosing mesoderm. In some Chondrichthyes the paired fins are at first represented on each side by a continuous ridge or fold, which only subsequently becomes divided into anterior and posterior portions—the rudiments respectively of the pectoral and pelvic fins. Into these folds penetrates a series of buds from the somites: these, the *muscle-buds*, give rise to the fin-muscles; at first, from their mode

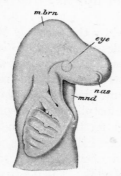

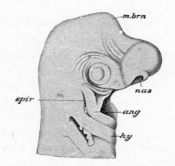

FIG. 177.—Side view of head of embryo of **Scyliorhinus canicula**, with the rudiments of the gills on the first and second branchial arches. *eye*, eye; *m. brn*. midbrain; *mnd*. mandible; *nas.* nasal sac. (After Sedgwick.)

FIG. 178.—Side view of the head of **Scyliorhinus canicula** at a somewhat later stage. The gill-filaments have increased in number and are present on the mandibular arch. *ang.* angle of the jaw; *hy.* hyoid; *m. brn*. mid-brain; *nas.* nasal sac; *spir.* spiracle. (After Sedgwick.)

of origin, they present a metameric arrangement, but this is in great measure lost during development.

Ethology and Distribution.—The habits of the active, fierce, and voracious Sharks, which live in the surface-waters of the sea, waging war on all and sundry, contrast strongly with those of the more sluggish Rays, which live habitually on the bottom, usually in shallow water, and feed chiefly on crustaceans and molluscs, with the addition of such small fishes as they can capture. As a group, the Chondrichthyes, more particularly the Sharks, are distinguished by their muscular strength, the activity of their movements, and also by the acuteness of their senses of sight and smell.

Nearly all are marine: some ascend rivers: a very few live habitually in fresh water.

[1] In a species of *Trygon* a number of the villi of the uterus project into the pharynx of the foetus through the spiracles, and nourishment is probably received by this means.

None of the Chondrichthyes is of very small size, and comprised among them are the largest of living Fishes : the harmless Basking Sharks (*Cetorhinus*) sometimes attain a length of 35 feet or more, the formidable Great Blue Shark (*Carcharodon*) sometimes reaches 30 feet, and some of the Rays also attain colossal dimensions. In this respect, however, recent Sharks and Rays are far behind some of the fossil forms, certain of which, if their general dimensions were in proportion to the size of their teeth, must have reached a length of as much as 80 feet.

Sub-Class Holocephali.

The Holocephali appear first in the lower Jurassic as a branch from the Bradyodont stock (p. 174), and replaced that group after its extinction during the Permian period.

Although definitely Chondrichthyes, as is shown by the presence of claspers in the male, by the large egg-cases, the placoid scales when present (in modern species the skin is naked [1]), and by the general similarity of anatomical structure to that of the Euselachii, the group has nevertheless a number of well-defined characters which entitle its representatives to be placed in a separate sub-class. In the first place, the holostylic jaw suspension is characteristic (see p. 74), as are the extra claspers on the head and in front of the normal pair on the abdomen. The numerous calcified rings round the unconstricted notochord and the presence of an operculum are characters which differentiate the Holocephali from the Euselachii. The dentition is also highly peculiar in the composition of the tooth-plates, as well as in their shape. There is no enamel, but, instead, a layer of vitro-dentine, and the pulp cavity is much reduced. The teeth are in the form of tritural plates formed, no doubt, by a fusion of originally separate denticles. Of these plates there are two pairs in the upper jaws, a small anterior and a larger posterior pair, and one large pair on the lower jaws. The arrangement of these plates producing the " parrot "-like beak has contributed largely to the peculiar modification of the whole skull. The microscopic structure of the teeth is much like that of the Bradyodonti.

The earliest known representatives of the Holocephali differ very little in essential characters from the living forms. *Squaloraja* (Fig. 179) and *Myriacanthus* are representative and fairly completely known examples.

The existing representatives of the Holocephali are included under the single family *Chimæridæ*, containing three genera—*Chimæra*, *Callorhynchus*, and *Harriotta*. Even taking in fossil forms, the group is a very small one ; it agrees in many fundamental characteristics with the Elasmobranchii, and is sometimes included in that sub-class. Of the recent genera, Chimæra, the so-called " King of the Herrings " (Fig. 180, *I*), is found on the coasts of

---

[1] A few placoid scales occur on the claspers.

Europe, Japan, and Australia, the west coast of North America, and at the Cape of Good Hope; Callorhynchus (Fig. 180, II) is tolerably abundant in the South Temperate seas; Harriotta (Fig. 180, III) is a deep-sea form.

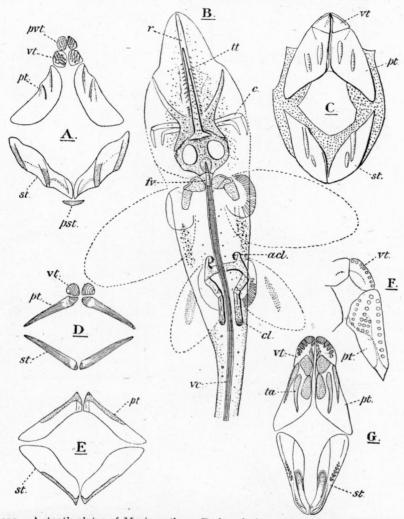

FIG. 179.—A, tooth-plates of *Myriacanthus*; B, dorsal view of *Squaloraja*; C, tooth-plates of *Callorhynchus*; D, tooth-plates of *Squaloraja*; E, tooth-plates of *Rhynchodus*; F, tooth-plates of *Hariotta*; G, tooth-plates of *Elasmodus*. A. *cl.* anterior clasper; *c.* paired cartilages; *cl.* clasper; *f.r.* fused post-occipital vertebræ; *pst.* predentary tooth; *pt.* palatine tooth; *p. vt.* prevomerine tooth; *r.* rostrum; *st.* tooth plate of lower jaw; *t. a.* tritoral area; *tt.* tentaculum; *v. c.* vertebral column; *v. t.* vomerine tooth. (From Goodrich.)

External Characters.—The general form of the body is Shark-like, but the large, compressed head and small mouth are strikingly different from the

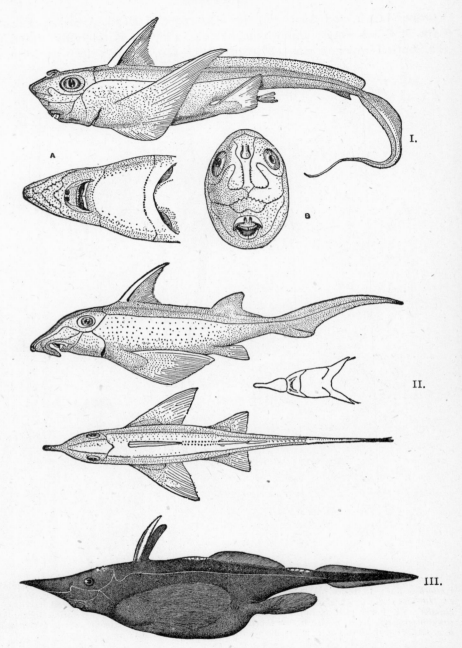

FIG. 180.—I. *Chimæra monstrosa*, male. A. ventral, B. Front view of head. II. *Callorhynchus autarcticus*. Dorsal, lateral and ventral views. III. *Harriotta raleighana*. (From Goodrich.)

depressed, shovel-headed head and wide mouth of most Selachians. The mouth is bounded by lip-like folds, two of which, placed laterally and supported by labial cartilages, resemble the folds in which the premaxillæ and maxillæ of many Bony Fishes are enclosed : a third fold, external to and concentric with the mandible, is also supported by labial cartilages and has the appearance of a second or external lower jaw. In *Chimæra* the snout is blunt, in *Harriotta* long and pointed ; in *Callorhynchus* it is produced into a rostrum, from the end of which depends a large cutaneous flap abundantly supplied with nerves and evidently serving as an important tactile organ.

A still more important difference from Sharks and Rays is the possession of only a single external branchial aperture, owing to the fact that a fold of skin, the *operculum*, extends backwards from the region of the hyoid arch and covers the true gill-slits, which thus come to open into a common chamber situated beneath the operculum and communicating with the exterior by a single secondary branchial aperture placed just anterior to the shoulder-girdle : there is no spiracle. Equally characteristic is the circumstance that the urinogenital aperture is distinct from and behind the anus, there being no cloaca.

There are two large dorsal fins and a small ventral ; the caudal fin is of the ordinary *heterocercal* type in the adult *Callorhynchus*, but in the young (Fig. 186) the extremity of the tail proper is not upturned, and the fin-rays are arranged symmetrically above and below it, producing the form of tail-fin called *diphycercal*. In *Chimæra* the tail may be produced into a long whip-like filament. The pectoral and pelvic fins are both large, especially the former.

In the male there is a horizontal slit situated a little in front of the pelvic fins ; it leads into a shallow glandular pouch, from which can be protruded a peculiar and indeed unique apparatus, the *anterior clasper*, consisting of a plate covered with recurved dermal teeth, to which is added, in *Callorhynchus*, a plate rolled upon itself to form an incomplete tube. The use of this apparatus is not known. A rudiment of the pouch occurs in the female, although the clasper itself is absent.   The male possesses, in addition, a pair of the ordinary *myxopterygia* or posterior claspers, and is further distinguished by the presence of a little knocker-like structure, the *frontal clasper*, on the dorsal surface of the head.   In *Harriotta* the paired claspers are poorly developed, and the frontal clasper is absent.

The lateral line is an open groove in *Chimæra*, a closed tube in *Callorhynchus*, and there are numerous sensory pits, arranged in curved lines, on the head.   The skin is smooth and silvery, and bears for the most part no exoskeletal structures.   There are, however, delicate, recurved dermal teeth on the anterior and frontal claspers, and the first dorsal fin is supported by an immense bony spine or *dermal defence*. In the young, moreover, there is a double row of small dermal teeth along the back.

Endoskeleton.—The *vertebral column* consists of a persistent notochord with cartilaginous arches. In *Chimæra*, but not in *Callorhynchus*, there are calcified rings (Fig. 181, *c. r.*) embedded in the sheath of the notochord. The anterior neural arches are fused to form a high, compressed, vertical plate, to which the first dorsal fin is articulated. The *cranium* (Figs. 182 and 183) has a very characteristic form, largely owing to the compression of the region between

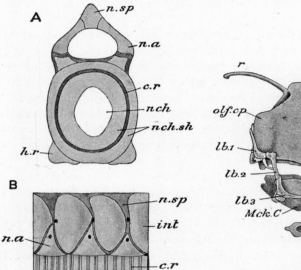

FIG. 181.—**Chimæra monstrosa.** *A*, transverse section of the vertebral column; *B*, lateral view of the same. *c. r.* calcified ring; *h. r.* hæmal ridge; *int.* intercalary piece; *n. a.* neural arch; *nch.* position of notochordal tissue; *nch. sh.* sheath of notochord; *n. sp.* neural spine. (After Hasse.)

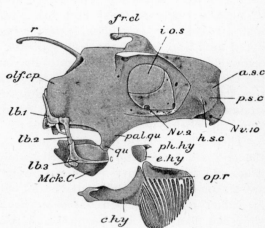

FIG. 182.—**Chimæra monstrosa,** lateral view of skull. *a. s. c.* position of anterior semicircular canal; *c.hy.* ceratohyal; *e.hy.* epihyal; *fr.cl.* frontal clasper; *h. s. c.* position of horizontal semicircular canal; *i. o. s.* interorbital septum; *lb. 1, lb. 2, lb. 3,* labial cartilages; *Mck. C.* mandible; *Nv. 2,* optic foramen; *Nv. 10,* vagus foramen; *olf. cp.* olfactory capsule; *op. r.* opercular rays; *pal.qu.* palatoquadrate; *ph.hy.* pharyngohyal; *p. s. c.* position of posterior semicircular canal; *qu.* quadrate region; *r.* rostrum. (After Hubrecht.)

and in front of the large orbits, which are separated from the cranial cavity only by membrane in *Callorhynchus* (Fig. 183, *or.*); in *Chimæra* they lie above the level of the cranial cavity and are separated from one another by a median vertical partition of fibrous tissue (Fig. 182, *i. o. s*). At first sight the palatoquadrate, or primary upper jaw, appears to be absent, but a little consideration shows it to be represented by a triangular plate (*pal. qu.*) which extends downwards and outwards from each side of the cranium and presents at its apex a facet for the articulation of the mandible. The palatoquadrate is therefore fused with the cranium and furnishes the sole support for the lower jaw; in a word the skull is *holostylic*. The pituitary fossa (Fig. 183, *s. t.*) is very deep and inclined backwards; on the ventral surface of the basis cranii is a pit (*pt.*) for the extra-cranial portion of the pituitary body. The posterior portion of the cranial cavity is very high; the anterior part—containing most of the fore-brain—is low and tunnel-like, and has above it a cavity of almost equal size (*Nv. 5 o'.*) for the ophthalmic branches of the fifth nerves. The greater part of the membranous labyrinth is lodged in a series of pits on the side-walls of the cranium (*a. s. c., p. s. c.*), and is separated from the brain by membrane only. The occipital region articulates with the vertebral column by a single saddle-shaped surface or *condyle* (*oc. cn.*). There is a great development of labial cartilages, particularly noticeable being a large plate which, in *Callorhynchus*, lies just externally to the mandible, nearly equalling it in size and having the appearance of a secondary or external jaw. In *Callorhynchus* the snout is supported by three cartilaginous rods growing forward from the cranium, of which one (*r.*) is median and dorsal and represents the rostrum; these, as well as the great lower labial, are represented by comparatively small structures in *Chimæra* (Fig. 182, *lb.3*).

The hyoid resembles the branchial arches in form and is little superior to them in size. Above the epihyal (Fig. 182, *e. h.y*) is a small cartilage (*ph.hy.*), evidently serially homologous with the pharyngobranchials, and therefore to be considered as a *pharyngohyal*. It represents the hyomandibular of Selachians, but, having no function to perform in the support of the jaws, it is no larger than the corresponding segments in the succeeding arches. Long cartilaginous rays (*op. r.*) for the support of the operculum are attached to the ceratohyal.

The first dorsal fin is remarkable for having all its pterygiophores fused in a single plate, which articulates with the coalesced neural arches already referred to. The remaining fins are formed quite on the Selachian type, as is also the shoulder girdle. The right and left halves of the pelvic arch are separate from one another, being united in the middle ventral line by ligament only; each presents a narrow iliac region and a broad flat pubo-ischial region perforated by two apertures or fenestræ closed by membrane, one of them of great size in *Callorhynchus*. The skeleton of the anterior clasper articulates with the pubic region.

Digestive Organs.—The *teeth* (Figs. 179, 183) are very characteristic, having the form of strong plates with an irregular surface and a sharp cutting edge. In the upper jaw there is a pair of small *vomerine teeth* (*vo. t.*) in front, immediately behind them a pair of large *palatine teeth* (*pal. t.*), and in the lower jaw a single pair of large *mandibular teeth* (*mnd. t.*). They are composed of vasodentine, and each palatine and mandibular tooth has its surface slightly raised into a rounded elevation of a specially hard substance, of whiter colour than the rest of the tooth, and known as a *tritor* (*tr.*). The *stomach* is almost obsolete, the enteric canal passing in a straight line from gullet to anus; there is a well-developed *spiral valve* in the intestine.

Respiratory Organs.—There are three pairs of *holobranchs* or complete gills borne on the first three branchial arches, and two *hemibranchs* or half-gills, one on the posterior face of the hyoid, the other on the anterior face of the fourth branchial arch. The fifth branchial arch is, as usual, gill-less, and there is no cleft between it and its predecessor.

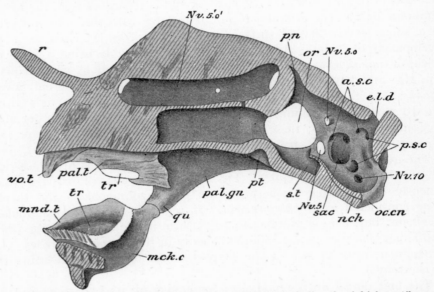

FIG. 183.—**Callorhynchus antarcticus,** sagittal section of skull; the labial cartilages are removed. *a.s.c.* apertures through which the anterior semicircular canal passes from the cranial cavity into the auditory capsule; *e.l.d.* aperture for endolymphatic duct; *mck. c.* Meckel's cartilage; *mnd. t.* mandibular tooth; *nch.* notochord; *Nv. 5*, trigeminal foramen; *Nv. 5. o.* foramen for exit of ophthalmic nerves; *Nv. 5.'o'*, canal for ophthalmic nerves with apertures of entrance and exit; *Nv. 10*, vagus foramen; *oc. cn.* occipital condyle; *or.* fenestra separating cranial cavity from orbit; *pal. gn.* palatoquadrate; *pal. t.* palatine tooth; *pn.* position of pineal body; *pt.* pit for extra-cranial portion of pituitary body; *p.s.c.* apertures through which the posterior semicircular canal passes into the auditory capsule; *qu.* quadrate region of palatoquadrate; *r.* rostrum; *sac.* depression for sacculus; *s. t.* sella turcica; *tr.* tritor; *vo. t.* vomerine teeth.

The small **heart** resembles that of the Dog-fish in all essential respects, being formed of sinus venosus, atrium, ventricle, and conus arteriosus, the last with three rows of valves.

The **brain** (Fig. 184), on the other hand, is very unlike that of *Scyliorhinus*, but presents a fairly close resemblance to that of *Scymnorhinus*. The medulla oblongata (*med. obl.*) is produced laterally into large frill-like *restiform bodies* (*cp. rst.*), which bound the hinder half of the cerebellum (*cblm.*). The diencephalon (*dien.*) is extremely long, trough-shaped, and very thin-walled, without pronounced optic thalami; it is continued without change of diameter into a distinct prosencephalon, which gives off the cerebral hemispheres (*crb. h.*) right and left.   The combined diacœle and prosocœle (*di. cœ.*) are widely open above in a brain from which the membranes have been removed (*A*), but in the entire organ (*B*) are roofed over by a conical, tent-like *choroid*

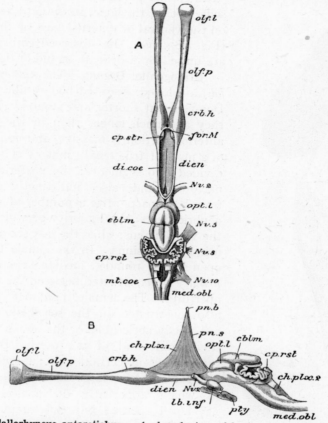

FIG. 184.—**Callorhyncus antarctichus.** *A*, dorsal view of brain after removal of the membranes; *B*, side view with the membranes in place. *cblm.* cerebellum; *ch. plx 1*, choroid plexus of fore-brain, and *ch. plx. 2*, of hind-brain; *cp. rst.* corpus restiforme; *cp. str.* corpus striatum; *crb. h.* cerebral hemisphere; *di. cœ.* diacœle; *dien.* diencephalon; *for. M.* foramen of Monro; *lb. inf.* lobus inferior; *med. obl.* medulla oblongata; *mt. cœ.* metacœle; *Nv. 2*, optic nerve; *Nv. 5*, trigeminal; *Nv. 8*, auditory; *Nv. 10*, vagus; *olf. l.* olfactory bulb; *olf. p.* olfactory peduncle; *opt. l.* optic lobe; *pb. b.* pineal body; *pn. s.* pineal stalk; *pty.* pituitary body.

plexus (*ch. plx. 1*).   The cavities of the small, spindle-shaped hemispheres (*crb. h.*), sometimes regarded as corresponding to olfactory lobes only, communicate with the third ventricle by wide foramina of Monro (*for. M.*), partly blocked up by hemispherical corpora striata (*cp. str.*).   Each hemisphere is continued in front into a slender thin-walled tube, the *olfactory peduncle* (*olf. p.*), bearing at its extremity a compressed olfactory bulb (*olf. l.*).

The optic nerves (*Nv. 2*) form a chiasma. The *pineal body* (*pn. b.*) is a small rounded vesicle borne in a hollow stalk (*pn. s.*) which runs just outside the posterior wall of the tent-like choroid plexus. The *pituitary body* (*pty.*) consists of intra- and extra-cranial portions, the former lodged in the sella turcica, the latter in the pit already noticed on the ventral or external face of the skull-floor (Fig. 183, *pt.*). In advanced embryos the two are united by a delicate strand of tissue.

Urinogenital Organs.—The *kidneys* (Fig. 185, *kd.*) are lobed, deep-red bodies, like those of the Dog-fish, but shorter and stouter. In the male they are much longer than in the female; the anterior portion is massive, and consists mainly of a mass of true renal tubules; it is indistinctly divided into segments: the posterior portion is narrower and also indistinctly segmented; from both parts arise a number of ducts (mesonephric ducts) the majority of which open into the vas deferens, while the last six open into the urinogenital sinus. In the female the ducts all open into a rounded median *urinary bladder* or *urinary sinus*, situated between the two oviducal apertures. The female reproductive organs are also constructed on the selachian pattern, and are chiefly noticeable for the immense size of the shell-glands and of the uteri. But the male organs present certain quite unique characters. The *testes* (*ts.*) are large ovoid bodies the tubules of which apparently do not contain fully-developed sperms, but only immature sperm-cells. These latter are probably passed through vasa efferentia into the vas deferens, which is coiled in a highly complicated manner to from a body of considerable size, commonly termed the epididymis, closely applied to the surface of the anterior part of the kidney. In this the sperms become aggregated into *spermatophores* in the form of small ovoidal capsules surrounded by a resistant membrane and full of a gelatinous substance in which bundles of sperms are imbedded. The lower end of the vas deferens (*v. df.*)

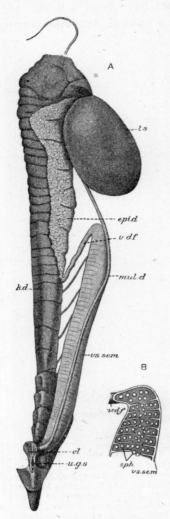

FIG. 185.—**Callorhynchus ant-arcticus.** *A*, male urinogenital organs of left side-ventral aspect; *B*, anterior part of vesicula seminalis in section. *cl.* cloaca; *epid.* epididymis; *kd.* kidney; *mul. d.* Müllerian duct; *sph.* spermatophores; *ts.* testis; *u.g.s.* opening of urinogenital sinus; *v. df.* vas deferens; *vs. sem.* vesicula seminalis. (*A* after Redeke.)

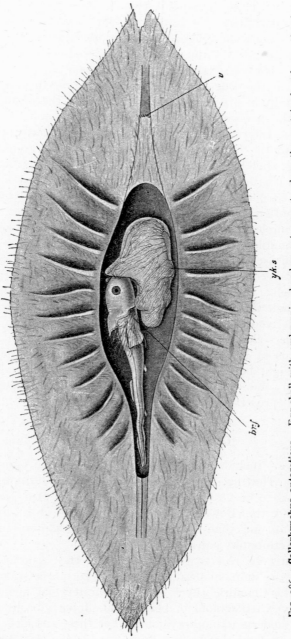

Fig. 186.—**Callorhynchus antarcticus.** Egg-shell with embryonic chamber cut open to show the contained embryo. *br. f.* branchial filaments; *v.* valve through which young fish escapes; *yk. s,* yolk-sac.

is dilated to form a large cylindrical *vesicula seminalis* (*v. sem.*) imperfectly divided into compartments by transverse partitions (*B*) and filled with a greenish jelly. The spermatophores (*sph.*) are passed into these compartments and finally make their way through the central passage into the urinogenital sinus (*u. g. s.*). The vestigial Müllerian ducts (*mul. d.*) are much more fully developed than in the Dog-fish : they are complete, though narrow, tubes opening in front by a large common aperture into the cœlome, and behind connected with the urinogenital sinus.

Development.—Internal fertilisation takes place, and the egg becomes surrounded, as in the Dog-fish, by a horny egg-shell secreted by the shell-glands. The egg-shell of *Callorhynchus* (Fig. 186) is of extraordinary size— about 25 cm. in length, or fully five-sixths as long as the abdominal cavity— and the elongated chamber for the embryo is surrounded by a broad, flat expansion covered on one side with yellow hair-like processes, and giving the shell a close resemblance, doubtless protective, to a piece of kelp. The early development resembles that of the Selachians ; but the yolk becomes divided into nucleated masses which divide into smaller segments, and the smallest break away and become dissolved in a milky nutrient liquid which fills the spaces of the shell : the advanced embryo has elongated gill-filaments (*br. f.*) projecting through the branchial aperture (and probably serving to absorb the nutriment derived from the yolk), a diphycercal tail, and a curiously lobed and nearly sessile yolk-sac (*yk. s.*).

Fossil remains of Holocephali are known from the Lower Jurassic rocks upwards. As might be expected, they consist mostly of teeth and of dorsal fin-spines, but in some cases, and notably in *Squaloraja*, practically the whole of the skeleton is preserved.

CLASS ACTINOPTERYGII.

In this class are included all the commonest and most familiar fishes, such as the Cod, Sole, Herring, Eel, Salmon, etc., and, in addition, some of those fishes which used to be termed " Ganoids "—viz. the Sturgeons, the Garpike (*Lepidosteus*) and the Bowfin (*Amia*). *Polypterus* and *Calamoichthys* (or *Erpetoichthys*), at one time placed with the Crossopterygii, are now also thought to be Actinopterygians.

The Actinopterygii receive their name from the structure of the paired fins as seen in the more modern representatives of the group. Unlike the paired fins of the Chondrichthyes or the archipterygial fins of certain other fishes which have cartilaginous or bony basal supports projecting outside the body-wall, the modern actinopterygian fin has these supports reduced almost to vanishing point, and the fin web lying outside the body-wall is supported by the fin rays alone. To this statement the Polypterini and Chondrostei (sturgeons) and some of the early Palaeoniscoids, being in a somewhat more primitive condition as regards their fin structure, must be regarded as exceptions.

The structure of the scales, being ganoid as opposed to cosmoid (see p. 65), is an important diagnostic feature. The scales of most of the group, however, especially in the more recent forms, have gradually become modified by the loss of many elements, and may be reduced to thin horny structures, or, on occasions, may even be absent, and it is only from a knowledge of the ancestry that their essentially ganoid structure can be presumed. The endo-skeleton, at first cartilaginous, gradually becomes more and more ossified and more perfect mechanically. The tail, at first heterocercal, becomes semi-heterocercal, and finally homocercal or, more rarely, diphycercal. The investing bones of the skull and jaws can be compared with those of the Choanichthyes, but show a certain amount of reduction in number and modification in shape. Of the anatomy of the soft parts, the earlier forms, to judge by what we can see in the persisting forms of the more primitive groups, such as the Sturgeons, Polypterini, *Amia* and *Lepidosteus*, there were present spiracles, abdominal pores, and a spiral valve in the intestine, structures which the modern forms have lost. The gill structure has changed from a condition near the laminar type to the fully filamentar (Fig. 68). In exchange for a valvular conus in the heart a large elastic *bulbus arteriosus* has been evolved, the conus becoming reduced to one or, at most, two rows of valves. There is a gradual alteration of the genital ducts towards the specialised type of the teleosts. The brain structure is characteristic in the large corpora striata, cerebellum and medulla, presence of the valvula cerebelli, and in the absence of cerebral lobes.

The class appears first in the Middle Devonian (*Cheirolepis*), and expanded into many lines, of which the majority became extinct, until finally the Teleosts alone remain, with the exception of the Sturgeons and a few others, to form the most numerous, most varied and most modern of all living fishes.

Owing to a lack of continuity over large tracts of the geological record, the classification of the Actinopterygii, especially in its details, presents much difficulty. The earliest known forms are placed in a group, probably a complex one, termed the Palæoniscoidei, of which the first examples are found in the Middle Devonian and which, after an expansion during the Carboniferous and Permian periods, subsequently contracted and became finally extinct in the early part of the Cretaceous. During the Trias, however, a number of lines evolved from the Palæoniscoid stock, most of which also became extinct, although three branches persisted, one to lead to the modern Sturgeons, one to the Polypterini and the other expanded into a large number of parallel lines, collectively known as the Holostei. From this evolution during the Jurassic period arose the Teleostei, while two other, rather more primitive, lines still persist to the present day in *Amia* and *Lepidosteus*. The Polypterini, represented by *Polypterus* and *Calamoichthys* from the fresh waters of Central Africa, are considered to be survivors of the old Palæoniscoid stock (see below, p. 232).

Owing to their more primitive fin structure, the Chondrostei and Polypterini are grouped with the Palæoniscoids as the Palæopterygii, to distinguish them from later actinopterygians, whose fins are without basal supports outside the body-wall which are termed the Neopterygii.

A condensed classification may therefore be written as follows :

CLASS ACTINOPTERYGII.

Sub-class Palæopterygii

      Orders : PALÆONISCOIDEI
                  CHONDROSTEI
                  POLYPTERINI (CLADISTIA)

Sub-class Neopterygii

      Orders : GINGLYMODI (*Lepidosteus*) ⎱
                  PROTOSPONDYLI (*Amia*) ⎰ HOLOSTEI
                  and many extinct lines ⎰
                  ISOSPONDYLI (" Soft-rayed fishes) ⎱
                  ACANTHOPTERYGII (" Spine-rayed fishes ") ⎰ TELEOSTEI

Sub-class Palæopterygii.

ORDER PALÆONISCOIDEI.

The Palæoniscoidei may be supposed to have arisen from some ancestor common to themselves and the Choanichthyes. Palæoniscoids, however, have some points of difference from the Osteolepids, Cœlacanths and Dipnoi on the one hand, and others, perhaps less deep-seated, by which they can be distinguished from the later actinopterygians which have arisen from them.

The main differences between these early actinopterygians and the crossopterygians can be seen by comparing two such forms as *Palæoniscus* and *Osteolepis*, when it will be seen that the former has large eyes with no more than four sclerotic plates, as against the large eyes and many sclerotic plates of the latter. In *Palæoniscus* (Fig. 187) the maxilla has a wide post-orbital extension which runs far backwards, and which is firmly supported by a large preopercular, which functionally replaces the squamosal of *Osteolepis*, and the cheek extends dorsally as far as the upper surface of the skull, and helps to obliterate the spiracular cleft. In *Osteolepis* (Figs. 260, 261) the squamosal is a large bone, and the preopercular is very small, and the maxilla itself is smaller. The osteolepid skull is further characterised by the internal nostril, by the transverse meso-cranial joint and by peculiarities in the dentition (p. 285), all of which are entirely unrepresented in the actinopterygian skull. In the fins of palæoniscoids, while some of them have a series of divergent radials which form a short, rounded lobe, there is no defined central axis, and they are in no way archipterygial. The structure of the scales is ganoid and not cosmoid (p. 65), and their arrangement on the

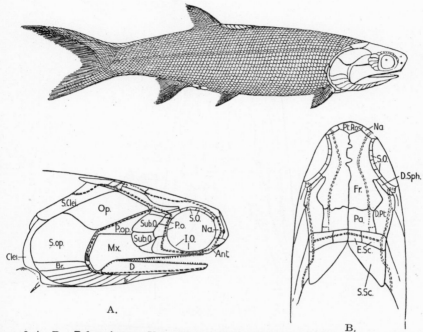

FIG. 187A, B.—**Palæoniscus.** Upper figure **Palæoniscus macropomus** from Nicholson and Lydekker. A, lateral, and B, dorsal, aspect of head. *Ant.* antorbital; *Br.* branchiostegals; *Clei.* cleithrum; *D.* dentary; *D. Pt.* dermo-pterotic; *D. Sph.* dermo-sphenotic; *E. Sc.* extra-scapulas; *Fr.* frontal; *I. O.* infra-orbitals; *Mx.* maxilla; *Na.* nostril; *Op.* opercular; *PA.* parietal; *P. op.* pre-opercular; *P. o.* post-orbital; *Pt. Ros.* rostral; *S. O.* supra-orbitals; *Sub. O.* sub-orbitals; *S. Clei.* supra-cleithrum; *S. op.* sub-opercular; *S. Sc.* supra-scapular. (After Westoll.)

tail is characteristic, in that there is an apparent break of pattern in the lines of scales on the upper lobe of the tail which appear to run in a different direction from those on the body. There is only one dorsal fin, as against two in the osteolepid.

The Palæoniscids are essentially palæozoic fishes which became replaced during the mesozoic period by offshoots which specialised in various directions from the older-fashioned stock that was then dying out. Of these offshoots only a bare remnant has persisted in the four lines represented by the Sturgeons, *Polypterus*, *Lepidosteus* and *Amia*. There were, however, many

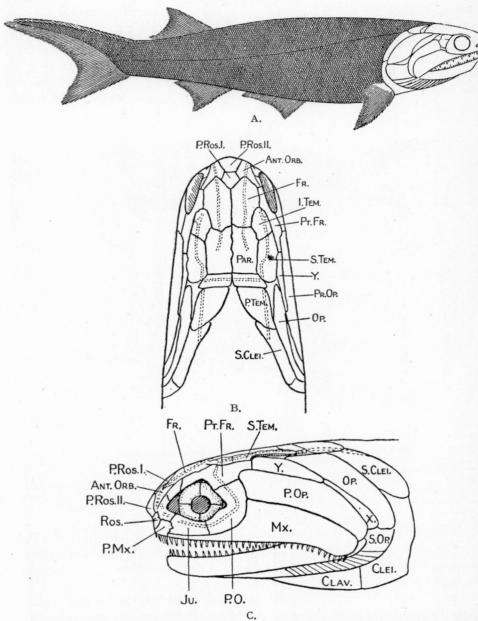

FIG. 188.—**Cheirolepis trailli.** A, restoration by Traquair, from Smith Woodward ; B, dorsal,
and C, ventral views of head.   *Ant. Orb.* antorbital ; *Clav.* clavicle ; *Clei.* cleithrum ; *Fr.* frontal ;
Ju. jugal ;   *Mx.* maxilla ;   *Op.* opercular ; *P. Op.* pre-opercular ; *Pt. Fr.* post-frontal ; *P. Ros. I.
II.* pre-rostrals ;   *P. Mx.* pre-maxilla ;   *Par.* parietal ;   *P. Tem.* post-temporal ; *I. Tem.* inter-
temporal ; *S. Op.* sub-opercular ; *S. Clei.* supra-cleithrum ; *X. Y.* bones of uncertain homology.
(After Watson.)

other families evolved during the late Palæozoic and Mesozoic periods, all pursuing their own evolutionary lines, only to become extinct.   All these may be placed in a rather loosely defined group, the Holostei, which cannot be clearly defined from the earlier palæoniscoids on the one hand, nor their later representatives from the Teleosts on the other.   It is largely a matter of various trends of evolution, but the Holostei show all of them a general trend which is quite separable from that of the Sturgeons (Chondrostei), in that there is no considerable loss of bone nor reduction of jaws.   The fin structure and gradual loss of many primitive characters also differentiate them from *Polypterus*.   The general trend of evolution away from their earlier palæoniscoid ancestors is shown by the forward movement of the point of suspension of the lower jaw and the greater freedom of movement of the maxilla so as to allow a wider gape.   The fins become more definitely

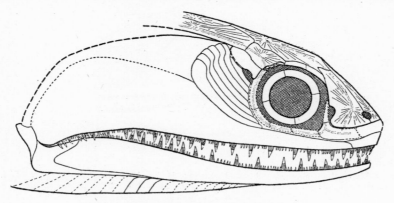

FIG. 189.—**Birgeria grœnlandica.**   (After Stensiö.)

actinopterygian, and the tail more and more homocercal.   The whole skeleton becomes more mechanically efficient.

The superfamily Palæoniscoidei therefore, for the present, must be regarded as a collection of families of separate lines of evolution whose actual relations one to another is still uncertain.   A review of known forms of the Devonian period shows that several lines had already become differentiated, and so diverse that it is not possible to select one as absolutely typical of the whole group.   *Cheirolepis* (Fig. 188), although the earliest known species, was already specialised in several respects.   The small scales are atypical in shape, the eyes are unusually small, the skull has a very large posterior extension and its dorsal surface is flat instead of rounded.

The families that may be placed in this order are the Palæoniscidæ (*e.g.*, *Palæoniscus* (Fig. 187), *Cheirolepis* (Fig. 188), *Birgeria* (Fig. 189).   Platysomidæ, deep-bodied fishes (*e.g.*, *Cheirodus*, *Platysomus*).   Saurichthyiidæ, long-bodied fishes (*e.g.*, *Saurichthys*, *Belonorhynchus*). Catopteridæ (*e.g.*, *Catopterus*). Perleididæ (*e.g.*, *Helichthys* (Fig. 190), *Perleidus*).

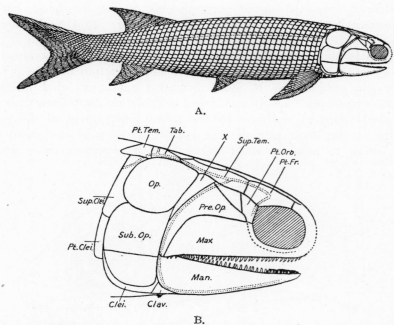

FIG. 190.—**Helichthys elegans.** A, restoration; B, head. *Tab.* tabular; *Pt. Clei.* post-cleithrum; *Man.* lower jaw. Other letters as in Fig. 188. (After Brough.)

ORDER CHONDROSTEI.

This order is represented at the present time by the Sturgeons—viz., *Acipenser* (Fig. 191), a genus of about twenty species living in the rivers of Europe, North America and Asia; *Scaphirhynchus*, the " Shovel-nosed

FIG. 191.—**Acipenser ruthenus** (Sturgeon). *b.* barbels; *c. f.* caudal fin; *d. f.* dorsal fin; *pct. f.* pectoral fin; *pv. f.* pelvic fin; *sc.* scutes; *v. f.* ventral fin. (After Cuvier.)

sturgeon " of North America and Central Asia; *Polyodon*, the " Spoonbill sturgeon " of the Mississippi and *Psephurus*, a primitive sturgeon from China. The group as a whole shows a mixture of primitive and secondarily degenerate characters. In the first category are such characters as the un-constricted notochord, the persistence of basi- and inter-dorsals and of basi-and inter-ventrals as separate elements in the vertebræ (Fig. 192), the retention of a clavicle in the shoulder-girdle, the primitive structure of the fins with their broad bases, the fulcral scales on the dorsal and caudal fin, the heterocercal tail, the spiracle and spiracular pseudobranch, the spiral valve and the arrangement of the urogenital organs. In the second category are certain characters which are more developed in the earlier than in the later forms, and which are therefore known to have become degenerate or lost, such as the reduction of the jaws owing to the suctorial method of feeding which has been acquired ; the loss of ganoine on the scales and head bones ; the reduction of the scales to a few rows on the sides of the body ; the irregularity and loss of some of the head bones and secondary multiplica-tion of centres on ossification of others. There is also a general loss of ossification in the whole skeleton.

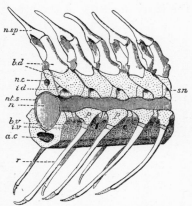

FIG. 192.—Pre-caudal vertebræ of Sturgeon. *a. c.* aortic canal formed by the union of ingrowths from the basi- and interventrals of opposite sides; *b. d.* basidorsals; *b. v.* basiventrals; *i. d.* interdorsals; *i. v.* interventrals; *n.* notochord; *n. c.* neural canal; *n. sp.* neural spine; *nt. s.* sheath of notochord; *P.* parapophysis; *R.* rib; *s. n.* foramen for root of spinal nerve. (From the *Cambridge Natural History*.)

A Mesozoic species, *Chondrosteus acipenseroides* (Fig. 193), the earliest

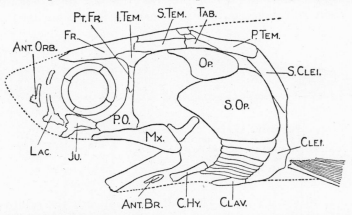

FIG. 193.—**Chondrosteus acipenseroides.** *Ant. Br.* anterior branchiostegal; *Ant. Orb.* antorbi-tal; *C. Hy.* ceratohyal; *Clav.* clavicles; *Clei.* cleithrum; *Fr.* frontal; *I. Tem.* intertemporal; *Ju.* jugal; *Lac.* lachrymal; *Mx.* maxilla; *Op.* opercular; *O. P.* subopercular; *P. O.* postorbital; *P. Tem.* post-temporal; *Pt. Fr.* post-frontal; *S. Clei.* supracleithrum; *S. Op.* subopercular; *S. Tem.* supratemporal; *Tab.* tabular. (After Watson.)

known true sturgeon, is transitional in structure, and although degeneration has already set in, suggests a palæoniscid origin through some such form as *Coccocephalus* (Fig. 194). There is still, however, a lack of evidence as to the early ancestry of the group.

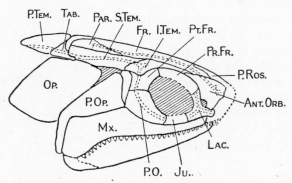

FIG. 194.—**Coccocephalus wildi.**   *Ant. Orb.* antorbital; *Clav.* clavicle; *Clei.* cleithrum; *Fr.* frontal; *Ju.* jugal; *Mx.* maxilla; *Op.* opercular; *P. Op.* pre-opercular; *Pt. Fr.* post-frontal; *P. Ros. I. II.* pre-rostrals; *P. Mx.* pre-maxilla; *Par.* parietal; *P. Tem.* post-temporal; *I. Tem.* inter-temporal; *S. Op.* sub-opercular; *S. Clei.* supra-cleithrum; *X. Y.* bones of uncertain homology.   (After Watson.)

ORDER POLYPTERINI (CLADISTIA).

At one time *Polypterus* (Fig. 195) and *Calamoichthys*, the only known members of the order, were classed as crossopterygians. There are, however, difficulties in accepting this view, and although, from a complete lack of any fossil evidence, their position is still somewhat obscure, the balance of evidence favours an origin from some palæoniscid stock.[1] The scales, for instance, are

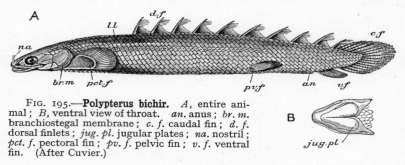

FIG. 195.—**Polypterus bichir.**   *A*, entire animal; *B*, ventral view of throat.   *an.* anus; *br. m.* branchiostegal membrane; *c. f.* caudal fin; *d. f.* dorsal finlets; *jug. pl.* jugular plates; *na.* nostril; *pct. f.* pectoral fin; *pv. f.* pelvic fin; *v. f.* ventral fin.   (After Cuvier.)

ganoid in composition, the skull lacks the division into the orbito-ethmoidal and occipito-otic regions so characteristic of the crossopterygian skull (p. 285). The position of the nostrils on the dorso-lateral surface of the snout is typically actinopterygian as is the anatomy of the soft parts such as a pyloric cæcum in the

[1] Goodrich, ' *Polypterus* a palæoniscid ? "   Palæobiologica.   1928, Vol. I, p. 87.

gut and the teleostean-like character of the urogenital organs. The teeth are simple in structure, and are without the peculiar structure and method of replacement found in the Crossopterygii. The structure of the paired fin is peculiar, with its long posterior axis and preaxial radials (Fig. 247) and muscular lobe lying outside the body-wall. The resemblance to the fin of the Chondrichthyes is superficial; it is, however, quite unlike the archipterygial type of the Crossopterygii, and can perhaps best be interpreted as a modification of the actinopterygian pattern.

On the other hand, the more primitive, or rather less modified, structure of the scales; the fin structure just mentioned and various characters of the skull prevent any close association of these two fishes with other Actinopterygii and, for the present, they are best considered as representing a persistent line of palæoniscid affinity.

There are a few species of the genus *Polypterus* from the Congo and Upper Nile, and another, *Calamoichthys calabaricus*, a smaller and more elongated,

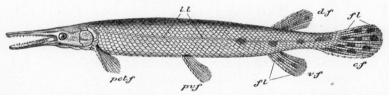

FIG. 196.—**Lepidosteus platystomus** (Bony Pike). *c. f.* caudal fin; *d. f.* dorsal fin; *fl.* fulcra; *l. l.* lateral line; *pct. f.* pectoral fin; *pv. f.* pelvic fin; *v. f.* ventral fin. (After Cuvier.)

but otherwise very similar, form from Old Calabar. The most noticeable points are the rhomboid scales, the presence of a pair of gular plates between the rami of the lower jaws, the lobed pectoral fins, the abbreviate heterocercal tail and the division of the dorsal fin into a series of repeated finlets, each supported by an anterior spine.

Sub-class Neopterygii.

ORDER GINGLYMODI.

The Ginglymodi are a Holostean group ranging from the Upper Permian, and comprising as families the Semionotidæ, Pycnodontidæ and Lepidosteidæ. This last family originated in the Eocene, and is represented at the present day in the fresh waters of North and Central America by the sole living genus, *Lepidosteus*, the Gar-pikes.

The group, as exemplified by *Lepidosteus* (Fig. 196), shows a number of primitive features, such as a long valvular conus to the heart and a corresponding absence of a bulbus arteriosus, a tail still hemi-heterocercal, an air bladder with cellular walls, thick rhombic scales with a complete covering of ganoine, fulcral scales have still been retained, and traces of a clavicle have been observed.   On the other hand, the central jugal plate has been lost, and the spiracle is closed.   The presence of pyloric cæca and the structure of the generative organs are teleostean features.   There are also some specialised characters that appear to be peculiar to the genus, such as the reduced maxilla

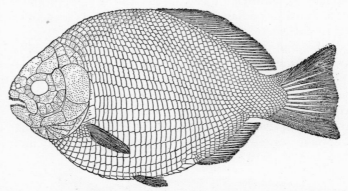

FIG. 197.—**Dapedius politus.**   (After Smith Woodward.)

and its functional replacement by a number of tooth-bearing infra-orbital elements, the numerous small cheek plates and, above all, the opisthocœlous vertebræ as opposed to the much more common amphicœlous vertebræ of most actinopterygian fishes.

There are several living species of *Lepidosteus*, of which *L. tristœchus* is said to attain a length of ten feet.

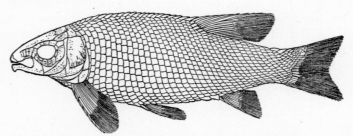

FIG. 198.—**Lepidotus minor.**   (After Smith Woodward.)

Of the extinct families under this grouping, the Semionotidæ are fusiform fishes and the Pycnodontidæ very deep and flattened from side to side.   The most noticeable character common to both families is the way in which the jaw suspension has swung forwards as compared with the ancestral palæoniscid condition.   The strong complete ganoid scales are present, but the clavicle is becoming reduced or is absent.   The vertebral column is composed of hemivertebræ and the notochord is unconstricted. Fulcra are present on the fins of the Semionotidæ, but not of the Pycnodontidæ.

Semionotus, *Dapedius* (Fig. 197), *Lepidotus* (Fig. 198) and *Acentrophorus* are characteristic and well-known genera of the Semionotidæ and *Mesodon* (Fig. 199), and *Pycnodus* of the Pycnodontidæ.

ORDER PROTOSPONDYLI.

This order is represented at the present day by a sole living species, *Amia calva* (Fig. 200), the Bow-fin, from the fresh waters of the United States. Like the Gar-pikes, *Amia* shows a mixture of primitive and advancing characters. Of the former the lung is dorsal, but bilobed and cellular, so that a certain amount of air-breathing is still possible. A vestigial spiral valve

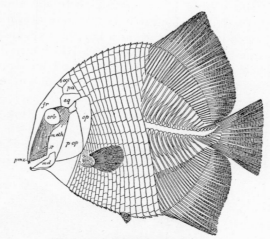

FIG. 199.—**Mesodon macropterus.**
(After Smith Woodward.)

is present in the intestine, and a small valvular conus in the heart, but this is accompanied at the same time by a considerable bulbus arteriosus. There is one large jugal plate between the rami of the lower jaws and well-developed branchiostegal rays like the teleosts. Unlike the latter, there are no pyloric cæca, and the lower jaws still retain the full number of elements. Of progressive characters the scales have become thin and cycloid, and have lost the ganoine layer, the fins have lost all fulcra, the tail is practically homocercal, the vertebræ solid and amphicœlous

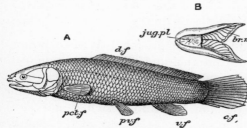

FIG. 200.—**Amia calva** (Bow-fin). *A*, the entire animal ; *B*, ventral view of throat. *br. m.* branchiostegal membrane ; *c. f.* caudal fin ; *d. f.* dorsal fin ; *jug. pl.* jugular plate ; *pct. f.* pectoral fin ; *pv. f.* pelvic fin ; *v. f.* ventral fin. (After Günther.)

(except in the tail region where separate basidorsals and ventrals still occur).

Protospondyli are first found in the Triassic, and, beside the Amiidæ, the other families, all extinct, are the Eugnathidæ, Pachycormidæ, Aspidorhynchidæ and Pholidophoridæ ; from this last family arose the Leptolepidæ which may be considered as the ancestors of the teleosts.

EXAMPLE OF A TELEOST FISH—THE BROOK TROUT (*Salmo fario*).

The Brook Trout is common in the rivers and streams of Europe, and has been acclimatised in other parts of the world, notably in New Zealand. It varies greatly in size according to the abundance of food and the extent of the water in which it lives : it may attain sexual maturity, and therefore be looked upon as adult, at a length of 18–20 cm. (seven or eight inches), but in large lakes it may grow to nearly a metre in length. Other species of Salmo, such as the Salmon (*S. salar*), the Lake Trout (*S. trutta*), the American Brook Trout (*Salvelinus fontalis*), are common in the Northern Hemisphere and differ only in details from *S. fario*.

External Characters.—The *body* (Fig. 201) is elongated, compressed, thickest in the middle, and tapering both to the head and tail. The *mouth* is terminal and very large ; the upper jaw is supported by two freely movable bones, the *premaxilla* (Figs. 202, 206, *pmx.*) in front and the *maxilla* (*mx.*) behind,

FIG. 201.—**Salmo fario.** *a.l.* adipose lobe of pelvic fin ; *an.* anus ; *c. f.* caudal fin ; *d. f. 1*, first dorsal fin ; *d. f. 2*, second dorsal or adipose fin ; *l. l.* lateral line ; *op.* operculum ; *pct. f.* pectoral fin ; *pv. f.* pelvic fin ; *v. f.* ventral fin. (After Jardine.)

both bearing sharp curved *teeth* arranged in a single row. When the mouth is opened a row of *palatine teeth* is seen internal and parallel to those of the maxilla, and in the middle line of the roof of the mouth is a double row of *vomerine teeth*. The lower jaw (*md.*) is mainly supported by a bone called the *dentary* and bears a row of teeth : on the throat each ramus of the mandible is bounded mesially by a deep groove. The floor of the mouth is produced into a prominent *tongue* (*t.*) bearing a double row of teeth. In old males the apex of the lower jaw becomes curved upwards like a hook.

The large *eyes* have no eyelids, but the flat cornea is covered by a transparent layer of skin. A short distance in front of the eye is the double *nostril* (*na1, na2*), each olfactory sac having two external apertures, the anterior one (*na1*) provided with a flap-like valve. There is no external indication of the ear.

On each side of the posterior region of the head is the *operculum* (Fig. 202, *op.*) or gill-cover, a large flap which, when raised, displays the gills ; between it and the flank is the large crescentic gill-opening, from which the respiratory current makes its exit.   The operculum is not a mere fold of skin, as in Holocephali, but is supported by three thin bones the outlines of which can be made out through the skin ; they are the *opercular* (Fig. 206, *op.*), *sub-opercular* (*s. op.*), and *inter-opercular* (*i. op.*) ; the last is attached to the angle of the mandible.   The *pre-opercular* (*p. op.*) is not an opercular support but is one of the cheek bones following the outline of the hyomandibular.   The ventral portion of the operculum is produced into a thin membranous extension, the *branchiostegal membrane* (*br. m.*), supported by twelve flat, over-lapping bones, the *branchiostegal rays*.   The narrow area on the ventral surface of the throat which separates the two gill-openings from one another is called the *isthmus*.   The *gills*, seen by lift-

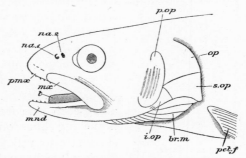

ing up the operculum, are four red comb-like organs, each having a double row of free gill-filaments ; alternating with the gills are the five vertically elongated *gill-slits*, opening into the mouth.

The Trout breathes by the draw-ing in of water through the mouth and its passage outwards through the gill-slits.   The *inspiration* or inward movement of the water is effected by the opercula being moved outwards, the space internal to them thus being widened, and water flow-ing in through the open mouth to

FIG. 202.—Head of female **Salmo fario.**   *br. m.* branchiostegal membrane ;   *i. op.* inter-opercular ;   *mnd.* mandible ;   *mx.* maxilla ;   *na. 1,* anterior, and *na. 2,* posterior external nostril ;   *op.* opercular ;   *pct. f.* pectoral fin ;   *pmx.* pre-maxilla ;   *p. op.* preopercular ;   *s. op.* suboper-cular ;   *t.* tongue.

fill the vacuum, the branchiostegal membrane at the same time closing the gill-opening and thus preventing the water from flowing in from behind.   *Expiration* is brought about by the opercula moving inwards and forcing the water out.   Owing to the action of a pair of transversely directed membranous folds, the *respiratory valves*, one attached to the roof, the other to the floor of the mouth, which are so directed as to become expanded and block the passage when water presses on them from behind, the water is compelled to make its exit through the gill-slits.

On the ventral surface of the body, at about two-thirds of the distance from the snout to the end of the tail, is the *anus* (Fig. 201, *an.*) ; behind it is the *urinogenital aperture*, of almost equal size and leading into the *urinogenital sinus*, into which both urinary and genital products are discharged.

The region from the snout to the posterior edge of the operculum is counted as the *head* ;   the *trunk* extends from the operculum to the anus ;   the post-anal region is the *tail*.

There are two *dorsal fins* :   the *anterior dorsal* (Fig. 201, *d. f. 1*) is large and triangular, and is supported by thirteen bony fin-rays; the *posterior dorsal* (*d. f. 2*) is small and thick, and is devoid of bony supports: it is distinguished as an *adipose fin*. The *caudal fin* (*c. f.*) is the chief organ of locomotion; it differs markedly from that of most Chondrichthyes in being, as far as its external appearance is concerned, quite symmetrical, being supported by fin-rays which radiate regularly from the rounded end of the tail proper; such outwardly symmetrical tail-fins are called *homocercal*. There is a single large *ventral fin* (*v. f.*) supported by eleven rays. The *pectoral fin* (*pct. f.*) has fourteen rays and is situated, in the normal position, close behind the gill-opening, but the *pelvic fin* (*pv. f.*) has shifted its position and lies some distance in front of the vent: it is supported by ten rays, and

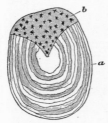

has a small process or *adipose lobe* (*a. l.*) springing from its outer edge near the base.

The body is covered by a soft, slimy skin through which, in the trunk and tail, the outlines of the *scales* can be seen; on the head and fins the skin is smooth and devoid of scales. A well-marked *lateral line* (*l. l.*) extends along each side from head to tail, and is continued into branching lines on the head. The skin is grey above, shading into yellowish below, and is covered with minute black pigment-spots which, on the sides and back, are aggregated to form round spots two or three millimetres in diameter. In young specimens orange-coloured spots are also present.

FIG. 203.—Scale of **Salmo fario.** *a.* anterior portion covered by overlap of preceding scales; *b.* free portion covered only by pigmented epidermis.

Skin and Exoskeleton.—The *epidermis* contains unicellular glands, from which the mucus covering the body is secreted, and pigment-cells, to which the colours of the animal are due. The *scales* (Fig. 203) are lodged in pouches of the dermis and have the form of flat, nearly circular plates of bone but marked with concentric lines which represent the annual growth stages, having no Haversian canals, lacunæ, or canaliculi. They have an imbricating arrangement, overlapping one another from before backwards, like the tiles of a house, in such a way that a small three-sided portion (*b*) of each scale comes to lie immediately beneath the epidermis, while the rest (*a*) is hidden beneath the scales immediately anterior to it. Besides the scales, the fin-rays belong to the exoskeleton, but will be most conveniently considered in connection with the endoskeleton.

Endoskeleton.—The *vertebral column* shows a great advance on that of the two previous classes in being thoroughly differentiated into distinct bony *vertebræ*. It is divisible into an anterior or *trunk region* and a posterior or *caudal region*, each containing about twenty-eight vertebræ.

A typical trunk vertebra consists of a dice-box-shaped *centrum* (Fig. 204, **CN**) with deeply concave anterior and posterior faces, and perforated in the centre by a small hole. The edges of the centra are united by ligament and the biconvex spaces between them are filled by the remains of the notochord; there are also articulations between the arches by means of little bony processes, the *zygapophyses* (**N, ZYG., H. ZYG.**). To the dorsal surface of the centrum is attached, by ligaments in the anterior vertebræ, by *ankylosis* or actual bony union in the posterior, a low *neural arch* (**N. A.**), which consists in the anterior vertebræ of distinct right and left moieties, and is continued above into a long, slender, double *neural spine* (**N. SP.**), directed upwards and backwards. To the ventro-lateral region of

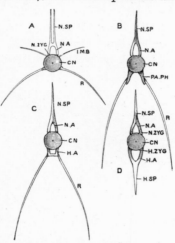

FIG. 204.—**Salmo fario.** *A*, one of the anterior, and *B*, one of the posterior trunk vertebræ; *C*, one of the anterior, and *D*, one of the posterior caudal vertebræ. **CN.** centrum; **IMB.** intermuscular bone; **HA.** hæmal arch; **H. SP.** hæmal spine; **H. ZYG.** hæmal zygapophysis; **N. A.** neural arch; **N. SP.** neural spine; **N. ZYG.** neural zygapophysis; **PA. PH.** parapophysis; **R.** pleural rib.

the vertebra are attached by ligament a pair of long, slender *pleural ribs* (**R.**) with dilated heads, which curve downwards and backwards between the muscles and the peritoneum, thus encircling the abdominal cavity. In the first two vertebræ they are attached directly to the centrum, in the rest to short downwardly directed bones, the *parapophyses* (**PA. PH.**), immovably articulated by broad surfaces to the centrum. At the junction of the neural arch with the centrum are attached, also by fibrous union, a pair of delicate *inter-muscular bones* (**I. M. B.**), which extend outwards and backwards in the fibrous septa between the myomeres. The first and second abdominal vertebræ bear no ribs. In the last three the neural spines (*B*, **N. SP.**) are single.

In the caudal vertebræ the outgrowths corresponding to the parapophyses are fused with the centrum and unite in the middle ventral line, forming a *hæmal* arch (*C*, **H. A.**), through which the caudal artery and vein run. In the first six caudals each hæmal arch bears a pair of ribs (**R.**); in the rest the arch is produced downwards and backwards into a *hæmal spine* (*D*, **H. SP.**).

The centra as well as the arches of the vertebræ are formed entirely from the skeletogenous layer, and not from the sheath of the notochord as in Elasmobranchs (see pp. 70 and 179).

The posterior end of the caudal region is curiously modified for the support of the tail-fin. The hindmost centra (Fig. 205, **CN.**) have their axes not horizontal, but deflected upwards, and following the last undoubted centrum is a rod-like structure, the *urostyle* (**UST.**), consisting of the partly ossified end of the notochord, which has thus precisely the same upward flexure as in the

Dogfish. The neural and hæmal spines (**N. SP., H. SP.**) of the last five
vertebræ are very broad and closely connected with one another, and are
more numerous than the centra; and three or four hæmal arches are attached
to the urostyle. In this way a firm vertical plate of bone is formed, to the
edge of which the caudal fin-rays (*D.F.R.*) are attached fanwise in a symmetrical manner. It will be obvious, however, that this homocercal tail-fin
is really quite as unsymmetrical as the heterocercal fin of the Dogfish, since,
its morphological axis being constituted by the notochord, nearly the whole
of its rays are, in strictness, ventral.

The *skull* (Fig. 206) is an extremely complex structure, composed of
mingled bone and cartilage. The cartilage has no superficial mosaic of lime-
salts such as we find in many Chondrichthyes, but certain portions of it are

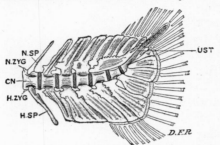

replaced by bones, and there are in
addition numerous investing bones developed in the surrounding connective-
tissue. As in the Dogfish, the skull
may be divided into cranium, upper
and lower jaws, with their suspensory
apparatus, and hyoid and branchial
arches.

FIG. 205.—**Salmo fario,** caudal end of
vertebral column. **CN.** centrum; *D. F. R.*
dermal fin-rays; **H. SP.** hæmal spine; **H.
ZYG.** hæmal zygapophysis; **N. SP.** neural
spine; **N. ZYG.** neural zygapophysis; **UST.**
urostyle.

The *cranium* (Fig. 207) is a somewhat wedge-shaped structure, its apex
being directed forwards. At first sight
the distinction between replacing and
investing bones is not obvious, but
after maceration or boiling certain flat

bones (the paired parietals, *PA.*, frontals, *FR.*, and nasals, *NA.*, and the
unpaired supra-ethmoid, *S. ETH.*) can be easily removed from the dorsal
surface; and two unpaired bones (the parasphenoid, *PA, SPH.*, and vomer,
VO.) from the ventral surface. These are all investing bones: they are
simply attached to the cranium by fibrous tissue, and can readily be prised
off when the latter is sufficiently softened by maceration or boiling. We thus
get a distinction between the cranium as a whole, or *secondary cranium*,
complicated by the presence of investing bones, and the *primary cranium*,
neurocranium or *chondrocranium*, left by the removal of these bones and
corresponding exactly with the cranium of a Dogfish.

The primary cranium contains the same regions as that of *Scyliorhinus*.
Posteriorly is the *occipital region*, surrounding the foramen magnum, presenting
below that aperture a single concave *occipital condyle* for the first vertebra,
and produced above into an *occipital crest*. The *auditory capsules* project
outwards from the occipital region, and between them on the dorsal surface
of the skull are paired oval *fontanelles* (*fon.*) closed in the entire skull by the

frontal bones.   The posterior region of the cranial floor is produced downwards
into paired longitudinal ridges, enclosing between them a groove which is
converted into a canal by the apposition of the parasphenoid bone and serves
for the origin of the eye-muscles.   In front of the auditory region the cranium
is excavated on each side by a large *orbit*, a vertical plate or *inter-orbital
septum* (**OR, SPH.**) separating the two cavities from one another.   In front of
the orbital region the cranium broadens out to form the *olfactory capsules*,

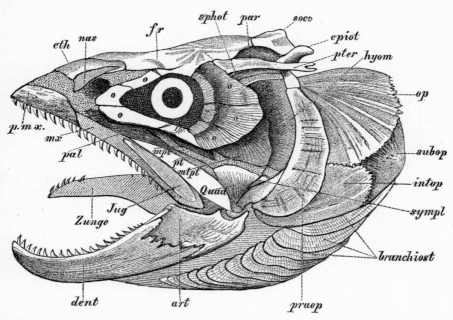

FIG. 206.—**Salmo,** the entire skull, from the left side.   *art.* articular ; *branchiost.* branchiostegal
rays ; *dent.* dentary ; *epiot.* epiotic ; *eth.* supraethmoid ; *fr.* frontal ; *hyom.* hyomandibular ; *intop.*
interopercular ; *Jug.* supra-maxillary ; *mpt.* mesopterygoid ; *mtpt.* metapterygoid ; *mx.* maxilla ;
nas. nasal ; *o.* circumorbitals ; *op.* opercular ; *pal.* palatine ; *par.* parietal ; *pmx.* premaxilla ;
praop. preopercular ; *pt.* pterygoid ; *pter.* pterotic ; *Quad.* quadrate ; *socc.* supraoccipital ; *sphot.*
sphenotic ; *subop.* subopercular ; *sympl.* symplectic ; *Zunge,* basihyal. (From Wiedersheim's
Vertebrata.)

each excavated by a deep pit (*olf. s.*) for the olfactory sac, and anterior to
these is a blunt snout or *rostrum*.   The occipital region is formed as usual
from the parachordals of the embryonic skull, the auditory region from the
auditory capsules, and the rest of the cranium from the trabeculæ.

The replacing bones, formed as ossifications in the chondrocranium, correspond in essentials with the typical arrangement already described (pp. 70–76).
In the occipital region are four bones ; the *basi-occipital* (**B. OC.**), forming
the greater part of the occipital condyle and the hinder region of the *basis
cranii* or skull-floor ; the *ex-occipitals* (**EX. OC.**), placed one on each side of

the foramen magnum and meeting both above and below it ; and the *supra-occipital* (**S. OC.**), forming the occipital crest already noticed. Each auditory capsule is ossified by five bones—*i.e.*, two more than the typical number (p. 75) : the *pro-otic* (**PR. OT.**), in the anterior region of the capsule, uniting with its fellow of the opposite side in the floor of the brain-case, just in front of the basi-occipital ; the *opisthotic*, in the posterior part of the capsule, external to the ex-occipital ; the *sphenotic* (**SPH. OT.**), above the pro-otic and forming part of the boundary of the orbit ; the *pterotic* (**PT. OT.**), above the ex-occipital and opisthotic, forming a distinct lateral ridge and produced behind into a prominent *pterotic process* ; and the *epiotic* (**EP. OT.**), a small bone, wedged in between the supra- and ex-occipitals and pterotic, and produced into a short *epiotic process*. On the external face of the auditory capsule, at the junction of the pro-, sphen-, and pter-otics, is an elongated facet (*h.m.*) covered with cartilage and serving for the articulation of the hyomandibular.

The trabecular region of the cranium contains six bones. Immediately in front of the conjoined pro-otics, and forming the anterior end of the basis cranii, is a small unpaired Υ-shaped bone, the *basisphenoid* (**B. SPH.**). Above it, and forming the anterior parts of the side-walls of the brain-case, are the large paired *alisphenoids* (**AL. SPH.**). In the inter-orbital septum is a median vertical bone, representing fused *orbitosphenoids* (**OR. SPH.**). Lastly, in the posterior region of each olfactory capsule, and forming part of the boundary of the orbit, is the *ecto-ethmoid* (**EC. ETH.**).

The investing bones already referred to are closely applied to the roof and floor of the chondrocranium, and modify its form considerably by projecting beyond the cartilaginous part, and concealing apertures and cavities. The great *frontals* (*FR.*) cover the greater part of the roof of the skull, concealing the fontanelles, and furnishing roofs to the orbits. Immediately behind the frontals is a pair of very small *parietals* (*PA.*) ; in front of them is an unpaired *supra-ethmoid* (*S. ETH.*), to the sides of which are attached a pair of small *nasals* (*NA.*). On the ventral surface is the large *parasphenoid* (*PA. SPH.*), which forms a kind of clamp to the whole cartilaginous skull-floor ; and in front of and below the parasphenoid is the toothed *vomer* (*VO.*). Encircling the orbit is a ring of scale-like bones, the *circum-orbitals* (Fig. 206, *o.*).

In the jaws, as in the cranium, we may distinguish between primary and secondary structures. The primary upper jaw or *palatoquadrate* is homologous with the upper jaw of the Dogfish, but instead of remaining cartilaginous, it is ossified by five replacing bones : the toothed *palatine* (**PAL.**) in front, articulating with the olfactory capsule ; then the *pterygoid* (**PTG.**) on the ventral, and the *mesopterygoid* (**MS. PTG.**) on the dorsal edge of the original cartilaginous bar ; the *quadrate* (**QU.**) at the posterior end of the latter, furnishing a convex condyle for the articulation of the lower jaw ; and projecting upwards from the quadrate the *metapterygoid* (**MT. PTG.**). These bones do not, however, enter into the gape, and do not therefore constitute the actual upper jaw of the adult fish : external to them are two large investing bones, the *premaxilla* (*PMX.*) and the *maxilla* (*MX.*), which together form the actual or secondary upper jaw : they both bear teeth. A small scale-like bone, the *jugal* (*JU.*), is attached to the posterior end of the maxilla.

The lower jaw is similarly modified. Articulating with the quadrate is a large bone, the *articular* (**ART.**), continued forwards by a narrow pointed rod of cartilage : the latter is the unossified distal end of the primary lower jaw or Meckel's cartilage ; the articular is its ossified proximal end, and therefore a replacing bone. Ensheathing Meckel's cartilage and forming the main part of the secondary lower jaw is a large toothed investing bone, the *dentary* (*DNT.*), and a small investing bone, the *angular* (*ANG.*), is attached to the lower and hinder end of the articular.

The connection of the upper jaw with the cranium is effected partly by the articulation of the palatine with the olfactory region, partly by means of a *suspensorium* formed of two bones separated by a cartilaginous interval : the larger, usually called the *hyomandibular* (**HY. M.**), articulates with the auditory capsule by the facet already noticed, and the small, pointed *symplectic* (**SYM.**) fits into a groove in the quadrate. Both bones are attached by fibrous tissue to the quadrate and metapterygoid, and in this way the suspensorium and palatoquadrate together form an inverted arch, freely articulated in front with the olfactory and behind with the auditory capsule, and thus giving rise to an extremely mobile upper jaw. As its name implies, the hyomandibular (together with the symplectic) is commonly held to be the upper end of the hyoid arch and the homologue of the hyomandibular of the Chondrichthyes, but there is some reason for thinking that it really belongs to the mandibular arch, and corresponds with the dorsal and posterior part of the triangular palatoquadrate of Holocephali : a perforation in the latter would convert it into an inverted arch having the same general relations as the upper jaw *plus* suspensorium of the Trout, but fused, instead of articulated, with the cranium at either extremity.

The hyoid cornu is articulated to the cartilaginous interval between the hyomandibular and symplectic through the intermediation of a small rod-like bone, the *interhyal* (**I. HY.**), which is an ossification in a ligament. It is ossified by three bones : an *epihyal* (**E. HY.**) above, then a large *ceratohyal* (**C. HY.**), and below a small double *hypohyal* (**H. HY.**). The right and left hyoid bars are connected by a keystone-piece, the unpaired, toothed *basihyal* (**B. HY.**), which supports the tongue.

Connected with the hyomandibular and hyoid cornu are certain investing bones serving for the support of the operculum. The *opercular* (Fig. 206, *op.*) is articulated with a backward process of the hyomandibular ; the *sub-opercular* (*subop.*) is below and internal to the opercular ; and the *inter-opercular* (*intop.*)

fits between the lower portions of the three preceding bones, and is attached by ligament to the angle of the mandible. The twelve sabre-shaped *branchiostegal rays* (*branchiost.*) are attached along the posterior border of the epi- and cerato-hyal, and below the basi-hyal is an unpaired bone, the *basibranchiostegal* or *urohyal*.

There are five branchial arches, diminishing in size from before backwards

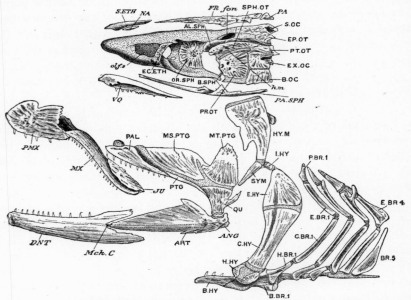

FIG. 207.—**Salmo fario.** Disarticulated skull with many of the investing bones removed. The cartilaginous parts are dotted. *fon.* fontanelle; *h. m.* articular facet for hyomandibular; *Mck. C.* Meckel's cartilage; *olf. s.* hollow for olfactory sac. Replacing bones—**AL. SPH.** alisphenoid; **ART.** articular; **B. BR.** *1*, first basibranchial; **B. HY.** basihyal; **B. OC.** basioccipital; **BR.** *5*, fifth branchial arch; **B. SPH.** basisphenoid; **C. BR.** *1*, first ceratobranchial; **C. HY.** ceratohyal; **EC. ETH.** ecto-ethmoid; **E. BR.** *1*, first epibranchial; **E. HY.** epi-hyal; **EP. OT.** epiotic; **EX. OC.** ex-occipital; **H. BR.** *1*, first hypobranchial; **H. HY.** hypohyal; **HY. M.** hyomandibular; **I. HY.** interhyal; **MS. PTG.** mesopterygoid; **MT. PTG.** metapterygoid; **OR. SPH.** orbitosphenoid; **PAL.** palatine; **P. BR.** *1*, first pharyngobranchial; **PTG.** pterygoid; **PT. OT.** petrotic; **QU.** quadrate; **S. OC.** supraoccipital; **SPH. OT.** sphenotic; **SYM.** symplectic. Investing bones—*ANG.* angular; *DNT.* dentary; *FR.* frontal; *JU.* jugal; *MX.* maxilla; *NA.* nasal; *PA. SPH.* parasphenoid; *PMX.* premaxilla; *VO.* vomer.

(Fig. 207). The first three present the same segments as in the Dogfish : *pharyngobranchial* (**PH. BR.**) above, then *epibranchial* (**E. BR.**), then a large *ceratobranchial* (**C. BR.**), and a small *hypobranchial* (**H. BR.**) below. The right and left hypobranchials of each arch are connected by an unpaired *basibranchial* (**B. BR.**). All these segments are ossified by replacing bones, and the basibranchials are connected with one another and with the basihyal by cartilage, so as to form a median ventral bar in the floor of the pharynx. In the fourth arch the pharyngobranchial is unossified, and the hypobranchial absent, and the fifth arch (**BR.** 5) is reduced to a single bone on each side. Small spine-like ossifications are attached in a single or double row along the inner aspect of each of the first four arches: these are the *gill-rakers*; they serve as a sieve to prevent the escape of food by the gill-slits.

The comparison of this singularly complex skull with the comparatively simple one of the Dogfish is much facilitated by the examination of the skull of a young Trout or Salmon. In the latter, at about the second week after hatching, the only ossifications present are a few investing bones; when these are removed we get a purely cartilaginous skull (Fig. 208), exactly comparable

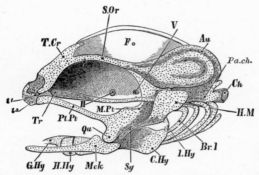

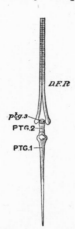

FIG. 208.—Skull of young **Salmon,** second week after hatching; the investing bones removed. *Au.* auditory capsule; *Br. 1,* first branchial arch; *Ch.* notochord; *C. Hy.* hyoid cornu; *Fo.* fontanelle; *G. Hy.* basihyal; *H. Hy.* hypohyal; *H. M.* hyo-mandibular; *1. Hy.* interhyal; *l¹, l²,* labial cartilages; *Mck.* Meckel's cartilage; *M. Pt.* metapterygoid region of primary upper jaw; *Pa. ch.* parachordal; *Pl. Pt.* palatopterygoid region; *Qu.* quadrate region; *S.Or.* supraorbital region of cranium; *Sy.* symplectic region of suspensorium; *T. Cr.* cranial roof; *Tr.* trabecula; *II,* optic foramen; *V,* trigeminal foramen. (From Parker and Bettany's *Morphology of the Skull.*)

FIG. 209.—**Salmo fario.** A dermal fin-ray with its supports. *D.F.R.* dermal fin-ray; **PTG.** *1,* proximal pterygiophore (interspinous bone); **PTG.** *2,* middle pterygiophore; *ptg. 3,* distal pterygiophore (cartilaginous.)

with that of a Shark or Ray. There is a cranium devoid of replacing bones and divisible only into regions; the upper jaw is an unossified palatoquadrate (*Pl. Pt., M. Pt., Qu.*) and the lower jaw (*Mck.*) a large Meckel's cartilage; the suspensorium is an undivided hyomandibular (*HM.*), and the hyoid and branchial arches are unsegmented.

The *first dorsal* and the *ventral fins* are supported each by a triple set of pterygiophores, so that the fin-skeleton is multiserial, as in the Dogfish. The proximal series consists of slender bony rays—the *interspinous bones* (Fig. 209, **PTG.** *1*), lying in the median plane, between the muscles of the right and left sides, and more numerous than the myomeres of the regions in which they occur. Their distal ends are broadened, and with them are connected the second series (**PTG.** *2*) in the form of small dice-box-shaped bones; to these, finally, are attached small nodules of cartilage (*ptg. 3*) forming the third series of radials. The *dermal fin-rays* or *lepidotrichia* (*D.F.R.*), which lie in the substance of the fin itself, are slender bones, jointed like the antennæ of an Arthropod, and mostly branched in the sagittal plane (Fig. 209, *D.F.R.*). Each is formed of distinct right and left pieces (Fig. 209), in close contact for the most part, but diverging below to form a forked and dilated end, which fits over one of the cartilaginous nodules (*ptg. 3*). In the caudal fin (Fig. 205) the dermal rays (*D.F.R.*) are similarly seated on the

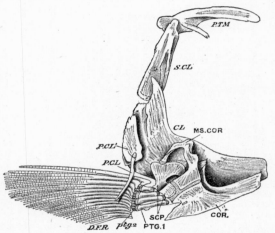

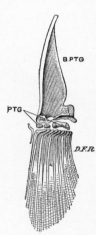

FIG. 210.—**Salmo fario.** Left half of shoulder-girdle and pectoral fin, from the inner surface. *C.L.* = cleithrum; **COR.** coracoid; *D.F.R.* dermal fin-rays; **MS. COR.** mesocoracoid; *P.C.L.*, *P.C.L.*[1], post-clavicles; **PTG.** *1*, proximal, and *ptg. 2*, distal pterygiophores; *P.T.M.* post-temporal; *S.C.L.* supraclavicle; **SCP.** scapula.

FIG. 211.—**Salmo fario.** Skeleton of left pelvic fin, dorsal aspect. **B. PTG.** basipterygium; *D. F. R.* dermal fin-rays; **PTG.** distal pterygiophores.

broad hæmal arches of the posterior caudal vertebræ. The second dorsal or adipose fin has, as already noticed, no bony support.

The *shoulder-girdle* (Fig. 210), like the skull, consists of a *primary shoulder-girdle*, homologous with that of a Dogfish, and of several investing bones. The primary shoulder-girdle in the young fish is formed of distinct right and left bars of cartilage, which do not unite with one another ventrally. In the adult each bar is ossified by three bones, a *scapula* (**SCP.**), situated dorsally to the glenoid facets, and developed partly as a replacing, partly as an investing bone; a *coracoid* (**COR.**), situated ventrally to the glenoid facet, and a *meso-coracoid* (**MS. COR.**), situated above the coracoid and anterior to the scapula. Externally to these is found a very large investing bone, the *cleithrum* (*CL.*), extending downwards under the throat: its dorsal end is connected by means of a *supra-clavicle* (*S. CL.*) to a forked bone, the *post-temporal* (*P.T.M.*), one branch of which articulates with the epiotic, the other with the pterotic process. To the inner surface of the cleithrum are attached two flat scales of bone (*P. CL'.*), with a slender rod-like *post-clavicle* (*P. CL.*) passing backwards and downwards among the muscles.

The structure of the *pectoral fin* is very simple. Articulated to the posterior border of the scapula and coracoid are four dice-box-shaped bones, the proximal pterygiophores or radials (**PTG.** *1*), followed by a row of small nodules of cartilage (*ptg. 2*) representing distal pterygiophores. The main body of the fin is supported by dermal fin-rays, which resemble those of the median fins, and have their forked ends seated upon the distal pterygiophores : the first ray, however, is larger than the rest, and articulates directly with the scapula.

There is no pelvic girdle, its place being taken by a large, flat triangular bone, the *basipterygium* (Fig. 211, **B. PTG.**), probably representing fused proximal pterygiophores : to its posterior border are attached three partly ossified nodules, the distal pterygiophores (**PTG.**), and with these the dermal fin-rays are articulated. The adipose lobe of the pelvic fin is supported by a small scale-like bone.

The **muscles** of the trunk and tail are arranged, as in the Dogfish, in zigzag myomeres : there are small muscles for the fins, and the head has a complex musculature for the movement of the jaws, hyoid, operculum, and branchial arches.

The **cœlome** is divisible into a large *abdomen* (Fig. 212) containing the chief viscera, and a small *pericardial cavity*, situated below the branchial arches, and containing the heart.

Digestive Organs.—The *mouth* (Figs. 206 and 212) is very large and has numerous small, recurved, conical teeth, borne, as already mentioned, on the premaxillæ, maxillæ, palatines, vomer, dentaries and basihyal. They obviously serve merely to prevent the escape of the slippery animals used as food and are of no use for either rending or chewing. The *pharynx* (*ph.*) is perforated on each side by four vertically elongated gill-slits, fringed by the bony tooth-like gill-rakers. Each gill-slit is V-shaped, the epihyal being bent upon the ceratohyal so that the dorsal and ventral moieties of the branchial arches touch one another when the mouth is closed.

The pharynx leads by a short *gullet* (*gul.*) into a U-shaped *stomach* (*st.*) consisting of a wide cardiac and a narrow pyloric division : between the latter and the intestine is a ring-shaped pyloric valve. The *intestine* passes at first forwards as the *duodenum* (*du.*), then becomes bent upon itself (*int.*) and passes backwards, without convolution, to the anus (*an.*). Its posterior portion has the mucous membrane raised into prominent annular ridges which simulate a spiral valve.

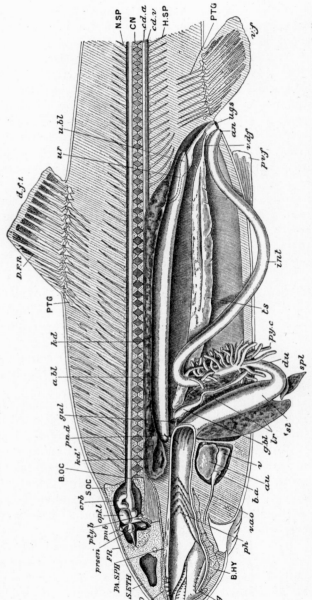

Fig. 212.—**Salmo fario.** Dissection from the left side. *a. bl.* air-bladder, opened; *an.* anus; *au.* atrium; *b. a.* bulbus arteriosus; **B.HY.** basihyal; **B. OC.** basi-occipital; *cd. a.* caudal artery; *cd. v.* caudal vein; **CN.** centrum; *crb.* cerebellum; *d. f. r,* first dorsal fin; *D.F.R.* dermal fin-rays; *du.* duodenum; *FR.* frontal; *g. bl.* gall-bladder; *gul.* gullet; **H. SP.** hæmal spine; *int.* intestine; *kd.* kidney; *kd'.* degenerate portion of kidney; *lv.* liver; **N. SP.** neural spine; *opt. l.* optic lobes; *PA. SPH.* parasphenoid; *ph.* pharynx; *pn. b.* pineal body; *pn. d.* bristle passed into pneumatic duct; *prsen.* prosencephalon; *pty. b.* pituitary body; **PTG.** pterygiophores; *pv. f.* pelvic fin; *py. c.* pyloric cæca; *S. ETH.* supra-ethmoid; **S. OC.** supra-occipital; *spl.* spleen; *st.* stomach; *tg.* tongue; *ts.* testis; *u. bl.* urinary bladder; *u. g. s.* urinogenital sinus; *ur.* urinary duct; *v.* ventricle; *v. ao.* ventral aorta; *v. df.* vas deferens; *v. f.* ventral fin; *VO.* vomer.

The *liver* (*lr.*) is imperfectly divided into right and left lobes, and there is a large gall-bladder (*g. bl.*). Opening into the duodenum are about forty blind glandular tubes, the *pyloric cæca* (*py. c.*). There is a large *spleen* (*spl.*) attached by peritoneum to the fundus of the stomach. The stomach, duodenum, and pyloric cæca are surrounded by loose folds of peritoneum loaded with fat.

Lying below the kidneys and extending the whole length of the abdominal cavity is the **air-bladder** (*a.bl.*), a thin-walled sac serving as an organ of flotation. Anteriorly its ventral wall presents a small aperture leading, by a short *pneumatic duct* (*pn. d.*), into the œsophagus on the dorsal side somewhat to the right of the middle line.

Respiratory Organs.—There are four pairs of *gills* each with a double row of branchial filaments, united proximally but having their distal ends free : interbranchial septa are practically obsolete (see Fig. 68). The gills are borne on the first four branchial arches, the fifth arch bearing no gill. On the inner surface of the operculum is a comb-like body, the *pseudo-branchia*, formed of a single row of branchial filaments, and representing the vestigial gill (hemibranch) of the hyoid arch.

Circulatory Organs.—The *heart* (Fig. 212) consists of sinus venosus, *atrium* (*au.*), and ventricle (*v.*). There is no conus arteriosus, but the proximal end of the ventral aorta is dilated to form a *bulbus arteriosus* (*b. a.*), a structure which differs from a conus in being part of the aorta, and not of the heart ; its walls do not contain striped muscle, and are not rhythmically contractile.

In accordance with the atrophy of the hyoid gill there is no afferent branchial artery to that arch, but a *hyoidean artery* springs from the ventral end of the first efferent branchial and passes to the pseudobranch. The right branch of the caudal vein is continued directly into the corresponding cardinal, the left breaks up in the kidney, forming a renal-portal system. There are no lateral veins, but the blood from the paired fins is returned to the cardinals. The red blood-corpuscles are, as in other fishes, oval nucleated discs.

Nervous System.—The brain (Fig. 213) is very different from that of Chondrichthyes, and is in many respects of a distinctly more specialised type. The *cerebellum* (*H.H.*) is very large, and bent upon itself. The *optic lobes* (*M.H.*) are also of great size, and on the ventral surface are large bean-shaped *lobi inferiores* (*U.L.*). The *diencephalon* is much reduced, and, indeed, is indicated dorsally only as the place of origin of the pineal body (*G. p.*) : ventrally it is produced into the lobi inferiores with the infundibulum between them giving attachment to the pituitary body (*Hyp.*). Hence, seen from above, the small undivided *prosencephalon* (*V.H.*) comes immediately in front of the mid-brain : it has a non-nervous roof (*Pall.*) and its floor is raised into prominent corpora striata (*BG., Bas. G.*). The *olfactory bulbs*, situated in close apposition with the prosencephalon without intervening olfactory peduncles or olfactory tracts such as are present in *Scyliorhinus* (*L.ol.*), are nearly as large as the corpora striata, and each contains a small cavity or

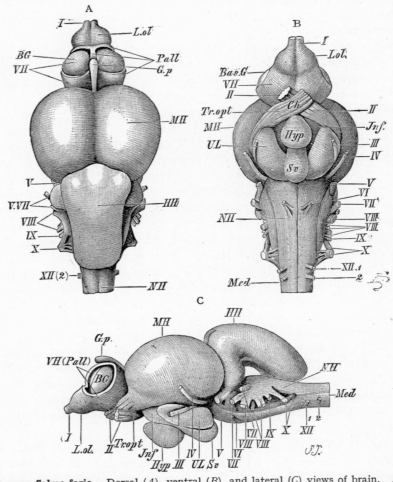

FIG. 213.—**Salmo fario.** Dorsal (*A*), ventral (*B*), and lateral (*C*) views of brain. *BG., Bas. G.* corpora striata; *ch.* crossing of optic nerves; *G. p*, pineal body; *HH.* cerebellum; *Hyp,* pituitary body; *Inf.* infundibulum; *L. ol.* olfactory bulbs; *Med,* spinal cord; *MH.* optic lobes; *NH.* medulla oblongata; *Pall.* non-nervous roof of prosencephalon; *Sv.* saccus vasculosus; *Tr. Opt.* optic tracts; *UL.* lobi inferiores; *VH,* prosencephalon; *I—X,* cerebral nerves; *XII, 1,* first spinal (hypoglossal) nerve; *2,* second spinal nerve. (From Wiedersheim's *Vertebrata*.)

rhinocœle in communication with the undivided prosocœle. Three transverse bands of fibres connect the right and left halves of the fore-brain, an *anterior commissure* joining the corpora striata, a *posterior commissure* situated just behind the origin of the pineal body, and an *inferior commissure* in front of the infundibulum. The *pineal body* (*G.p.*) is rounded and placed at the end of a hollow stalk : a shorter offshoot of the roof of the diencephalon may perhaps represent a rudimentary pineal eye. Behind the pituitary body is a *saccus vasculosus* (*s. v.*). The anterior part of the cerebellum does not bulge outwards in the way it does in the Dogfish ; instead it pushes forwards under the roof of the mesencephalon to form the *valvula cerebelli* (Fig. 214), which is very characteristic of teleost fishes. The hinder part of the cerebellum bulges outwards in the usual manner. The *optic nerves* do not form a chiasma, but simply cross one another, or decussate (*Ch.*), on leaving the brain, the right nerve going to the left, and the left nerve to the right eye.

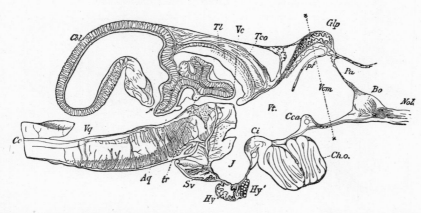

FIG. 214.—Median longitudinal section of the brain of a trout. *Aq.* aqueductus sylvii; *Bo.* olfactory lobe; *Cbl.* cerebellum; *C.c.* canal of spinal cord; *Cca.* anterior commissure; *Ch.o.* optic nerve; *Ci.* inferior commissure; *Glp.* pineal body; *Hy. Hy′.* hypophysis; *J.* infundibulum; *Nol.* olfactory nerve; *Pa.* roof of telencephalon; *p. f.* velum transversum; *S. v.* saccus vasculosus; *Tco.* pia mater; *tr.* crossing fibres of fourth nerve; *V. c.* valvula cerebelli; *V. cm.* ventricle of telencephalon; *V. q.* fourth ventricle; *Vt.* third ventricle. (From Goodrich, after Rabl-Rückhard.)

Sensory Organs.—The most distinctive feature of the *olfactory sac* is the possession of two small apertures, the anterior provided with a valve.

The *eye* (Fig. 215) has a very flat *cornea* (*cn.*) with which the globular *lens* (*l.*) is almost in contact, so that the aqueous chamber of the eye is extremely small. Between the cartilaginous *sclerotic* (*scl.*) and the vascular *choroid* (*ch.*) is a silvery layer or *argentea* (*arg.*), which owes its colour to minute crystals in the cells of which it is composed. There are no choroid processes. In the posterior part of the eye, between the choroid and the argentea, is a thickened ring-shaped structure (*ch. gld.*) surrounding the optic nerve, and called the *choroid gland* : it is not glandular, but is a complex network of blood-vessels, or *rete mirabile*. It is supplied with blood by the efferent artery of the pseudobranch. Close to the entrance of the optic nerve a vascular fold of the choroid, the *fulciform process* (*pr. fl.*), pierces the retina, and is continued to the back of the lens, where it ends in a knob, the *campanula Halleri* (*cp. hal.*), which contains smooth muscular fibres. The falciform process with the campanula Halleri takes an important part in the process of *accommodation* by which the eye becomes adapted to forming and receiving images of objects at various distances. Accommodation in the Bony Fish is effected, not by an alteration in the curvature of the lens as in higher vertebrates, but by changes in its position, by which it becomes more approximated towards, or further withdrawn from, the retina. In bringing about these changes of position the structures in question appear to play the principal part.

The *auditory organ* (Fig. 216) is chiefly remarkable for the large size of the otoliths (*ot. 1*). They are three in number; one, called the *sagitta* (*ot. 1*), is

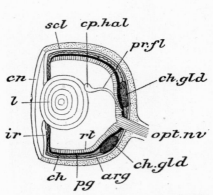

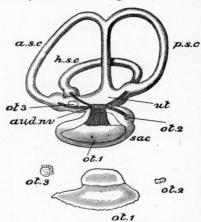

Fig. 215.—**Salmo fario.** Vertical section of eye (semi-diagrammatic). *arg.* argentea; *ch.* choroid; *ch. gld.* choroid gland; *cn.* cornea; *cp. hal.* campanula Halleri; *ir.* iris; *l.* lens; *opt. nv.* optic nerve; *pg.* pigmentary layer; *pr. fl.* processus falciformis; *scl.* sclerotic (dotted).

Fig. 216.—**Salmo fario.** The right auditory organ, from the inner side; the otoliths are shown separately below. *a. s. c.* anterior semi-circular canal; *aud. nv.* auditory nerve; *h. s. c.* horizontal canal; *ot. 1—3*, otoliths; *p. s. c.* posterior canal; *sac.* sacculus; *ut.* utriculus.

fully 6 mm. in length, and almost fills the sacculus: another, the *asteriscus* (*ot. 2*), is a small granule lying in the lagena or rudimentary cochlea: the third, the *lapillus* (*ot. 3*), is placed in the utriculus close to the ampullæ of the anterior and horizontal canals.

Urinogenital Organs.—The *kidneys* (Fig. 212, *kd.*, and Fig. 217, *R*) are of great size, extending the whole length of the dorsal wall of the abdomen, above the air-bladder, and partly fused together in the middle line. They are derived from the mesonephros of the embryo. Their anterior ends (Fig. 212, *kd*, Fig. 217, *R*) are much dilated and consist in the adult of lymphatic tissue, thus ceasing to discharge a renal function. The mesonephric ducts (*ur.*) unite into a single tube, which is dilated to form a *urinary bladder* (Fig. 212, *u. bl.*, Fig. 212, *v.*), and discharges into the urinogenital sinus.

The *gonads* are of great size in the sexually mature fish. The *testes* (Fig. 212, *ts.*) are long, smooth, pinkish paired organs, extending the whole length of the abdominal cavity; each is continued posteriorly into a duct (*v. df.*) which opens into the urinogenital sinus, and the homology of which with the ducts of the primitive nephridial system is still uncertain. The ovaries are

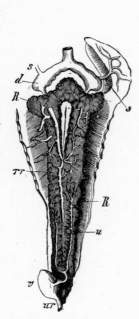

FIG. 217.—**Salmo fario.** The kidneys and adjacent parts. *d,* precaval vein; *R* (to the right), kidney; *R* (to the left), degenerate anterior portion of kidney; *rr,* efferent renal vein; *s.* subclavian vein; *u, ur,* mesonephric duct; *v.* bladder. (From Gegenbaur's *Comparative Anatomy*).

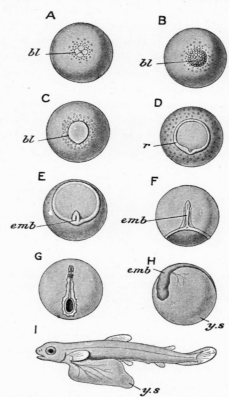

FIG. 218.—Nine stages in the development of **Salmo fario.** *A—H,* before hatching; *I,* shortly after hatching. *bl.* blastoderm; *emb.* embryo; *r.* thickened edge of blastoderm; *y. s.* yolk-sac. (*A—G* after Henneguy.)

also of the full length of the abdominal cavity and are much wider than the testes; they are covered with peritoneum on their inner or mesial faces only, and the numerous ova, which are about 4 mm. in diameter, are discharged when ripe from their outer faces into the cœlome. There are no oviducts, but the anterior wall of the urinogenital sinus is pierced by a pair of *genital pores* through which the ova make their way to the exterior. There is reason for thinking that these pores are to be looked upon as degenerate oviducts, and in no way homologous with the abdominal pores of the Chondrichthyes.

Development.—Impregnation is external, the male shedding his milt or seminal fluid on the newly-laid eggs. The ovum is covered by a thick membrane, the *zona radiata*, perforated by an aperture, the *micropyle*, through which the sperms find access : it is formed of a superficial layer of protoplasm surrounding a mass of transparent fluid yolk of a pale yellow colour. At one pole the protoplasm accumulates to form an elevated area or *germinal disc*, in which cleavage takes place (Fig. 218, *A*, *B*) in much the same way as in Chondrichthyes, except that, owing to the smaller proportion of yolk, the resulting blastoderm (*bl.*) and the embryo formed therefrom are proportionally much larger, and the yolk-sac (*y.s.*) correspondingly smaller, than in the two previous classes. Epiboly takes place as in Chondrichthyes, the blastoderm gradually growing round and enclosing the yolk (*C–F*). The embryo (*emb.*) arises as an elevation growing forwards from the thickened edge of the blastoderm, and, as it increases in length, appears as a clear colourless band (*H*, *emb.*) winding round the yellow yolk, and kept in close contact with it by

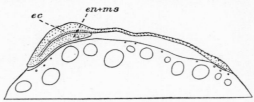

FIG. 219.—Longitudinal section of blastoderm of **Salmo**, at about the stage represented in *D* of Fig. 218. *ec.* ectoderm ; *en + ms*, infolding giving rise to endoderm and mesoderm. (After O. Hertwig.)

the enclosing zona radiata. There is no open medullary groove, the nervous system being formed, as in Lampreys, from a fold of ectoderm the walls of which are in apposition so as to form a keel-like ridge. The endoderm and mesoderm are formed as a result of a process of infolding of the posterior edge of the blastoderm (Fig. 219). Gradually the head and tail become free from the yolk, and at the time of hatching the yolk-sac (*I*, *y.s.*) is a shoe-shaped body sessile upon the ventral surface of the transparent embryo.

Systematic Position of the Example.

Salmo fario is one of several species of the genus *Salmo*, belonging to the family *Salmonidæ*, and the order " *Teleostei*."

The absence of a spiral valve and of a conus arteriosus, the presence of a bulbus *arteriosus*, and the decussation of the optic nerves indicate its position among the Teleostei. It belongs to the Isospondyli in virtue of possessing a pneumatic duct, none but jointed fin-rays, and abdominal pelvic fins. The characters which place it among the Salmonidæ are the presence of an adipose fin and of pseudobranchiæ, the absence of oviducts, and the fact that the maxilla enters into the gape of the mouth.   The genus *Salmo* is distinguished by its small scales, well-developed conical teeth, absent on the pterygoids, a short anal fin with fewer than fourteen rays, numerous pyloric appendages, and comparatively large ova.   The distinctive characters of the various species of *Salmo* depend upon comparatively minute points, such as the relative proportions of various parts, and are often difficult of determination owing to individual variations correlated with different environments.   In *S. fario* the posterior margin of the operculum is evenly curved, the maxilla is longer than the snout, and the vomerine teeth are in a double series and persist throughout life.

The remaining orders of the Neopterygii, which include the great majority of living fishes, are usually placed under the general heading of Teleosts. Representatives of the group first appear in the Upper Liassic period as an off-shoot of the holostean phase of evolution.   The process of separation was gradual, and a definite line of demarcation is not easy to make.   During the very early tertiary period the Teleosts expanded enormously and replaced the older phase of evolution to such an extent that at the present time the teleosts are, with the few exceptions already noted, the only bony fishes in existence. It is, moreover, very probable that the full tide of evolution has not yet been reached, and that new species are still in process of formation.   Teleosts have penetrated into every kind of environment, and show an amazing range of adaptation to different foods and habits, and give a striking picture of what is known as " adaptive radiation," of which a condensed account is given further on (p. 262).

The marks whereby a teleost, whatever its shape and appearance may be, can be recognised are partly in the loss of certain characters which are still preserved by the more primitive actinopterygians, such as the Palæopterygii, Protospondyli and Ginglymodi, and partly the presence of a number of structures which are new or, at least, definite modifications of old ones.

The characters that are lost are : the spiracle ; the spiral valve, the conus arteriosus in the heart which is reduced to one or at most two rows of valves, a loss which is compensated by the great enlargement of the bulbus arteriosus ; ganoine disappears from the exoskeleton and scales ; there are no longer any fulcral scales on the fins ; gular bones, with very few exceptions where they are much reduced, have disappeared or rather have been replaced by branchiostegal rays (Fig. 240).   The dermal bones tend more and more to sink beneath the skin and to come into closer association with the endocranium than is the case with the more primitive Palaeoniscids, Crossopterygians or Dipnoi.   The bones of the lower jaw are reduced to three elements only : the dentary, angular and articular.   The pectoral girdle loses the clavicle.

Of new or highly modified characters, the gills are now fully filamentar p. 86), the tail is externally, and in many cases internally, homocercal or even gephyrocercal. The skull, which shows an extreme range of variation in shape, always has a single instead of a paired vomer and, at the posterior dorsal surface, a single supraoccipital bone which is sometimes stated to be formed by the fusion of the neural arches of some of the anterior vertebræ, and which does not occur in any other fishes.[1] The vertebræ are amphicœlous. There are additional " ribs " known as the intermuscular bones. In the paired fins the radials are reduced to a few brachial ossicles, and the fin is completely fan-like, and without any trace of an axis. The urogenital organs have become highly specialised in that both ovaries and testes have acquired new ducts. In the male there is no longer any connection between the testis and meso-nephros. In the female in some cases—e.g., the trout (p. 253)—there is still an open-mouthed oviduct leading from the cœlom, but usually the oviduct sur-rounds the ovary so that the ova pass directly to the exterior without being previously shed into the cœlom. The teleost brain is also specialised, in that the upper walls of the cerebrum are very thin (the enlarged corpora striata on the ventral surface show through and give a false impression of cerebral hemis-pheres). The mid- and hind-brains are, however, often very large. There is a great development of the valvula cerebelli (Fig. 214), and the optic nerves cross over outside the brain without mixing (the absence of the so-called optic chiasma.)

A satisfactory classification of the twenty thousand, or more, living species of teleosts is, in the present state of our knowledge, a matter of great difficulty, and the number of extinct forms, great as it is, still leaves us in the dark as to the actual course of evolution of the many groups which go to form the teleostei. The essential teleost characters are present in all, however great the diversity in shape, and to make a classification on single anatomical characters or external appearance involves the danger of mistaking adaptive convergence for evidence of true affinity.

Certain broad groupings, however, can be made by taking into consideration stages of structure and the appearance of species in geological time. The earliest known fishes that can definitely be accepted as teleosts are placed in the genus *Leptolepis*, itself a derivative of the holostean family the Pholido-phoridæ, which occurs in the Upper, and perhaps in the Lower, Lias. These little fishes, from three to four inches long, show all the teleost characters of skull and skeleton that can be shown by a fossil, but with a few characters, such as the presence of a small gular bone, a perforation of the amphicœlous vertebræ by the notochord and the retention of some ganoine on the bones and scales, all characters showing that *Leptolepis* had not quite fully emerged from the holostean condition.

---

[1] The earliest known supraoccipital bone, however, is found in the Pholidophoridæ, a family transitional between the Holostei and Teleostei, where this bone appears to be a neurocranial ossification.

Taking *Leptolepis* (Fig. 220) as the starting-point, a number of the more primitive of living and extinct teleosts can be grouped around it as probable

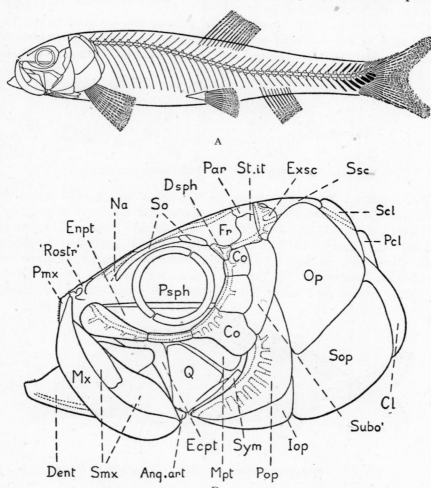

FIG. 220.—**Leptolepis bronni.** A, restoration; B, skull. *Ang. art.* angulo-articular; *Cl.* cleithrum; *Co.* circumorbital; *Dent.* dentary; *Dsph.* dermosphenotic; *Ecpt.* ectopterygoid; *Exsc.* extrascapular; *Fr.* frontal; *Iop.* interopercular; *Mpt.* metapterygoid; *Mx.* maxilla; *Na.* nasal; *Op.* opercular; *Par.* parietal; *Pcl.* postcleithrum; *Pmx.* premaxilla; *Pop.* pre-opercular; *Psph.* parasphenoid; *Q.* quadrate; *Rostr.* rostral bone; *Scl.* supracleithrum; *Smx.* supramaxilla; *So.* supraorbital; *Sop.* sub-opercular; *Ssc.* suprascapular; *St. it.* supratemporo intertemporal; *Subo.* suborbital; *sym.* symplectic. (After Dorothy H. Rayner.)

derivatives. This order is termed the Isospondyli, its members all being characterised by having an open duct from the air-bladder to the throat (known as the physostomous condition), by the fin rays being soft and flexible, by the backward position of the pelvic fins on the body and by the presence of a mesocoracoid element in the shoulder girdle. The cranial bones also often remain in the primitive position near the surface.

Excluding some extinct families, the Isospondyli are represented at the present time by the following seven sub-orders. Clupeoidea (Herrings, Shad, Sprats, Pilchard, Anchovy, Tarpon, etc.); Salmonoidea (Salmon, Trout, Char,

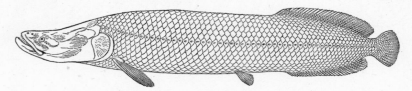

FIG. 221a.—**Arapaima gigas.**   (From *Cambridge Natural History*.)

Smelt, Grayling, Argentines, etc.); Osteoglossoidea (Tropical fresh-water fishes, some of very large size, *e.g.*, *Arapaima* (Fig. 221)); Notopteroidea (a small family of fresh-water fishes from Africa and the Orient, rather specialised in shape—*e.g.*, *Notopterus* (Fig. 237)); Mormyroidea (fresh-water fishes from Africa specialised in having the snout sometimes much elongated—*e.g.*, *Gymnarchus, Mormyrus* (Fig. 221 *b*)); Gonorhynchoidea (*Gonorhynchus* the sole living species of a family dating from the Cretaceous); Stomiatoidea

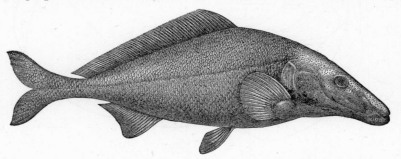

FIG. 221b.—**Mormyrus caballus.**   (From *Cambridge Natural History*.)

(deep-sea fishes usually with well-developed phosphorescent organs and often of very aberrant shape).

Although many members of the above sub-orders are often specialised in one way or another, they are all based on a primitive and generalised ground plan. Allied to them, but showing further anatomical changes, such as the loss of the mesocoracoid, frequent closure of the pneumatic duct, etc., is another group of orders, such as the Haplomi (Pikes and their allies); Iniomi (Lantern fishes); Lyomeri (deep-sea fishes of aberrant shape—*e.g.*, *Saccopharynx* (Fig. 222)); Apodes (Eels); Synentognathi (Garfishes, Flying-fishes, etc.); Micro-

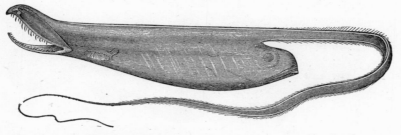

FIG. 222.—**Saccopharynx ampullaceus.** (From *Cambridge Natural History.*)

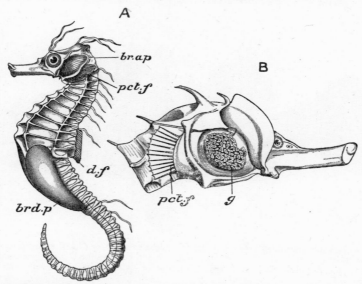

FIG. 223.—**Hippocampus** (Sea-horse). In *B* the operculum is removed to show the gills. *br. ap.* branchial aperture; *brd. p.* brood-pouch; *d. f.* dorsal fin; *g.* gills; *pct. f.* pectoral fin. (From Claus and Günther.)

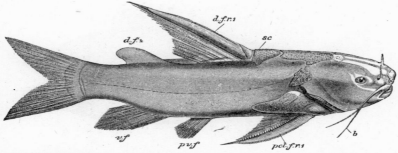

FIG. 224.—**Rita buchanani**, one of the Siluroids. *b.* barbel; *d. f. r. 1*, first dorsal fin-ray; *d. f. 2*, adipose fin; *pct. f. r. 1*, first pectoral fin-ray; *pv. f.* pelvic fin; *v. f.* ventral fin. (After Day.)

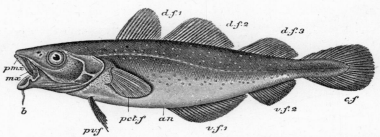

FIG. 225.—**Gadus morrhua** (Cod). *an.* anus; *c. f.* caudal fin; *d. f. 1—3*, dorsal fins; *mx.* maxilla; *pct. f.* pectoral fin; *pmx.* premaxilla; *pv. f.* pelvic fin; *v.f. 1* and *2*, ventral fins. (After Cuvier.)

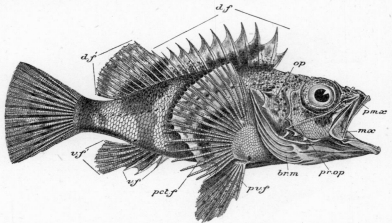

FIG. 226.—**Sebastes percoides.** *br. m.* branchiostegal membrane; *d. f.* spiny portion of dorsal fin; *d. f'.* soft portion; *mx.* maxilla; *op.* opercular; *pct. f.* pectoral fin; *p.mx.* premaxilla; *pr. op.* pre-opercular; *pv. f.* pelvic fin; *v. f.* spiny portion of ventral fin; *v.f'.* soft portion. (After Richardson.)

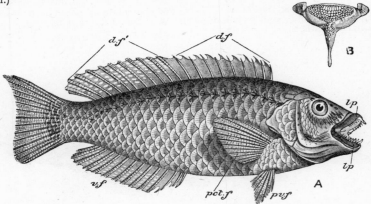

FIG. 227.—**Labrichthys psittacula** (Wrasse). *d. f.* hard dorsal fin; *d. f'.* soft dorsal; *lp.* lips; *pct. f.* pectoral fin; *pv. f.* pelvic fin; *v. f.* ventral fin. *B*, inferior pharyngeal bone of Labrichthys. (*A*, after Richardson; *B*, after Owen.)

cyprini; Allotriognathi (Oar- and Ribbon-fishes); Solenichthyes (Pipe-fishes, Sea-horses (Fig. 223), etc.), and Salmopercæ (" Trout-perch "). All these, although some of them number several hundred species, are relatively small groups. The Ostariophysi, however, which are characterised by a peculiar chain of bones, the " Weberian ossicles," connecting the air-bladder with the ear region, form one of the largest orders of fishes and include the Cyprinoids (Carp, Roach, Tench, Dace, Loach, Bream, Goldfish, Electric Eel), the Siluroids, (Cat-fishes, Rita), (Fig. 224), and indeed the majority of fresh-water fishes. The Anacanthini, the last of this series to be mentioned (Cod (Fig. 225), Haddock, Whiting, Hake, and the less commonly known Macrurids) are an important group, in that they afford so great a proportion of food fishes.

All fishes in the above-mentioned series have soft fin-rays. The remaining orders together form a super group, the Acanthopterygii, whose members have

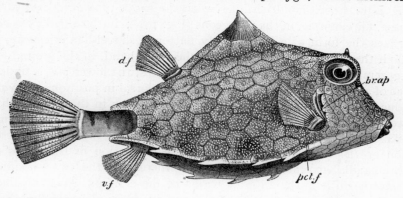

FIG. 228.—**Ostracion** (Coffer-fish). *br. ap.* branchial aperture; *d. f.* dorsal fin; *pct. f.* pectoral fin; *v. f.* ventral fin. (After Day.)

reached the highest degree of anatomical separation from the Leptolepid starting-point. The fins are now supported by rigid and frequently unsegmented spines, the pelvic fins have moved so far forward that they have become attached to the cleithrum, the cranial bones are deeply sunk and may be covered by scales, and the pneumatic duct, if present, is closed (physoclistous condition). The orders in this group are the Berycomorphi (the most primitive of the orders, with the pneumatic duct still open and the fin spines less developed); Zeomorphi (John Dories, Boar fish, etc.); Percomorphi (Perches, Sea bream (Fig. 226), Bass, Sunfish, Blennies, Angle-fish, Mullet, Tile-fish, Wrasses (Fig. 227), Sword-fish, etc.); Gobiomorphi (Gobies); Scleroparei (Gurnards, Miller's Thumb, etc.); Thoracostei (Sticklebacks); Heterosomata (Flat-fishes); Plectognathi (File- Trigger- Sun- Globe- (Fig. 228) and Porcupine-fishes); Pediculati (Angler-fishes), Opisthomi (Spiny Eels), and Symbranchii (Eel-like fishes without pectoral fins).

3. General Organisation.

External Form.—A typical form of the bony fishes is very fairly represented by that of the Trout (Fig. 201)—a long, compressed body, nearly half of which is formed by the tail, pointed anterior and posterior ends, a large vertical tail-fin, a head of moderate size, and a terminal mouth. Such a form is eminently fitted for rapid progression through the water. But from this characteristic fish-form there are many striking deviations. The body may be greatly elongated and almost cylindrical, as in the Eels; or of great length and strongly flattened from side to side, as in the Ribbon-fishes; or the head may be of immense proportional size and strongly depressed, as in certain bottom living fishes, such as the " Fishing-frog "; or, as in the beautiful Reef-fishes, the whole body may be as high as it is long. The mouth sometimes has a ventral position, as in most Chondrichthyes, with the snout prolonged over it. This is the case, for example, in the Sturgeons (Fig. 191); in the allied *Polyodon* the snout takes the form of a horizontally flattened shovel-like structure, about one-fourth the length of the body. On the other hand, in the ground-feeding " Star-gazers " and some other spiny-rayed fishes, the lower jaw is underhung like that of a bull-dog, and the mouth becomes dorsal in position. A *beak* may be produced by the prolongation of the upper jaw, as in the Sword-fish, or of the lower jaw, as in the Half-beak, or of both jaws, as in the Gar-fish (Fig. 196) and Pike. Such a projection is not to be confounded with the snout of the Sturgeon or *Polyodon*, being formed by the elongation of the bones of the jaws (premaxilla, maxilla, dentary, etc.), whereas in the two Chondrostean forms referred to it is the anterior region of the cranium which is prolonged. Still another form of " snout " is produced in many Teleostei by the great mobility of the jaws, allowing of their protrusion in the form of a short tube. In the Wrasses or " lip-fishes " the mouth is bounded by fleshy lips (Fig. 227, *lp.*).

Adaptation—the apparent suitability, that is to say, of an organism to its surroundings—is a phenomenon which is widespread throughout the animal and vegetable kingdoms. The results of this adaptation can be viewed from two aspects. One result is to bring about a resemblance between animals of *different* stocks that have taken up similar environments, a condition known as *convergent* adaptation. The other aspect, known as *divergent* adaptation or *adaptive radiation*, is when animals of *allied* stock have entered different environments and have come to differ superficially from one another, sometimes to a surprising degree.

Fishes, and in particular the Teleosts, from the abundance of species living and the great variety of their environments, afford excellent examples of both these related aspects of evolution. As an illustration of converged evolution may be quoted the superficial resemblance between the extinct holostean

Thoracopterus (Fig. 229) and *Exocœtus* (Fig. 230), a teleost of the Synentognathi. Both are " flying-fishes," and both, in their enlarged pectoral fins and hypobatic tails, show a striking similarity in general body form, while retaining, of course, the deeper-seated anatomical differences of their respective classes.

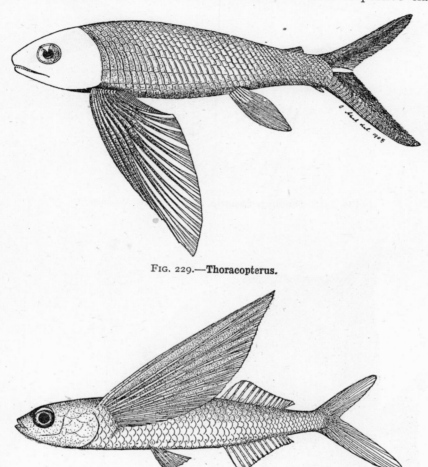

FIG. 229.—**Thoracopterus.**

FIG. 230.—**Exocœtus.**

A third "flying-fish" may be mentioned, *Chirothrix* (Fig. 231), which, like *Exocœtus*, is a teleost, but is extinct and of a different family. This form acquired its flying shape by a different road, since it was the pelvic, and not the pectoral, fins that became enlarged to form the gliding-planes. This is a reminder that adaptive evolution can attain similar functional ends by different means, and that the resemblance between convergent animals is one of varying

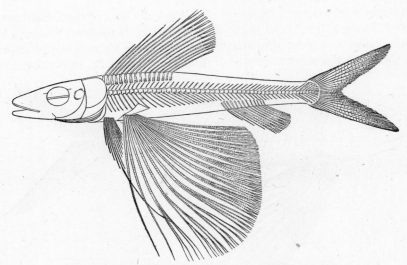

FIG. 231.—**Chirothrix libanicus.** (After Smith Woodward.)

FIG. 232.—**Microdon wagneri.** (From Smith Woodward after Thiollière.)

FIG. 233.—**Psettus sebæ** (After Gregory.)

degree, and never amounts to an identity of structure. Many fishes of very different families, or even classes, have acquired similar body-forms adapted presumably to some particular needs, such, for example, as the deep laterally compressed body shown by *Microdon* (Fig. 232), an Upper Jurassic holostean, by the still-living teleosts *Psettus sebæ* (Fig. 233) and *Pterophyllum* the "Angel-fish," amongst many others. Many, again, have independently acquired the eel-like shape or the peculiar whip-like tail of several different

Fig. 234.—**Notacanthus bonapartii.** (From *Cambridge Natural History*.)

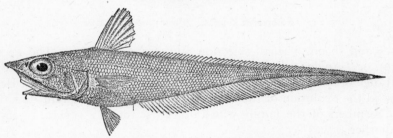

Fig. 235.—**Macrurus carminatus.** (From *Cambridge Natural History*.)

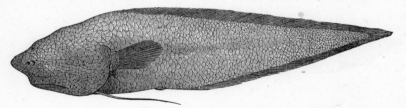

Fig. 236.—**Typhlonus nasus.** (From *Cambridge Natural History*.)

deep-sea fishes, such as *Notacanthus* (Fig. 234) (Heteromi), *Macrurus* (Fig. 235) (Anacanthini), *Typhlonus* (Fig. 236), and others.[1] In fact, any examination of the fishes will reveal a host of instances in which diverse fishes of similar habits have come to resemble one another to a greater or lesser degree, either in general shape, in fin structure, in dentition or in some or other character.

[1] But here again *Notopterus* (Fig. 237), a fresh-water and not a deep-sea fish has a very similar shape. It must therefore be conceded that, while this peculiar shape may be one of several possible shapes suitable for deep-sea life, it may also be convenient in another environment. It shows that in the present state of our knowledge no absolute rule can be laid down, and that conclusions must not be reached too easily.

The teleosts, taken as a whole, in themselves afford an example of adaptive radiation. While retaining their well-defined and diagnostic characters, they have assumed an almost infinite variety of shape and construction in accordance with the many different environments into which they have migrated. Apart from those fishes which have a " normal " body, it will be enough to mention such forms as the flat-fishes, eels, pipe-fishes, procupine-fishes, the curious

FIG. 237.—**Notopterus kapirat.** (From Goodrich, after Day.)

sea-horses and so on, a small selection out of a vast range. The Pediculati (Fig. 239), or " Angler-fishes," give a good example of adaptive radiation over a small range of structure, and within the limits of a single family. Here can be observed the evolution of the tentacle on the head in different directions in different members of the family which otherwise retain a general resemblance to one another.

The process by which an animal, or an organ, becomes adapted to a particular function is still one of the unsolved problems of evolution, nor can it always be

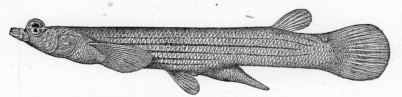

FIG. 238.—**Anableps tetrophthalmus.** (From *Cambridge Natural History*.)

stated with certainty that every character is adapted. Some characters that appear (perhaps from our own ignorance) to have no particular adaptive significance may be remnants of a former stage of evolution which, owing to some change in environment, have ceased their useful function. A structure once useful may, under changed circumstances, even become harmful in which case extinction would sooner or later be the result. On the other hand, there are many characters which are clearly adaptive, as, for example, the specialised modification of the breathing organs in *Anabas*, the " Climbing Perch," or the division of the eye into an upper and lower section for vision above and below water respectively in *Anableps tetrophthalmus* (Fig. 238), the " Four-eyed Fish." All characters such as these, it must be presumed, have been gradually perfected by natural selection, and will continue so long as the particular environment, nature of food and habits remains unchanged. It is not easy to explain the majority of adaptations in any other way.

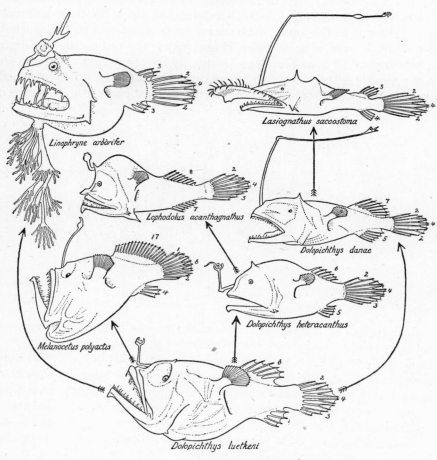

Linophryne arborifer

Lasiognathus saccostoma

Lophodolus acanthagnathus

Dolopichthys danae

Melanocetus polyactis

Dolopichthys heteracanthus

Dolopichthys luetkeni

FIG. 239.—" Angler fishes." (From Gregory, after Regan.)

Tactile processes or *barbels* sometimes arise from the head; the most familiar example is that on the chin of the Sturgeon (Fig. 191 *b*) Cod or Haddock (Fig. 227, *b*.). An *operculum* is always present, and is supported by a variable number of investing bones; it is continued below into a *branchiostegal membrane* (Fig. 240), which, except in Crossopterygii and the Sturgeons, is supported by bony rays. In *Polypterus* a pair of bony *jugular plates* (Fig. 195, *B*, *jug. pl.*) are placed at the lower end of the branchiostegal membrane, between the rami of the mendible : *Amia* has a single plate (Fig. 200, *B*, *jug. pl.*) in the same position. *Spiracles* are present only in *Polypterus* (Fig. 246) and some Sturgeons.

The commonest number of *median fins* is two dorsals, one caudal, and one ventral, but this number may be increased or diminished (Figs. 225 and 227), or there may be a continuous median fin extending along the back and round the end of the tail to the anus. The dorsal fin is sometimes partly or wholly represented by a series of small *finlets* (Figs. 195). The tail fin may be diphycercal, heterocercal, or homocercal, and is usually the chief organ of progression. But in the Sea-horse (Fig. 223) there is no caudal fin, and the tail is prehensile, being used in the position of rest to coil, in the vertical plane, round sea-weeds,

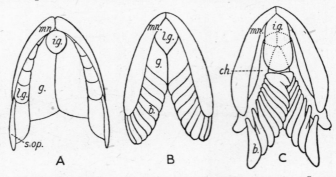

FIG. 240.—Ventral view of gular plates and branchiostegal rays in A, a Crossopterygian ; B, *Elonichthys*, a palæoniscid ; C, *Amia* ; *G*, gular plates ; *i.g.* intergular ; *l. g.* lateral gulars ; *s. op.* sub-opercular ; *b.* branchiostegals ; *ch.* ceratohyal ; *mn.* mandible. (After Regan.)

etc. : when swimming it hangs downwards, having no lateral movement, and locomotion is effected mainly by the vibration of the dorsal fin.

The *dermal-rays* of the caudal fin are always jointed, as in the Trout, but in the Acanthopterygian type of fishes more or fewer of the foremost rays of the dorsal, anal, and pelvic fins are unjointed, forming *spines* (Figs. 226 and 227, *d. f.*), sometimes large and strong enough to recall the dermal defences of some Sharks and of Holocephali. In *Polypterus* (Fig. 195) each finlet is supported along its anterior edge by a strong spine, to which the soft rays are attached.

The anterior dorsal fin may attain an immense size, and is subject to some curious variations. In the Fishing-frog or Angler (*Lophius*) its foremost rays are elongated and bear lobes or lures by which small fishes are attracted as to the bait on a fishing-line.

In the Sucking-fish (*Echeneis*) the anterior dorsal fin is modified into an adhesive disc by means of which the fish attaches itself to the bodies of Sharks and Turtles.

The portion of the *paired fins* visible externally is usually very thin, and supported entirely by dermal rays. But in *Polypterus* (Fig. 247) the rays form a fringe round a thick basal lobe, which is supported by endoskeletal structures (*vide infra*). This condition of things forms an approach to the structure met with in Elasmobranchii and Holocephali. The pectorals vary considerably in size, and in the Flying-fishes (Exocetidæ) and flying Gurnards (Dactylopteridæ) form large, wing-like expansions, capable of sustaining the animal in its long leaps into the air. In many fishes the pelvics are reduced to filaments or scales, and in some cases a sucking-disc is developed in connection with them. The pectorals always retain their normal position, just behind the gill-clefts, but the pelvics often become more or less shifted forwards from the typical position beside the vent. The change in position is least in the " ganoid " orders [1] (Figs. 191, 195, 196, and 200) and in the Isospondyli and allied orders (Fig.

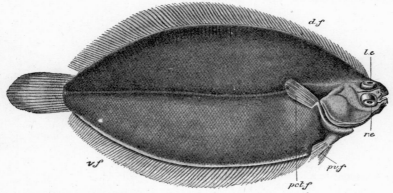

FIG. 241.—**Glyptocephalus cynoglossus** (Craig-fluke), from the right side. *d. f.* dorsal fin ; *l. e.* left eye ; *pct. f.* pectoral fin ; *pv. f.* pelvic fin ; *r. e.* right eye ; *v. f.* ventral fin. (After Cuvier.)

201), in which they are usually between the middle of the abdomen and the anus, and are said to be *abdominal* in position ; but in a large proportion of the fishes in the remaining orders of Teleostei they come to be placed almost beneath the pectorals (Fig. 227, *pv. f.*), when their position is called *thoracic*, or on the throat (Fig. 225), when they are said to be *jugular* in position.

A very remarkable deviation from the typical form occurs in the Flat-fishes (Heterosomata). The body (Fig. 241) is very deep and strongly compressed : the fish habitually rests on the bottom, in some species on the right, in others on the left side, partly covering itself with sand, and occasionally swimming with an undulating movement. The under side is usually pure white, the upper side dark. The eyes (*r. e.*, *l. e.*) are both on the upper or dark-coloured side, and the skull is distorted so as to adapt the orbits to this change of position.

[1] In this section the term " ganoid " has been left unaltered. It may be read as covering the Palæopterygii (Sturgeons and *Polypterus*) together with *Amia* and *Lepidosteus*.

The abdominal cavity is very small, the anus placed far forward, and the dorsal and anal fins are sometimes continuous. Young Flat-fishes swim in the ordinary vertical position, but after a time they lie on one side and assume the adult peculiarities, the eye on the lower side gradually rotating until it reaches the upper surface.

Many shore-fishes exhibit protective characters, the tints and markings of the skin being harmonised with those of the rocks, sea-weeds, etc., among which they live. The effect may be heightened by fringes and lobes of skin, resembling sea-weed, and often giving the fish a most grotesque appearance. The colours are often adaptable : Trout, for instance, alter their colour by the contraction or expansion of their pigment-cells, according to whether the streams in which they live have a muddy or a sandy bottom. In some shore-fishes, such as those of the coral reefs, the colours are of the most brilliant description ; vivid reds, blues, and yellows, spots or stripes of gold or silver, are common, and

FIG. 242.—**Stomias boa.** The white dots are the luminous organs.   FIG. 243.—Ctenoid scale.
(From Hickson, after Filhol.)   (After Günther.)

although the combination of tints may sometimes seem to our eye rather crude and glaring, they appear to be distinctly protective, harmonising with the brilliant hues of the coral polypes and other members of the reef fauna. Pelagic fishes, such as the Mackerel and Herring, are usually steely-blue above, white beneath.

Many deep-sea Teleostei are phosphorescent : in some of these definite *luminous organs* (Fig. 242) are arranged in longitudinal rows along the body, each provided with a lens and other accessory parts, like those of the eye, the whole organ having the character of a minute bull's eye lantern. Some species of the same order, such as the Weever (*Trachinus*), possess *poison-glands*, opening either on one of the dorsal spines, or on a spinous process of the operculum, or, as in the Cat-fishes (Siluridæ), on the spine of the pectoral fin.

Exoskeleton.—In many bony fishes, such as *Polyodon* and many Eels, the skin is devoid of hard parts, but in most cases a dermal exoskeleton is present. In *Amia* and in the majority of Teleostei this takes the form, as in the Trout, of *scales*, rounded plates of bone imbedded in pouches of the dermis and over-lapping one another from behind forwards. When the free border of the scales presents an even curve, as in *Amia* and most Physostomi and Anacanthini, they are called *cycloid* scales (Fig. 203); when, as in most "spiny-rayed" fishes, the free edge is produced into small spines (Fig. 243), they are dis-tinguished as *ctenoid* scales. Usually the integument is continued as a thin layer over the surface of the scales, but in a good many cases this investment is absent. In exceptional cases the scales by a redeposition of bone may be so large and strong as to form a rigid armour. In the Sturgeon (Fig. 191) there is a strong armour, formed of stout bony plates, or *scutes*, produced into enamelled spines and articulating with one another by suture. Scutes are also found in many Siluroids (Fig. 226) and in Lophobranchii (Fig. 223) and some Plectognathi (Fig. 228); while in other Plectognathi the exoskeleton takes the form, as in the File-fishes, of minute spines like the shagreen of Sharks, or, as in many Globe-fishes, of long, outstanding, bony spines. Lastly, in *Polypterus* and *Lepidosteus* are found *ganoid* scales in the form of thick, close-set, rhomboidal plates formed of bone, covered externally by a layer of enamel-like material (*ganoin*) and joined together by pegs and sockets. In many Ganoids the anterior fin-rays of both median and paired fins bear a row of spine-like scales called *fulcra* (Fig. 196, *fl.*). True dermal teeth similar to those of the Chondrichthyes occur scattered over the scales and lepidotrichia in some of the bony fishes (*e.g., Lepidosteus, Polypterus*) : these may be fixed or movable (Siluroids).

Endoskeleton.—In the Sturgeons the *vertebral column* (Fig. 192 and 245) consists of a persistent notochord with cartilaginous arches, and is fused anteriorly with the cranium. In the remaining orders bony vertebræ are present ; the centra are biconcave, except in some Eels, in which the anterior face is flat or even convex, and in *Lepidosteus*, in which the anterior face is distinctly convex. Vertebræ of this form, *i.e.*, having the centrum convex in front and concave behind, are called *opisthocœlous*. Ribs are usually present : in *Polypterus* each vertebra has two pairs, a dorsal pair (Fig. 244, *R, I—V*) of considerable length, running between the dorsal and ventral muscles, and a short ventral pair (†) between the muscles and the peritoneum : the former answer to the ribs of Chondrichthyes, the latter to the ribs (*pleural ribs*) of the remaining bony fishes, which are always placed immediately beneath the peritoneum. There may be one or more sets of intermuscular bones, attached either to the neural arch (*epineurals*), to the centrum (*epicentrals*) or the ribs (*epipleurals*), not preformed in cartilage, but developed as ossifications of the intermuscular septa. The posterior end of the vertebral column is turned up in the Sturgeons, *Lepidosteus*, and *Amia*, resulting in a *heterocercal* tail-fin : in *Amia*, however, the fin-rays are so disposed that the fin appears almost symmetrical. Among Teleostei the tail-fin is very usually *homocercal*, as in the

Trout, with a more or less disguised asymmetry: in many cases in the adult the development of the large, fan-shaped, posterior hæmal arches completely hides the upturned end of the notochord, and in some the spinal column

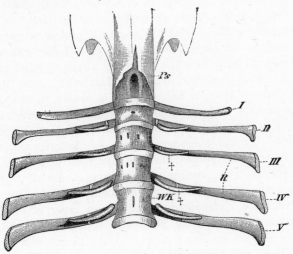

FIG. 244.—Anterior end of vertebral column of **Polypterus.** *PS.* parasphenoid; *R. I—V,* dorsal ribs; *WK,* centra; †, ventral (pleural) ribs. (From Wiedersheim's *Comparative Anatomy.*)

ends simply in a somewhat compressed centrum around which the fin-rays are symmetrically disposed; such truly symmetrical tail-fins are called *diphycercal.*

In the structure of the *skull,* the cranium of the Chondrostei (Fig. 245) is an undivided mass of cartilage with a few isolated replacing bones. The roofing

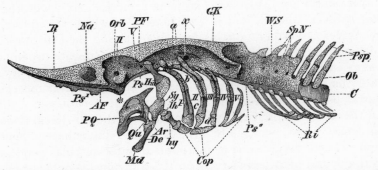

FIG. 245.—Skull of **Sturgeon,** with the investing bones removed. *a.* pharyngo-branchials; *AF.* antorbital process; *AR.* articular; *b.* epibranchial; *c.* ceratobranchial; *C,* notochord; *Cop.* basibranchials; *d.* hypobranchial; *De.* dentary; *GK.* auditory capsule; *HM.* hyomandibular; *hy.* hyoid cornu; *Ih.* interhyal; *Md.* mandible; *Na.* nasal capsule; *Ob.* neural arches; *PF.* post-orbital process; *PQ.* palatoquadrate; *Ps. Ps'. Ps''.* parasphenoid; *Psp.* neural spines; *Qu.* quadrate; *R.* rostrum; *Ri.* ribs; *Sp. N.* foramina for spinal nerves; *Sy.* symplectic; *WS.* vertebral column; *x.* vagus foramen; *I—V,* branchial arches. (From Wiedersheim's *Comparative Antomy.*)

investing bones lie in the dermis, so as to be practically superficial, and behind pass insensibly into the scutes covering the trunk; the fact that these bones (parietals, frontals, etc.) are exoskeletal structures is here perfectly obvious. The same is the case in *Polypterus* (Fig. 246), in which, however, the replacing bones are better developed. In *Lepidosteus*

and *Amia*, and especially the latter, the skull resembles that of the Trout in all essential respects, the main differences consisting in the absence of certain bones, such as the supra-occipital, and in the presence of additional investing bones. Among Teleostei it is only in the Isospondyli that the investing bones remain separable from the chondrocranium in the adult; in the remaining orders, *e.g.* in the Cod, Haddock, or Perch, they become grafted on to the chondrocranium and so closely united with the replacing bones that they can be removed only by pulling the whole skull to pieces; most of the original cartilage frequently disappears in the adult and the cranium thus becomes a firm bony mass in which no distinction between replacing and investing bones is discernible.

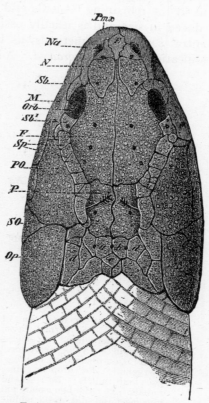

FIG. 246.—Skull of **Polypterus**, from above. *F.* frontal; *M.* maxilla; *N.* nasal; *Na.* nostril; *Op.* opercular; *Orb.* orbit; *P.* parietal. The remaining letters point to less important investing bones. The arrow is passed into the spiracle. (From Wiedersheim's *Comparative Anatomy*.)

The varying size of the gape, which is so noticeable a feature in the fishes, depends upon the inclination of the suspensorium: in wide-mouthed Fishes (Fig. 227) the axis of the hyomandibular and suspensorium is nearly vertical or even inclined backwards; in small-mouthed forms (Fig. 228) it is strongly inclined forwards, and the length of the jaws is proportionately reduced. In the branchial arches the pharyngobranchials of each side are very commonly fused, and constitute what are called the *superior pharyngeal bones*: the reduced fifth branchial bars, or *inferior pharyngeal bones*, bite against them. In some Percoid fishes are distinguished by having the inferior pharyngeal bones united into a single bony mass of characteristic form (Fig. 227, *B*). The gill-rakers are often very highly developed, and may form a mesh capable of retaining even microscopic organisms.

In the *shoulder-girdle*, of the Chondrostei there is a primary shoulder-girdle consisting of large paired cartilages, not united in the middle ventral line, and unossified : each is covered externally by a large scute-like investing bone, the *cleithrum*. In *Polypterus* a clavicle and cleithrum are also present, but in the remaining Ganoids and in Teleostei the primary shoulder-girdle is reduced in size and is usually ossified by two bones, a dorsal *scapula* and a ventral *coracoid* : sometimes, as in the Trout, there may be an additional ossification, the *mesocoracoid*. Additional investing bones—*supra-cleithrum,*

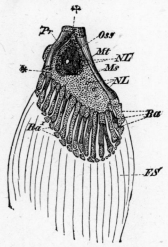

Fig. 247.—Pectoral fin of **Polypterus.** *FS.* dermal rays; *MS.* mesopterygium; *MT.* metapterygium; *NL.* nerve-foramina; *Oss.* ossification in mesopterygium; *Pr.* propterygium; *Ra.* first radials; *Ra¹.* second radials. At * the bony marginal rays meet and shut off the middle region from the shoulder-girdle. (From Wiedersheim's *Comparative Anatomy.*)

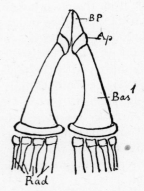

Fig. 248.—Pelvic fin of young **Polypterus.** *Ap.* part of basal; *Bas¹.* basal; *BP.* pelvic cartilages (fused in adult); *Rad.* radials. (From Wiedersheim.)

post-cleithrum, etc.—are added, and one of them, the *post-temporal*, serves to articulate the shoulder-girdle with the skull (Fig. 210).

In the skeleton of the *pectoral fin* of *Polypterus* (Fig. 247) the basal lobe of the fin is supported by a rod-like ossified propterygium (*Pr*), a broad cartilaginous, partly ossified, mesopterygium (*MS*), and an ossified metapterygium (*MT*) ; to these, two rows of elongated radials (*Ra, Ra¹*) are articulated fanwise, and these in their turn give attachment to the fin-rays (*FS*). In all the remaining orders the basalia (pro-, meso-, and meta-pterygium) are absent, and the endoskeleton of the fin consists only of a single or double row of radials (Fig. 210).

In *Polypterus* there is a vestigial *pelvic girdle* (Fig. 248, *BP*) in the form of a small rhomboidal cartilage to which the anterior ends of the basalia (*Bas*[1]) are attached. In all the remaining orders the pelvic girdle appears to be atrophied. The *pelvic fin* is supported by a single bone of variable form (Fig. 211, **B. PTG**) and apparently arising from the fusion of proximal pterygiophores. Between its posterior end and the dermal rays irregular nodules, representing radials, may be interposed.

The distinction between hard or unjointed fin-rays, or spines, and soft or jointed fin-rays has already been referred to. The first ray of the dorsal and pectoral fins sometimes, *e.g.* in Siluroids (Fig. 224), has the form of a very strong spine articulated by a bolt-and-shackle joint, *i.e.* by the interlocking of two rings. In some cases the first dorsal spine springs from the skull.

The texture of the bones is subject to wide variation: in some " Spiny-rayed " fishes they are very thick and strong, in some places almost like ivory; while in the Lump-fish (*Cyclopterus*), the huge Sunfish (*Mola*), and in many deep-sea forms, such as the Ribbon-fishes (*Regalecus* and *Trachypterus*), the amount of mineral matter is so small that the bones are easily cut with a knife and weigh astonishingly little when dry.

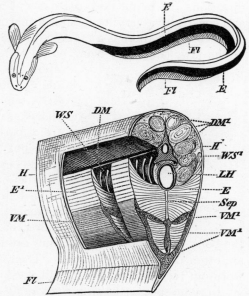

FIG. 249.—**Electrophorus electricus**, A, showing the extent of the electric organ (*E*). *Fl*, ventral fin. B, small portion of tail, in section. *DM. DM'*. dorsal muscles. *E. E'*. electric organ; *Fl*, ventral fin; *H*, skin; *LH*. caudal canal; *Sep*. fibrous septum; *VM. VM'*. ventral, muscles; *WS, WS'*, vertebral column, with spinal nerves. (From Wiedersheim's *Comparative Anatomy*.)

Electric Organs.—Three genera of bony fishes possess electric organs, the Electric Cat-fish (*Malapterurus*), one of the Siluridæ, found in the fresh waters of tropical Africa, the Electric Eel (*Cyprinoid*), *Electrophorus* occurring in Brazil and the Guianas, and an American Star-gazer of the genus *Astroscopus*. In *Malapterurus* the electric organ extends over the whole body, beneath the skin; in *Electrophorus* (Fig. 249) there is a pair of batteries in the ventral half of the greatly elongated tail; in *Astroscopus* the electric organs are situated on the upper surface of the head just behind the eyes. As in the Chondrichthyes, the electric organs are formed by modification of muscular tissue.

Digestive Organs.—Some fishes are toothless; but in most instances *teeth* are present, and may be developed on the pre-maxilla, maxilla, palatine, pterygoid, vomer, parasphenoid, dentary, basihyal, and bones of the branchial arches. It is characteristic of most Teleostei, with the exception of Isospondyli, that the maxilla is edentulous and does not enter into the gape (Fig. 226). In a large majority of species the teeth are small, conical, and recurved, suitable for preventing the struggling prey from slipping out of the mouth, but quite unfitted for either tearing or crushing. In some fishes, such as the Pike, the teeth are hinged backwards so as to offer no resistance to the passage of the prey towards the gullet, but effectually barring any movement in the other direction. In many deep-sea fishes (Fig. 222) the teeth are of immense size and constitute a very formidable armature to the jaws. A number of instances occur in which there is a marked differentiation of the teeth, those in the front of the jaws (Fig. 250) being pointed or chisel-edged, and adapted for seizing, while the back teeth have spherical surfaces adapted for crushing. In the Wrasses (Fig. 227, *B*) strong crushing teeth are developed on the pharyngeal bones. In the Globe-fishes the teeth are apparently reduced to one or two in each jaw, but each "tooth" in this case really consists of numerous calcified plates fused together. The teeth may be either simply embedded in the mucous membrane so as to be detached when the bones are macerated or boiled, or they may be implanted in sockets of

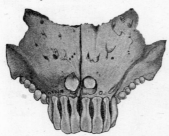

FIG. 250.—Premaxillæ of **Sargus**, showing teeth. (After Owen.)

the bone, or ankylosed to it. They are formed of some variety of dentine, and are often capped with enamel. Their succession is perpetual, *i.e.* injured or worn-out teeth are replaced at all ages.

In some species the *alimentary canal* shows little differentiation into regions, but, as a rule, gullet, stomach, duodenum, ileum, and rectum are more or less clearly distinguishable. The *stomach* is generally V-shaped, but its cardiac region may be prolonged into a blind pouch; it is often very distensible, allowing some of the deep-sea Teleostei to swallow fishes as large as themselves. In the Globe-fishes the animal can inflate the gullet with air or water when it floats upside down. The Ganoids have a *spiral valve* in the intestine, which is very well developed in *Polypterus* and the Sturgeon, vestigial in *Lepidosteus* (Fig. 252, *sp. v.*) and *Amia*: it is absent in all Teleostei, except possibly in *Chirocentrus*, one of the Isospondyli and a trace occurs in the Herring. The liver is usually large; a pancreas may be present as a compact gland, as in Chondrichthyes, or may be widely diffused between the layers of the mesentery, or in part surrounded by the liver. *Pyloric cæca* are commonly present, and vary in number from a single one to two hundred. The anus is always distinct from, and in front of, the urinogenital aperture.

Respiratory Organs.—The gills are usually comb-like, as in the Trout, the branchial filaments being free, owing to the atrophy of the interbranchial septa.   In the Sturgeon, however, the septa are fairly well developed, reaching half-way up the filaments, so that the latter are free only in their distal portions ; this arrangement is obviously intermediate between the chondrichthyan and teleostean conditions (Fig. 68).   The most striking deviation from the normal structure occurs in Syngnathidæ, in which the gill-filaments are replaced by curious tufted processes (Fig. 223, *B*, *g*.).   As a rule gills (holobranchs) are developed on the first four branchial arches, but the fourth is frequently

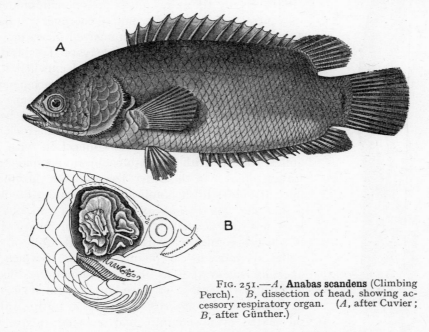

FIG. 251.—*A*, **Anabas scandens** (Climbing Perch).   *B*, dissection of head, showing accessory respiratory organ.   (*A*, after Cuvier ; *B*, after Günther.)

reduced to a hemibranch, and further reduction takes places in some cases. The pseudobranch or vestigial hyoidean gill may either retain the characteristic comb-like structure, as in the Trout, or may be reduced, as in the Cod, to a gland-like organ formed of a plexus of blood-vessels and called a *vaso-ganglion* or *rete mirabile*.   In most Teleosts the mechanism of respiration is similar to what has already been described in the case of the Trout, and respiratory valves are developed in the mouth-cavity.   But there are considerable differences in details, more especially as regards the relative importance of the opercula and the branchiostegal membranes in carrying on the movements of inspiration and expiration.

In additon to the gills some Teleostei possess accessory organs of respiration. In *Amphipnous*, an Indian physostome, the gills are poorly developed and are functionally replaced by a vascular sac occurring on each side of the body and opening in front into the first (hyobranchial) gill-cleft. Such sacs are physiologically, though not morphologically, lungs. In the Climbing Perch (*Anabas*) of the Oriental Region (Fig. 251) the superior pharyngeal bones are developed into folded plates (*B*) covered with vascular mucous membrane and capable of retaining water for a considerable period : the fish is able to traverse the land, and is even said to climb trees, holding on alternately by the spines of its pre-operculum and of its ventral fins. It has become so thoroughly a land-animal that it is drowned if immersed in water. In the little armoured siluroid *Callichthys* anal respiration takes place, air being drawn into and expelled from the rectum. Lastly, in the curious little goggle-eyed *Periophthalmus* of the Indian and Pacific Oceans the tail-fin seems to serve as a respiratory organ, being kept in the water while the fish perches on a rock.

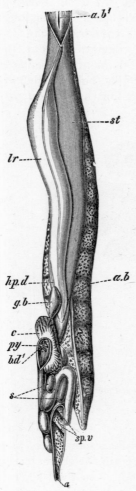

FIG. 252.—Digestive organs and air-bladder of **Lepidosteus.** *a.* anus; *a. b.* air-bladder; *a. b'.* its aperture in the pharynx; *b. d'.* aperture of bile-duct; *c.* pyloric cæca; *g. b.* gall-bladder; *hp. d.* hepatic duct; *lr.* liver; *py.* pyloric valve; *s.* spleen; *sp. v.* spiral valve; *st.* stomach. (From Wiedersheim's *Comparative Anatomy,* after Balfour and Parker.)

The **air-bladder** retains its connection with the gullet (rarely with the stomach) in Ganoids and Physostomes ; in the other Teleostei the pneumatic duct atrophies in the adult and the bladder becomes a shut sac. In *Polypterus* it consists of two lobes, a large left and a smaller right. The pneumatic duct is always connected with the dorsal wall of the gullet or stomach, except in *Polypterus*, in which the aperture is ventral. The bladder is sometimes divided into compartments or produced into lateral offshoots : in *Amia* and *Lepidosteus* (Fig. 252, *a. b.*) its wall is sacculated or raised into anastomosing ridges, enclosing more or less well-marked chambers and thus resembling a lung. In *Polypterus* its lung-like character is enhanced by the ventral position of the opening and by the blood being conveyed to it (as is also the case in *Amia*) by a pair of *pulmonary arteries* given off from the last pair of epibranchial arteries, as in the Dipnoi.

The air-bladder seems to be capable of acting as a sort of accessory respiratory organ ; it has been found that in a perch, asphyxiated in stagnant water, the oxygen in the bladder, which normally amounts to 20 or 25 per cent., is entirely absorbed and replaced by nitrogen and carbonic acid. Its normal function, however, is hydrostatic, *i.e.*, it serves to keep the fish of the same specific gravity as the water. The specific gravity of the fish as a whole, rising or falling as it must on account of the increase or decrease of pressure at various depths as the fish descends or ascends causing greater or less compression of the gases in the air-bladder, can be brought to approximate to that of the surrounding water by increase or decrease in the quantity of the contained gas. This is brought about by secretion or absorption, often by means

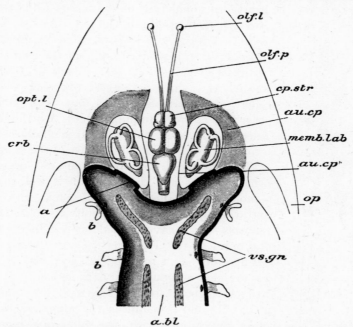

FIG. 253.—Horizontal section of posterior portion of head and anterior end of air-bladder in **Pseudophycis bachus,** one of the Gadidæ or Cods (semi-diagrammatic). *a.* thickened portion of air-bladder fitting into fenestra in posterior wall of auditory capsule; *a. bl.* air-bladder; *au. cp.* outer wall of auditory capsule; *au. cp'.* inner (membranous) wall; *b.* hollow offshoots of air-bladder; *cp. str.* corpora striata; *crb.* cerebellum; *memb. lab.* membranous labyrinth; *olf. l.* olfactory bulbs; *olf. p.* olfactory peduncles (olfactory tracts); *op.* operculum; *opt. l.* optic lobes; *vs. gn.* vaso-ganglia.

of vaso-ganglia or *red glands* (Fig. 253, *vs. gn*). These are elevations of the wall of the bladder, abundantly supplied with blood, and containing tubular glands which open into the cavity of the bladder. In fishes with a pneumatic duct the red glands are absent, but in the Eels and others their place is taken by *red bodies* of similar appearance, but with non-glandular epithelium. In some forms with closed air-bladder the anterior end of the organ is forked, and each branch (Fig. 253, *a*) fits closely against a membranous space in the posterior wall of the auditory capsule, while laterally it extends outwards in the region of the shoulder-girdle, and comes to lie immediately beneath the skin; any change in volume of the air bladder is thus communicated to the auditory organ. A more sensitive apparatus exists in the carps and siluroids, in which a chain of bones connects the air bladder with the ear, forming the Weberian apparatus. Both mechanisms control by reflex action the passage of gas to and from the bladder, tending to maintain the volume of this organ constant at all depths. This ensures that the equilibrium will not change during a sufficiently slow migration to shallower or deeper water.

The structure of the **heart** forms one of the most striking differences between the " Ganoid " orders and the Teleostei. In Ganoids there is a muscular conus arteriosus with rows of valves, as in the Chondrichthyes; in Teleostei a vestige of the conus containing two rows of valves has been found in *Albula* (Physostomi), and similar vestiges occur in several other genera of the same sub-order, but in all the rest of the order it is entirely unrepresented. On the other hand, Teleostei always have a large bulbus arteriosus, formed as a dilatation of the base of the ventral aorta.

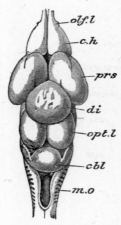

FIG. 254.—Brain of **Lepidosteus,** dorsal view. *cbl.* cerebellum; *c. h.* olfactory part of prosencephalon; *di.* diencephalon; *m. o.* medulla oblongata; *olf. l.* olfactory bulbs; *opt. l.* optic lobes; *prs.* corpora striata. (After Balfour and Parker.)

In the **brain** the cerebellum and optic lobes are usually large; the diencephalon is well developed in Ganoids, almost obsolete in Teleostei. In the Teleostei and Ganoidei the prosencephalon has the general features which have been described in the account of the brain of the Trout: it is not divided into hemispheres and has a roof which, except in *Amia*, is completely non-nervous; its floor consists of a pair of massive corpora striata (Fig. 254, *prs.*, and Fig. 213, *BG.*). In most instances the olfactory bulbs are in close apposition with the olfactory region of the prosencephalon without the intervention of olfactory stalks or tracts; but in some cases, as in the Cod (Fig. 253, *olf. p.*), they are borne on long *olfactory peduncles* or *olfactory tracts*. The Ganoids agree with Chondrichthyes in the fact that the optic nerves form a chiasma, while in Teleostei they simply cross one another or decussate. Here also, however, the distinction is not quite absolute, since in the Herring and some other Physostomes one nerve passes through a slit in the other. In some Plectognaths the spinal cord undergoes a remarkable shortening: in a Sun-fish 2½ metres in length and weighing a ton and a half the cord is only 15 millimetres long, being actually shorter than the brain.

Urinogenital Organs.—The *kidney* (Fig. 212, *kd.*) is formed from the mesonephros of the embryo, and usually attains a great size; the pronephros usually atrophies. The urinary duct (*ur.*) is the undivided pronephric duct: it unites with its fellow of the opposite side before opening either directly on to the exterior or into a urinogenital sinus. A *urinary bladder* is formed as a single or double dilatation of the duct. The right and left kidneys undergo more or less fusion, and their anterior ends are usually converted into adenoid or lymphatic

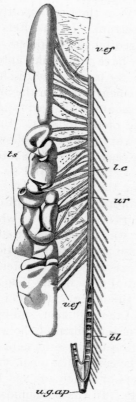

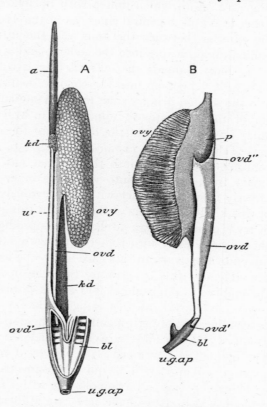

FIG. 255.—Male organs of **Lepidosteus**. *bl.* bladder; *l. c.* longitudinal canal; *ts.* testis; *u.g. ap.* urinogenital aperture; *ur.* urinary duct; *v. ef.* vasa efferentia. (After Balfour and Parker.)

FIG. 256.—Female organs of **Lepidosteus** (*A*) and **Amia** (*B*). *a*, degenerate anterior portion of kidney; *bl.* bladder; *kd.* kidney; *ovd.* oviduct; *ovd.'* aperture of oviduct into bladder; *ovd."* peritoneal aperture; *ovy.* ovary; *p.* peritoneum; *u.g. ap.* urinogenital aperture; *ur.* urinary duct. (*A*, after Balfour and Parker; *B*, after Huxley.)

tissue (*kd.'*), so that, while resembling the rest of the organ in external appearance they do not discharge a renal function.

The *male organs* of *Lepidosteus* may be taken as an example of those of Ganoids. The testis (Fig. 255, *ts.*) is a paired, lobulated organ, the secretion of which is carried by a large number of vasa efferentia (*v. ef.*) into a longitudinal canal (*l. c.*) lying alongside the urinary duct (*ur.*). From this canal tubes

are given off which communicate with the urinary tubules of the kidney or open directly into the duct, so that the seminal fluid has to traverse the latter in order to reach the urinary bladder (*bl.*) and make its escape by the common urinogenital aperture (*u.g. ap.*). In Teleostei there are no vasa efferentia, but the posterior end of the testis is directly continued into a duct (Fig. 212, *v. d.*) which unites with its fellow of the opposite side and opens either into a urinogenital sinus, as in the Trout, or, as in the Cod, directly on the exterior, between the anus and the urinary aperture. In the Eels the seminal fluid escapes into the cœlome and is discharged by genital pores.

In most Ganoids the *oviducts* (Fig. 256, *B, ovd.*) have funnel-like anterior ends (*ovd.''*) opening into the cœlome, while posteriorly (*ovd.'*) they discharge into the dilated urinary duct (*bl.*). A similar arrangement occurs in the Smelt, one of the Physostomi (Salmonidæ), in which the eggs are discharged from the outer or lateral face of the ovary into the open end of the oviduct. But in most Teleostei and in *Lepidosteus* (Fig. 256, *A*) the ovary (*ovy.*) is a hollow sac continued posteriorly into the oviduct (*ovd.*) : the eggs are set free into its cavity from the folds into which its inner surface is produced, and so pass directly into the oviduct without previously entering the cœlome. An ovary of this kind reminds us of the state of things in Arthropods, in which also the ovary is a hollow organ discharging its products into its internal cavity, whence they pass directly into the continuous oviduct. It was pointed out that the lumen of the ovary in this case was to be looked upon as a shut-off portion of the cœlome : this is certainly the case in *Lepidosteus* and the Teleostei. In the embryo a longitudinal fold grows from the ventral edge of the then solid ovary, and turns upwards along the lateral face of the organ : it is met by a descending fold of peritoneum from the dorsal wall of the abdomen, and by the union of the two folds a cavity is enclosed, which is the lumen of the ovary. The oviduct is developed as a backward continuation of these folds of peri-toneum, and appears to be quite unconnected with the embryonic renal system, and therefore not to be homologous with the oviducts of Selachians and Holo-cephali, which, as we have seen, are Müllerian ducts. In the Salmonidæ and the Eels oviducts are absent, and the ova are discharged by genital pores, which are probably to be looked upon as degenerate oviducts. True abdominal pores are present in Ganoids and in some Physostomi. Most fishes are diœcious, but *Serranus*, one of the Perch family, is hermaphrodite and self-impregnating ; *Chrysophrys* is hermaphrodite and successively male and female ; and there are many well-known species, such as the Cod and the Herring, which exhibit the hermaphrodite condition as an occasional variation. Regan has described interesting cases of small parasitic males which become permanently attached to the female in the Ceratioids (Oceanic Angler fishes).

Reproduction and Development.—Most bony fishes are oviparous, the eggs being fertilised after they are laid, but in some Teleostei, such as the Viviparous

Blenny (*Zoarces*), internal fertilisation takes place; the young are developed in the hollow ovary and are brought forth alive.   Many instances of parental care of the young are known, the most familiar being that of the male Stickleback (*Gasterosteus*), which constructs a nest of weeds, fastened together by a

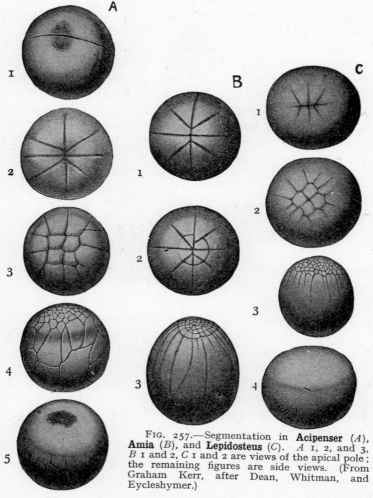

FIG. 257.—Segmentation in **Acipenser** (*A*), **Amia** (*B*), and **Lepidosteus** (*C*).   *A* 1, 2, and 3, *B* 1 and 2, *C* 1 and 2 are views of the apical pole; the remaining figures are side views.   (From Graham Kerr, after Dean, Whitman, and Eycleshymer.)

glutinous secretion of the kidneys, and jealously guards the developing young. In the Sea-horse (*Hippocampus*) and the Pipe-fishes (*Syngnathidæ*) the young are developed in a pouch (Fig. 223, *brd. p.*) on the abdomen of the male.   In the Siluroid *Aspredo* the eggs are pressed into the soft spongy skin of the belly and thus carried about by the parent.   The ova are always small as compared with those of Chondrichthyes, never exceeding 5–10 mm. in diameter, and being usually much smaller. They are rarely protected by an egg-shell. They are produced in immense numbers, a single female sometimes laying several millions : in such cases the mortality among the unprotected embryos and young is immense. The eggs may be *pelagic, i.e.* so light as to float when laid, as in the Cod, Haddock, Turbot, Sole, etc. ; or *demersal, i.e.* so heavy as to sink to the bottom, as in the Herring, Salmon, Trout, etc. In some cases (*Chilobranchus*) they become cemented to the surface of a rock.

In all the Ganoids hitherto investigated, with the exception of *Lepidosteus*, cleavage is complete. In *Acipenser* and *Amia* (Fig. 257, *A* and *B*) it is very unequal, the macromeres being immense as compared with the micromeres : in *Polypterus* it is subequal at first, becoming unequal later : the process may be said to be intermediate between the holoblastic and meroblastic types. In *Lepidosteus* (Fig. 257, *C*) the segmentation is meroblastic, the fissures not extending much beyond the equator of the egg. In Teleostei segmentation is

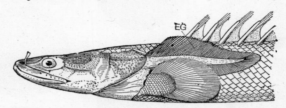

FIG. 258.—**Polypterus bichir.** Head of advanced larva. *E.G.* external gill.
(From Dean, after Steindachner.)

always partial and discoidal. The general features of development are much the same as in the Trout, except that in the Sturgeon and *Polypterus*, as in Craniates in general, there is an open medullary groove which becomes closed in to form a medullary canal. There is frequently a metamorphosis : in *Lepidosteus*, for instance, the newly-hatched young is provided with a sucking-disc, and the proportions of the head are quite different from those of the adult. In the larval Sturgeon provisional teeth are present, and in many Teleostei the young differ from the adult in the presence of large spines. The pelagic larvæ of Eels are strongly compressed, perfectly transparent, and have colourless blood. They are sometimes known as " Glass-fish," and were formerly placed in the genus *Leptocephalus*, their real nature being unknown. *Polypterus* (Fig. 258), has *external gills*, as in Dipnoi and Amphibia (*vide infra*), and the same holds good of *Cobitis*, *Heterotis*, and *Gymnarchus* among the Teleostei.

CLASS CHOANICHTHYES.[1]

Although in point of numbers and variety this class has never approached the Actinopterygii, and is, at the present time, reduced to one recently dis-

[1] This term is adopted from Romer. C. L. Hubbs has suggested the term Amphibioidei " Science," New Series, XLIX, 1919.

covered Actinistian and to the few species of Dipnoi, themselves members of a side line, it has been of the greatest importance, in that it gave rise to all the land living vertebrates of the world.

The apparently trivial feature that made this enormous change possible was the acquisition of a nostril inside the mouth, whereby the lung, already in partial use, was enabled to assume a much greater rôle.

The cosmoid structure of the scales and head bones is a characteristic feature. The general anatomy of the soft parts can be presumed, allowing for some specialisations and degeneration, from the still-living lung-fishes.

The earliest appearance of the Choanichthyes is during the Middle Devonian period by which time three separate orders, the Rhipidistia, Dipnoi, and only a little later the Actinistia were already clearly established. The Rhipidistia and Actinistia together form the old group known as the Crossopterygii (after the removal of *Polypterus* to the Actinopterygii).

Sub-class Crossopterygii.

Order Rhipidistia.

Although the members of this order are in some respects too specialised to be themselves ancestral to the other two, or to the Tetrapods, the order may nevertheless be considered as the central one from whose earlier less specialised roots the other two and the Tetrapods branched off on their own lines of evolution.

Osteolepis macrolepidotus (Figs. 259, 260), the earliest species that is well known, may be described as illustrating all the main features of the class, as well as the particular features of the order. As compared with a primitive Actinopterygian, such as *Palæoniscus*, there are several points of difference, beside those of the internal nostril and scale structure already mentioned, such as two dorsal fins instead of one, a smaller eye with numerous sclerotic plates and paired fins of the archipterygial type with a single basal element articulating with the shoulder-girdle. The dentition shows two peculiar features. The premaxilla, maxilla and dentary are supplied with a number of small, sharp, conical teeth, such as occur in many fishes, but the prevomer, palatine and ectopterygoid have, in addition, a series of larger teeth of a characteristic structure and method of replacement. The dentine is much folded and replacement is alternate, a second tooth growing up beside the first, so that there is a large and a small socket side by side. It is interesting that these two features have also been transmitted from some earlier ancestor to the tetrapods, as is shown by the " labyrinthodont " teeth of the early amphibia.

The tail of the Rhipidistia having a small epichordal lobe is partly heterocercal. The composition of the skull is, in general, not unlike that of a palæoniscid, but there is one important and characteristic point of difference, in that in all Crossopterygii there is a line running transversely across the skull between the frontal and parietal bones which divides it into two portions. This feature alone would prevent any known crossopterygian from being regarded as ancestral either to the dipnoan or tetrapod lines.

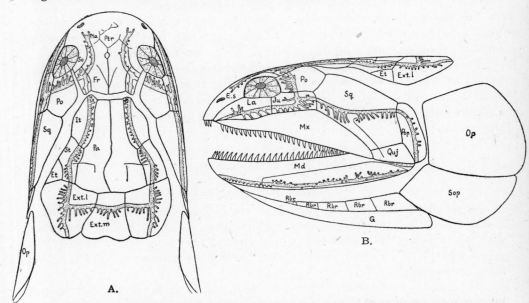

FIG. 259.—**Osteolepis macrolepidotus.** A, dorsal; B, side views. *Ang.* angular; *Clei.* cleithrum; *D.* dentary; *D. Sph.* dermosphenotic; *Ext. L. Ext. M.* or *E.* extrascapulars; *Fr.* frontal; *Gu.* gular; *I. T.* intertemporal; *Ju.* jugal; *La.* lachrymal; *Lat. Gu.* lateral gulars; *Md.* mandible; *M. Gu.* median gular; *Mx.* maxilla; *Na.* nasal; *Op.* opercular; *Pa.* parietal; *P. Gu.* principal gular; *P. O.* post-orbital; *P. Op.* pre-opercular; *P. Ros.* post-rostral; *P. sp.* post-splenial; *Qu. J.* quadrato-jugal; *S. Ang.* sur-angular; *S. O.* supra-orbital; *S. op.* sub-opercular; *Sp.* splenial; *Sq.* squamosal; *S. T.* supra-temporal; *n.* external nostril; *p.* pineal foramen. (After Säve-Söderbergh.)

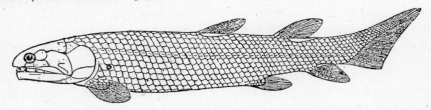

FIG. 260.—**Osteolepis macrolepidotus.** (After Traquair.)

There is likewise a curious feature of the skull bones and scales which is observable both in crossopterygians and early dipnoans in that there is an alternate deposition and resorption of the outer layer of cosmine during the life of the individual fish. As much of the detailed classification of the crossopterygii has been based on the structure of the scales, the recognition of this phenomenon [1] is likely on fuller investigation to alter considerably the current views on the composition of the order, which is at present divided into four families, the Osteolepidæ (*Osteolepis* (Fig. 260), *Megalichthys*,

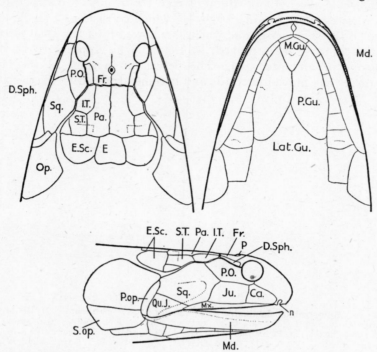

FIG. 261.—**Diplopterax trailli.** *Ang.* angular; *Clei.* cleithrum; *D.* dentary; *D. Sph.* dermo-sphenotic; *Ext. L. Ext. M.* or *E.* extrascapulars; *Fr.* frontal; *Gu.* gular; *I.T.* intertemporal; *Ju.* jugal; *La.* lachrymal; *Lat. Gu.* lateral gulars; *Md.* mandible; *M. Gu.* median gular; *Mx.* maxilla; *Na.* nasal; *Op.* opercular; *Pa.* parietal; *P. Gu.* principal gular; *P.O.* post-orbital; *P. Op.* pre-opercular; *P. Ros.* post-rostral; *P. sp.* post-splenial; *Qu. J.* quadrato-jugal; *S. Ang* sur-angular; *S. O.* supra-orbital; *S. op.* sub-opercular; *Sp.* splenial; *Sq.* squamosal; *S. T.* supra-temporal; *n.* external nostril; *p.* pineal foramen. (After Westoll.)

Thursius, etc.). The Rhizodontidæ (*Eusthenopteron*, *Rhizodus*, *Sauripterus*, *Glyptopomus*, *Diplopterax* (Fig. 261), etc). The Urostheneidæ (*Urosthenes*) and the Holoptychiidæ (*Holoptychius*) (Fig. 262), *Glyptolepis*.

ORDER ACTINISTIA.

The Actinistia, represented by the single family of the Cœlacanthidæ, are a side-line of the Choanichthyes, ranging from the Upper Devonian to the present day. With the same general organisation of skull and scale

[1] T. S. Westoll, *Geological Magazine*, April 1936.

structure as the Rhipidistia, the group acquired some very definite specialisations of its own, the structure of the fins and tail and the peculiar feature of an ossified air-bladder being highly characteristic. The paired fins have the appearance, superficially at least, of an actinopterygium. There is a short, blunt and scale-covered lobe around which the fin-rays are attached as a fan. There is, however, an internal skeleton, which consists of a single basal piece attached to the shoulder-girdle, which is followed by a few axial pieces around which the fin-rays are arranged, so that the fin appears to be essentially mesorhachic or archipterygial. The pelvic fin in some of the later forms (*e.g.*, *Laugia*) has moved forwards and become attached to the pectoral girdle,

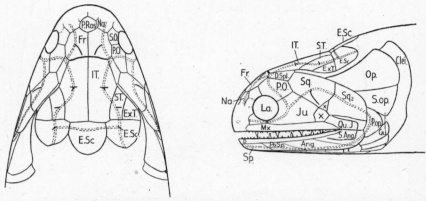

FIG. 262.—**Holoptychius flemingi.** *Ang.* angular; *Clei.* cleithrum; *D.* dentary; *D. Sph.* dermosphenotic; *Ext. L. Ext. M.* or *E.* extrascapulars; *Fr.* frontal; *Gu.* gular; *I.T.* intertemporal; *Ju.* jugal; *La.* lachrymal; *Lat. Gu.* lateral gulars; *Md.* mandible; *M. Gu.* median gular; *Mx.* maxilla; *Na.* nasal; *Op.* opercular; *Pa.* parietal; *P. Gu.* principal gular; *P.O.* post-orbital; *P. Op.* pre-opercular; *P. Ros.* post-rostral; *P. sp.* post-splenial; *Qu. J.* quadratojugal; *S. Ang.* sur-angular; *S. O.* supra-orbital; *S. op.* sub-opercular; *Sp.* splenial; *Sq.* squamosal (double in *Holoptychius*); *S. T.* supra-temporal; *n.* external nostril; *P.* pineal foramen; *X.* additional cheek bones in Holoptychius. (After Westoll.)

just as in the later acanthopterygian teleosts, a case of convergence. Of the two dorsal fins the anterior is supported by a bony plate, the posterior by a bony structure not unlike that of the pectoral fin. The tail is diphycercal, with a small central projecting lobe, and the fin-rays are attached each one singly to a dorsal or ventral spine of a vertebra, which is another point of convergence with the later teleosts. The vertebral column, apart from the spines, is unossified and the notochord is unconstricted.

The skull, while showing a number of specialisations, is like that of the Rhipidistia in having the hinge on the dorsal surface between the parietals and frontals. This feature, together with the traces of cosmoid covering of the bones and scales, is good evidence of the common ancestry of the two orders. While these sheets were going through the press the surprising news arrived of the discovery of a still living species of Cœlacanth.   Only the skin has been preserved, but in all the external features this specimen, *Latimeria chalumnæ*, closely resembles *Macropoma* and *Undina*.

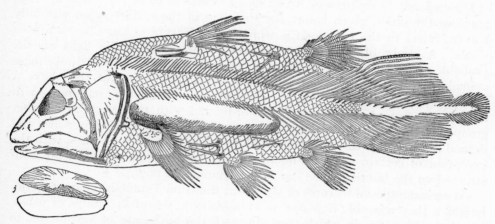

FIG. 263.—**Undina penicillata.**   *J,* jugal plates.   (From Smith Woodward.)

FIG. 264.—**Latimeria chalumnæ.**   A living Cœlacanth.   The arrow points to the opening of the spiracle.   (By courtesy of Dr. J. L. B. Smith.)

It was found in 40 fathoms off East London, South Africa, and will be described by Dr. J. L. B. Smith in the Transactions of the Royal Society of South Africa.   Representative examples are *Cœlacanthus, Undina* (Fig. 263), *Macropoma, Laugia,* etc., and the living *Latimeria* (Fig. 264).

VOL. II.   U

Sub-class Dipnoi (Dipneusti Dipneumones).

The third order of Choanichthyes, the Dipnoi, still has a few living representatives in the " Lung-fishes "—*i.e.*, *Ceratodus*, the " Burnett Salmon " of Queensland, *Protopterus* of Africa and *Lepidosiren* of South America. The name of the order, given before the structure of the extinct types was fully known, refers to the two nostrils which are a feature of the Choanata as a whole. A study of the living members throws considerable light on the probable anatomy of the soft parts of the extinct forms. Not only do these animals breathe by means of gills, like ordinary Fishes, but they have a highly-developed apparatus for the respiration of air—a lung or lungs—with an arrangement of the circulation co-ordinated with this, such as in other groups is indicated only in *Polypterus* and *Amia*. They have bony scales and dermal fin-rays, but the paired fins, unlike those of any other Fishes, with the exception of certain extinct Chondrichthyes and Crossopterygians, are constructed on the biserial type (" archipterygium," see p. 79).

With some special features of their own the Dipnoi combine characteristics in which they resemble now one, now another, of the other groups of fishes, together with a few in which they approach the next class of vertebrates to be dealt with, viz., the Amphibia and even the higher vertebrates. The brain and the heart are quite peculiar : the former in its undivided, or almost undivided, mid-brain ; the latter in its partially divided atrium, and spirally-twisted conus. The pallium of the cerebral hemispheres in the Dipneumona with its layers of nerve-cells has no parallel among the lower Vertebrates.

The order, of which the first genus and species *Dipterus valenciennesi* (Figs. 265 *A*, 266) occurs in the Middle Devonian, is as early as any of the bony fishes. It was never a large one, but a succession of genera is known which leads without difficulty to the modern species. A number of characters is common to all members of the order. The internal nostril, cosmine covering of the bones and scales and the mesorhachic fin show that the Dipnoi evolved originally from an ancestor in common with the other Choanichthyes. The autostylic jaw suspension and characteristic pattern of the teeth are peculiar to the order. During the long history of the group its component members, while retaining all the essential anatomical features, show a gradual degeneration of certain parts, notably in the bones of the skull and a loss of cosmine and an alteration from the normal two dorsal fins and heterocercal tail to the almost eel-like body of the latest member, *Lepidosiren*, with its fused dorsal fins, gephyrocercal tail, thread-like paired limbs and reduced scales (Fig. 267).

Dipterus valenciennesi, the most primitive form, has a body covered with stout cycloid scales covered, as are the bones of the head, with cosmine. The archipterygial paired fins are moderately long, there are two small dorsal fins, a heterocercal tail with a small epichordal lobe and an anal fin. The skull

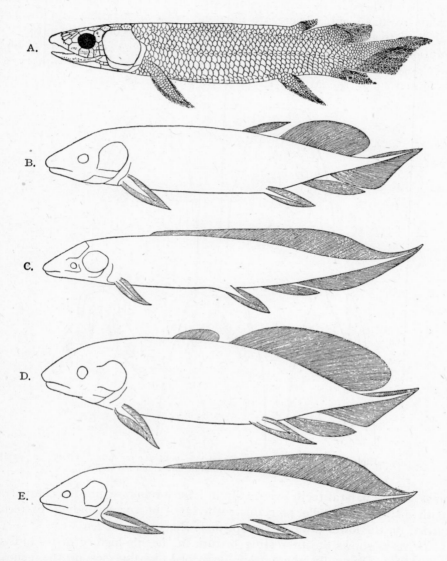

FIG. 265.—A, *Dipterus valenciennesi*, Middle Devonian; B, *Pentlandia macropterus*, Upper Middle Devonian; C, *Phaneropleuron andersoni*, Upper Middle Devonian; D, *Scaumenacia curta*, Upper Devonian; E, *Uronemus lobatus*, Lower Carboniferous. (A after Forster-Cooper; B–E after Dollo.)

(Fig. 266) is completely roofed in by bones so numerous that their homologies, especially of those in the front region, with the head bones of other fishes are difficult to make out.   There are no premaxillæ or maxillæ, and the bones of the palate are firmly fixed to the neurocranium to produce the autosystylic condition.   There is a double series of gular bones between the rami of the lower jaws.   The upper teeth are borne on the vomers and palato-pterygoids, the former small, the latter a larger series of tubercles arranged as a pair of

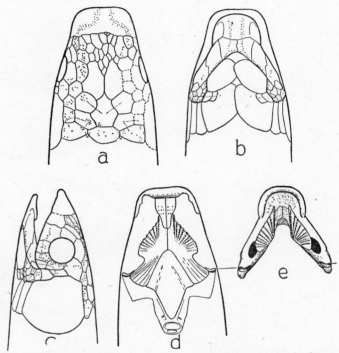

FIG. 266.—**Dipterus valenciennesi.** *a.* dorsal; *b.* ventral; *c*, lateral views; *d,* palate; *e,* lower jaws.   (After Graham-Smith and Westoll.)

fans.   These palatal teeth eventually in later forms fuse into the characteristic tooth plates.   A single pair of tooth-plates of corresponding pattern are carried on the lower jaws by the splenials (Figs. 266, D, E).

Dipterus shows an interesting feature in the life-history of its individual specimens.   Originally there were described two species of the genus, *D. platycephalus* and *D. valenciennesi*, both found preserved in the same horizons. The specific differences between the two lay in the fact that *D. platycephalus* had a completely bony snout, and the bones of the head and the scales are covered by a thick, smooth and finely pitted outer layer of cosmine, which hides the underlying pattern of the scales, whereas *D. valenciennesi* has the front part of the snout without bone and the scales lack the outer layer, so that the pattern is clearly visible (Fig. 266, *a*). It now appears that these apparently different conditions are to be explained as seasonal differences of a single species (*D. valenciennesi*). At recurring intervals during the life of the fish the outer layer of cosmine is resorbed to allow of growth to take place and is then redeposited. Specimens have been found in the intermediate condition (see T. S. Westoll, *loc. cit.*, p. 287). This phenomenon is known to occur in other Choanichthyes, and may prove to be a widespread occurrence in the class and to have a material effect on our ideas of classification.

Representative genera of Dipnoi are *Dipterus* (Middle Devonian), *Pentlandia*, *Phaneropleuron*, *Scaumenacia* (Upper Devonian), *Uronemus* (Lower Carboniferous), *Conchopoma* (Lower Permian), *Ctenodus*, *Sagenodus* (Carboniferous and Permian). Of the living forms *Ceratodus* is known from the Triassic onwards and *Protopterus* from the Miocene.

1. EXAMPLE OF THE SUB-CLASS—*Epiceratodus* (*Ceratodus*, *Neoceratodus*) *forsteri*.

The Ceratodus or " Burnett Salmon " (Fig. 268) is the largest of the Dipnoi, attaining a length sometimes of 4 or 5 feet. It occurs at the present day only in the Burnett and Mary Rivers in Queensland, but fossil teeth [1] referred to the same or nearly related genera have been found in abundance in Palæozoic and Mesozoic beds in Europe, America, the East Indies, Africa, and Australia. *Ceratodus forsteri* lives in still pools in which the water in the dry season becomes extremely stagnant and overladen with decomposing vegetable matter; and at that season it is only by rising to the surface occasionally, and taking air into its lung, that it is enabled to obtain sufficient oxygen for purposes of respiration. Its food consists of such small animals as live among the water-plants and decaying leaves, and in order to obtain a sufficient amount of such food, it swallows relatively large quantities of vegetable matter, which passes with little or no alteration through its enteric canal. Its movements are for the most part very sluggish, and are chiefly effected by the agency of the tail-fin. The paired fins are employed in steering and balancing and in the ascending and descending movements: owing to their great flexibility they are entirely incapable of supporting the body when the fish is removed from the water, but the pectoral fins may be employed as props when it lies in a resting condition at the bottom.

External Characters.—The body is fish-like with a diphycercal caudal fin. The surface is covered with thin, bony, imbricated cycloid scales, very large on the head and trunk, somewhat smaller towards the tail end, and very much smaller over the fins and the posterior part of the operculum.

The limbs have a characteristic shape, being in the form of two pairs of

---

[1] The fusion of the teeth into a large and a small pair of plates in the upper jaw and a pair in the lower is characteristic of the group from the earliest period.

elongated, leaf-like, pointed paddles. The marginal parts of the paired fins and the whole extent of the unpaired or caudal fin are supported by a double

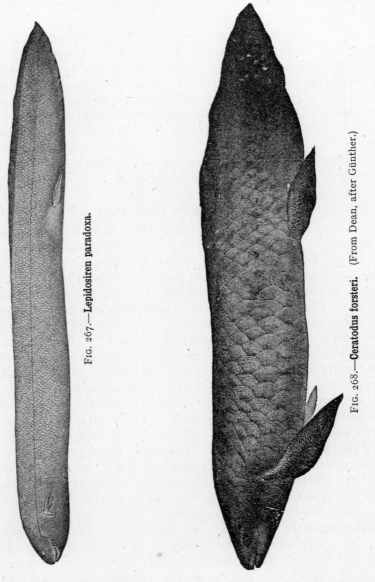

FIG. 267.—Lepidosiren paradoxa.

FIG. 268.—Ceratodus forsteri. (From Dean, after Günther.)

series of slender fibre-like unjointed, partly ossified, dermal rays (*camptotrichia*), which are much more numerous than the endoskeletal rays and which are covered by small surface-scales.

The mouth is situated on the ventral surface of the head, close to the anterior extremity of the snout. The external nares differ from those of other Vertebrates in being situated immediately outside the aperture of the mouth, enclosed within the upper lip. A pair of internal nares opens not far behind them into the anterior part of the mouth-cavity. At the root of the tail is the cloacal aperture with an abdominal pore on either side of it. There is an operculum similar to that of the bony fishes, with a single slit-like branchial aperture behind it. There are no spiracles. There is a well-marked lateral line.

Endoskeleton.—The *spinal column* (Fig. 269) is represented by a persistent notochord, enclosed in a thick fibrous sheath, together with neural and hæmal arches.

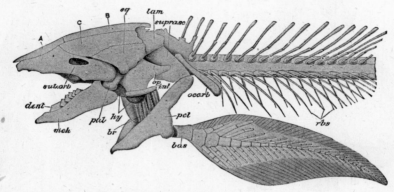

FIG. 269.—**Ceratodus forsteri.** Lateral view of the anterior portion of the skeleton. *A* anterior median investing bone of the roof of the skull; *B*, posterior median investing bone; *C*, inner lateral investing bone; *bas.* basal cartilage of the pectoral fin; *br.* branchial arches; *dent.* tooth of lower jaw; *hy.* hyoid arch; *int.* interoperculum; *lam.* plate overhanging branchial region; *mck.* Meckel's cartilage; *occ. rb.* occipital rib; *op.* operculum; *pal.* palatoquadrate; *pct.* pectoral arch; *rbs.* ribs; *sub. orb.* sub-orbital bones; *sq.* so-called squamosal; *supra. sc.* post-temporal.

A series of neural or basidorsal cartilages form the bases of the neural arches, and hæmal or basiventral cartilages are similarly related below to a series of pleural ribs in the precaudal region, and to a series of hæmal arches in the caudal. These two sets of basal cartilages are not precisely opposite throughout, and regularly alternate for some distance in front. They are embedded in the sheath of the notochord, but no centra are formed, and the notochord, though pressed upon above and below by the series of basal cartilages, is not constricted in the usual annular manner. At the posterior end it becomes surrounded by cartilage. The neural and hæmal arches are ossified; each is surmounted by a rod-like neural or hæmal spine which forms part of a continuous three-jointed ossified rod, the proximal segment being the spine, and the two others radials. The pleural ribs are curved bony rods extending downwards and somewhat backwards in the body-wall immediately outside the peritoneal membrane, like the pleural ribs of the bony fishes. The first pair—the *occipital ribs*—(Fig. 269, *occ. rb.*), thicker and straighter than the rest, are connected with the skull in its vertebral portion.

The *skull* (Figs. 269, 270, and 271) consists of an undivided mass of cartilage, devoid of fontanelles, narrowest between the orbits, and broadening before and behind; posteriorly it is prolonged into a plate (*lam.*) overhanging the branchial region. Embedded in the cartilage of the posterior part are a pair of small replacing bones which appear to represent the most anterior of the spinal elements fused with the skull. On the upper surface are two

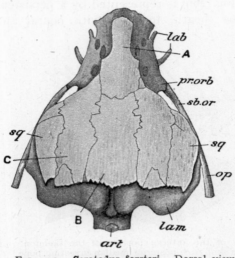

FIG. 270.—**Ceratodus forsteri.** Dorsal view of the skull. *A*, anterior median investing bone; *art.* articular surface for second fin-ray; *B*, posterior median investing bone; *C*, inner lateral investing bone; *lab.* labial cartilages; *lam.* process projecting over gills; *op.* operculum; *pr. orb.* pre-orbital process of chondrocranium; *sb. or.* sub-orbital bones; *sq.* outer lateral investing bone. (After Huxley.)

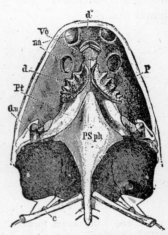

FIG. 271.—**Ceratodus forsteri.** Ventral view of the skull. *c*, occipital rib; *d*, palatine teeth; *d'*, vomerine teeth; *na.* anterior and posterior nares; *P.* palatine region of palatopterygoid; *P. Sph.* parasphenoid; *Pt.* pterygoid; *Qu.* quadrate region; *Vo.* vomer. (From Dean, after Günther.)

unpaired (*A* and *B*) and four paired (*C* and *sq.*) investing bones, the homologies of all of which are undetermined. Premaxillæ, maxillæ, and nasals are absent. On the ventral surface is a large investing bone (Fig. 271, *P.Sph.*) representing the parasphenoid of the teleosts. In front is a pair of small upper labial or nasal cartilages. A palatoquadrate cartilage (Fig. 269, *pal.*), firmly fixed to the side-wall of the cranium, gives attachment to the mandible, so that the skull is autostylic; the quadrate element is distinct in the larva and independently developed. In front the palatoquadrate contains a palato-pterygoid ossification which forms the support for the large composite tooth of the upper jaw. The mandible consists of Meckel's cartilage with an angular bone behind, and a large splenial, which bears the tooth, in front. The dentary is vestigial. The hyomandibular is only represented by a small vestige. Opercular (*op.*) and interopercular (*int.*) bones support the operculum. The hyoid (*hy.*) and branchial arches (*br.*) are cartilaginous. Of the latter, four are completely developed, and a fifth is represented by a vestige. There are no branchial rays, but the branchial arches bear a series of gill-rakers with cartilaginous supports.

The pectoral arch (Fig. 269, *pct.*) is a stout cartilage with two pairs of investing bones, the *clavicles* on the coracoid, and the *cleithra* on the scapular regions. The latter are connected with the skull by post-temporals. The skeleton of the pectoral fin consists of a stout basal cartilage (*bas.*), an elongated, tapering, central axis made up of a number of short cartilaginous segments, and two rows of jointed cartilaginous rays extending out on either

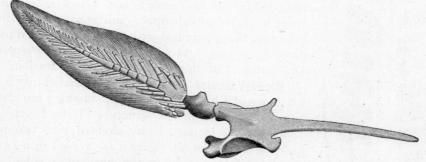

FIG. 272.—**Ceratodus forsteri.** Pelvic arch and skeleton of pelvic fin. (After Günther.)

side of the axis so as to support the middle part of the expanse of the fin. The pelvic arch is a single cartilage, produced forwards into an elongated rod-like epipubic process (Fig. 272). The skeleton of the pelvic fin is similar to that of the pectoral.

Digestive Organs.—The *teeth* (Fig. 271) are of a remarkable and characteristic shape. There are two pairs of large compound teeth of similar character, one pair (the *palatine*, *d*) on the roof of the mouth (palatopterygoid bone) and the other (*splenial*) on the lower jaw. Each is a curved plate with the convex border, which is directed inwards and somewhat backwards, entire; while the concave border presents a series of six or seven vertical, ridge-like projections or cusps. In addition to these, there are, in front of the palatine pair, a pair of much smaller, simple, somewhat chisel-like *vomerine* teeth (*d'*) placed close together and directed vertically. In the embryo each tooth is represented by a number of separate denticles which subsequently coalesce.

In the *enteric canal* the chief feature of special interest is the presence, throughout the length of the intestine, of a spiral valve similar to that of the

Elasmobranchs and " Ganoids." The rectum opens into a small cloaca. A pair of abdominal pores open just behind this.

Organs of Respiration.—*Ceratodus* combines aquatic respiration by means of gills similar to those of ordinary fishes, with aërial respiration by means of a lung.

There are four pairs of *gills*, each consisting of a double row of gill-filaments supported on the branchial arches. A rudimentary hyoidean gill or *pseudobranch* is present as well. The *lung* (Fig. 273) is an elongated median sac connected by a pneumatic duct with a muscular chamber or vestibule opening into the œsophagus on its ventral side by a slit-like aperture or *glottis*. The internal surface of the lung is sacculated, and a regularly-arranged series of blind pouches opens out of the main central cavity. This lung of *Ceratodus* corresponds morphologically to the air-bladder of Ganoids and Teleosts, but differs from it in its blood-supply and consequently in its function, being supplied with blood by a special paired *pulmonary artery* (as is also the case in *Polypterus*) and acting as an important organ of respiration.

FIG. 273.—**Ceratodus forsteri.** Posterior half of the lung with the ventral wall slit up so as to show the interior. (After Günther.)

Blood-Vascular System.—Co-ordinated with the existence of a lung and distinct pulmonary circulation, is a complication in the structure of the heart. The *sinus venosus* is imperfectly divided into two parts, and the cavity of the atrium is divided into two by an incomplete septum in the form of a ridge. The venous blood enters the right-hand division of the sinus venosus and passes thence through the right-hand division of the atrium to the ventricle; the *pulmonary vein*, by which the blood is returned from the lung, passes through the sinus, and its blood reaches the ventricle through the left-hand division of the atrium. There are no atrio-ventricular valves guarding the opening between the atrium and the ventricle. A contractile conus arteriosus is present, and has a remarkable spirally-twisted form ; in its interior are four longitudinal rows of valves, one of which is modified to form an incomplete longitudinal septum. The channel on the left side of this septum, which receives the blood of the pulmonary vein, is in communication in front with the first two aortic arches (afferent branchials), that on the right with the last two.

The blood-vessels (Fig. 274) present an arrangement which is intermediate in some respects between that which has been already described as observable in the Chondrichthyes and that which will be found to characterise the

Amphibia. The four afferent branchial arteries (*aff.*) take their origin close together, immediately in front of the conus, so that a ventral aorta can hardly be said to exist. Each branchial arch has two efferent branchial arteries. A hyoid artery (*hy. art.*) is connected with the most anterior of these. The eight efferent vessels unite in pairs to form four epibranchial arteries (*epi.*). The

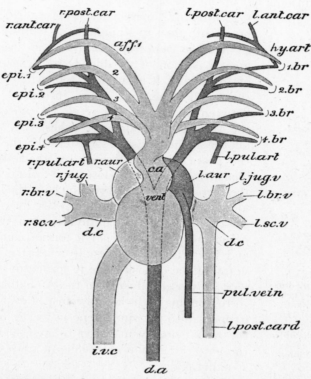

Fig. 274.—**Ceratodus forsteri.** Diagrammatic view of the heart and main blood-vessels, as seen from the ventral surface. *aff. 1, 2, 3, 4,* afferent vessels ; *1 br, 2 br, 3 br, 4 br,* position of gills ; *c. a.* conus arteriosus ; *d. a.* dorsal aorta ; *d. c.* precaval vein ; *epi. 1, epi 2, epi. 3, epi. 4,* epibranchial arteries ; *hy. art.* hyoidean artery ; *i. v. c.* postcaval vein ; *l. ant. car.* left anterior carotid artery ; *l. aur.* left atrium ; *l. br. v.* left brachial vein ; *l. jug. v.* left jugular vein ; *l. post. car.* left posterior carotid artery ; *l. post. card.* left cardinal vein ; *l. pul. art.* left pulmonary artery ; *l. sc. v.* left subscapular vein ; *r. ant. car.* right anterior carotid artery ; *r. aur.* right atrium ; *r. br. v.* right brachial vein ; *r. jug.* right jugular vein ; *r. post. car.* right posterior carotid ; *r. pul. art.* right pulmonary artery ; *r. sc. v.* right subscapular vein ; *vent.* ventricle. (After Baldwin Spencer.)

latter unite dorsally to form a main trunk, which combines with the corresponding trunk of the opposite side to form the median *dorsal aorta* (*d. a.*). The head is supplied by *carotid* branches given off from the first epibranchial (*l. post. car.* and *r. post. car.*) and from the hyoidean arteries (*l. ant. car.* and *r. ant. car.*), and the latter also gives off a *lingual artery* to the tongue. From the last (fourth) epibranchial artery arises the *pulmonary artery* (*l. pul. art.* and *r. pul. art.*), carrying blood to the lung.

There are two *precavals* or *ductûs Cuvieri* (*d. c.*), as in the Dogfish (p. 189). The right is formed by the union of *jugular* (*l. jug. v.* and *r. jug. v.*), *brachial* (*l. br. v.* and *r. br. v.*), and *subscapular* veins (*l.sc. v.* and *r. sc. v.*). The left receives in addition a left *cardinal vein* (*l. post card.*). A large *lateral cutaneous* vein, running superficially along the side of the body, opens into the sub-scapular.

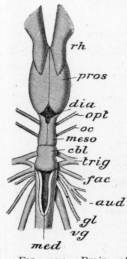

A large *postcaval vein* (*i. v. c.*) brings back the greater portion of the blood from the posterior parts of the body; it is situated somewhat to the right of the middle line, and opens into the sinus venosus between the two *hepatic veins*. A postcaval occurs in the Dipnoi alone amongst fishes, but is universal in all the higher classes. Posteriorly the cardinal and the post-caval are formed by the bifurcation of a median *caudal vein*; close to its origin each receives the *efferent renal veins* bringing back the blood from the kidney. The blood from the pelvic fin is brought back by an *iliac vein* which divides into two branches— *pelvic* and *renal portal*. The former, running forwards and inwards, unites mesially with the corresponding vessel of the opposite side to form a median *abdominal vein*—a vessel universal in the Amphibia, and perhaps corresponding to the lateral veins of the Chondrichthyes; it opens into the sinus venosus. The other branch— the *renal portal* vein—after receiving tributaries from the posterior region of the body passes to the corresponding kidney.[1]

FIG. 275.—Brain of **Ceratodus forsteri,** dorsal view. *aud.* auditory nerve; *cbl.* cerebellum; *dia.* diencephalon; *fac.* facial nerve; *gl.* glossopharyngeal; *med.* medulla oblongata; *meso.* mesencephalon; *oc.* oculomotor nerve; *opt.* optic nerve; *pros.* prosencephalon; *rh.* rhinencephalon (olfactory lobe with olfactory tract and bulb); *vg.* vagus nerve. (Chiefly after Sanders.)

Brain.—The whole brain (Fig. 275) is enclosed in a tough and thick membrane, which becomes glandular in two positions—on the roof of the diacœle, and on that of the metacœle. In the former position this glandular development of the enclosing membrane, or *choroid plexus*, passes downwards into the diacœle and is developed into a spongy mass which is prolonged forwards to the anterior end of the prosencephalon. The prosencephalon (*pros.*) presents two elongated hemispheres, which are completely separated except posteriorly, where they are united by a narrow commissure. The contained cavity is divided into two by the prolongation of the choroid plexus already referred to. The nervous wall of the hemisphere (*pallium*) is very

[1] How far this arrangement combines Fish-like and Amphibian characters will be best understood at a later stage.

thin and is incomplete dorsally and internally : basally it forms a massive *tuberculum olfactorium* from which the olfactory nerve-fibres are derived. There is a pair of large olfactory lobes (*rh.*), each with its cavity, and each prolonged into an olfactory peduncular tract, which ends in front in an olfactory bulb in close apposition with the nasal capsule.

The pineal body is situated on the summit of a conical membranous cap on the roof of the third ventricle. The infundibulum develops a pair of lobi inferiores. The mesencephalon (*meso.*) is bilobed, but the division is not strongly pronounced. The cerebellum (*cbl.*) is very small, being little more than a transverse bridge of nerve-matter over the anterior end of the fourth ventricle. The medulla (*ed.*) is of relatively large size.

Urinogenital Organs.—The *kidneys* are short, being confined to the posterior portion of the body-cavity, and are firmly attached to the ovaries or testes. Each has a thick-walled duct which joins its fellow, the passages, however, remaining distinct to near the opening into the urinogenital division of the cloaca, when the right opens into the left.

There are two elongated *ovaries* (Fig. 276, *l. ov., r. ov.*), which remain distinct throughout. The *oviducts* (*l. ovd.* and *r. ovd.*) are a pair of thick-walled, greatly convoluted tubes which extend along the whole length of the body-cavity, into which they open in front (*cœl. ap.*) ; posteriorly they coalesce immediately before opening into the cloaca. The *testes* are long, compressed bodies which remain distinct from one another throughout their length. The efferent ducts from the testes open into certain of the tubules of the mesonephros, and the sperms are thus enabled to pass out through the mesonephric duct. The Müllerian ducts in the male are remarkably well-developed.

In the early stages of its **development** (Fig. 277) *Ceratodus* exhibits resemblances, on the one hand, to *Petromyzon* (p. 144), and on the other to the next class to be studied—the Amphibia. The ova become enclosed, while passing down the oviduct, in a gelatinous envelope which swells up considerably when it comes in contact with the water. At what stage fertilisation takes place is not exactly known. Cleavage is complete and unequal, and results in the formation of a lens-shaped blastula (*A*) with smaller cells on one of the convex surfaces (the future dorsal), and larger on the other (the future ventral). A blastopore (*bl. p.*) first appears on the dorsal surface as a short transverse slit, which grows into a semicircle (*B*) or a horse-shoe. The free ends of this grow in towards one another and unite to enclose an irregularly circular or elliptical space filled in by a mass of large cells—the *yolk-plug* (*C, yk. pl.*). Soon, however, this wide aperture becomes narrowed to a small longitudinal slit, the lips of the anterior part of which then unite, only the most posterior part remaining open (*D*) and subsequently giving rise to the anus. A narrow medullary groove (*E, blp. sut.*) appears along the dorsal surface, and a pair of medullary folds are seen at the sides of the blastopore

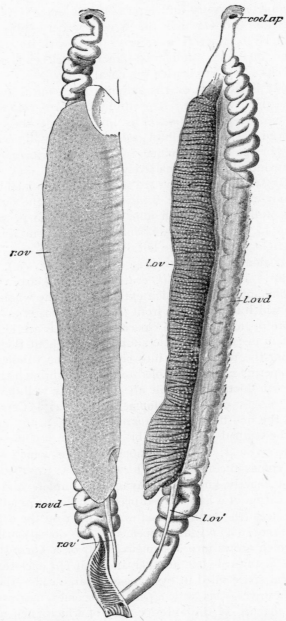

FIG. 276.—**Ceratodus forsteri.** Reproductive organs of female; the inner surface of the right and the outer surface of the left ovary shown. *cœl. ap.* cœlomic aperture of oviduct; *liv.* portion of the liver; *l. ov.* left ovary; *l. ov'.* its posterior termination; *l. ovd.* left oviduct; *r. ov.* right ovary; *r. ovd.* right oviduct; *r. ov'.* its posterior termination. (After Günther.)

(*E*) and are coalescent in front of it. From the medullary folds and the groove between them the neurocœle, and subsequently the entire nervous system, are developed as in Craniata in general (see pp. 95 *sqq.*). The portion of the blastoderm destined to give rise to the embryo becomes to a slight extent folded off from the rest, which forms an ill-defined rounded mass, or *yolk-sac*, to be subsequently absorbed as development proceeds.

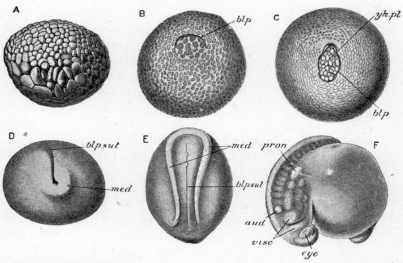

Fig. 277.—**Ceratodus forsteri.** Stages in the development. *A*, lens-shaped blastula; *B*, stage with semicircular blastopore (*bl. p.*); *C*, later stages in which the blastopore (*bl. p.*) has taken the form of a ring-like groove enclosing the yolk-plug (*ylk. pl.*); *D*, stage in which the narrow medullary groove (*blp. sut.*) has appeared with the rudiment of the medullary folds (*med.*); *E*, stage in which the medullary folds (*med.*) have become well developed; *F*, later stage with well-formed head with two visceral arches (*visc.*) and rudiments of eye (*eye*) and ear (*aud.*); *pron.* mesonephros. (After Semon.)

2. Distinctive Characters and Classification.

The Dipnoi are Pisces in which the notochord is persistent, there are no vertebral centra, and the primary cranium persists with little ossification, but has added to it a number of investing bones. The skull is autostylic, the lower jaw articulating with a palatoquadrate process which is immovably fixed to each side of the skull. There are four to six cartilaginous branchial arches. The dermal fin-rays are slender more or less ossified fibres, and are supported by numerous cartilaginous or ossified pterygiophores. The caudal fin is diphycercal. The paired fins are of the character of " archipterygia." The pectoral arch is a single cartilage with a pair of superficial investing bones on each side. The pelvic arch is well-developed and cartilaginous. There are gills attached to the branchial arches, and in addition a single or double lung opening into the œsophagus by a ventral aperture. The gills are covered over by an operculum.   There is a dermal skeleton in the form of overlapping cycloid scales.   There is a distinct cloaca.   The intestine contains a spiral valve.   The atrium and the sinus venosus are each imperfectly divided into two parts.   There is a contractile conus arteriosus, which has a spirally-twisted form, and is partly or completely divided internally by a longitudinal septum.   The afferent branchial vessels take their origin close together immediately in front of the conus. A pulmonary artery is given off from the afferent branchial system on either side ; a pulmonary vein opens into the left division of the auricle.   The optic nerves form a chiasma.   The oviducts open anteriorly into the cœlome.   The ova are of moderate size ; segmentation is entire.

The recent Dipnoi are classified as follows :—

ORDER I.—MONOPNEUMONA.

Dipnoi in which the lung is single, and the lateral jointed rays of the "archiptery-gium" are well developed.

This order comprises only the Australian *Ceratodus* (Fig. 268).

ORDER 2.—DIPNEUMONA.

Dipnoi in which the lung is double, and the lateral rays of the "archiptery-gium" are vestigial or absent.

This order includes *Protopterus* (Fig. 278) of Tropical Africa, and *Lepidosiren* of South America (Fig. 267).

GENERAL REMARKS.

The three genera of living Dipnoi are closely allied in all the most essential features of their structure, and it will only be necessary now to mention the principal points in which *Protopterus* and *Lepidosiren* differ from *Ceratodus*.

The limbs (Fig. 278) are long and very narrow, and the limb-skeleton is correspondingly modified, consisting of a slender, jointed axis without, or with only vestiges of, the lateral rows of rays.   A blind dorsal diverticulum of

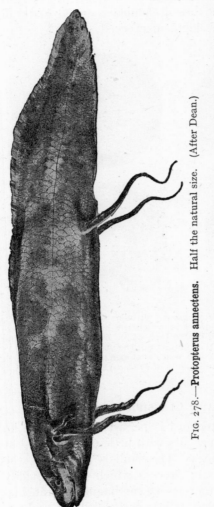

FIG. 278.—**Protopterus annectens.**   Half the natural size.   (After Dean.)

the cloaca, derived developmentally from the urinogenital sinus, is present, and perhaps corresponds to the sperm-sacs of the Chondrichthyes. There are two lungs, the anterior portions of which are united to form a median chamber, to which the presence of numerous trabeculæ gives a spongy character. There are five (or six) reduced rod-like branchial arches, of which the last three bear the internal gills; in addition there is a series of *external* gills in the larva, vestiges of which persist in the adult *Protopterus* (Fig. 279, K). In the males

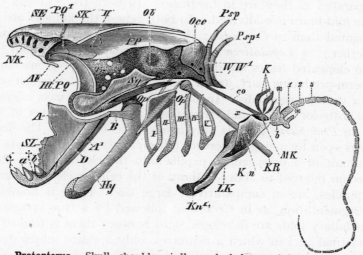

FIG. 279.—**Protopterus.** Skull, shoulder-girdle, and skeleton of fore-limb. AA^1, splenial; *AF*, pre-orbital process; *a* and *b* (on lower jaw), and *S.L.* teeth; *b*, basal cartilage of pectoral fin; *B*, ligamentous band connecting the mandible with the hyoid; *co.* ligamentous band connecting the dorsal end of the pectoral arch with the skull; *D*, angular; *FP*, frontoparietal; *Ht*, membranous fenestra perforated by the foramen for the optic nerve (*II*); *Hy.* hyoid; *K*, external gills; *Kn, Kn¹*, cartilage of the pectoral arch; *KR*, occipital rib; *LK* and *MK*, investing bones of the pectoral arch; *NK*, olfactory capsule; *Ob*, auditory capsule; *Occ.* supra-occipital; *Op.* and *Op¹*. rudimentary opercular bones; *PQ.* palatoquadrate; *Psp. Psp¹*. spinous processes of the anterior vertebræ; *SE.* supra-ethmoid bone; *SK*, roofing investing bones; *Tr.* palatoquadrate cartilage; *WW¹*, anterior vertebræ coalescent with the skull; *I—V*, branchial arches (that marked *I* is forked and the anterior bar may represent the first, in which case there are six branchial arches); *1, 2, 3*, segments of axis of pectoral fin; *, *, vestigial lateral rays of pectoral fin. (From Wiedersheim.)

of *Lepidosiren*, vascular filaments, which may be accessory respiratory organs, are developed on the paired fins during the breeding season. The conus arteriosus is completely divided by a longitudinal septum. The pulmonary artery is given off from the point of union of the epibranchial arteries into a single lateral trunk. In *Protopterus* there is usually a single abdominal pore opening on the dorsal wall of the cloaca; this leads into a cavity into which the true abdominal pores, which are very minute, lead. In *Lepidosiren* abdominal pores are absent.

The brain in both *Lepidosiren* and *Protopterus*, as well as in *Ceratodus*, differs from that of fishes in general, and resembles that of Amphibia in the presence of long and relatively narrow cerebral hemispheres. In the two former these have a pallium or nervous roof with a stratified layer of nerve-cells. In all the Dipnoi the part of the hemisphere (olfactory lobe and tuberculum) from which the olfactory nerve-fibres pass to the bulbus olfactorius is of relatively large size, but smaller in *Protopterus* and *Lepidosiren*. In *Protopterus* and *Lepidosiren* the olfactory tract is not distinguishable, bulbus and lobus being in immediate apposition instead of being widely separated as they are in *Ceratodus*. In both these genera the dorsal part of the mid-brain is undivided. In both genera the kidneys are relatively more elongated than in *Ceratodus*; in *Protopterus* the posterior portions are fused together; in *Lepidosiren* they remain separate throughout. In both genera the elongated testes are distinguishable into two regions—an anterior longer, sperm-producing part, and a posterior shorter part which serves as a duct and a vesicula seminalis. In *Lepidosiren* about six vasa efferentia arise from this posterior region and enter the Malpighian capsules of the mesonephros: in *Protopterus* there is only a single vas efferens. The ducts of the two kidneys open by a single aperture (*Protopterus*) or two separate apertures on the summit of a urinogenital papilla into the cloaca at the base of the cloacal cæcum referred to above. Many of the cellular elements, such as the blood-corpuscles, are of comparatively large size. There is holoblastic, but unequal, segmentation, as in *Ceratodus*, followed by a true invagination. A pair of medullary folds are developed, and between them is formed a median solid ectodermal keel in which a neurocœle only appears subsequently. The larva has well-developed external gills.

CLASS AMPHIBIA.

The Amphibia, the first vertebrates to become adapted to life on land, may be distinguished from the choanate fishes, their predecessors, by their pentadactyle limbs, by the absence of fin-rays in the unpaired fins when these are present and by the presence of a middle ear (see page 327).

The class includes the frogs and toads, newts and salamanders, the worm-like Apoda and a number of extinct orders which are for convenience grouped together as the Stegocephalia.

Typically the amphibia breathe by means of external gills in the larval stage and by lungs when adult, but the gills are retained by the adults of some Urodeles, and the skin, which is usually naked, may play an important part in assisting respiration. Some modern amphibia, in fact, have lost both gills and lungs, and depend entirely for respiration on the skin and bucco-pharyngeal cavity.

The skull is autosystylic (page 73), and the free hyomandibula has been converted into a *columella auris*, which lies in the upper part of the spiracle between the inner ear and the tympanic membrane stretched on the outer part of the skull. In all but a few of the early forms there is an opening in the side of the ear capsule, the *fenestra ovalis*, through which the columella auris conveys sound-vibrations to the inner ear.

A number of points should be noted with regard to the skeleton. The skull has become movably attached to the vertebral column by means of either one, or two, condyles; an interclavicle soon became added to the shoulder-girdle of the early forms to brace the two halves together, and the pelvis became attached to the vertebral column, typically by a single sacral vertebra. In all modern forms there are only ten intracranial nerves, but some of the Stegocephalia had twelve.

FIG. 280.—**Rana temporaria.** (From Mivart.)

1. Example of the Class.[1]—The Common Frog (*Rana temporaria*), or the Edible Frog (*Rana esculenta*).

Rana temporaria is the common British species of Frog, found in ponds and damp situations all over the country, and occurring also in America; *R. esculenta* is the large green edible Frog found on the continent of Europe and occasionally in England; *R. pipiens* is the commonest North American species of the genus. Other species of the same genus occur in all parts of the world except New Zealand, the southern part of South America, and the various oceanic islands.

---

[1] It has long been the custom to use the frog as an elementary type in the study of vertebrate morphology, largely because of its abundance and cheapness, and because of the clear demonstration of many points of its internal anatomy, which are easily displayed by merely opening the body cavity. The student, however, must realise that the Anura are very specialised vertebrates. The skull is greatly modified by the reduction of several elements, and the whole of the post-cranial skeleton is profoundly modified for jumping, and is far removed from a typical vertebrate condition.

External Characters.—The *trunk* is short and stout, and is continued, without the intermediation of a neck, into the broad, depressed *head*. There is no trace of a tail, the anus being terminal. The *mouth* also is terminal, and is characterised by its extraordinary width, the gape extending considerably behind the eye. On the dorsal surface of the snout are the small *nostrils*; the *eyes* are large and prominent, and each is provided with an *upper eyelid* in the form of a thick fold of skin; and a *nictitating membrane*, a much thinner fold, which arises from the lower margin of the eye and can be drawn up over it. Close behind the eye is a circular area of tensely-stretched skin, the *tympanic membrane*, a structure not met with in any fish: as we shall see, it is an accessory part of the auditory organ. There is no trace of branchial apertures.

The back has a peculiar bend or hump, in the sitting posture, marking the position of the sacral vertebra. The limbs are of very unequal size. The *fore-limbs* are short, and each consists of an *upper arm*, which, in the ordinary position, is directed backwards and downwards from the shoulder-joint; a *fore-arm*, directed downwards and forwards from the elbow; and a *hand*, ending in four short, tapering *digits*, directed forwards. The *hind-limb* is of great size; in the usual squatting posture the *thigh* is directed downwards, outwards, and forwards from the thigh-joint, the *shank* inwards, backwards, and upwards from the knee. The *foot* consists of two parts: a *tarsal region* directed downwards from the heel-joint, and five long, slender *digits* united by thin folds of skin or *webs*. Thus the limbs are placed in such a way that the elbow and knee face one another, and the first digit—that of the hand representing the *index-finger*, that of the foot, the *hallux* or great toe—is turned inwards or towards the median plane of the body.

The *skin* is greyish-brown in *R. temporaria*, greenish in *R. esculenta*, and is mottled, in both species, with dark brown or black; in *R. temporaria* there is a large black patch over the tympanic region. Sexual differences occur in both species; in *R. temporaria* there is a large, black, glandular swelling on the inner side of the hand of the male, and in *R. esculenta* the male has, at each angle of the mouth, a loose fold of skin, the *vocal* sac, which can be inflated from the mouth into a globular form. The skin is soft and slimy owing to the secretion of mucous glands; there is no trace of exoskeleton.

Endoskeleton.—The *vertebral column* (Fig. 281) is remarkable for its extreme shortness; it consists of only nine vertebræ (**V. 1**—**V. 9**), the last followed by a slender, bony rod, the *urostyle* (**U. ST.**). The second to the seventh vertebræ have similar characters. The *centrum* (B. *cn.*) is somewhat depressed and has a concave anterior and a convex posterior face—a form known as *procœlous*. Each half of the *neural arch* consists of two parts: a pillar-like *pedicle* (*dp.*) springing from the centrum and extending vertically upwards, and a flat, nearly horizontal *lamina* (*lm.*), forming, with its fellow, the roof of the neural

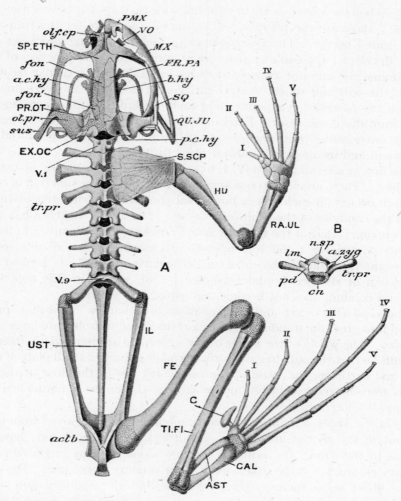

FIG. 281.—**Rana temporaria.** A, the skeleton from the dorsal aspect; the left half of the shoulder-girdle and the left fore- and hind-limbs are removed, as also are the investing bone on the left side of the skull. Cartilaginous parts dotted. Names of replacing bones in thick, those of investing bones in italic capitals, other references in small italics. *a, c. hy.* anterior cornu of hyoid; *actb.* acetabulum; **AST.** astragalus; *b. hy.* basi-hyal; **C.** calcar; **CAL.** calcaneum; **EX. OC.** exoccipital; **FE.** femur; *fon. fon'.* fontanelles; *FR. PA.* fronto-parietal; **HU.** humerus; **IL.** ilium; *MX.* maxilla; *olf. cp.* olfactory capsule; *ot. pr.* otic process; *p. c. hy.* posterior cornu of hyoid; *PMX.* premaxilla; **PR. OT.** pro-otic; *QU.JU.* quadrato-jugal; **RA.UL.** radio-ulna; **SP.ETH.** sphenethmoid; *SQ.* paraquadrate; **S.SCP.** supra-scapula; *sus.* suspensorium; **TI.FI.** tibio-fibula; *tr. pr.* transverse process; **UST.** urostyle; **V.1,** cervical vertebra; **V.9,** sacral vertebra; *VO.* vomer; *II—V,* digits of hand; *I,* the prepollex, a sesamoid bone; *I—V,* digits of hind foot. B, the fourth vertebra, anterior face. *a. zyg.* anterior zygapophysis; *cn.* centrum; *lm.* lamina; *n. sp.* neural spine; *pd.* pedicle; *tr. pr.* transverse process. (After Howes, slightly altered.)

canal.   When the vertebræ are in position, wide gaps are left between successive pedicles ; these are the *intervertebral foramina*, and serve for the transmission of the spinal nerves.   The *zygapophyses* (*a. zyg.*) or yoking processes are far better developed than in any fish ; they spring from the junction of pedicle and lamina, the anterior zygapophysis having a distinct articular facet on its dorsal, the posterior on its ventral surface.   Thus when the vertebræ are in position the posterior zygapophyses of each overlap the anterior zygapophyses of its immediate successor.   Laterally the neural arch gives off on each side a large outstanding *transverse process* (*tr. pr.*) ; its crown is produced into a very small and inconspicuous *neural spine* (*n. sp.*).

The first or *cervical vertebra* (**V. 1**) has a very small centrum and no transverse processes.   There are no anterior zygapophyses, but at the junction of centrum and arch occurs on each side a large oval concave facet for articulation with one of the condyles of the skull (*vide infra*).   The eighth vertebra has a biconcave centrum ; that of the ninth or *sacral vertebra* (**V. 9**) is convex in front and presents posteriorly a double convexity articularing with a double concavity on the anterior end of the urostyle.   The latter (**U. ST.**) is formed by the ossification of the perichordal tube (see p. 69), which, in this region of the vertebral column, does not become segmented into vertebræ.

The *skull* (Figs. 281 and 282) consists of a narrow *brain-case*, produced behind into great outstanding *auditory capsules*, and in front into large *olfactory capsules*.   The whole of the bones of the *upper jaw* are immovably fixed to the cranium, so that the only free parts are the *lower jaw* and a small plate of mingled bone and cartilage, the *hyoid apparatus*, which lies in the floor of the mouth and is the sole representative in the skull of the entire hyobranchial or gill-bearing skeleton of fishes.

As in the Trout, a number of investing bones can be removed from the skull without injury to the underlying chondrocranium.   The latter, however, is not, as in the Trout, the primary cranium alone, but, as in the Dipnoi, the primary cranium *plus* the palatoquadrate or primary upper jaw.   The cranium in the strict sense includes the brain-case and the auditory and olfactory capsules : the palatoquadrate (*pal. qu.*) is not a solid mass fused throughout its length with the cranium, as in the Dipnoi, but is a slender rod attached to the cranium at either end, but free in the middle.   It is divisible into three regions : a posterior *quadrate-region* or *suspensorium* (*sus.*), an intermediate *pterygoid region*, and an anterior *palatine region*.   The suspensorium extends backwards, outwards, and downwards from the auditory region of the cranium, to which it is immovably united by its forked proximal end, one branch of the fork—the *otic process* (Fig. 282, *ot. pr.*)—being fused with the auditory capsule, the other—the *pedicle* (*ped.*)—with the trabecular region immediately anterior to the auditory capsule.   Ventrally the suspensorium furnishes an articular facet for the mandible, and is connected with the delicate rod-like pterygoid region ;

this passes forwards and joins the palatine region, which is a transverse bar fused at its inner end with the olfactory capsule.

The occipital region of the cranium contains only two bones: the *exoccipitals* (**EX. OC.**), which lie one on each side of the foramen magnum (*for. mag.*) and meet above and below it: there is no trace of supra- or basi-occipital. Below the foramen magnum are a pair of oval projections, the *occipital condyles* (*oc. cn.*), furnished by the exoccipitals and articulating with the cervical vertebra.

Each auditory capsule is ossified by a single bone, the *pro-otic* (**PR. OT.**);

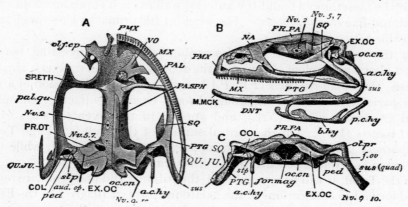

FIG. 282.—**Rana temporaria.** The skull. A, from beneath, with the investing bones removed on the right side (left of figure); B, from the left side, with mandible and hyoid; C, from behind, the investing bones removed at *sus*. *a. c. hy.* anterior cornu of hyoid; *aud. cp.* auditory capsule; *b. hy.* body of hyoid; **COL.** columella; *DNT.* dentary; **EX.OC.** exoccipital; *for. mag.* foramen magnum; *f. ov.* fenestra ovalis; *FR.PA.* fronto-parietal; **M.MCK.** mento-meckelian; *MX.* maxilla; *NA.* nasal; *Nv. 2,* optic foramen; *Nv. 5, 7,* foramen for fifth and seventh nerves; *Nv. 9, 10,* foramina for ninth and tenth nerves; *oc. cn.* occipital condyle; *olf. cp.* olfactory capsule; *ot. pr.* otic process; *PAL.* palatine; *pal. qu.* palato-quadrate; *PA.SPH.* parasphenoid; *p. c. hy.* posterior cornu of hyoid; *ped.* pedicle; *PMX.* premaxilla; **PR.OT.** pro-otic; *PTG.* pterygoid; *QU.JU.* quadrato-jugal; **SP.ETH.** sphenethmoid; *SQ.* paraquadrate; *stp.* stapes; *sus. (quad.)* suspensorium (quadrate); *VO.* vomer. (After Howes, slightly altered.) A minute investing bone, the *septo-maxillary*, which is present above the maxilla, close to the nostril, is not here represented.

there are no other ossifications of the auditory region (p. 313). In the adult the pro-otic fuses with the exoccipital: it presents on its outer surface, behind the otic process of the suspensorium, a small aperture, the *fenestra ovalis*, closed in the entire animal by membrane, and, when the latter is removed, leading into the cavity of the auditory capsule, containing the membranous labyrinth.

In front of the auditory capsules a considerable part of the cranial wall is formed of cartilage, and presents above a single large and a pair of small *fontanelles* (Fig. 281, *fon., fon.'*), but anteriorly it is ossified by the *sphenethmoid*, or *girdle-bone* (**SP. ETH.**), a short bony tube divided by a transverse partition into an anterior compartment which lodges the hinder ends of the olfactory sacs, and a posterior compartment which contains the olfactory bulbs. The anterior compartment is again divided by a vertical partition which separates the olfactory sacs from one another, and the transverse partition is perforated for the olfactory nerves. This very peculiar and characteristic bone may be taken to represent meso- and ecto-ethmoids and pre- and orbito-sphenoids all united together.

The olfactory capsules (Figs. 282, 283, *olf. cp.*) have a delicate cartilaginous roof and floor produced into irregular processes which help to support the olfactory sac. They are separated from one another by a vertical plate of cartilage, continuous behind with the girdle-bone and representing the unossified part of the mesethmoid; and the anterior wall of each is produced into a little curved, rod-like *rhinal process.* The whole of the primary palatoquadrate arch is unossified.

To this partly ossified chondrocranium the usual investing bones are applied above and below. Covering the roof of the brain-case is a single pair of bones, the *fronto-parietals* (*FR. PA.*), each formed by the fusion of a frontal and a parietal, distinct in the young Frog. Over the olfactory capsules are paired triangular *nasals* (*NA.*), and applied to their ventral surfaces small paired *vomers* (*VO.*). On the ventral surface of the skull is a large T-shaped *parasphenoid* (*PA. SPH.*), its stem underlying the basis cranii, while its two arms extend outwards beneath the auditory capsules.

In the Trout, it will be remembered, the palatine and pterygoid are replacing bones, formed as ossifications of the palatoquadrate cartilage. In the Frog this cartilage is, as we have seen, unossified, but to its ventral face two investing bones are applied, a small rod-like *palatine* (*PAL.*), and a three-rayed *pterygoid* (*PTG.*) having an anterior arm extending forwards to the palatine, an inner arm applied to the pedicle of the suspensorium, and an outer arm extending along the whole inner face of the suspensorium. It will thus be seen that bones originally preformed in cartilage may give place to investing bones, developed in corresponding situations, but altogether independent of the cartilage, the latter remaining unossified.

The suspensorium, as we have seen, is strengthened on its inner face by the outer arm of the pterygoid; externally it is similarly supported by a hammer-shaped investing bone, the *squamosal* (*SQ.*). The upper jaw is formed by three investing bones, the small *premaxilla* (*PMX.*) in front, then the long, narrow *maxilla* (*MX.*), and finally the short *quadratojugal* (*QU. JU.*), which is connected posteriorly with the quadrate.

The mandible contains a persistent *Meckel's cartilage*, as a sort of core, outside which are formed two bones: a long *angulo-splenial* on its inner face, and a short *dentary* (*DNT.*) on the outer face of its distal half. The actual distal end of Meckel's cartilage is ossified as a small replacing bone, the *mento-meckelian* (**M. MCK.**), not represented in fishes.

The *hyoid apparatus* consists of a shield-shaped plate of cartilage, the *body of the hyoid* (*b. hy.*), produced at its anterior angles into slender rods, the *anterior cornua* (*a. c. hy.*), which curve upwards and are fused with the auditory capsules, and at its posterior angles into partly ossified rods, the *posterior cornua* (*p. c. hy.*), which extend backwards, embracing the glottis.

Two other cranial structures remain to be noticed. External to the paraquadrate is a ring of cartilage, the *annulus tympanicus* (Fig. 295, *an. tymp.*), which supports the tympanic membrane as the frame of a tambourine supports the parchment. Inserted into the fenestra ovalis is a nodule of cartilage, the *stapes* (*stp.*), to which is attached the inner end of a small hammer-shaped structure, the *columella* (**COL.**), the handle of which is ossified, while its cartilaginous head, or *extra-columella*, is fixed to the inner surface of the tympanic membrane.

The comparison of the Frog's skull with those of Fishes is facilitated by a study of its development. In the tadpole or larval Frog there is a cartilaginous cranium (Fig. 283) connected on each side with a stout inverted arch, like the subocular arch of the Lamprey or the palatoquadrate of Chimæra or Ceratodus, and, like them, developed from the dorsal region of the mandibular arch. The quadrate region (*qu.*) of this primary upper jaw is well in front of the eye, the axis of the suspensorium being inclined forwards and the mandible very short, in correspondence with the small size of the tadpole's mouth. The quadrate

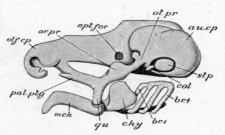

FIG. 283.—Skull of **Tadpole.** *au. cp.* auditory capsule; *br. 1—4,* branchial arches; *c. hy.* ceratohyal; *col.* columella; *mck.* Meckel's cartilage; *olf. cp.* olfactory capsule; *opt. for.* optic foramen; *or. pr.* orbital process of suspensorium; *ot. pr.* otic process; *pal. ptg.* palato-pterygoid bar; *qu.* quadrate; *stp.* stapes. (After Marshall, slightly altered.)

is fused by its pedicle with the trabecular region, the otic process (*ot. pr.*) which unites it with the auditory capsule being formed later. Behind the suspensorium are distinct hyoid (*c. hy.*) and branchial (*br. 1—4*) arches supporting the gills by which the tadpole breathes. As development goes on, the axis of the suspensorium is rotated backwards, producing the wide gape of the adult, and the stout palatopterygoid region of the subocular arch (*pal. ptg.*) gradually assumes the slender proportions it has in the adult. The greater part of the hyoid arch gives rise to the anterior cornua of the adult hyoid-apparatus, the body of which is formed from the basi-hyal and basi-branchials, and its posterior cornua probably from the fourth branchial arch. The columella is developed independently, but may perhaps represent a pharyngo-hyal or dorsal segment of the hyoid arch. The stapes is a detached portion of the outer wall of the auditory capsule. Thus, with the assumption of purely aërial respiration, the complex branchial skeleton is reduced to a simple structure for the support of the tongue.

The *shoulder-girdle* has essentially the structure already described (p. 79) in general terms as characteristic of the pentadactyle Craniata. The *scapula*

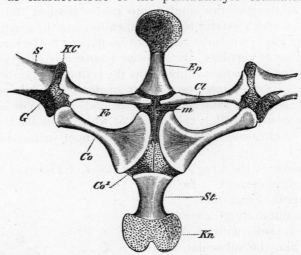

FIG. 284.—**Rana esculenta.** The shoulder-girdle from the ventral aspect. Cartilage dotted. *Co.* coracoid; *Co¹.* epicoracoid; *Cl.* clavicle; *Ep.* omosternum; *G.* glenoid cavity; *Fe.* fenestra between clavicle and coracoid; *KC.* cartilage separating scapula and clavicle; *Kn.* xiphisternum; *m.* junction of epicoracoids; *S.* scapula; *St.* sternum. (From Wiedersheim's *Comparative Anatomy.*)

(Fig. 284, S., Fig. 285, *scp.*) is ossified, and is connected by its dorsal edge with a *suprascapula* (Fig. 281, **S. SCP.,** Fig. 285, *s. scp.*) formed partly of bone, partly of calcified cartilage, and developed from the dorsal region of the embryonic

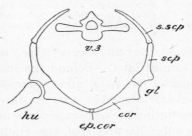

FIG. 285.—**Rana.** Diagrammatic transverse section through the shoulder-girdle. *cor.* coracoid; *ep. cor.* epicoracoid; *gl.* glenoid cavity; *hu.* humerus; *scp.* scapula; *s. scp.* suprascapula; *v. 3,* third vertebra. (From Parker's *Practical Zoology.*)

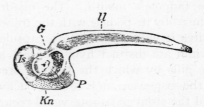

FIG. 286.—**Rana esculenta.** Pelvic girdle from the right side. *G.* acetabulum; *Il. P.* ilium; *Is.* ischium; *Kn.* pubis. (From Wiedersheim's *Comparative Anatomy.*)

shoulder-girdle. The *coracoid* (Fig. 284, *Co.,* Fig. 285, *cor.*) is also ossified, but the *procoracoid* is represented by a bar of cartilage having an investing bone, the *clavicle* (*Cl.*), closely applied to it. The suprascapula overlaps the anterior vertebræ ; the coracoid and procoracoid are connected ventrally by a cartilage, the *epicoracoid* (Fig. 284, *Co.*¹, Fig. 285, *ep. cor.*), which is in close contact with its fellow of the opposite side in the middle ventral line, so that the entire shoulder-girdle (Fig. 285), like that of the Dogfish, forms a single inverted arch.

Passing forwards from the anterior ends of the united epicoracoids is a rod of bone, the *omosternum* (Fig. 284, *Ep.*), tipped by a rounded plate of cartilage, and passing backwards from their posterior ends is a similar but larger bony rod, the *sternum* (*St.*), also tipped by a cartilaginous plate, to which the name *xiphisternum* (*Kn.*) is applied. These two structures are the first indication of a sternum we have yet met with, with the possible exception of the median ventral element of the shoulder-girdle of Heptranchias. The omosternum is developed as paired forward extensions of the epicoracoids which undergo fusion : the sternum and xiphisternum arise as paired rods lying posterior to the epicoracoids, and subsequently uniting with one another. This sternal apparatus of the Frog (and of the Amphibia in general) differs developmentally from the structures in the higher Vertebrates to which the same name is applied—the latter being formed from separated-off portions of embryonic ribs (*costal sternum*).

The *fore-limbs* deviate from the typical structure (p. 80) chiefly in the fusion of the radius and ulna into a single *radio-ulna* (Fig. 281, **RA. UL.**), and in the presence of only four complete digits with a vestigial one on the radial side. The last represents a sesamoid bone, and the complete digits are the second to the fifth of the typical hand. Six carpals only are present, the third, fourth, and fifth digits articulating with a single bone which has apparently risen by the fusion of the third, fourth, and fifth distalia and of at least one centrale.

The *pelvic girdle* (Fig. 286) is very peculiarly modified ; it resembles in form a Bird's " merrythought," consisting of two long, curved bars articulating in front with the transverse processes of the sacral vertebra (Fig. 281) and uniting posteriorly in an irregular vertical disc of mingled bone and cartilage which bears on each side a deep, hemispherical *acetabulum* (*G.*) for the articulation of the thigh-bone. The curved rods are the *ilia* (*Il., P.*) ; they expand posteriorly and unite with one another in the median plane to form the dorsal portion of the disc and about one-half of the acetabulum. The posterior portions of the disc and acetabulum are furnished by the *ischia* (*Is.*), fused with one another in the sagittal plane, their ventral portions by the similarly united *pubes* (*Kn.*). The ilium and ischium are formed of true bone, the pubis of calcified cartilage ; the union of the elements in the median plane is called the *symphysis*. In the larva the ilium is vertical, but during development it becomes lengthened and at the same time rotated backwards, thus bringing the articulation of the hind-limbs as far back as possible.

In the *hind-limb* the tibia and fibula are fused to form a single *tibio-fibula* (Fig. 281, **TI. FI.**), and the two bones in the proximal row of the tarsus—the tibiale or *astragalus* (**AST.**) and the fibulare or *calcaneum* (**CAL.**)—are greatly elongated and provide the leg with an additional segment. There are three tarsals in the distal row, one of which appears to represent the centrale, another the first distale, and the third the fused second and third distalia. There are five well-developed digits, and on the tibial side of the first is a spur-like structure or *calcar* (*c.*), formed of three bones, a metatarsal and two phalanges : such an additional digit is called a *pre-hallux*.

All the long bones of the limbs consist of the *shaft*, formed of true bone and of *extremities* of calcified cartilage. The distinction is a very obvious one, both in the freshly-prepared and in the dried skeleton.

The **muscular system** has undergone great modifications in correspondence with the complex movements performed by the limbs. The dorsal muscles of the trunk are no longer divisible into myomeres, but take the form of longitudinal or oblique bands (*extensores dorsi*, etc.), lying partly above the vertebræ, partly between the transverse processes, partly between the ilia and the urostyle. The ventral muscles are differentiated into a paired median band, the *rectus abdominis* (Fig. 287, *rct. abd.*), with longitudinal fibres, and a double layer of oblique fibres—*obliquus externus* (*obl. ext.*) and *internus* (*obl. int.*)—extending from the vertebral column to the recti. Both the extensor dorsi and the rectus abdominis are traversed at intervals by transverse bands of fibrous tissue, the *inscriptiones tendineæ* (*ins. ten.*), but the segments thus formed do not correspond with the embryonic myomeres. The right and left recti are united by a longitudinal band of tendon, the *linea alba* (*l. alb.*).

The muscles of the limbs are numerous and complex, each segment having its own set of muscles by which the various movements of which it is capable are performed. There are muscles passing from the trunk to the limb-girdles ; from the trunk or the limb-girdles to the humerus and femur ; from the humerus and femur to the radio-ulna and tibio-fibula ; from the fore-arm or shank to the digits ; and from one segment of a digit to another. For the most part the limb-muscles are elongated and more or less spindle-shaped, presenting a muscular portion or *belly* which passes at either end into a *tendon* of strong fibrous tissue serving to fix the muscle to the bones upon which it acts. The relatively fixed end of a muscle is called its *origin*, the relatively movable end its *insertion*, *e.g.* in the *gastrocnemius* muscle of the calf of the leg (*gstr.*) the proximal end attached to the femur is the origin, the distal end attached to the foot the insertion. According to their action, muscles are divided into *flexors* which bend, and *extensors* which straighten, one part upon another ; *adductors* which draw towards, and *abductors* which draw away from, the middle line ; *elevators* which raise, and *depressors* which lower, a part, such as the lower jaw. The names of the muscles may have reference to their position, *e.g. pectoralis* (*pct.*), the principal muscle of the chest ; or to their form, *e.g. biceps*, the two-headed muscle ; or to their action, *e.g. flexor tarsi* ; or to their origin and insertion, *e.g. coracohumeralis*.

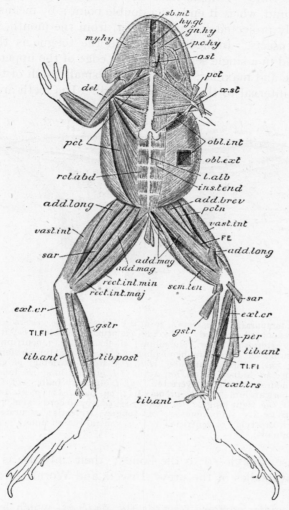

FIG. 287.—**Rana esculenta.** The muscles from the ventral aspect. On the left side (right of figure) many of the superficial muscles have been cut and reflected to show the deep layer. *add. brev.* adductor brevis ; *add. long.* adductor longus ; *add. mag.* adductor magnus ; *del.* deltoid ; *ext. cr.* extensor cruris ; *ext. trs.* extensor tarsi ; *FE.* femur ; *gn. hy.* genio-hyoid ; *gstr.* gastrocnemius ; *hy. gl.* hyoglossus ; *ins. ten.* inscriptio tendinea ; *l. alb.* linea alba ; *my. hy.* mylo-hyoid ; *obl. int.* obliquus internus ; *obl. ext.* obliquus externus ; *o.st.* omosternum ; *p. c. hy.* posterior cornu of hyoid ; *pct.* pectoralis ; *pctn.* pectineus ; *per.* peronæus ; *rct. abd.* rectus abdominis ; *rect. int. maj.* rectus internus major ; *rect. int. min.* rectus internus minor ; *sar.* sartorius ; *sb. mt.* sub-mentalis ; *sem. ten.* semi-tendinosus ; *tib. ant.* tibialis anticus ; *tib. post.* tibialis posticus ; *TI. FI.* tibio-fibula ; *vast. int.* vastus internus ; *x. st.* xiphisternum.

Digestive Organs.—The mouth leads into a wide *buccal cavity* having in its roof the *internal* or *posterior nares* (Fig. 288, *p. na.*), a pair of projections due to the downward bulging of the large eyes, and the openings of the *Eustachian tubes* (*eus. t., vide infra*). On its floor is the large *tongue* (*tng.*), attached in front and free behind, where it ends in a double point ; by means of its muscles it can be suddenly projected, point foremost, from the mouth, and is used in the capture of Insects. Immediately behind the tongue is the *glottis* (*gl.*). *Teeth* are arranged in a single series round the edge of the upper jaw, attached to the premaxillæ and maxillæ ; there is also a small patch of teeth (*vo. t.*) on each vomer just internal to the posterior nostril. The teeth are small conical

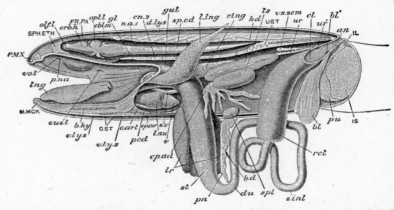

FIG. 288.—**Rana temporaria.** Dissection from the left side ; the viscera somewhat displaced. *an.* anus ; *b. d.* bile-duct ; *b. hy.* body of hyoid ; *bl.* urinary bladder ; *bl'.* its opening into the cloaca ; *c. art.* conus arteriosus ; *cblm.* cerebellum ; *cl.* cloaca ; *cn. 3,* centrum of third vertebra ; *cp. ad.* corpus adiposum ; *crb. h.* cerebral hemisphere ; *d. ly. s.* dorsal lymph sinus ; *du.* duodenum ; *ep. cor.* epicoracoid ; *eus. t.* Eustachian tube ; *FR. PA.* fronto-parietal ; *gl.* glottis ; *gul.* gullet ; *il.* ilium ; *is.* ischium ; *kd.* kidney ; *l. au.* left auricle ; *l. lng.* left lung ; *lr.* liver ; *M.* MCK. mento-meckelian ; *n. a 1,* neural arch of first vertebra ; *olf. l.* olfactory bulb ; *opt. l.* optic lobe ; O. ST. omosternum ; *pcd.* pericardium ; *PMX.* premaxilla ; *pn.* pancreas ; *p. na.* posterior naris ; *pu.* pubis ; *rct.* rectum ; *r. lng.* right lung ; *s. int.* ileum ; *sp. cd.* spinal cord ; SPH. ETH. sphenethmoid ; *spl.* spleen ; *st.* stomach ; *s. v.* sinus venosus ; *tng.* tongue ; *ts.* testis ; *ur.* ureter ; *ur'.* its aperture into the cloaca ; UST. urostyle ; *v.* ventricle ; *v. ly. s.* ventral lymph sinus ; *vo. t.* vomerine teeth ; *vs. sem.* vesicula seminalis.

bodies, their bases ankylosed to the bones ; their only use is to prevent the polished or slimy bodies of the prey—Insects and Worms—from slipping out of the mouth.

The buccal cavity narrows towards the *pharynx*, which leads by a short *gullet* (*gul.*) into a *stomach* (*st.*) consisting of a wide cardiac and a short, narrow, pyloric division. The *duodenum* (*du.*), or first portion of the small intestine, passes forwards parallel with the stomach ; the rest of the small intestine (*ileum*) is twisted into a coil. The large intestine or *rectum* (*rct.*) is very wide and short, and passes without change of diameter into the cloaca (*cl.*).

The *liver* (*lr.*) is two-lobed ; between the right and left lobes lies a large *gall-bladder* (Fig. 289, G.). The *pancreas* (P.) is an irregular gland surrounding the bile-duct, into which it pours its secretion ; the *spleen* (Fig. 288, *spl.*) is a small, red globular body attached near the anterior end of the rectum. The *thyroids* are small paired organs lying below the floor of the mouth in front of the glottis. The *thymus* is also paired, and is situated behind and below the tympanic membrane.

Respiratory Organs.—The *lungs* (*l. lng., r. lng.*) are elastic sacs lying in the anterior part of the cœlome above the heart and liver ; their size and appearance vary greatly according to their state of distension. Each contains a spacious cavity and has its walls raised into a complex network of ridges abundantly supplied with blood-vessels. The two lungs open anteriorly into a small *laryngo-tracheal chamber* which communicates with the mouth by the narrow, slit-like *glottis*. The walls of the laryngo-tracheal chamber are supported by a cartilaginous framework, and its mucous membrane is raised into a pair of horizontal folds, the *vocal chords*, by the vibration of which the croak of the Frog is produced.

In breathing, the Frog keeps its mouth closed, and by depressing the floor of the mouth, draws air into the buccal cavity through the nostrils. The floor of the mouth is then raised, the nostrils, which are valvular, are closed, and the air is forced through the glottis into the lungs. The skin also is an important respiratory organ.

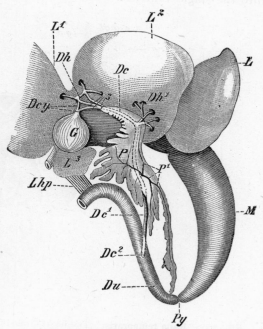

FIG. 289.—**Rana esculenta.** Stomach and duodenum with liver and pancreas. *Dc., Dc.*[1] common bile-duct ; *Dc.*[2] its opening into the duodenum ; *D. cy.* cystic ducts ; *Dh., Dh.*[1] hepatic ducts ; *Du.* duodenum ; *G.* gall-bladder ; *L, L*[1], *L*[2], *L*[3], lobes of liver, turned forwards ; *Lhp.* duodenohepatic omentum, a sheet of peritoneum connecting the liver with the duodenum ; *M.* stomach ; *P.* pancreas ; *P*[1], pancreatic duct ; *Py.* pylorus. (From Wiedersheim's *Comparative Anatomy*.)

Circulatory Organs.—The *pericardium* (Fig. 288, *pcd.*) is not situated in front of the general cœlome, as in Fishes, but lies in the cœlomic cavity between the gullet above and the epicoracoids below ; it consists, as usual, of a visceral layer closely adherent to the heart, and a loose parietal layer, the two being continuous at the bases of the great vessels and separated by a small quantity of pericardial fluid.

The *heart* consists of a sinus venosus (Figs. 290 and 288, *s. v.*), right and left auricles (*r. au., l. au.*), a ventricle (*v., vt.*), and a conus arteriosus (*c. art.*). The sinus venosus opens into the right auricle, the pulmonary veins into the left : a striking advance on the Dipnoi is seen in the greatly increased size of the left auricle and its separation by a complete partition, the *septum auricularum* (Fig. 290, *spt. aur.*), from the right. The two auricles open by a common auriculo-ventricular aperture, guarded by a pair of valves (*au. v. v.*) into the single ventricle. The latter has a transversely elongated cavity, and

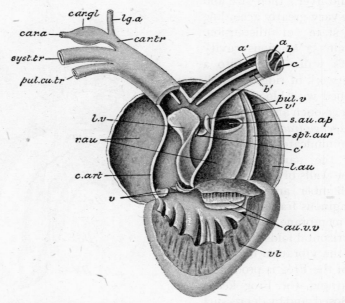

FIG. 290.—**Rana temporaria.** The heart from the ventral aspect with the cavities laid open. *a, a'*, bristle in left carotid trunk ; *au. v. v.* auriculo-ventricular valves ; *b. b'*, bristle in left systemic trunk ; *c, c'*, bristle in left pulmo-cutaneous trunk ; *car. a.* carotid artery ; *car. gl.* carotid labyrinth ; *c. art.* conus arteriosus ; *car. tr.* carotid trunk ; *l. au.* left auricle ; *lg. a.* lingual artery ; *l. v.* longitudinal valve ; *pul. cu. tr.* pulmo-cutaneous trunk ; *pul. v.* aperture of pulmonary veins ; *r. au.* right auricle ; *s. au. ap.* sinu-auricular aperture ; *spt. aur.* septum auricularum ; *v, v'*, valves ; *vt.* ventricle.

its dorsal and ventral walls are raised up into muscular ridges or trabeculæ with interstices between them. The conus springs from the right side of the base of the ventricle ; it is separated from the latter by three small semilunar valves (*v.*), and is traversed obliquely along its whole length by a large, flap-like, longitudinal valve (*l.v.*) which springs from its dorsal wall and is free ventrally. The conus passes without change of diameter into a *bulbus arteriosus*, the two being separated by a semilunar valve (*v¹.*) and by the free end of the longitudinal valve. The bulbus gives off two branches, right and left, each of them divided by two longitudinal partitions into three vessels, an inner or anterior, the carotid trunk (*car. tr.*), a middle, the *systemic trunk* or *aortic arch*, and an outer or posterior, the *pulmo-cutaneous trunk* (*pul. cu. tr.*). The systemic trunks communicate separately with the bulbus and the carotid trunks open slightly to the right of the junction of the two systemic trunks. The opening of the carotid trunks is guarded by a valve.

After being bound together in the way described for a short distance, the carotid, systemic, and pulmo-cutaneous trunks separate from one another. The carotid trunk divides into an *internal* (Figs. 290 and 291, *car.*) and *external carotid* (*lg.*) artery for the supply of the head, the former having at its base a small swelling, the *carotid "gland"* or *labyrinth* (*car. gl.*), with a spongy interior containing numerous cavities. The systemic trunks curve round the gullet and unite with one another above it to form the *dorsal aorta* (*d. ao.*), from which, or from one of the systemic trunks themselves, the arteries to all parts of the body, except the head, the lungs, and the skin, are given off. The pulmocutaneous trunk divides into two, a *pulmonary artery* (*pul.*) to the lung, and a *cutaneous artery* (*cu.*) to the skin.

In the tadpole there are four aortic arches, each consisting of an afferent and an efferent branchial artery connected by the capillaries of the gills. As the water-breathing larva undergoes metamorphosis into the air-breathing adult the gills disappear; the first aortic arch loses its connection with the dorsal aorta and becomes the carotid trunk; the second enlarges, retains its connection with the dorsal aorta, and becomes the systemic trunk; the

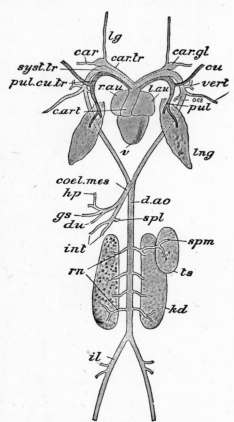

FIG. 291.—**Rana temporaria.** The arterial system, with the heart, lungs, kidneys, and left testis, from the ventral aspect. *car.* internal carotid artery; *car. gl.* carotid labyrinth; *c. art.* conus arteriosus; *car. tr.* carotid trunk; *cœl. mes.* cœliaco-mesenteric artery; *cu.* cutaneous artery; *d. ao.* dorsal aorta; *du.* duodenal artery; *gs.* gastric artery; *hp.* hepatic artery; *il.* iliac artery; *int.* intestinal arteries; *kd.* kidney; *l. au.* left auricle; *lg.* external carotid artery; *lng.* lung; *œs.* œsophageal artery; *pul.* pulmonary artery; *pul. cu. tr.* pulmo-cutaneous trunk; *r. au.* right auricle; *rn.* renal arteries; *scl.* subclavian artery; *spl.* splenic artery; *syst. ts.* systemic trunk; *spm.* spermatic artery; *ts.* testis; *v.* ventricle; *vert.* vertebral artery.

third disappears; and the fourth sends off branches to the lungs and skin,

loses its connection with the dorsal aorta, and becomes the pulmo-cutaneous trunk.

The blood from each side of the head is returned by *internal* (Fig. 292, *int. ju.*) and *external* (*ext. ju.*) *jugular veins* into the *precaval vein* (*pr. v.*), which also

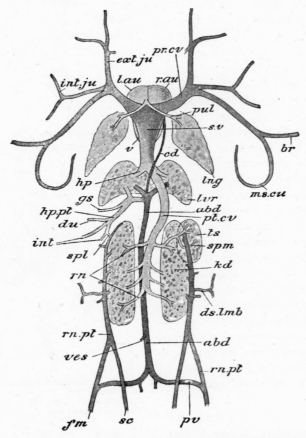

Fig. 292.—**Rana temporaria.** The venous system with the heart, lungs, liver, kidneys, and right testis, from the dorsal aspect. *abd.* abdominal vein; *br.* brachial vein; *cd.* cardiac vein; *ds. lmb.* dorso-lumbar vein; *du.* duodenal vein; *ext. ju.* external jugular vein; *fm.* femoral vein; *gs.* gastric vein; *hp.* hepatic vein; *hp. pt.* hepatic portal vein; *int.* intestinal veins; *int. ju.* internal jugular vein; *kd.* kidney; *l. au.* left auricle; *lng.* lung; *lvr.* liver; *ms. cu.* musculo-cutaneous vein; *pr. cv.* precaval vein; *pt. cv.* postcaval vein; *pul.* pulmonary vein; *pv.* pelvic vein; *r. au.* right auricle; *rn.* renal veins; *rn. pt.* renal portal vein; *sc.* sciatic vein; *spl.* splenic vein; *spm.* spermatic vein; *s. v.* sinus venosus; *ts.* testis; *ves.* vesical veins.

receives the *brachial vein* (*br.*) from the fore-limb, and the *musculo-cutaneous vein* (*ms. cu.*) from the skin and muscles of the side and back, and part of the head: the two precavals open separately into the sinus venosus.

The course of the blood from the posterior part of the body is very different from what we have met with in fishes, the differences being due partly to the absence of a tail, partly to a peculiar modification of the lateral veins, and partly to the replacement of the cardinals by a *postcaval vein*, found among fishes only in the Dipnoi.

The blood from the front part of the hind-leg is brought back by a *femoral vein* (*fm.*), which, on reaching the cœlome, divides into two branches, a dorsal and a ventral. The dorsal branch is the *renal portal vein* (*rn. pt.*): it receives the *sciatic vein* (*sc.*) from the back of the leg and passes to the kidney, in which it breaks up into capillaries. The ventral branch is the *pelvic vein* (*pv.*): it unites with its fellow of the opposite side to form the *abdominal vein* (*abd.*) which passes forwards in the ventral body-wall, between the linea alba and the peritoneum, to the level of the sternum, where it turns inwards and divides into two branches, both breaking up into capillaries in the liver. Just as it enters the liver it is joined by the *hepatic portal vein* (*hp. pt.*), bringing the blood from the stomach, intestine, spleen, and pancreas. The abdominal vein also receives *vesical veins* (*ves.*) from the urinary bladder, and a small *cardiac vein* from the heart (*cd.*). It represents the lateral veins of Chondrichthyes united in the middle ventral line: the pelvic veins are their posterior free portions.

The blood is collected from the kidneys by the *renal veins* (*rn.*), which unite to form the large unpaired *postcaval vein* (*pt. cv.*). This passes forward through a notch in the liver, receives the *hepatic veins* (*h.p.*) from that organ, and finally opens into the sinus venosus. Thus the blood from the hind-limbs has to pass through one of the two portal systems on its way back to the heart: part of it goes by the renal portal veins to the kidneys, and thence by the renal veins to the postcaval, part by the pelvic and abdominal veins to the liver, and thence by the hepatic veins to the postcaval. Lastly, the blood which has been purified in the lungs is returned by the *pulmonary veins* (*pul.*) directly to the left auricle.

It will be seen that there is no trace of cardinal veins in the Frog. But in the larva both anterior and posterior cardinal veins are present: during the metamorphosis the ductûs Cuvieri, in which, as in fishes, they unite, become converted into the precavals, while the posterior portions of the posterior cardinals contribute to the formation of the postcaval, and the anterior portions disappear.

It will be perceived that the blood poured into the right auricle is mostly impure or venous, that poured into the left fully aerated or arterial. When the auricles contract, which they do simultaneously, each passes its blood into the corresponding part of the ventricle, which then instantly contracts, before the venous and arterial bloods, kept separate as they are to some extent by the muscular trabeculæ acting as incomplete partitions, have time to mix. Since the conus arteriosus springs from the right side of the ventricle, it will at first receive only venous blood, which, on the contraction of the conus, might pass either into the bulbus aortæ or into the aperture of the pulmo-cutaneous trunks. But the carotid and systemic trunks are connected with a much more extensive capillary system than the pulmo-cutaneous, and the pressure in them is pro-

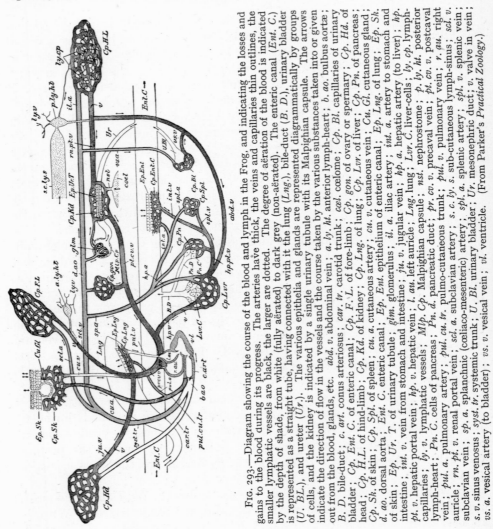

FIG. 293.—Diagram showing the course of the blood and lymph in the Frog, and indicating the losses and gains to the blood during its progress. The arteries have thick, the veins and capillaries thin outlines, the smaller lymphatic vessels are black, the larger are dotted. The degree of aëration of the blood is indicated by the depth of shade, from white (fully aërated) to dark grey (non-aërated). The enteric canal (*Ent. C.*) is represented as a straight tube, having connected with it the lung (*Lng.*), bile-duct (*B. D.*), urinary bladder (*U. BL.*), and ureter (*Ur.*). The various epithelia and glands are represented diagrammatically by groups of cells, and the kidney is indicated by a single urinary tubule with its Malpighian capsule. The arrows indicate the direction of flow in the vessels and the course taken by the various substances taken into or given out from the blood, glands, etc. *abd. v.* abdominal vein; *a. ly. ht.* anterior lymph-heart; *b. ao.* bulbus aortæ; *B. D.* bile-duct; *c. art.* conus arteriosus; *car. tr.* carotid trunk; *cœl.* coelome; *Cp. Bl.* capillaries of urinary bladder; *Cp. Ent. C.* of enteric canal; *Cp. F. L.* of fore-limb; *Cp. gon.* of ovary or spermary; *Cp. Hd.* of head; *Cp. H.L.* of hind-limb; *Cp. Kd.* of kidney; *Cp. Lng.* of lung; *Cp. Lvr.* of liver; *Cp. Pn.* of pancreas; *Cp. Sk.* of skin; *Cp. Spl.* of spleen; *cu. a.* cutaneous artery; *cu. v.* cutaneous vein; *Cu. Gl.* cutaneous gland; *d. ao.* dorsal aorta; *Ent. C.* enteric canal; *Ep. Ent.* epithelium of enteric canal; *Ep. Lng.* of lung; *Ep. Sk.* of skin; *Ep. Ur. T.* of urinary tubule; *glm.* glomerulus; *il. a.* iliac artery; *int. a.* artery to stomach and intestine; *int. v.* vein from stomach and intestine; *ju. v.* jugular vein; *hp. a.* hepatic artery (to liver); *hp. pt. v.* hepatic portal vein; *hp. v.* hepatic vein; *l. au.* left auricle; *Lng.* lung; *Lvr. C.* liver-cells; *ly. cp.* lymph-capillaries; *ly. v.* lymphatic vessels; *Mlp. Cp.* Malpighian capsule; *nst.* nephrostome; *p. ly. ht.* posterior lymph-heart; *Pn. C.* cells of pancreas; *Pn. d.* pancreatic duct; *prc. cv. v.* precaval vein; *pt. cv. v.* postcaval vein; *pul. a.* pulmonary artery; *pul. cu. tr.* pulmo-cutaneous trunk; *r. au.* right auricle; *rn. pt. v.* renal portal vein; *scl. a.* subclavian artery; *s. c. ly. s.* sub-cutaneous lymph-sinus; *scl. v.* subclavian vein; *sp. a.* splanchnic (coeliaco-mesenteric) artery; *spl. a.* splenic artery; *spl. v.* splenic vein; *s. v. sinus venosus*; *syst. tr.* systemic trunk; *U. Bl.* urinary bladder; *Ur.* mesonephric duct; *v.* valve in vein; *vs. a.* vesical artery (to bladder); *vs. v.* vesical vein; *vl.* ventricle. (From Parker's *Practical Zoology.*)

portionally great, so that it is easier for the blood to enter the pulmo-cutaneous trunks than to force aside the valves between the conus and the bulbus. A fraction of a second is, however, enough to get up the pressure in the pulmonary and cutaneous arteries, and in the meantime the pressure in the arteries of the head, trunk, etc., is constantly diminishing, owing to the continual flow of blood towards the capillaries. Very soon, therefore, the blood forces the valves aside and makes its way into the bulbus aortæ. This will therefore receive the next portion of blood, which, the venous blood having been mostly driven to the lungs, will be a mixture of venous and arterial. Finally, as the pressure rises in the systemic trunks, the last portion of blood from the ventricle, which, coming from the left side, is arterial, will pass into the carotids and so supply the head.

The *red blood-corpuscles* are, like those of fishes, oval, nucleated discs. The *lymphatic system* (Fig. 293) is very well developed, and is remarkable for the dilatation of many of its vessels into immense *lymph-sinuses*. Between the skin and muscle are large *subcutaneous sinuses* (Fig. 288, *v. ly. s.*), separated from one another by fibrous partitions, and the dorsal aorta is surrounded by a spacious *subvertebral sinus*. The lymph is pumped into the veins by two pairs of *lymph-hearts*, one situated beneath the suprascapulæ, the other beside the posterior end of the urostyle.

Nervous System.—The *brain* (Fig. 294) has a very small cerebellum, large optic lobes, a well developed diencephalon, and large hemispheres and olfactory bulbs, the latter fused in the median plane. The corpora striata, or basal ganglia of the cerebral hemispheres, are connected together, as in all Vertebrates, by an *anterior commissure* (*D, com.*, below, lower line), above which is another commissure (*com.*, below, upper line) partly representing the *hippocampal commissure* of the brain of Reptiles and Mammals. The metacœle is covered by a thick choroid plexus; the mesocœle is divisible into a median passage or *iter* (*i.*), and paired *optocœles* (*opt. v.*) in the optic lobes: the paracœles are large cavities each communicating with a rhinocœle in the corresponding olfactory bulb. The pineal body is vestigial in the adult, a lobe of the anterior choroid plexus, with a vestige of the stalk (*pin.*), taking the position which it usually occupies: in the larva it is found outside the skull and immediately beneath the skin.

The first spinal nerve performs the function of the hypoglossal (Fig. 294, *1Sp.*), supplying the muscles of the tongue: it passes out between the first and second vertebræ. The spinal cord is short and ends in a delicate filament, the *filum terminale*. In correspondence with the number of vertebræ there are only ten pairs of spinal nerves, of which the second and third unite to form a *brachial plexus* giving off the nerves to the fore-limb, while the seventh to the tenth join to form a *lumbo-sacral plexus* giving off the nerves to the hind-limb.

Sensory Organs.—The *olfactory sacs* have each two openings: the *anterior naris* or external nostril and the *posterior naris* (Fig. 288, *p. na.*) or internal nostril, which opens into the mouth immediately external to the vomer.

The *eye* and the *auditory organ* have the usual structure, but in connection with the latter there is an important accessory organ of hearing not hitherto met with. Bounded externally by the tympanic membrane and internally by the outer wall of the auditory capsule is a considerable space, the *tympanic cavity* (Fig. 295, *tymp. cav.*), which communicates with the pharynx by the short Eustachian tube (*eus. t.*) already noticed (Fig. 288, *eus. t.*), so that a probe thrust through the tympanic membrane from outside passes directly into the

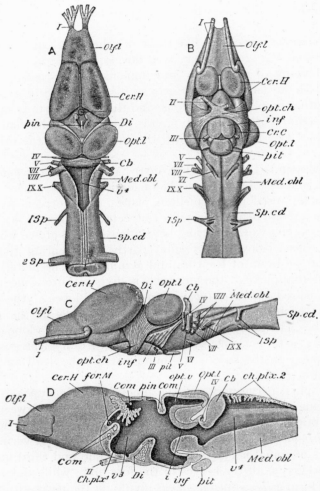

FIG. 294.—Brain of **Rana.** *A*, from above; *B*, from below; *C*, from the side; *D*, in longitudinal vertical section. *Cb.* cerebellum; *Cer. H.* cerebral hemispheres; *ch. plx*[1]. anterior, and *ch. plx*[2]. posterior choroid plexus (removed in *A*); *com.* commissures, the two in front the *anterior* and *hippocampal*, the two above the *superior* or *habenular* and the *posterior*; *Cr. C.* crura cerebri; *Di.* diencephalon; *for. M.* foramen of Monro; *i.* iter, or aqueduct of Sylvius; *inf.* infundibulum; *Med. obl.* medulla oblongata; *Olf. l.* olfactory bulb; *opt. ch.* optic chiasma; *Opt. l.* optic lobe; *opt. v.* optic ventricle; *pin.* stalk of pineal body; *pit.* pituitary body; *Sp. cd.* spinal cord; *v*[3]. third ventricle; *v*[4]. fourth ventricle; *I—X.* cerebral nerves; *1Sp. 2Sp.* spinal nerves. (From Parker's *Practical Zoology.* *A—C,* after Gaupp; *D,* from Wiedersheim's *Comparative Anatomy,* after Osborn.)

pharynx. In the roof of the tympanic cavity lies the columella (*col.*), its head, or extra-columella, attached to the inner surface of the tympanic membrane, its handle united to the stapes (*stp.*), which is fixed in the membrane of the fenestra ovalis (*fen. ov.*). Sonorous vibrations striking the tympanic membrane are communicated by the columella and stapes to the fenestra ovalis, thence to the perilymph, and thence to the membranous labyrinth. The connection of the eustachian tube with the pharynx obviates undue compression of the air in the tympanic cavity. There seems little doubt that the tympano-eustachian passage is homologous with the first or hyomandibular gill-cleft, although, in the Frog, it is formed independently of the clefts and never opens on the exterior.

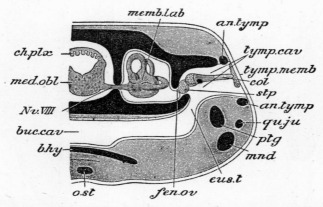

Fig. 295.—Transverse section of head of **Frog** to show the relations of the accessory auditory apparatus (diagrammatic). Skeletal structures black, with the exception of the columella. *an. tymp.* annulus tympanicus; *b. hy.* body of hyoid; *buc. cav.* cavity of pharynx; *ch. plx.* choroid plexus; *col.* columella; *eus. t.* Eustachian tube; *fen. ov.* fenestra ovalis; *med. obl.* medulla oblongata; *memb. lab.* membranous labyrinth; *mnd.* mandible; *Nv. VIII.* auditory nerve; *o. st.* omosternum; *ptg.* ptergyoid; *qu. ju.* quadrato-jugal; *stp.* stapes; *tymp. cav.* tympanic cavity or middle ear; *tymp. m.* tympanic membrane.

Urinogenital Organs.—The *kidneys* (Figs. 296 and 297, *N.*) are flat, somewhat oval bodies, of a dark red colour, lying in the posterior region of the cœlome. On the ventral face of each is an elongated, yellow *adrenal*, and irregularly scattered *nephrostomes* occur in considerable numbers on the same surface; these do not, however, communicate with the urinary tubules, but with the renal veins, and serve to propel the lymph from the cœlome to the venous system. The mesonephric ducts (*Ur.*) pass backwards from the outer borders of the kidneys and open into the dorsal wall of the cloaca (*Cl.*). The kidney is developed from the mesonephros of the embryo, the urinary duct from the mesonephric duct. In the larva a large pronephros is present and is, for a time, the functional kidney.

Opening into the cloaca on its ventral side is an organ (Fig. 288, *bl.*)

mentioned in the general account of the Craniata (p. 121), but here actually met with for the first time. It is a bilobed, thin-walled, and very delicate sac into which the urine passes by gravitation from the cloaca when the anus is closed. The sac is a *urinary bladder*, but, as it is quite different morphologically from the organ of the same name in Fishes, which is a dilatation of the mesonephric duct, it is distinguished as the *allantoic bladder*.

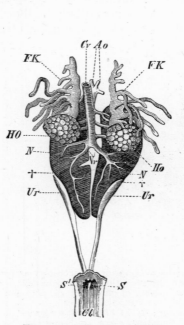

FIG. 296.—**Rana esculenta.** Urinogenital organs of the male. *Ao.* dorsal aorta; *Cl.* cloaca; *Cv.* postcaval vein; *FK*, fat-bodies; *HO*, testes; *N*, kidneys; *S*, *S'*, apertures of mesonephric ducts into cloaca; *Ur.* meso-nephric ducts. (From Wieders-heim's *Comparative Anatomy*.)

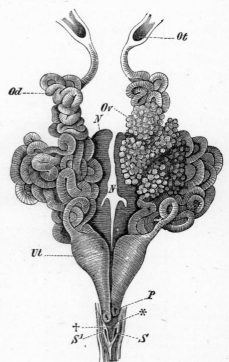

FIG. 297.—**Rana esculenta.** Urinogenital organs of the female. *N*, kidneys; *Od.* ovi-duct; *Ot.* its cœlomic aperture; *Ov.* left ovary (the right is removed); *P*, cloacal aper-ture of oviduct; *S*, *S'*, cloacal apertures of mesonephric ducts; *Ut.* uterine dilatation of oviduct. (From Wiedersheim's *Comparative Anatomy*.)

The *testes* (*HO*) are white ovoid bodies lying immediately ventral to the anterior ends of the kidneys, to which they are attached by folds of peritoneum. From the inner edge of each pass a number of delicate *vasa efferentia* which enter the kidney and become connected with the urinary tubules. The spermatic fluid is thus passed into the urinary tubules and carried off by the duct, which is therefore a urinogenital duct in the male Frog. A *vesicula seminalis* (Fig. 288, *vs. sem.*) opens by numerous small ducts into the outer side of the duct.

Attached to the testis are lobed bodies of a bright yellow colour, the *fat-bodies* (*FK*).

The *ovaries* (Fig. 297, *Ov.*) are large folded sacs on the surface of which the black-and-white ova project. A fat-body is attached to each. The *oviducts* (*Od.*) are greatly convoluted tubes, the narrow anterior ends of which open into the cœlome by small apertures (*Ot.*) placed close to the bases of the lungs. Their posterior ends are wide and thin-walled (*Ut.*), and open into the cloaca (*P*). The ova break loose from the surface of the ovary and enter the cœlomic apertures of the oviducts, the walls of which are glandular and secrete an albuminous fluid having the property of swelling up in water. The eggs receive a coating of this substance as they pass down the oviducts, and are finally stored up in the thin-walled posterior portions of those tubes, which, in the breeding season, become immensely dilated and serve as uteri.

Development.—The eggs are laid in water in large masses ; each has a black and white hemisphere, the former always directed upwards, and is surrounded by a sphere of jelly. The egg is telolecithal, the protoplasm being mainly accumulated on the pigmented hemisphere, while the white hemisphere is loaded with yolk. During oviposition the male sheds his spermatic fluid over the eggs, and the sperms make their way through the jelly and impregnate them. In a short time the jelly swells up and becomes thereafter impermeable to the sperms.

Segmentation begins by a vertical furrow dividing the oosperm into two cells (Fig. 298, *A*), and soon followed by a second vertical furrow at right angles to the first (*B*), and then by an equatorial furrow placed nearer the black than the white pole (*C*). Thus the eight-celled embryo consists of four smaller black cells and four larger white cells. Further divisions take place (*D*), the black cells dividing rapidly into micromeres (*mi.*), the white, more slowly, into megameres (*mg.*) : as in previous cases, the presence of yolk hinders the process of segmentation. The pigmented micromeres (*D—F, mi.*) give rise to the ectoderm, which is many-layered : the megameres (*mg.*) contribute to all three layers and are commonly called *yolk-cells*. During the process of segmentation a *blastocœle* (*E, bl. cœl.*) or segmentation-cavity appears in the upper hemisphere.

The black now begins to encroach on the white hemisphere ; cells, budded from the yolk-cells, take on the character of ectoderm, acquire pigment, and gradually extend the black area until it covers the whole embryo except a small patch, known as the *yolk-plug* (*G, H, yk. pl.*), at what will become the posterior end. This process is obviously one of epiboly : the margin of ectoderm cells surrounding the yolk-plug represents the blastopore.

The *archenteron* (*I, ent.*) arises by a split taking place among the yolk-cells, beginning at the edges of the blastopore and gradually extending forwards : the process is probably supplemented by a limited amount of invagination of

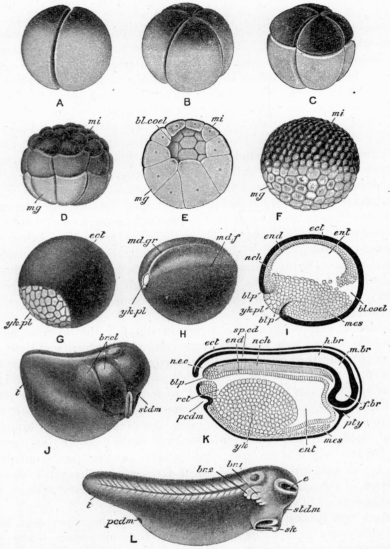

FIG. 298.—Development of the **Frog.** *A—F*, segmentation; *G*, overgrowth of ectoderm; *H, I*, establishment of germinal layers; *J, K*, assumption of tadpole-form and establishment of nervous system, notochord, and enteric canal; *L*, newly-hatched tadpole. *bl. cœl.* blastocœle; *blp. blp'*. blastopore; *br. 1, br. 2*, gills; *br. cl.* branchial arches; *e.* eye; *ect.* ectoderm; *end.* endoderm; *ent.* enteron; *f. br.* fore-brain; *h. br.* hind-brain; *m. br.* mid-brain; *md. f.* medullary fold; *md. gr.* medullary groove; *mes.* mesoderm; *mg.* megameres; *mi.* micromeres; *nch.* notochord; *n. e. c.* neurenteric canal; *pcdm.* proctodæum; *pty.* pituitary invagination; *rct.* commencement of rectum; *sk.* sucker; *sp. cd.* spinal cord; *st.dm.* stomodæum; *t.* tail; *yk.* yolk-cells; *yk. pl.* yolk-plug. (*A—D, F—H,* and *J* from Ziegler's models; *E, I, K,* and *L* after Marshall.)

the ectoderm. The archenteron is at first a very narrow cleft, but soon widens considerably : for a long time it does not actually communicate with the exterior, the blastopore being filled up with the yolk-plug. As the archenteron extends forwards the blastocœle gradually disappears. The yolk-cells soon become differentiated into a layer of endoderm cells (*I, end.*) immediately surrounding the archenteron, and several layers of mesoderm cells (*mes.*). Ventrally, however, a large mass of yolk-cells (*K, yk.*) remains undifferentiated and serves as nutriment to the growing embryo.

The edges of the lower margin of the blastopore now begin to approach one another, and, uniting in the median plane, give rise to a vertical groove, the *primitive groove.* In the meantime *medullary folds* (*H, md. f.*) appear and mark the dorsal surface : they are at first widely separated, but gradually approach one another and close over the medullary groove (*md. gr.*), thus giving rise to the central nervous system. Posteriorly they are continuous with the lips of the blastopore, so that when the neural groove becomes closed in behind, the archenteron, as in Amphioxus, communicates with the neurocœle by a *neurenteric canal* (*K, n. e. c.*).

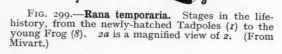

The embryo soon begins to elongate ; one end is broad, and, becoming separated by a slight constriction, is marked out as the *head* : the other end is bluntly pointed and is the rudiment of the *tail* (*t.*). On the ventral surface of the root of the tail a *proctodæum* (*pcdm.*) appears and communicates with the archenteron.

The head and tail become more distinctly marked off from the trunk. A pit—the *stomodæum* (*J—L, st.dm.*)—appears on the antero-ventral surface of the head, and, immediately behind it, a semilunar area with raised edges, the *sucker* (*sk.*). At each side of the head two branched processes appear : they are the *external gills* (*br. 1, br. 2*), and the regions from which they arise mark the positions of the first and second branchial arches.

The embryos are now hatched as *tadpoles*. They swim freely in the water or adhere to weeds by means of their suckers (Fig. 299, *1*). They are still blind and mouthless, the stomodæum not having yet communicated with the archenteron. Soon a third pair of external gills appears on the third branchial arch, and the first two pairs increase greatly in size (*2, 2a*) : the stomodæum joins the archenteron, gill-slits (branchial clefts) are formed between the branchial arches, and the eyes appear. The mouth is small, bounded by lips beset with horny papillæ and provided with a pair of horny jaws. The enteric canal grows to a great length and is coiled like a watch-spring, and the tadpole browses upon the water-weeds which form its staple food.

Soon the external gills show signs of shrivelling, and at the same time *internal gills*, like those of fishes, are developed in the branchial clefts. A fold of skin, the *operculum*, appears on each side, in front of the gills, growing from the region of the hyoid arch, and extending backwards until the gill-slits and external gills are covered and there is only a single small external branchial aperture on each side, as in Holocephali (*3, 4*). On the right side the operculum soon unites with the body-wall so as to close the branchial aperture, but on the left side the opening remains for a considerable time as the sole means of exit of the water. At this time the tadpole is to all intents and purposes a fish.

The lungs now appear, and the larva is for a time truly amphibious, rising periodically to the surface to breathe air : the single branchial aperture, however, soon closes and henceforth respiration is purely aerial.

In the meantime the limbs are developed. The hind-limbs appear as little rounded buds, one on each side of the root of the tail (*5*). The fore-limbs arise beneath the operculum and are therefore hidden at first ; soon, however, they emerge by forcing their way through the operculum. As the limbs increase in size the tail undergoes a progressive shrinking (*6–8*). The mouth widens by the backward rotation of the suspensorium, the intestine undergoes a relative diminution in length, and vegetable is exchanged for animal diet. The little, tailed Frog can now leave the water and hop about upon land ; its tail is soon completely absorbed, and the metamorphosis is complete.

CLASSIFICATION OF THE AMPHIBIA.

There are eight orders of Amphibia, five of which are extinct, and three living. The extinct orders have a completely roofed skull, whereas their modern descendants have the number of skull-bones greatly reduced. It has been customary to place the extinct orders together in a sub-class, the Stegocephalia, and the modern orders in another, the Lissamphibia, but this implies that the modern form are all descendants of a single group, whereas they are probably survivors of more than one of the early orders.

Order 1. *Ichthyostegalia.*—Very primitive Amphibia known from only a few skulls which were discovered quite recently in rocks which may be either Upper Devonian or Lower Carboniferous in age.

Order 2. *Labyrinthodontia.*—Amphibia with the dentine of the teeth typically infolded at the base, with vertebræ consisting of neural arches resting on an intercentrum and, in addition, in the early forms, on a pleurocentrum. This order includes the majority of the extinct Amphibia, and many of them reached a considerable size. Lower Carboniferous— Upper Trias.

Order 3. *Phyllospondylia.*—Small, newt-like Amphibia with only the neural arches of the vertebræ ossified. Lower Carboniferous—Lower Permian.

Order 4. *Lepospondylia.*—Amphibia with the neural arches co-ossified with the centra, which are of unknown composition. Frequently with the tabular bones enormously expanded. Lower Carboniferous—Lower Permian.

Order 5. *Adelospondylia.*—This order is known from only a few genera. The neural arches are not fused with the single centra, which have perforations at each side. The composition of these centra is unknown. Lower Carboniferous—Lower Permian.

Order 6. *Urodela.**—Newts and Salamanders. Amphibia with greatly reduced skulls, but retaining the primitive body form. Cretaceous— Recent.

Order 7. *Anura.**—Frogs and Toads. Tailless Amphibia with the hind limbs greatly enlarged for jumping. Trias—Recent.

Order 8. *Apoda.**—Limbless, worm-like Amphibia known only from living forms.

Systematic Position of the Example.

The genus Rana belongs to the sub-family *Raninæ* of the family *Ranidæ*, which, with two others, constitutes the sub-order *Diplasiocœla* of the order Anura.

The absence of a tail and the specialisations of the hind-limbs and vertebral column place the genus among the order Anura. It is placed in the sub-order Diplasiocœla by the articulations of the vertebral column; the first seven vertebræ being procœlous, the eighth biconcave and the sacral vertebra convex anteriorly and with paired articulations posteriorly for the urostyle; and also by certain specialisations of the thigh musculature. It is placed in the family Ranidæ on account of the cylindrical diapophyses and absence of intercalary cartilages, and in the sub-family Raninæ by the bony sternum and pointed or only slightly dilated tips of the digits, which have

* For a detailed classification of the modern orders, *see* Noble, *Biology of the Amphibia.*

no discs. The widespread genus *Rana*, which includes the great majority of the members of the sub-family, is difficult to define, differing only slightly from each of the other six genera. *R. temporaria* is distinguished from *R. esculenta* by its smaller size and brown colour, by the large black patch in the tympanic region, and by the absence of external vocal sacs in the male.

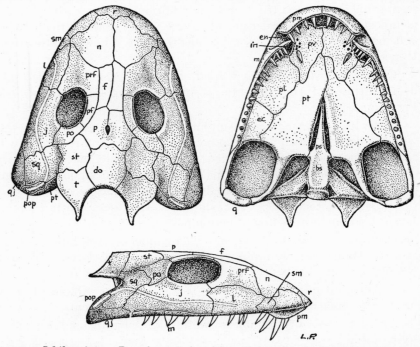

Fig. 300.—**Ichthyostega.** Dorsal, ventral and lateral aspects. *bs.* basisphenoid; *do.* supra-occipital; *ec.* ectopterygoid; *en.* external nares; *f.* frontal; *in.* internal nares; *j.* jugal; *l.* lachrymal; *m.* maxilla; *n.* nasal; *p.* parietal; *pf.* postfrontal; *pl.* palatine; *pm.* premaxilla; *po.* postorbital; *pop.* preopercular; *prf.* prefrontal; *ps.* parasphenoid; *pt.* pterygoid; *pv.* prevomer; *q.* quadrate; *qj.* quadrato-jugal; *r.* rostral; *sm.* septomaxillary; *sq.* squamosal; *st.* supratemporal; *t.* tabular. (After Romer.)

GENERAL ORGANISATION.

(a) *Extinct Orders.*

The classification of the Amphibia is unsatisfactory because, with the exception of one recent discovery, there are no known links between the various orders found in the late Palæozoic and early Mesozoic rocks and the three orders which survive to-day.

The earliest known Amphibia are the Ichthyostegalia, which have been found quite recently in rocks which may be either Upper Devonian or Lower Carboniferous in age. At present only the skull is known, but this shows three interesting features (Fig. 300). A pre-opercular persists on the back of the squamosal and quadratojugal bones as a relic of the fish opercular series; the septomaxilla forms part of the dermal covering of the skull; and the nose consists of a pit on the under side of the skull, which is bridged by a process of the maxilla and is divided into an anterior and posterior part. This last condition is similar to that found in the Dipnoi and some of the early Crossopterygians, while in all tetrapods the anterior opening of the nasal pit has migrated to the upper surface of the skull and has become completely closed off from the posterior opening so as to form true internal and external nares.

The next order, the Labyrinthodontia, includes the majority of the extinct forms. Appearing first in the Carboniferous, it became abundant during the Permian, but did not survive beyond the Trias. Some of the early forms are very important, as they show features which are fish-like, and at the same time provide possible ancestors of the reptiles. *Palæogyrinus* (Fig. 301 B) has a long, cylindrical body with a powerful tail and poorly developed limbs. It has no neck, the shoulder-girdle being attached to the back of the skull by a post-temporal bone, as in fishes. The build of the skull of these Carboniferous forms is very similar in general structure to that of the Osteolepid fishes (Fig. 301 B), except that the specialised hinge between the frontals and parietals is missing. An important feature is seen in the structure of the teeth, which have the dentine infolded at the base into complicated grooves, as in the Osteolepids. The vertebræ are of a type known as embolomerous, consisting of a neural arch resting on two notochordal centra, an anterior intercentrum and a posterior pleurocentrum (Fig. 302). The shoulder-girdle is similar to that of the Osteolepid fishes, particularly in retaining the post-temporal bone, except that an interclavicle has been added and the scapulocoracoid bone has increased in size (Fig. 303). The pelvis is peculiar in being the only one known among tetrapods which is not directly attached to the vertebral column, but was held in place by means of ligaments.

In the course of their evolution the Labyrinthodonts underwent a series of profound changes, one of the most important being in the structure of their vertebræ. The two centra present in each embolomerous vertebra of early forms were first reduced to two half-moon-shaped elements, and then the posterior pleurocentrum was further reduced to a pair of blocks of bone which lay behind the top of the intercentrum and the neural arch (Fig. 302). This condition is typical of the Permian forms, and is known as *rachitomous*. In the majority of Triassic Labyrinthodonts all trace of the pleurocentrum became lost (at least as a separate element), and the intercentrum re-developed into a solid centrum. This form of vertebra, composed only of the neural arch and the intercentrum, is termed *stereospondylous*. A convenient classification of the Labyrinthodonts is based on these changes, and the order is thereby divided into three grades, the *Embolomeri*, *Rachitomi* and *Stereo-*

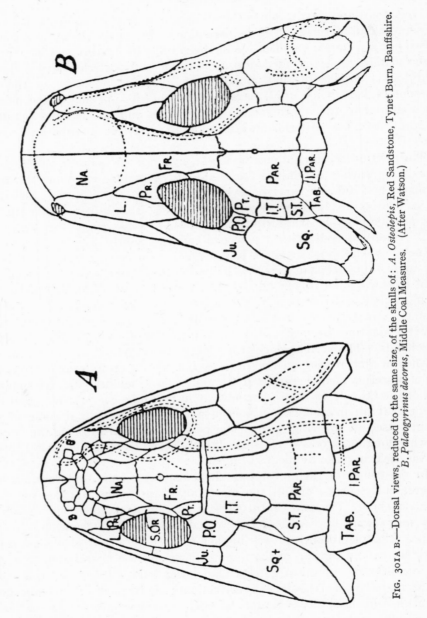

FIG. 301 A B.—Dorsal views, reduced to the same size, of the skulls of : *A. Osteolepis*, Red Sandstone, Tynet Burn, Banffshire. *B. Palæogyrinus decorus*, Middle Coal Measures. (After Watson.)

spondyli, typical respectively of the Carboniferous, Permian and Triassic periods. It must be remembered, however, that this classification is only one of convenience, and does not bear any phylogenetic significance.

Many other changes of importance took place in the skeleton. The skull and body became flattened, most of the bones forming the brain-case were reduced (the loss of the basioccipital resulted in the formation of paired exoccipital condyles typical of all but the earliest amphibia) and a separation

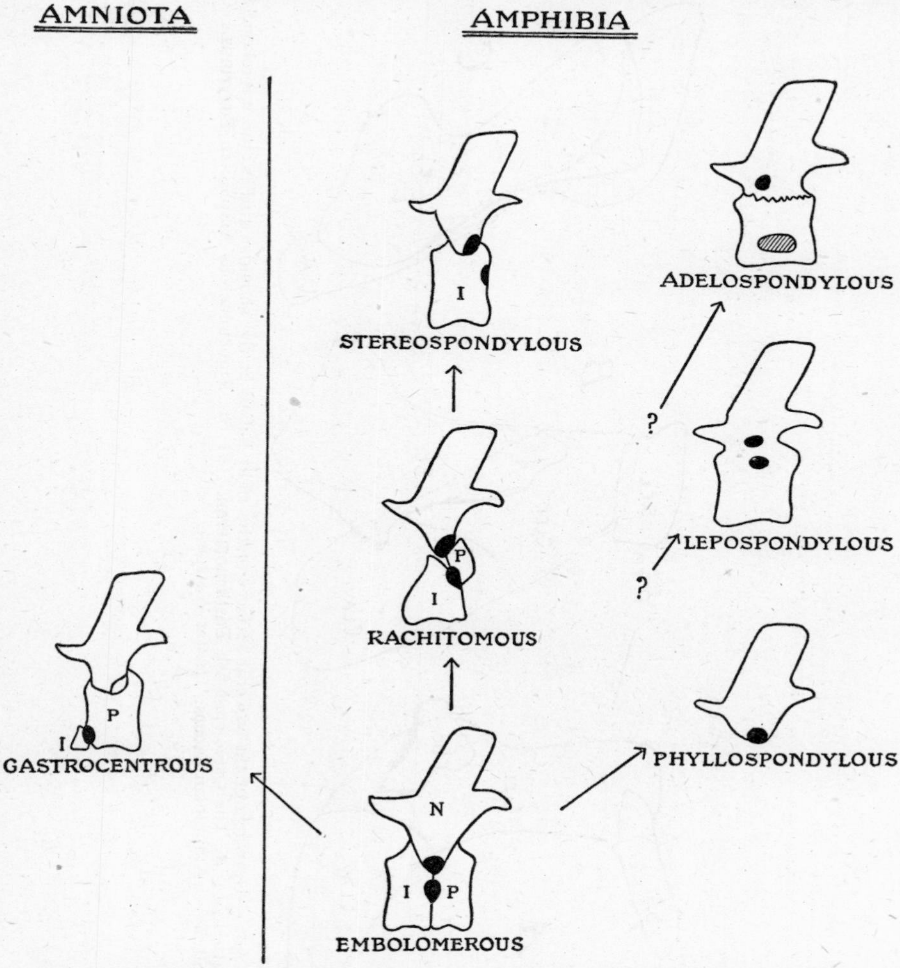

FIG. 302.—Diagrams of the composition of the main types of Tetrapod vertebræ. Rib facets are black. Excavation in adelospondylous centrum is shaded.

of the pterygoids from the parasphenoid in the mid-line resulted in the formation of large interpterygoid vacuities. *Eryops*, a form common in the Lower Permian rocks of North America, was much better fitted for life on land than *Eogyrinus*, the limbs being larger, the tail smaller and the lateral line system was apparently lost in the adult. By the Trias, however, the group returned to life in water, the head became relatively enormous, the limbs were reduced and the lateral line system persisted in the adult stage. It is interesting to notice that while the earliest members show fish-like

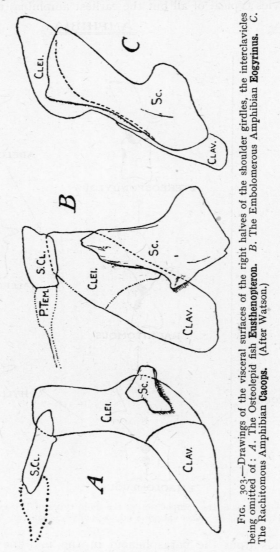

Fig. 303.—Drawings of the visceral surfaces of the right halves of the shoulder girdles, the interclavicles being omitted of: A. The Osteolepid fish **Eusthenopteron.** B. The Embolomerous Amphibian **Eogyrinus.** C. The Rachitomous Amphibian **Cacops.** (After Watson.)

features, and some had much in common with the earliest reptiles, the later members resembled the living frogs and newts in many features of their palates and brain-cases.

There are three other orders of Palæozoic Amphibia, distinguished by the structure of their vertebræ. The Phyllospondylia are abundant in some Carboniferous and Permian rocks of Europe and North America. They were small, newt-like forms which had only the neural arches of their vertebræ ossified. They had a complete roofing to their skull, but the brain-case was unossified, and the young had external gills which have been preserved in a number of specimens. The general build of these forms is so newt-like that many attempts have been made to ally them to the Urodeles, but positive evidence of this is still lacking.

The Lepospondylia were forms which had the neural arches and the centra of the vertebræ co-ossified, and their constituents are problematical. Although the order includes forms of a generalised build, they are for the most part bizarre animals, with the posterior corners of the skull roof enormously enlarged, and a few were legless. *Diplocaulus*, which is found in the Lower Permian of North America, is one of the best-known forms. It was about two feet long, with a huge triangular head and small limbs.

Only a few members of the Adelospondylia are known. Here the neural

FIG. 304.—**Necturus maculatus.** *an.* anus; *br. 1*—*br. 3* external gills; *br. cl. 1* and *2*, branchial clefts.

arches were loosely attached to single centra, which were hollowed out by an excavation on each side. One American form, *Lysorophus*, is peculiar among early Amphibia in that some reduction of the skull-bones has taken place, but unfortunately it is specialised, and gives no evidence of relationship with later forms.

(b) *Modern Amphibia.*

External Characters.—An excellent example of the Urodela with persistent gills is afforded by the great North American Water-newt, *Necturus maculatus* (Fig. 304). The animal attains a length of 30 cm. (more than a foot); the elongated trunk is separated by a slight constriction from the depressed head, and passes insensibly into the compressed tail, which is bordered by a continuous median fin unsupported by fin-rays. The limbs are small and weak in proportion to the size of the body, and in the ordinary swimming attitude are directed backwards, more or less parallel to the sagittal plane, the upper arm and thigh taking a direction backwards and slightly upwards, the fore-arm and hand and the shank and foot extending backwards and downwards. Each limb thus presents an external or dorsal and an internal or ventral surface, an anterior or *pre-axial* border, which terminates in the first digit, and a posterior or *post-axial* border, which terminates in the last digit. The eyes are small and have no eyelids, there is no tympanic membrane, and the mouth is wide and bordered by thick lips. On each side of the neck are two gill-slits (*br. cl. 1, br. cl. 2*) leading into the pharynx, the first between the first and second branchial arches, the other between the second and third. From the dorsal end of each of the three branchial arches springs a branched *external gill* (*br. 1—br. 3*). Very

FIG. 305.—**Siren lacertina.** (From Mivart.)

similar in its external characters is the blind, cave-dwelling *Proteus*; and *Siren* (Fig. 305) differs mainly in its elongated eel-like body and in the absence of hind-limbs. All three genera are *perennibranchiate* or persistent-gilled.

The remaining Urodela are often called *caducibranchiate* or deciduous-gilled, and furnish a complete series of transitions from *derotrematous* forms which, while losing the gills, retain the gill-clefts, to *salamandrine* forms in which all trace of branchiate organisation disappears in the adult. In *Amphiuma* (Fig. 306) the body is eel-like and the limbs are extremely small : there are no gills in the adult, but two pairs of gill-openings are retained throughout life. In

FIG. 306.—**Amphiuma tridactyla.** (From Mivart.)

Cryptobranchus there is a single branchial aperture, sometimes present on the left side only ; but, as in the previously mentioned genera, four branchial arches are retained. In *Megalobatrachus*, the Giant Salamander of Japan and China, all trace of gill-slits disappears, but two branchial arches persist. Lastly, in the Salamanders, such as the spotted Salamander (*Salamandra maculosa*, Fig. 307) of Europe, and the common British Newts (*Molge*), the adult has no trace either of gills or gill-slits, and the branchial arches are much reduced. The limbs, also, in the terrestrial Salamanders stand out from the trunk, and have the soles of the feet and hands applied to the ground with the toes directed forwards, so as to support the weight of the body. Moreover, all trace of the median fin disappears, the tail becoming nearly cylindrical.

In the Anura the body is always frog-like, the head being large and depressed, with a very wide mouth and large tympanic membranes, the trunk short, the tail absent, and the hind- much larger than the fore-limbs. In the Toads, such as the common British *Bufo vulgaris*, and most Tree-frogs, the webs between

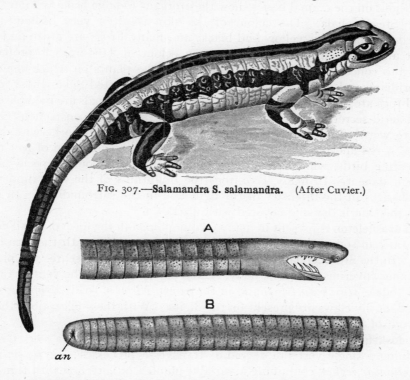

Fig. 307.—**Salamandra S. salamandra.** (After Cuvier.)

Fig. 308.—**Cæcilia pachynema.** *A*, anterior extremity from the right side; *B*, posterior extremity from beneath. *an.* anus. (After Boulenger.)

the hind-toes are reduced or absent, and in many species of *Hyla* the toes end in rounded sucking-discs.

In the Gymnophiona (Fig. 308) the body is greatly elongated and snake-like, the head is small and not depressed, and the limbs are absent. There is no tail, the anus (*an.*) being at the posterior end of the body on the ventral surface. The Stegocephala, or Labyrinthodonts as they are frequently called, were mostly salamander-like, having long tails and well-developed limbs: some, however, were snake-like and limbless, and probably retained their external

gills throughout life. They varied in length from 10 centimetres to several metres.

The skin of Amphibia is soft and usually slimy, owing to the secretion of the cutaneous glands, which is sometimes poisonous. In some forms, such as Bufo and Salamandra, there are large swellings on the sides of the head, formed of aggregated glands, and called *parotoids*. In the larvæ of both Urodela and Anura, and in the adult aquatic Urodeles, lateral sense-organs are present, and impressions on the cranial bones show these organs to have been well developed in the Stegocephala. The colour of the skin is often very brilliant : the Spotted Salamander is yellow and black, and many Frogs are green and gold, scarlet and black, and so on. The green colour of Tree-frogs is protective, serving to conceal them among the foliage of the plants on which they live. The brilliant and strongly contrasted hues of the spotted Salamander and of some Frogs are instances of " warning colours " ; the animals are inedible owing to the acrid secretion of their cutaneous glands, and their conspicuous colours serve to warn off the birds and other animals which would otherwise devour them. A red-and-blue Nicaraguan Frog is said to show no sign of fear of the Frog-eating birds, while the edible and more plainly coloured species are in constant danger. In many Tree-frogs the brightness of the coloration varies with changes in the intensity of the light and in the surroundings. In many Toads the skin is dry and covered with warts.

An **exoskeleton** is present in many Gymnophiona in the form of small dermal scales, and in some Anura in the form of bony plates beneath the skin of the back. In the Stegocephala a very complete armour of bony scutes was present, sometimes covering the whole body, sometimes confined to the ventral surface. In a Urodele, *Onychodactylus*, and in the South African Toad, *Xenopus*, small, pointed, horny claws are present on the digits. With these exceptions the skin is devoid of hard parts.

Endoskeleton.—The *vertebral column* is usually divisible into a *cervical region*, containing a single vertebra devoid of transverse processes ; an *abdominal* or *thoracolumbar region*, containing a variable number of vertebræ with transverse processes and often with ribs ; a *sacral region*, containing usually a single vertebra, the large transverse processes—or the ribs—of which give attachment to the ilia ; and a *caudal region*, forming the skeleton of the tail. In the Gymnophiona the caudal region is very short, and there is no sacrum : in the Anura the caudal region is represented by a single rod-shaped bone, the *urostyle*. The total number of vertebræ may reach 250 in Urodela and Gymnophiona : in Anura there are only nine vertebræ and a urostyle.

In the lower Urodela (Fig. 309, *A* and *B*) the centra are biconcave, as in fishes : they consist of dice-box-shaped shells of bone, lined at either end by cartilage (*Jvk.*), which is continuous between adjacent vertebræ. The bony shell is developed before the cartilage appears, so that the vertebræ are, in strictness, investing bones. The neural arches, on the other hand, are far more perfectly developed than in any fish, and have well-formed zygapophyses, which articulate with one another by synovial joints.

The Gymnophiona also have biconcave vertebræ, but in the higher Urodela (Fig. 309, *C* and *D*) and the Anura absorption of cartilage takes place between adjacent centra in such a way that the convex end of one fits into the concave

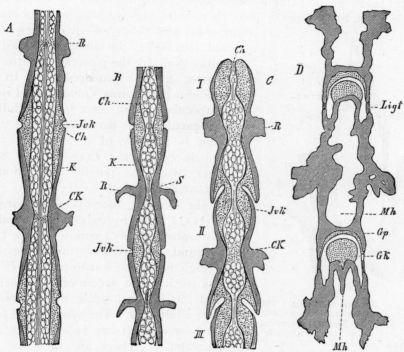

FIG. 309.—Longitudinal sections of vertebral centra of *A*. **Ranidens ;** *B*, **Amblystoma ;** *C*, **Spelerpes ;** and *D*, **Salamandrina.** *Ch*. notochord ; *CK*, intra-vertebral cartilage and fat-cells ; *Gk*. convex anterior face of centrum ; *Gp*. concave posterior face ; *Jvk*. inter-vertebral cartilage ; *K*, superficial bone of centrum ; *Ligt*. inter-vertebral ligament ; *Mh*, marrow-cavity ; *R*, transverse process ; *S*, intra-vertebral constriction. (From Wiedersheim's *Comparative Anatomy*.)

end of the next, forming a cup-and-ball joint. In the higher Urodela the convexity is on the anterior, the concavity on the posterior face of each centrum (*D*), and the vertebræ are said to be *ophisthocœlous* : in the Anura they are usually, as in the Frog, procœlous.

The first or cervical vertebra bears paired articular surfaces for the condyles of the skull, and between them the anterior face of the centrum gives off, in Urodela, a projection called the *odontoid process*. The Urodela, moreover, have *ribs* articulating with the transverse processes of the abdominal and sacral vertebræ : they are short bones, forked proximally, and the compressed transverse processes are correspondingly divided. The sacral ribs of Urodeles give attachment to the ilia, and the caudal vertebræ bear hæmal arches.

The *skull* of Urodela differs from that of the Frog in many important respects, the most striking of which is the fact that the trabeculæ do not meet either below the brain to form a basis cranii or above it to form a cranial roof. Thus, when investing bones are removed, the cranium (Fig. 310) is completed above and below in the parachordal or occipital region only : anterior to this it has side walls, but no roof or floor, there being above a huge superior cranial fontanelle, and below an equally large basi-cranial fontanelle, the former covered, in the entire skull, by the parietals and frontals, the latter by the parasphenoid. In the perennibranchiate forms *Necturus* and *Proteus* the trabeculæ remain, even in the adult, as narrow cartilaginous bars, and the chondro-cranium is actually of a lower or more embryonic type than that of any other Craniata, with the possible exception of Cyclostomata.

In the Urodela, moreover, the parietals (Fig. 311A, *P.*) and frontals (F.) are separate, the parasphenoid (*Ps.*) is not T-shaped, the palatine and vomer are sometimes represented by a single bone, the vomeropalatine (*Vop.*), bearing teeth. The suspensorium is inclined forwards, as in the tadpole, out backwards, as in the adult Frog. The hyoid arch is large, and its dorsal end may be separated as a hyomandibular. There are three or four branchial arches, which are large in the perennibranchiate forms, but undergo more or less reduction in caducibranch species, never, however, forming such a simple structure as that seen in the Frog. The stapes has no columella attached to it, and, in correspondence with this, there is no tympanic cavity or membrane.

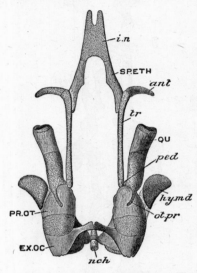

Fig. 310.—**Proteus anguinus.** The chondro-cranium from above. *ant.* antorbital process; **Ex.OC.** exoccipital and epiotic; *hy.md.* hyomandibular; *i.n.* internasal plate; *nch.* notochord; *ot. pr.* otic process; *ped.* pedicle; **PR.OT.** pro-otic; **QU.** quadrate; **SP.ETH.** sphenethmoid. (After W. K. Parker.)

In the Anura there is a very wide range of variation in the skull. Among the most important points are the presence, in a few species, of small supra- and basi-occipitals, and the fact that in others the roofing investing bones are curiously sculptured and so strongly developed as to give the skull a singularly robust appearance.

In the Gymnophiona (Fig. 312) very little of the original cartilage remains in the adult state, but the investing bones are very large and form an extremely

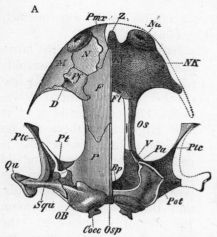

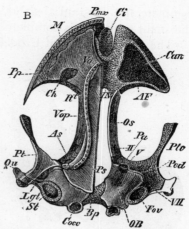

FIG. 311.—**Salamandra atra.** The skull. *A*, from above; *B*, from below. In both the investing bones are removed on the right side of the figure. *Af*, antorbital process; *As*, alisphenoid region; *Bp*, basal plate; *Can*, nasal cavity; *Ch*, posterior nares; *Ci*, process of internasal plate; *Cocc.* occipital condyles; *F*. frontal; *Fl*, olfactory foramen; *Fov*. fenestra ovalis; *IN*. internasal plate; *Lgt*. ligament connecting stapes with suspensorium; *M*. maxilla; *N*. nasal; *Na*. nasal aperture; *NK*, olfactory capsule; *OB*, auditory capsule; *os*, sphenethmoid (orbitosphenoid); *Osp*. supra-occipital region; *P*, parietal; *Pa*, ascending process of suspensorium; *ped*. pedicle; *Pf*. prefrontal; *Pmx*. premaxilla; *Pot*. otic process of suspensorium; *Pp*. palatine process of maxilla; *Ps*. parasphenoid; *Pt*. pterygoid bones; *Ptc*. pterygoid cartilage; *Rt*, foramen for ophthalmic branch of trigeminal; *Qu*. quadrate; *Squ*. paraquadrate (squamosal); *St*. stapes; *Vo*. vomer; *Vop*. vomero-palatine; *Z*, process of internasal plate; *II*, optic foramen; *V* trigeminal foramen; *VII*, facial foramen. (From Wiedersheim's *Comparative Anatomy*.)

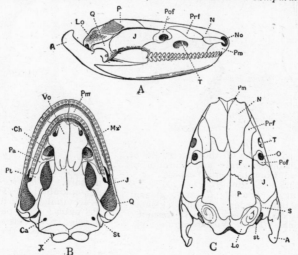

FIG. 312.—Skull of **Ichthyophis glutinosa,** × 3. *A*, Lateral; *B*, Ventral; *C*, Dorsal view. *A*, posterior process of the os articulare; *Ca*. carotid foramen; *Ch*. choana or posterior nasal opening; *F*. frontal; *J*. jugal; *LO*. exoccipital; *Mx*. maxilla; *N*. nasal; *No*. nostril; *O*. orbit; *P*. parietal; *Pa*. palatine; *Pm*. premaxilla; *Pof*. postfrontal; *Prf*. prefrontal; *Pt*. pterygoid; *Q*. quadrate; *S*. paraquadrate (squamosal); *St*. stapes; *T*. tentacular groove; *Vo*. vomer; *X*. exit of vagus nerve. (After Sarasin.)

complete and substantial structure, especially remarkable for the way in which the small orbit (*O.*) is completely surrounded by bones.

The *shoulder-girdle* of Urodela (Fig. 313) is chiefly remarkable for the great size of the unossified coracoids (*A*, *Co.*, *B*, *C.*) which overlap one another on the ventral body-wall. The procoracoid (*Cl.*) is also large, and there is no clavicle. The *sternum* (*St.*) is usually a more or less rhomboid plate of cartilage between the posterior ends of the coracoids, and there is no omosternum. In Necturus, however, the sternum presents a very interesting structure: it is a narrow, irregular, median bar, sending off branches right and left into the myocommas,

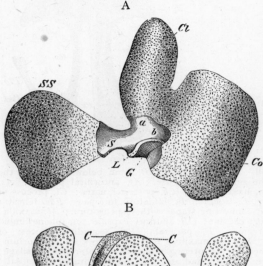

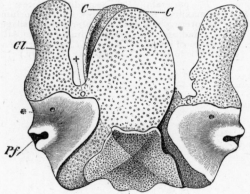

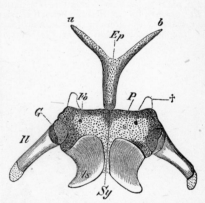

FIG. 313.—*A*, right side of shoulder-girdle of **Salamandra**; *B*, shoulder-girdle and sternum of **Amblystoma** (Axolotl) from the ventral aspect. *a, b*, processes of scapula; *C.* (in *B*), coracoid; *Cl.* procoracoid; *Co.* (in *A*), coracoid; *G.* (in *A*), glenoid cavity; *L*, its cartilaginous edge; *Pf.* (in *B*), glenoid cavity; *S.* scapula; *SS.* supra-scapula; *st.* sternum; *, †. nerve foramina. (From Wiedersheim's *Comparative Anatomy*.)

FIG. 314.—Pelvic girdle of **Salamandra**. *a, b*, processes of epipubis; *Ep.* epipubis; *Fo.* obturator foramen; *G.* acetabulum; *Il.* ilium; *Is.* ischium; *P.* pubis; *Sy.* pubo-ischiatic symphysis; †, process of pubis present in some Urodeles. (From Wiedersheim.)

a condition of things which suggests its origin by the fusion of *abdominal ribs*, or supporting structures developed between the ventral portions of the myomeres, just as the true ribs are formed between their dorsal portions. In the Anura the epicoracoids either simply meet one another in the middle ventral line, as in

Rana, or overlap, as in the Fire-toad (*Bombinator*) and the Tree-frogs (*Hyla*). The overlapping of the coracoids, in Anura as in Urodela, is sometimes correlated with the absence of an omosternum. In the Stegocephala there is a median ventral investing bone, the *inter-clavicle*, which is connected on each side with the clavicle, and extends backwards ventral to the sternum. There is also, on each side, a bone called the *cleithrum*, connected with the corresponding clavicle.

In the *pelvic girdle* of the Urodela the combined pubic and ischiatic regions (Fig. 314, *P.*, *Is.*) of the right and left sides are united to form an elongated cartilaginous plate which gives off on each side, above the acetabulum (*G.*), a slender vertical rod, the ilium (*Il.*). Ossifications are formed in the iliac and ischiatic regions, but the pubic region remains cartilaginous. The resemblance of the pelvis of the lower Urodela, and especially of Necturus, to that of Polypterus (p. 274) and of the Dipnoi (p. 297) is noteworthy. In Anura the pelvic girdle resembles that of the Frog.

Attached to the anterior border of the pubic region there occurs in many Urodela and in Xenopus a rod of cartilage, forked in front, the *epipubis* (*Ep.*). It is developed independently of the pelvis, and its relations to that structure are very similar to those of the sternum to the shoulder-girdle ; it has, in fact, been proposed to call it a *pelvi-sternum*.

The limbs of Urodela differ from the typical structure already described only in details : there are usually four digits in the fore-limb and five in the hind-limb. In Anura the limbs are modified by the fusion of the radius and ulna and of the tibia and fibula, and by the great elongation of the two proximal tarsals. A pre-hallux is frequently present.

Myology.—In the lower Urodela the muscles of the trunk and tail occur in the form of typical myomeres like those of fishes. In the higher forms the myomeres become converted into longitudinal dorsal bands—the *extensors of the back*, paired ventral bands—the *recti abdominis*, and a double layer of *oblique* muscles, covering the flanks.

Digestive Organs.—The *teeth* are always small and ankylosed to the bones : they may be singly or doubly pointed. They occur most commonly on the premaxillæ, maxillæ and vomers, but may also be developed on the dentaries, palatines and, in one instance, on the parasphenoid. In many Anura, such as the Common Toad, teeth are altogether absent.

The *enteric canal* is divisible into buccal cavity, pharynx, gullet, stomach, small intestine, rectum and cloaca. The stomach and duodenum together form a U-shaped loop in which the pancreas lies. The *tongue* in many Urodeles is fixed and immovable, like that of a fish : in most Anura it is free behind, as in the Frog ; but in Xenopus and Pipa (hence called *Aglossa*) it is absent.

Respiratory Organs.—With very few exceptions Amphibia possess *external gills* in the larval state, and, in the perennibranchiate Urodela, these organs are retained throughout life. They are branched structures, abundantly supplied with blood, and springing from the dorsal ends of the first three branchial arches. The epithelium covering them is ectodermal, so that they are cutaneous and not pharyngeal gills, and are of a totally different nature from the so-called external gills of the embryos of Elasmobranchii and Holocephali, which are only the filaments of the internal gills prolonged through the branchial apertures.

Internal gills are developed only in the larvæ of Anura. They appear as papillæ on the outer borders of the branchial arches below the external gills. They closely resemble the internal gills of fishes and appear to be homologous with them, although it seems probable that their epithelium is ectodermal.

In most adult Amphibia *lungs* are formed as outgrowths of the ventral wall

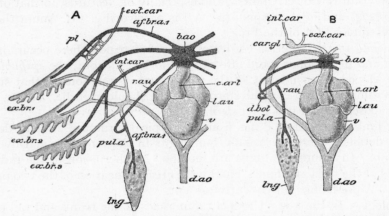

FIG. 315.—Heart and chief arteries of **Salamandra.** *A*, larva; *B*, adult. *af. br. a.* 1—4, afferent branchial arteries; *b. ao.* bulbus aortæ; *car. gl.* carotid labyrinth; *c. art.* conus arteriosus; *d. ao.* dorsal aorta; *d. bot.* ductûs Botalli; *ex. br.* 1—3, external gills; *ext. car.* external carotid; *int. car.* internal carotid; *l. au.* left auricle; *lng.* lung; *pl.* plexus, giving rise to carotid labyrinth; *pul. a.* pulmonary artery; *r. au.* right auricle; *v.* ventricle. (Altered from Boas.)

of the œsophagus. The right and left lungs communicate with a common *laryngo-tracheal chamber*, supported by the cartilages of the larynx and opening into the mouth by a longitudinal slit, the *glottis*. In the more elongated forms, such as Siren, Amphiuma and the Gymnophiona, the laryngo-tracheal chamber is prolonged into a distinct *trachea* or wind-pipe, supported by cartilages. In many species of Salamanders the lungs are absent, and respiration is exclusively cutaneous and pharyngeal.

Circulatory Organs.—The *heart* always consists of a sinus venosus, right and left auricles, ventricle and conus arteriosus. The sinus venosus opens into the right auricle, the pulmonary veins enter the left, and the two are separated by a septum auricularum which forms a complete partition in Anura, but in Urodela and Gymnophiona is more or less fenestrated, *i.e.* formed of a network of muscular strands with intervening spaces. The conus arteriosus has no longitudinal valve in the lower Urodela and the Gymnophiona, but is separated both from the ventricle and from the bulbus aortæ by transverse rows of valves.

In the perennibranchiate Urodela and in the larvæ of the air-breathing forms the circulation is essentially like that of a fish. The bulbus aortæ (Fig. 315, *A*, *b. ao.*), which represents an abbreviated ventral aorta, gives off four *afferent branchial arteries* (*af. br. a.* 1—4), three to the external gills, and a fourth which curves round the gullet and joins the dorsal aorta directly. From each gill an *efferent branchial artery* brings back the purified blood, and the efferent arteries unite, in a somewhat irregular way, to form the dorsal aorta (*d. ao.*). Each afferent with the corresponding efferent artery constitutes an *aortic arch*. Short connecting branches unite the afferent and efferent arteries of each gill, carotids (*ext. car.*, *int. car.*) arise from the first efferent artery, and, when the lungs appear, a *pulmonary artery* (*pul. a.*) is given off from the dorsal portion of the fourth aortic arch of each side. In those Urodela which in the adult condition are devoid of gills, when the latter atrophy (*B*) the first aortic arch loses its connection with the dorsal aorta, and becomes the carotid trunk; the second increases in size, forming the main factor of the dorsal aorta, and becomes the systemic trunk; the third undergoes great reduction, and the fourth becomes the pulmonary artery, its dorsal portion retaining its connection with the systemic trunk in the form of a small connecting branch, the *ductüs Botalli* (*d. bot.*). In the Anura, as we have seen (p. 321), the third arch vanishes completely, and there is no ductüs Botalli.

As to the *venous system*, the Urodela exhibit very clearly the transition from the fish-type to the condition already described in the Frog. The blood from the tail is brought back by a *caudal vein* (Fig. 316, *Caud. V.*), which, on reaching the cœlome, divides into two *renal portal veins*, one going to each kidney. From the kidney the blood is taken, in the larva, into paired *cardinal veins*, each of which joins with the corresponding *jugular* to form a *precaval vein*. In the adult the anterior portions of the cardinals undergo partial atrophy, becoming reduced to two small *azygos veins* (*Card. post.*) which receive the blood from the region of the back: their posterior portions unite and are continued forwards by a new unpaired vein, the *postcaval* (*V. cava. inf.*), which, joined by the hepatic veins, pours its blood into the sinus venosus. The iliac vein from the hind-leg divides into two branches: one joins the renal portal, the other, representing the lateral vein of Elasmobranchs, unites with its fellow in the middle ventral line to form the *abdominal vein* (*Abd. V.*) and joins the hepatic portal, its blood after traversing the capillaries of the liver, being returned by the hepatic vein into the post-caval.

The red corpuscles are oval and nucleated, and are remarkable for their unusual size. Those of Amphiuma are the largest known, being about $\frac{1}{14}$ mm. in diameter, or eight times that of a human red corpuscle.

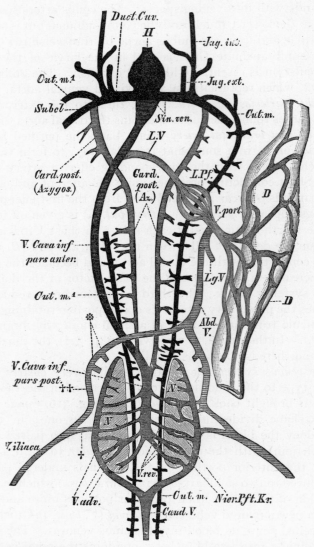

FIG. 316.—**Salamandra maculosa.** Venous system, diagrammatic, from the ventral aspect. *Abd. V.* abdominal vein; *Card. post.* (*Az.*), azygos vein; *Caud. V.* caudal vein; *Cut. m,* left musculo-cutaneous vein; *Cut. m¹,* the same on the right side (partly removed); *D,* intestine; *Duct. Cuv.* precaval vein; *H.* heart; *Jug. ext.* external jugular; *Jug. int.* internal jugular; *Lg. V.* mesenteric vein; *L. Pf.* hepatic portal system; *L. V.* hepatic vein; *N,* kidney; *Nier. Pft. Kr.* renal portal system; *Sin. ven.* sinus venosus; *Subcl.* subclavian vein; *V. adv.* branches of renal portal vein; *V. Cava inf.* postcaval; *V. iliaca,* iliac vein; *V. rev.* renal veins; *,* cloacal veins; †. branch of iliac to renal portal vein; ††, lateral vein. (From Wiedersheim's *Comparative Anatomy.*)

Nervous System and **Sense-Organs.**—The *brain* of Urodela differs from that of the Frog in its more elongated and slender form, in the comparatively small size of the optic lobes, and in the non-union of the olfactory bulbs. The *olfactory sacs* always open into the mouth by *posterior nares* situated behind or external to the vomers. The *eye* has no lids in the lower forms and is degenerate in the cave-dwelling Proteus and in some Gymnophiona. The Urodela, the

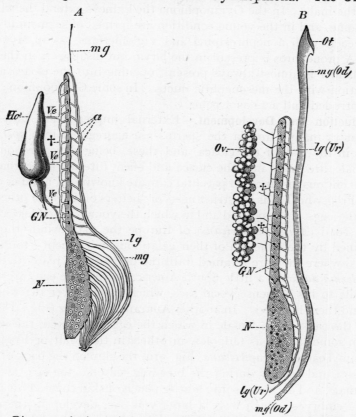

Fig. 317.—Diagrams of urinogenital organs of male (*A*) and female (*B*) **Urodele.** *a*, collecting tubes; *GN*, sexual portion of kidney; *Ho*, testis; *lg.* (*Ur*) Wolffian duct; *mg. mg'.* vestigal Müllerian duct of male; *mg.* (*Od*), oviduct; *N*, non-sexual portion of kidney; *Ov.* ovary; *Ve*, vasa efferentia; †, longitudinal canal. (From Wiedersheim's *Comparative Anatomy*, after Spengel.)

Gymnophiona, and some Anura have no tympanic cavity or membrane, and no columella; there is, however, a *stapes* (Figs. 295, *stp.*) in the form of a nodule of cartilage inserted in the fenestra ovalis. In the perennibranchiate Urodeles and in the larvæ of the air-breathing forms *lateral-line sense-organs* are present. There was an extensive lateral-line system, leaving its impress on the bones of the skull, in the Stegocephala.

Urinogenital Organs.—In the Urodela the *kidneys* (Fig. 317, *N*) are much

elongated and are divided into two portions, a broad posterior part, the functional kidney (*GN*), and a narrow anterior sexual part connected in the male with the efferent ducts of the testis. Numerous ducts leave the kidney and open into the Wolffian (mesonephric) duct [*lg.* (*Ur.*)], which thus acts as a "ureter" in the female, as a urinogenital duct in the male. The oviduct [*mg.* (*Od.*)] is developed from the Müllerian duct, a rudiment of which (*mg.*, *mg′.*) occurs in the male. In the Gymnophiona the kidneys extend the whole length of the cœlome, and in the young condition are formed of segmentally arranged portions, each with a nephrostome and a glomerulus, as in Myxinoids (see p. 144). A pronephros is present in the larva, but disappears in the adult. A urinary bladder is almost always present, opening into the cloaca and having no connection with the mesonephric ducts. In some Gymnophiona the cloaca can be protruded and acts as a penis.

Reproduction and **Development.**—External impregnation takes place in Anura, but in many Urodela the sperms are aggregated into *spermatophores* by glands in the wall of the cloaca, and these, being deposited on the body of the female, are taken into the cloaca and effect internal impregnation.

Several curious instances of parental care are known. A number of different species of Frogs and Toads construct nests or shelters of leaves or other materials in which the eggs are deposited and in which the young are developed. In the Obstetric Toad (*Alytes obstetricans*) of Europe the male winds the strings of eggs—formed by the adhesion of their gelatinous investment—round his body and thighs, where they are retained until the tadpoles are ready to be hatched. In *Rhinoderma darwini*, a little South American Frog, the eggs are transferred by the male to his immense vocal sacs, which extend over the whole ventral surface, and there hatched. In another Anuran, *Nototrema* (Fig. 318), there is a pouch on the back of the female in which the eggs are stored, the young being hatched in some species as tadpoles, in others in the adult or Frog form. In the Surinam Toad (*Pipa americana*, Fig. 319) the skin on the back of the female becomes soft and spongy during the breeding season : the eggs are placed on it by the male, and each sinks into a little pouch of skin covered by a gelatinous film. The embryos, which have a large yolk-sac, develop in these pouches ; they never possess external gills, and are hatched in the adult form. In the case of several species the tadpoles are carried about by the female, adhering to her dorsal surface by suckers or by a viscid secretion. Another Anuran *Pseudis paradoxa*, is remarkable for the fact that the tadpole is many times larger than the adult.

Some Salamanders (*S. maculosa* and *S. atra*) and a species of Cæcilia are viviparous. In the Black Salamander (*S. atra*), though many eggs are developed only two larvæ survive, one in each oviduct, these being nourished in later stages by means of the remainder of the eggs. The larva in this species possesses long plume-like external gills during its existence in the oviduct, shedding them before birth. If, however, the unborn young is removed from the oviduct and placed in water, it swims about like an ordinary aquatic larva, losing its long gills and developing a new and shorter set. Most Gymnophiona lay their eggs in burrows, but the larvæ in some cases lead an aquatic life for a time, and

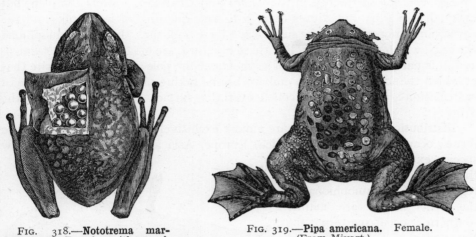

FIG. 318.—**Nototrema marsupiatum.** Female, with pouch opened. (From Mivart.)

FIG. 319.—**Pipa americana.** Female. (From Mivart.)

during this period possess, like tadpoles, a tail with a tail-fin which afterwards undergoes absorption. The larvæ of most Gymnophiona have long external gills (Fig. 320).

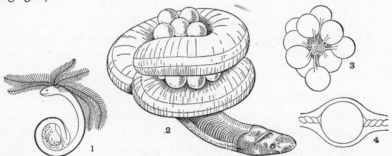

FIG. 320—.**Ichthyophis glutinosa,** × 1. *1*, a nearly ripe embryo, with gills, tail-fin, and still with a considerable amount of yolk; *2*, female guarding her eggs, coiled up in a hole underground; *3*, a bunch of newly-laid eggs; *4*, a single egg, enlarged, schematised to show the twisted albuminous strings or chalazæ within the outer membrane, which surrounds the white of the egg. (After P. and F. Sarasin.)

A very interesting case of *pædogenesis* is furnished by the Axolotl (*Amblystoma tigrinum*). This animal frequently undergoes no metamorphosis, but breeds in the gilled or larval state (Fig. 321). But under certain circumstances the gills are lost, the gill-slits close, and a terrestrial salamandrine form is assumed.

It is to the branchiate stage that the name Axolotl properly applies ; before the metamorphosis was discovered its connection with Amblystoma was not suspected, and it was placed in a distinct genus, *Siredon*, among the Perenni-branchiata.

Segmentation of the egg in the Anura and Urodela is always complete but unequal. In Pipa and Alytes there is a large quantity of food-yolk, and the developing embryo lies on the surface of a large yolk-sac. In the Gymnophiona the eggs, which are singularly like those of a bird, are of large size, and segmentation is partial, the formation of segments at the pole of the egg opposite that at which the formation of the embryo begins taking place only at the stage of gastrulation : the embryo is coiled over the surface of the yolk as in the Trout.

Distribution.—The Urodela are almost exclusively Palæarctic and Nearctic forms, occurring in North America, Europe, Asia and North Africa : a few species extend southwards into the Neotropical and Oriental regions. The Gymnophiona, on the other hand, are mainly southern, occurring in the Neotropical, Ethiopian and Oriental regions, but are absent in Australasia and the Pacific Islands. The Anura are almost universally distributed, and are abundant in all the greater zoo-

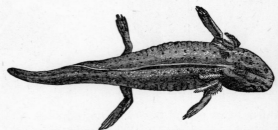

FIG. 321.—**Amblystoma tigrinum.** Larval or Axolotl stage. (From Mivart.)

geographical regions : they are, however, represented by only one species in New Zealand, and are absent in most oceanic islands, a fact due to the fatal effects of salt water upon the eggs and embryos of Amphibia as well as upon the adults.

THE ORIGIN AND RELATIONSHIPS OF THE AMPHIBIA.

Since Amphibia were the first vertebrates to adapt themselves to life on land, much of their interest lies in the way in which they fulfilled the various requirements for such a profound change of environment. A fish which is to adapt itself to life on land must be able to breathe oxygen directly from the air as it would no longer be able to use gills ; to move without the aid of water to support its weight ; to resist loss of water through its skin. The lateral-line sense-organ can no longer function, and soon disappears except in the larvae and some primitive forms. A comparison of the earliest Amphibia with some palæozoic fishes shows many resemblances between the embolomerous Labyrinthodonts and the Osteolepids of the Devonian. This is particularly marked in the general structure of the skulls (Fig. 301 B) ; in the similar " labyrinthodont " pattern of the teeth ; in the possession of large palatal " tusks," and the persistent fish-like character of the shoulder-girdle of such forms as *Eogyrinus*. And the comparison of the two types throws some light on the probable mode of origin of some of the tetrapod structures.

That lungs of a simple type had already been evolved by the early bony fishes is demonstrated by the development of *internal* and external nares in some of the Osteolepids, by the retention of functional lungs in the modern Dipnoi, and of the air-bladder, a modified lung, in the Teleosts.   For supporting the weight on land the limb-girdles were strengthened by the addition of an interclavicle bracing the two halves of the shoulder-girdle together, and by the attachment of the pelvic girdle to sacral ribs.   Unfortunately we know as yet no animal with a limb-structure intermediate between that of the fish paired fin and the pentadactyl limb, but fishes are known to-day in which the pectoral fins have the anterior part modified and strengthened, so that while they use the fin when swimming, it can also be used to support the body on the bottom or, in some cases, on land, and the structure of the fins of some of the Osteolepids suggests that the pentadactyl limb may have arisen in an analogous way.   The early Amphibia tended to inherit the scales of their fish ancestors, but later these were lost, and in the living forms there are mucous glands in the skin which prevent excessive loss of water.   The lateral line system was lost in the land-living adults, but was retained in the larvæ, and is present in the larvæ of modern Amphibia.

It is plain from a study of the Amphibia that the Permian and later forms had already become far too specialised to have been ancestral to the reptiles (traces of which order are found in the Carboniferous), but the earliest reptiles are so similar to the carboniferous Labyrinthodonts that it is often hard to distinguish between them, and their relationship seems very close.   The principal difference between them lies in the composition of the vertebræ, for while the amphibia tended to reduce the posterior pleurocentra, the reptiles reduced the anterior intercentra and evolved what are known as gastrocentrous vertebrae (Fig. 302).

The recent discovery of a Frog ancestor, *Protobatrachus massinoti*, may solve the problem of the origin of the order Anura.   In this animal the skull is similar to those of modern Frogs, except that an opisthotic has been retained, the ribs are short, and the skin impression shows it had a frog-like waist.   The presacral vertebræ are reduced in number, although there are more than eight, and there are free caudal vertebræ.   The form is frog-like in having an elongated ilium and a fairly long femur, but the radius and ulna and the tibia and fibula are not fused.   The critical question, the structure of the vertebræ, is not yet settled, but the centra were evidently well ossified.   *Palæobatrachus* was found in the Lower Trias of Madagascar, while the earliest true Frog remains occur in the Upper Jurassic.

CLASS. REPTILIA:

INTRODUCTION.

Reptiles, birds, and mammals are grouped together because they have certain features in common in which they differ from the lower vertebrates. The most important of these is the occurrence in all three classes of two embryonic membranes termed the *amnion* and *allantois*, to be described subsequently. In addition, they have gastrocentrous vertebræ (p. 337) and a metanephric kidney. Accordingly the term Amniota is used for the group formed by these three highest classes of the vertebrates, while the Fishes and Amphibia are referred to as the Anamniota.

The division of the Amniota into three classes—the reptiles, birds, and mammals—is kept because it is convenient, but it is unsatisfactory, since it does not present the true phylogeny. It has been shown that the amniote stem divided at a very early stage, one line giving rise to a number of orders of mammal-like " reptiles " and the mammals, whilst the other gave rise to the majority of " reptilian " orders and to the birds. In view of this history it would be better to express the phylogeny by placing the earliest, amphibian-like members in a class PROTOSAURIA, the mammal-like reptiles and their descendants, the mammals, in a class THEROPSIDA, and the typical reptiles and the birds in a class SAUROPSIDA. This diphyletic evolution, together with the fact that reptiles were extremely abundant and varied in form during the Mesozoic era, makes it very difficult to give an entirely satisfactory definition of a reptile, which can only be described as an amniote which lacks the diagnostic features of either mammals or birds.

The class Reptilia comprises four orders having living representatives, in addition to many extinct orders. In the Mesozoic period the class reached its maximum both in the number of its representatives and the size which many of them attained ; at that period they were very unmistakably the dominant class of the Animal Kingdom. In the Tertiary period they underwent a decline, while the birds and, in a yet higher degree, the mammals, were gaining a preponderance over them. The living reptiles are the Lizards and Chamæleons; the Snakes; the Tuataras; Tortoises, and Turtles; and the Crocodiles and Alligators. Though horny scales are not by any means present in all the reptiles, their occurrence as a complete covering is characteristic of the group and almost peculiar to it. When scales are not present, the epidermis is always hardened and cornified so as to form plates of horny material, such as the horny plates of the Tortoises, which protect the underlying parts from injury and desiccation. Bony plates are frequently present as well. In most respects the internal structure of the Reptilia shows a very decided advance on that of the modern Amphibia. The skull and the pectoral and pelvic arches are more completely ossified, and both vascular and nervous systems show a higher grade of organisation.

EXAMPLE OF THE CLASS.—A LIZARD (*Lacerta*).

The most striking external differences between the Lizard (Fig. 322) and the Frog are the covering of scales, the comparative smallness of the head, and the presence of a distinct neck, the great length of the caudal region, the shortness of the limbs, and the approximate equality in length of the anterior and posterior pairs. The anterior limbs are situated just behind the neck, springing from the trunk towards the ventral surface. The fore-limb, like that of the Frog, is divided into three parts : the upper-arm or *brachium*, the fore-arm or *anti-brachium*, and the hand or *manus* ; there are five digits provided with horny

FIG. 322.—**Lacerta viridis.** (After Brehm.)

claws, the first digit or pollex being the smallest. The hind-limbs arise from the posterior end of the trunk towards the ventral aspect ; each, like that of the Frog, consists of three divisions—thigh or *femur*, shank or *crus*, and foot or *pes*. The pes, like the manus, terminates in five clawed digits, of which the first or hallux is the smallest. The head is somewhat pyramidal, slightly depressed : the openings of the external nares are situated above the anterior extremity. The mouth is a wide slit-like aperture running round the anterior border of the head. At the sides are the eyes, each provided with upper and lower opaque, movable eyelids and with a transparent third eyelid or *nictitating membrane*, which, when withdrawn, lies in the anterior angle of the orbit. Behind the eye is a circular brown patch of skin—the *tympanic membrane*—corresponding closely to that of the Frog, but somewhat sunk below the general

level of the skin.   The trunk is elongated, strongly convex dorsally, flatter at
the sides and ventrally.   At the root of the tail on the ventral surface is a slit-
like transverse aperture—the *anus* or *cloacal aperture*.   The tail is cylindrical,
thick in front, gradually tapering to a narrow posterior extremity ; it is nearly
twice as long as the head and trunk together.

There is an **exoskeleton** of horny *scales* covering all parts.   These are formed
from folds of the dermis, each covered with a thick horny epidermal layer.
In size they differ in different positions.   On the dorsal surface of the trunk
they are small, hexagonal, and indistinctly keeled ; on the ventral surface they
are larger and are arranged in eight longitudinal rows.   Immediately in front
of the cloacal aperture is a large *pre-anal plate*.   A collar-like ridge of larger
scales surrounds the throat.   On the tail the scales are elongated, keeled, and
arranged in regular transverse (annular) rows, giving the tail a ringed appearance.   On the surface of the limbs the scales of the pre-axial (radial or tibial)
side are larger than those of the post-axial (ulnar or fibular).   The scales on
the upper surface of the head (*head-shields*) are large, and have regular and
characteristic arrangement.

Endoskeleton.—The *vertebral column* is of great length and made up of a
large number of vertebræ.   It is distinctly marked out into regions, a cervical
of eight vertebræ, a thoraco-lumbar of twenty-two, a sacral of two, and a caudal
of a considerable but indefinite number.   A vertebra from the anterior thoracic
region (Fig. 323, *A*, *B*) presents the following leading features.   The centrum
(*cent.*) is elongated and strongly *procœlous*, i.e., the anterior surface is concave,
the posterior convex ; the neural arch bears a short neural spine (*sp.*).   There
are pre- and post-zygapophyses (*pr. zy. pt. zy.*), the former with their articular
surfaces directed upwards, the latter downwards.   On each side at the junction
of centrum and neural arch is a facet—the *capitular facet*—for the articulation
of a rib.   The cervical vertebræ in general are similar in essential respects to
those of the trunk, but are somewhat shorter.   The first two, however, differ
greatly from the others.   The first is the *atlas* (*C*, *D*).   It has no distinct centrum,
but is in the form of a ring ; ventrally on its anterior face it bears a smooth
articular facet for the occipital condyle of the skull.   It consists of three distinct
ossifications, one ventral, the others dorso-lateral : the latter do not quite meet
dorsally, being separated by a space bridged over by membrane.   The second
or *axis* (*E*) has a short conical process—the *odontoid process* (*od.*)—projecting
forwards from its centrum.   In the natural position of the parts the odontoid
process—which is a part of the centrum of the atlas, and is not actually fused
with, though firmly fixed to, the axis—lies in the lower or ventral part of the
opening of the atlas, separated by a ligamentous band from the upper portion,
which corresponds to the neural arch, and lodges the anterior end of the spinal
cord.   On the ventral surface of the axis and of each of the following five or six
vertebræ is a distinct bony nodule, sometimes termed the *intercentrum* or

hypapophysis (*hyp.*).   The sacral vertebræ have short centra and strong expanded processes—the *transverse processes*—which abut against the ilia ; these are separately ossified, and are to be looked upon as *sacral ribs.*   The anterior caudal vertebræ are like the sacral, but have the centra longer, the transverse processes more slender, and the neural spines longer.   The posterior caudal vertebræ become gradually smaller as we pass backwards, and the various processes reduced in prominence, until, at the posterior end of the tail, the whole vertebra is represented merely by a rod-like centrum.   Attached to the ventral faces of the centra of a number of the anterior caudal vertebræ are Y-shaped

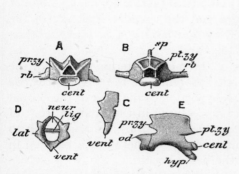

FIG.   323.—Vertebræ of **Lizard.** *A,* anterior ; *B,* posterior view of a thoracic vertebra ; *C,* lateral, *D,* anterior view of atlas vertebra ; *E,* lateral view of axis. *cent.* centrum ; *hyp.* hypapophysis of axis ; *lat.* lateral piece of atlas ; *lig.* ligamentous band dividing the ring of the atlas into two ; *neur.* neural arch of atlas ; *od.* odontoid process ; *pr. zy.* prezygapophysis ; *pt. zy.* post-zygapophysis ; *rb.* rib ; *sp.* spine ; *vent.* ventral piece of atlas.

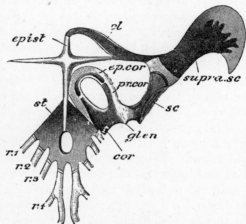

FIG. 324.—Pectoral arch and sternum of **Lacerta agilis.** *cl.* clavicle ; *cor.* coracoid ; *ep. cor.* epicoracoid ; *epist.* episternum ; *glen.* glenoid cavity for head of humerus ; *pr. cor.* procoracoid ; *r. 1—r. 4* first to fourth sternal ribs ; *sc.* scapula ; *st.* sternum ; *spura. sc.* suprascapula. (After Hoffmann.)

bones—the *chevron bones*—the upper limbs of the Y articulating with the vertebra, while the lower limb extends downwards and backwards.   In nearly all the caudal vertebræ the centrum is crossed by a narrow transverse unossified zone through which the vertebra readily breaks.   The ribs are slender curved rods, the vertebral ends of which articulate only with the capitular facets of the corresponding vertebræ, there being no direct articulation with the transverse processes.   The ribs of the five anterior thoracic vertebræ are connected by means of cartilaginous *sternal ribs* with the sternum.   The posterior thoracic ribs do not reach the sternum, the sternal ribs being very short, and free at their ventral ends.   The *cervical ribs,* which are present on all the cervical vertebræ with the exception of the first three, are all shorter than the thoracic ribs, and none of them is connected with the sternum.   Thus, as regards the structure of the vertebræ themselves, there is nothing to distinguish the posterior cervical from the anterior thoracic ; but, for convenience of description, the first thoracic is defined as the first vertebra having ribs connected with the sternum.

The *sternum* (Fig. 324, *st.*) is a rhomboidal plate of cartilage with a small central space, or *fontanelle*, completed by membrane. Posteriorly it is produced into two slender flattened processes. On its antero-lateral borders are articular surfaces for the bones of the pectoral arch, and on its postero-lateral borders and the processes are small facets for the sternal ribs.

In the *skull* (Fig. 325) the chondrocranium, though persistent, is replaced by bones to a much greater extent than in the Frog, and the number of investing bones is much greater. On the dorsal and lateral surface are a large number of dermal roofing bones. At the posterior end the rounded aperture of the foramen magnum (*for. mag.*) is surrounded by four bones—a *basioccipital* (*bas. oc.*) below, *exoccipitals* (*ex. oc.*) at the sides, and a *supraoccipital* (*supr. oc.*) above. The basioccipital forms the floor of the most posterior portion of the cranial cavity ; posteriorly it bears a rounded prominence, the *occipital condyle* (*oc. cond.*). In front of it, forming the middle portion of the floor of the cranial cavity, is the basisphenoid (*bas. sph.*), not represented in the Frog, in front of which again is an investing bone, the *parasphenoid* (*para.*), corresponding to the bone of the same name in the Frog and Trout, but here much reduced in size and importance and ankylosed with the basisphenoid.

In the wall of the auditory capsule are three ossifications—*pro-otic, epiotic,* and *opisthotic* (*op. ot.*). The first remains distinct, the second becomes merged in the supraoccipital, and the third in the exoccipital. The exoccipital and opisthotic are produced outwards as a pair of prominent horizontal processes, the *parotic processes.*

The large orbits are closely approximated, being separated only by a thin vertical *interorbital septum*. The cranial cavity is roofed over by the *parietals* (*par.*) and *frontals* (*fr.*). The former are united together ; in the middle is a small rounded aperture—the *parietal foramen* (*par. f.*). The frontals remain separated from one another by a median *frontal suture* : between them and the united parietals is a tranverse *coronal suture*. The nasal cavities are roofed over by a pair of *nasals* (*nas.*). A small *pre-frontal* (*pr. fr.*) lies in the front of the frontal, and helps to bound the orbit anteriorly, and another small bone—the *lacrymal* (*lcr.*)—perforated by an aperture for the lacrymal duct, lies at the anterior extremity of the orbit, just within its border. A row of small bones—the *supra-orbitals* (*s. orb.*)—bounds the orbit above, and behind is a *post-orbital* or *lateral post-frontal* (*pt. orb.*) articulating with the frontal. Just behind the post-orbital is a *supra-temporal* bone (*supra t. 1*), in close relation to which are the *quadrato-jugal* (*sq.*) and *squamosal* (*supra t.2*),[1] the former bending

---

[1] There is not as yet any agreement as to the true homologies of some of these bones. They are also called squamosal and tabular.

forwards and upwards to form with the post-orbital the *superior temporal arch.*
At the anterior extremity of the snout is a median bone formed by the coal-

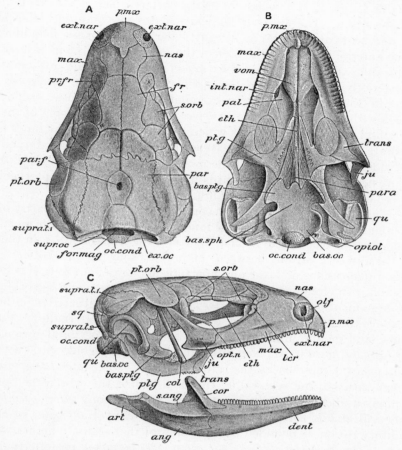

FIG. 325.—Skull of **Lacerta agilis.** *A*, from above; *B*, from below; *C*, from the side. *ang.* angular; *art.* articular; *bas. oc.* basi-occipital; *bas. ptg.* basipterygoid processes; *bas. sph.* basisphenoid; *col.* epipterygoid; *cor.* coronary; *dent.* dentary; *eth.* ethmoid; *ex. oc.* exoccipital; *ext. nar.* external nares; *for. mag.* foramen magnum; *fr.* frontal; *int. nar.* internal nares; *ju.* jugal; *lcr.* lacrymal; *max.* maxilla; *nas.* nasal; *oc. cond.* occipital condyle; *olf.* olfactory capsule; *opi. ot.* opisthotic; *opt. n.* optic nerve; *pal.* palatine; *par.* parietal; *para.* parasphenoid; *par. f.* parietal foramen; *p. mx.* premaxillæ; *pr. fr.* pre-frontal; *ptg.* pterygoid; *pt. orb.* post-orbital or lateral post-frontal; *qu.* quadrate; *s. ang.* supra-angular; *s. orb.* supra-orbitals; *sq.* paraquadrate; *supra t.* 1. supratemporal 1; *supra t.* 2. squamosal; *trans.* transverse or ectopterygoid; *supr. oc.* supra-occipital; *vom.* vomer. The unlettered bone internal to *pt.orb.* in *A* is the post-frontal. The transverse line behind *fr.* is a superficial mark, not a suture. (After W. K. Parker.)

escence of the two *premaxillæ* (*p. mx.*) ; this bears the four anterior teeth of each
side. On each side behind the premaxilla is the *maxilla* (*max.*), consisting of
two portions, an *alveolar* bearing all the rest of the teeth, and a *palatine*

extending inwards on the roof of the mouth, together with an ascending process articulating with the nasal and pre-frontal above. Articulating behind with each maxilla is a *jugal* (*ju.*), which forms the posterior half of the ventral boundary of the orbit. The *quadrate* (*qu.*) articulates movably with the parotic process, and bears at its distal end the articular surface for the mandible.

In the anterior portion of the roof of the mouth, articulating in front with the premaxillæ and maxillæ, are the vomers (*vom.*). Behind and embracing them posteriorly are the flat *palatines* (*pal.*). The elongated *pterygoids* (*ptg.*) articulate in front with the posterior extremities of the palatines : behind each articulates with the corresponding *basi-pterygoid process* (*bas. ptg.*) of the basi-sphenoid, and sends back a process which becomes applied to the inner face of the quadrate. A stout bone which extends between the maxilla externally and the pterygoid internally is termed the *transverse bone* or *ecto-pterygoid* (*trans.*). Extending nearly vertically downwards from the pro-otic to the pterygoid is a slender rod of bone, the *epi-pterygoid* (*col.*).

The *columella* is a small rod partly composed of cartilage and partly of bone the outer end of which is fixed into the inner surface of the tympanic membrane, while the inner is attached to a small aperture, the *fenestra ovalis*, in the outer wall of the auditory capsule between the pro-otic and the opisthotic.

Certain depressions or fossæ and apertures or foramina are to be observed in the skull. The foramen magnum, the parietal foramen and the orbits have already been mentioned. The *posterior temporal fossa* is situated on either side of and above the foramen magnum, bounded above and externally by the roofing bones, and on the inner side by the bones of the occipital region. The *inferior temporal fossa* is bounded internally by the pterygoid, and is separated from the palatine foramen by the transverse bone. The *lateral temporal fossa* is the wide space in the side wall of the skull behind the orbit ; the bony bar which limits it above is the *superior temporal arch* ; a bony *inferior temporal* or *quadratojugal arch* is here absent. The *tympano-eustachian fossa*, situated in the auditory region, is bounded by the bones of that region together with the quadrate. The *posterior* or *internal nares* are bounded posteriorly by the palatines. The *anterior* or *external nasal aperture* is situated at the anterior extremity of the skull bounded by the nasals and premaxillæ.

Each ramus of the *mandible* consists of six bony elements in addition to the slender persistent *Meckel's cartilage*. The proximal element is the *articular* (*art.*), which bears the articular surface for the quadrate, and is produced backwards into the *angular process*. The *angular* (*ang.*) is a splint-like bone covering the ventral edge and the lower half of the outer surface of the articular. The *supra-angular* (*s. ang.*) overlies the dorsal edge and upper half of the outer surface of the same bone. The *dentary* (*dent.*) forms the main part of the distal portion of the mandible, and bears all the mandibular teeth. The *splenial* is a flat splint applied to the inner face of the dentary. The *coronary* (*cor.*), a small, somewhat conical bone, forms the upwardly directed *coronoid process* immediately behind the last tooth. All these, with the exception of the articular, are investing bones.

The *hyoid apparatus* (*vide* Fig. 330, *b. hy.*) consists (1) of a median cartilaginous rod, the *basi-hyal*, (2) of the *anterior cornua*, elongated cartilaginous rods which, connected ventrally with the basi-hyal, curve round the gullet and end in close relation with the ventral surface of the auditory capsule, (3) of the *middle cornua*, rods of cartilage ossified at their proximal ends, and (4) of the *posterior cornua*, cartilaginous rods arising from the posterior edge of the basi-hyal and passing backwards and outwards. The middle cornua are vestiges of the first, the posterior of the second branchial arch.

In the *pectoral arch* (Fig. 324) the *coracoids* are flat bones articulating with the antero-lateral border of the sternum, and bearing the ventral half of the glenoid cavity (*glen.*) for the head of the humerus ; a cartilaginous *epicoracoid* (*ep. cor.*) element lies on the inner side of the procoracoid and coracoid ; a large gap or fenestra divides each coracoid into a narrow anterior portion—the *procoracoid* (*pr. cor.*), and a broader posterior portion, the *coracoid* proper (*cor.*). The *scapulæ* (*sc.*) articulate with the outer ends of the coracoids, and each bears the dorsal half of the glenoid cavity. Dorsally, the scapulæ become expanded, and each has connected with it a thin plate of partly calcified cartilage—the *suprascapula* (*supra. sc.*), which extends inwards towards the spinal column on the dorsal aspect of the body. An element not hitherto met with, except in the Stegocephala (p. 355), is the *interclavicle* or *episternum* (*epist.*), a cross-shaped investing bone, the stem of which is longitudinal and is in the posterior portion of its extent closely applied to the ventral surface of the anterior part of the sternum, while the cross-piece is situated a little in front of the scapula. The *clavicles* (*cl.*) are flat curved bones articulating with one another in the middle line and also with the anterior end of the interclavicle. The bones of the fore-limb consist of a proximal bone or *humerus*, a middle division composed of two bones—the *radius* and *ulna*—and a distal division or *manus*. In the natural position of the parts the humerus is directed, from the glenoid cavity with which it articulates, backwards, upwards, and outwards ; the radius and ulna pass from their articulation with the humerus downwards and slightly forwards, while the manus has the digits directed forwards and outwards. When the limb is extended at right angles to the long axis of the trunk, it presents, like that of the Frog, dorsal and ventral surfaces, and pre-axial and post-axial borders. In this radius is seen to be pre-axial, the ulna post-axial. In the natural position the pre-axial border of the humerus is external, and the distal end of the fore-arm is rotated in such a way that, while the pre-axial border looks forwards and outwards at the proximal end, it faces directly inwards at its distal end, the manus being rotated so that its pre-axial border looks inwards.

The *humerus* is a long bone consisting of a *shaft* and two *extremities*, each of the latter being formed of an *epiphysis* of calcified cartilage, the proximal rounded, the distal (*trochlea*) pulley-like, with two articular surfaces, one for the radius and the other for the ulna. The *radius* is a slender bone consisting like the humerus, of a shaft and two epiphyses; the distal extremity has a concave articular surface for the carpus, and is produced pre-axially into a *radial styloid process*. The proximal end of the *ulna* is produced into an upwardly directed process—the *olecranon*: the distal end bears a convex articular surface for the carpus. The *carpus* (Fig. 326) is composed of ten small polyhedral or rounded carpal bones. These consist of a proximal row containing three,

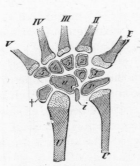

Fig. 326.—Carpus of **Lacerta agilis,** (left) from above. *R.* radius; *U.* ulna; *c.* centrale; *i.* intermedium; *r.* radiale; *u.* ulnare; *1—5,* the five distal carpals; †, pisiform; *I—V,* the five metacarpals. (From Wiedersheim's *Comparative Anatomy*.)

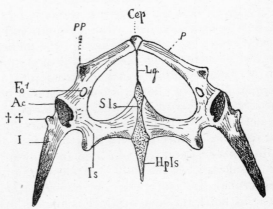

Fig. 327.—Pelvis of **Lacerta vivipara,** from the ventral side. *Ac.* acetabulum; *Cep.* epipubis. *Fo'.* foramen for obturator nerve; *Hp. Is.* hypoischium; *I.* ilium; ††, process representing the pre-acetabular part of the ilium; *Lg.* ligament; *Is.* ischium; *p.* pubis; *pp.* prepubis; *S. Is.* ischiatic symphysis. (From Wiedersheim's *Comparative Anatomy*.)

viz., the *radiale* (*r.*) *ulnare* (*u.*), and *intermedium* (*i.*), of a *centrale* (*c.*), and of a distal row of five (*1–5*); with an accessory or *pisiform* (†) bone attached to the distal epiphysis of the ulna on its post-axial side. The first digit or *pollex* consists of a metacarpal and two phalanges, the second of a metacarpal and three phalanges, the third of a metacarpal and four phalanges, the fourth of a metacarpal and five phalanges, and the fifth of a metacarpal and three phalanges. The number of phalanges in the first four digits is, therefore, one more than the serial number of the digit.

The *pelvic arch* (Fig. 327) consists of two triradiate bones, the *ossa innominata*, each ray being a separate bone. On the outer side at the point from which the rays diverge is a concave articular surface—the *acetabulum* (*Ac.*)—. for the head of the femur. From the region of the acetabulum one of the rays, the *ilium* (*I.*), a compressed rod, passes upwards and backwards to articulate with the sacral region of the spinal column. A second ray—the *pubis* (*p.*)—passes downwards and forwards to meet its fellow in the middle line, the articulation being termed the *pubic symphysis*. In the middle line in front, between the anterior ends of the pubes, is a small nodule of calcified cartilage, the *epipubis* (*Cep.*). The third ray or *ischium* (*Is.*) runs downwards and backwards, and articulates with its fellow in the *ischiatic symphysis*, the ventral ends of the two bones being separated by a plate of calcified cartilage (*S. Is.*). Between the pubes and ischia is a wide space, the *obturator foramen*, divided by a median ligament (*lg.*) into a pair of apertures, and a smaller aperture in each pubis (*Fo.*) transmits the obturator nerve. A small rod of bone, the *os cloacæ*, or *hypoischium* (*Hp. Is.*), passes backwards from the ischiatic symphysis and supports the ventral wall of the cloaca.

The hind-limb consists, like the fore-limb, of three divisions; these are termed respectively the proximal or *femur*, the middle or *crus*, and the distal or *pes*. The proximal division consists of one bone, the *femur*; the middle division of two, the *tibia* and *fibula*; the distal of the *tarsal* and *metatarsal* bones and the *phalanges*. When the limb is extended at right angles with the trunk, the tibia is pre-axial and the fibula post-axial : in the natural position of the parts the pre-axial border is internal in all three divisions of the limb. The *femur* is a stout bone consisting of a shaft and two epiphyses. The proximal epiphysis develops a rounded *head* which fits into the acetabulum ; near it on the pre-

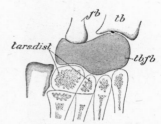

FIG. 328.—Tarsus of **Lacerta agilis**, *fb.* fibula ; *tb.* tibia ; *tb. fb.* tibio-fibulare ; *tars. dist.* distal tarsals. (After Gegenbaur.)

axial side is a prominence, the *lesser trochanter*, and a nearly obsolete prominence on the post-axial side represents the *greater trochanter*. The distal extremity is pulley-shaped, with internal and external prominences or *condyles* for articulation with the tibia ; immediately above the external condyle is a prominence or tuberosity for articulation with the fibula. The *tibia* is a stout, curved bone, along the anterior (dorsal) edge of which runs a longitudinal ridge, the *cnemial ridge* : the proximal extremity presents two articular surfaces for the condyles of the femur. The *fibula* is a slender bone, the proximal end articulating with the external tuberosity of the femur, the distal with the tarsus.

The *tarsus* (Fig. 328) comprises only three bones in the adult, one large proximal bone, the *tibio-fibulare* (*tb. fb.*), and two smaller distal (*tars. dist.*). Each digit consists of a metatarsal bone and phalanges, the number of the latter being respectively two, three, four, five, and three. The first and second metatarsals articulate with the tibial side of the tibio-fibulare, the rest with the distal tarsals.

Digestive System.—The upper and lower jaws, forming the boundary of the aperture of the mouth, are each provided with a single row of small conical teeth, and there is a patch of similar teeth (*palatine teeth*) on the palatine. On the floor of the mouth-cavity is the tongue, a narrow elongated fleshy organ, bifid in front.

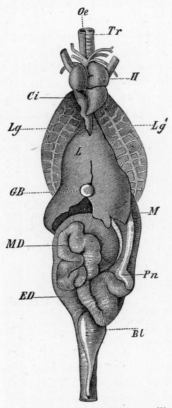

FIG. 329.—**Lacerta agilis.** General view of the viscera in their natural relations. *Bl.* urinary bladder; *Ci.* post-caval vein; *ED*, rectum; *GB*, gall-bladder; *H.* heart; *L.* liver; *Lg, Lg'.* the lungs; *M*, stomach; *MD*, small intestine; *Oe.* œsophagus; *Pn.* pancreas; *Tr.* trachea. (From Wiedersheim's *Comparative Anatomy*.)

The *stomach* (Fig. 329, *M*, Fig. 331, *St.*) is a cylindrical organ but little wider than the œsophagus, and with thick muscular walls. At the point where the small intestine joins the large intestine or rectum, the latter is produced into a short *cæcum* (Fig. 331, *coec.*). The *liver* (*lr.*) is divided into right and left lobes, and a gall-bladder (Fig. 329, *GB.*; Fig. 330, *g.b.*; Fig. 331, *g.bl.*) lies at the lower margin of the right lobe. The *pancreas* (*pn.*) is situated in the loop between the stomach and first part of the small intestine or duodenum. The stomach is attached to the body-wall by a fold of peritoneum, the *mesogaster*, the small intestine by a fold termed the *mesentery*, the rectum by a *mesorectum*. From the dorsal surface of the liver to the stomach extends a thin fold, the *gastro-hepatic omentum*; and this is continued backwards as the *duodeno-hepatic omentum*, connecting the liver with the first portion of the small intestine.

Vascular System.—The *heart* is enclosed, like that of the Frog, in a thin transparent membrane, the *pericardium*. It consists of a *sinus venosus, right* and *left auricles*, and an incompletely divided *ventricle*. The *sinus venosus* (Fig. 330, *s. v.*), into which the large veins open, is thin-walled, and has a smooth inner surface. From it a sinu-auricular aperture, guarded by a two lipped valve, leads to the right auricle. The *auricles* have their inner surfaces raised up into a network of muscular ridges, the *musculi pectinati*. Both auricles open into the cavity of the ventricle, the aperture of communication, or *auriculo-ventricular aperture*, being divided into two by the auricular septum, and guarded by the auriculo-ventricular valve, consisting of two semilunar flaps. The *ventricle* (Fig. 330, *v.*; Fig. 331, *vent.*) has very thick spongy walls and a small cavity divided into two parts by an incomplete muscular partition. From the part of the ventricular cavity to the right of the partition arises the pulmonary artery; from the part to the left are given off the right and left aortic arches. When the two auricles contract, the blood from the right auricle (venous blood)

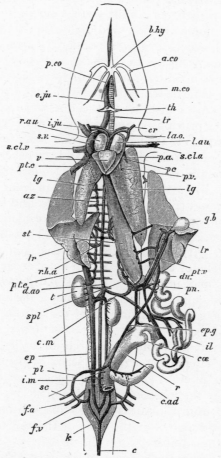

FIG. 330.—**Lacerta viridis.** Dissection from the ventral aspect showing the alimentary, circulatory, respiratory, and urinogenital organs (nat. size). The liver (*lr.*) is divided longitudinally and its two halves are displaced outwards; the alimentary canal is drawn out to the animal's left; the cloaca with the urinary bladder and posterior ends of the vasa deferentia is removed, as also is the right adipose body. *a. co.* anterior cornu of hyoid; *az.* azygos or cardinal vein; *b. hy.* body of hyoid; *c.* caudal vein; *c. ad.* adipose body; *c. m.* cœliaco-mesenteric artery; *cœ.* cæcum; *cr.* carotid artery; *d. ao.* dorsal aorta; *du.* duodenum; *e. ju.* external jugular vein; *ep.* epididymis; *ep. g.* epigastric vein; *f. a.* femoral artery; *f. v.* femoral vein; *g. b.* gall-bladder; *i. ju.* internal jugular vein; *il.* ileum; *i. m.* posterior mesenteric arteries; *k.* kidney; *la. o.* left aortic arch; *l. au.* left auricle; *lg.* lungs; *lr.* liver; *m. co.* middle cornu of hyoid; *p. a.* pulmonary artery; *pc.* pericardium; *p. co.* posterior cornu of hyoid; *pn.* pancreas; *pl.* pelvic vein; *pt. c.* postcaval vein; *pt. v.* hepatic portal vein; *p. v.* pulmonary vein; *r.* rectum; *r. au.* right auricle; *r. h. a.* right hepatic artery; *sc.* sciatic vein; *scl. a.* subclavian artery; *scl. v.* subclavian vein; *spl.* spleen; *st.* stomach; *s. v.* sinus venosus; *th.* thyroid gland; *tr.* trachea; *t.* testis; *v.* ventricle. (From Parker's *Zootomy*.)

tends to run more to the right-hand portion of the cavity of the ventricle while that from the left auricle (arterial) occupies the left-hand portion. When the ventricle begins to contract, its walls come in contact with the dorsal and ventral edges of the ventricular partition, thus completing the separation of the right-hand part of the cavity, containing venous blood, from the left-hand part, containing arterial and mixed blood ; and the further contraction results in the driving of the venous blood through the pulmonary artery to the lungs and of the rest through the aortic arches to the head and body. (*Vide* Fig. 385.)

From the *right aorta* arise the *carotid arteries* (Fig. 330, *cr.* ; Fig. 331, *car. art.*), and each runs for some distance parallel with the corresponding aortic arch, with which it anastomoses distally (the connecting part being termed the *ductus caroticus*), having previously given off the carotid artery proper, by means of which the blood is carried to the head The two aortic arches curve backwards round the œsophagus, one on the right hand and the other on the left, and meet in the middle line dorsally to form the median *dorsal aorta* (Fig. 330, *d. ao.* ; Fig. 331, *dors. aort.*). From the right arch, just in front of the junction, arise the two *subclavian arteries* (Fig. 330, *s. cl. a.*), right and left, each running outwards to the corresponding fore-limb. From the dorsal aorta the first important branch given off is the *cœliaco-mesenteric* (*c. m.*). This shortly divides into two trunks, a *cœliac* (Fig. 331, *cœl. a.*) supplying the stomach, spleen, pancreas, duodenum, and left lobe of the liver, and an *anterior mesenteric* supplying the posterior part of the small intestine. Three small *posterior mesenteric* arteries given off farther back supply the large intestine. Posteriorly, after giving off *renal* and *genital* branches, and a pair of large *iliacs* to the hind-limb, the dorsal aorta is continued along the tail as the *caudal artery* (Fig. 331, *caud. art.*). Throughout its length, in addition to the larger branches mentioned, the dorsal aorta gives origin to a regularly-arranged series of pairs of small vessels, the *intercostal* and *lumbar* arteries, giving off branches that enter the neural canal and others that supply the muscles and integument.

The venous blood from the tail is brought back by means of a *caudal vein* (Fig. 330, *c.*). This bifurcates at the base of the tail to form the two *pelvic* (*lateral*) *veins* (*pl.*) ; these unite to form the median *epigastric* or *abdominal* (*ep. g.*), which eventually enters the left lobe of the liver. Entering the pelvic veins are the *femoral* and *sciatic veins* from the hind-limb. Arising from the pelvic are the *renal portal veins* distributed to the substance of the kidneys. The *efferent renal veins*, carrying the blood from the kidneys, combine to form a pair of large trunks, which soon unite to form the median *postcaval*. The postcaval runs forwards towards the heart, and, after receiving the wide *hepatic vein* from the liver, enters the sinus venosus.

Two *precavals*, right and left, carry the blood from the anterior extremities and the head to the sinus venosus. The right precaval is formed by the union of the *internal* and *external jugular* and the *subclavian*. On the left side the

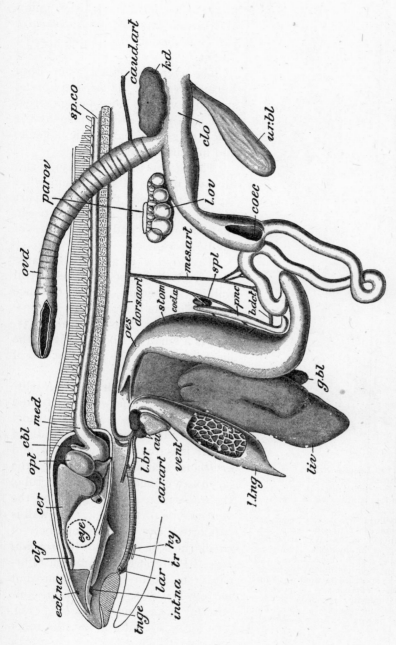

Fig. 331.—Lateral dissection of female **Lizard** (semi-diagrammatic). *au.* auricle; *b. dct.* bile-duct; *car. art.* carotid artery; *caud. art.* caudal artery; *cbl.* cerebellum; *cer.* cerebral hemispheres; *clo.* cloaca; *coec.* caecum; *cœl. a.* cœliac artery; *dors. aort.* dorsal aorta; *ext. na.* external nares; *eye,* eye; *g. bl.* gall-bladder; *hy.* basi-hyal; *int. na.* internal nares; *kd.* kidney; *lar,* larynx; *l. br.* left bronchus; *liv.* liver; *l. lng.* left lung, opened to show internal structure; *l. ov.* left ovary; *med.* medulla oblongata; *mes. art.* mesenteric artery; *œs.* œsophagus; *olf.* olfactory bulb; *opt.* optic lobe; *ovd.* oviduct (turned aside); *parov.* parovarium; *pnc.* pancreas; *sp. co.* spinal cord; *spl.* spleen; *stom.* stomach; *tnge.* tongue; *tr.* trachea; *ur. bl.* urinary bladder; *vent.* ventricle.

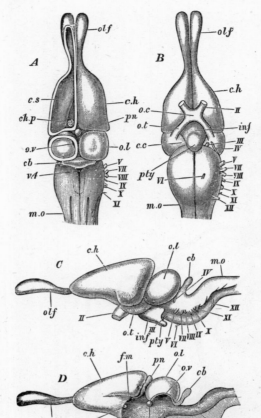

FIG. 332.—Brain of **Lacerta viridis.** *A,* from
above, with the left hemisphere (*c. h.*) and optic
lobe (*o. l.*) opened. *B,* from beneath. *C,* from
the left side. *D,* in longitudinal vertical section.
a. c. anterior commissure; *aq. s.* aqueduct of
Sylvius; *cb.* cerebellum; *c. c.* crura cerebri;
c. h. cerebral hemispheres; *ch. p.* choroid plexus;
c. s. corpus striatum; *f. m.* foramen of Monro;
inf. infundibulum; *m. o.* medulla oblongata;
o. c. optic chiasma; *o. l.* optic lobes; *olf.*
olfactory bulbs with their peduncles or tracts;
o. t. optic tracts; *o. v.* aperture between aqueduct
of Sylvius and optic ventricle; *p. c.* posterior
commissure; *pn.* pineal apparatus; *pty.*
pituitary body; *v. 3,* diacœle; *v. 4,* metacœle;
I—XII, cranial nerves. (From Parker's
Zootomy.)

precaval is formed by the union
of *internal jugular* and *subclavian,*
the left external jugular being
absent.

The liver is supplied, as in other
Vertebrates, by a *hepatic portal*
system of vessels, blood being carried
to it by a *portal vein,* formed by the
union of gastric pancreatic, splenic,
and mesenteric veins.

The *adipose bodies* (Fig. 330, *c. ad.*)
are two masses of fat of somewhat
semilunar shape in the posterior part
of the abdominal cavity, between
the peritoneum and the muscles of
the body-wall.

The *thyroid* is a whitish, transversely-elongated body on the ventral
wall of the trachea, a short distance
in front of the heart.

The *spleen* (Figs. 330 and 331,
spl.) is a small red body lying in the
mesogaster, near the posterior end of
the stomach.

Organs of Respiration.—A slit-
like aperture, the *glottis,* situated
behind the tongue, leads into a short
chamber, the *larynx,* the wall of
which is supported by *cricoid* and
arytenoid cartilages. From the
larynx an elongated cylindrical tube,
the *trachea,* passes backwards on the
ventral side of the neck. Its wall is
supported by a large number of
small rings of cartilage, the *tracheal
rings.* Posteriorly the trachea bifurcates to form two similar but
narrower tubes, the *bronchi,* one
entering each lung. The *lung* (Fig.
330, *lg.*) is a fusiform sac, the inner
lining of which is raised up into a

network of delicate ridges, having the appearance of a honeycomb; these ridges are much closer and more numerous towards the anterior than towards the posterior end of the lung.

The **brain** (Figs. 332 and 333) presents all the parts that have been described in the brain of the Frog (p. 325), with some minor modifications. The two cerebral hemispheres (parencephala) (Fig. 332, *c. h.*) are oval bodies, somewhat narrower in front than behind, closely applied together. Each is prolonged anteriorly into the corresponding *olfactory peduncle* or *tract*, somewhat dilated in front to form the *olfactory bulb* (*olf.*) from which the olfactory nerve arises. In the interior of each is a cavity, the *lateral ventricle* or *paracœle*, sending a prolongation forwards into the olfactory bulb, and communicating behind by a small aperture, the *foramen of Monro* (*D, f. m.*), with the diacœle (*v. 3*). Through the foramen of Monro there passes into each paracœle a vascular process of pia mater, the *choroid plexus* (*ch. p.*) : immediately above and behind this is a *hippocampal commissure* (*c.p.a.*) connecting together two areas known as *hippocampi*, one on the mesial surface of each hemisphere. On the floor of each paracœle is a thickened mass of nerve-matter, the *corpus striatum* (*c. s.*), and between them passes a transverse band of nerve-fibres, the *anterior commissure* (*a. c.*). The *diencephalon* is a small rounded lobe between the paracœles and the mid-brain, containing a laterally compressed cavity, the *diacœle* (*v. 3*). Its roof is extremely thin. Its lateral walls are formed of two thickenings, the *optic thalami*, behind which passes a transverse band, the *posterior commissure* (*p. c.*). Behind and below the thalami are the *optic tracts* (*o. t.*) continued into the optic nerves. Behind the optic tracts the floor is produced downwards into a tubular process, the *infundibulum* (*inf.*), ending below in a rounded body, the *pituitary body* or *hypophysis* (*pty.*). The roof is produced into a median outgrowth, the *pineal apparatus* (Fig. 332, *D, pn.*; Fig. 333, *Z*), which is divided into two parts, one of which has connected with its distal extremity an eye-like structure, the *parietal organ* or *pineal eye* (Fig. 333, *pa.*), lying in the parietal foramen, while the other is the *pineal organ* or *epiphysis*. In front of the epiphysis, in the *velum transversum* (*v. t.*), a transverse fold of the thin roof of the brain marking the anterior limit of the diencephalon, is another commissure, the *aberrant commissure* (*c.p.p.*), which connects together the posterior and dorsal parts of the parencephala ; this is not represented either in the Frog or in higher vertebrates. The *mid-brain* consists dorsally of two oval *optic lobes* (*corpora bigemina*, Fig. 332, *o. l.*) and ventrally of a mass of longitudinal nerve-fibres, the *crura cerebri* (*c. c.*), passing forwards to the fore-brain. Each optic lobe contains a cavity (*optocœle*) communicating with the *iter*, a narrow passage leading from the diacœle to the metacœle. The *cerebellum* (*cb.*) is, like that of the Frog, of small size, being a small anteroposteriorly flattened lobe overlapping the anterior portion of the metacœle. The *metencephalon* (medulla oblongata, *m. o.*), broad in front, tapers behind to where it passes into the anterior portion of the spinal cord. The *metacœle* is a

shallow space on the dorsal aspect of the medulla oblongata, overlapped in
front for a short distance by the cerebellum, and behind covered only by the
pia mater, containing a network of vessels, the *choroid plexus* of the metacœle
(Fig. 333, *pch.*).   At the point where medulla oblongata and spinal cord meet is
a strong *ventral flexure*.

The *spinal cord* is continued backwards throughout the length of the
neural canal, becoming slightly dilated opposite the origins of the two pairs of
limbs and tapering greatly towards the posterior end of the tail.

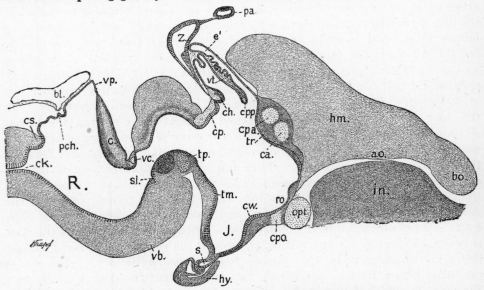

FIG. 333.—Longitudinal section of brain of an embryo of **Lacerta vivipara,** × 26.   *ab*, olfactory
area ; *bl*, blood-sinus ; *bo*, olfactory bulb ; *c*, cerebellar commissures ; *ca.* anterior commissure ;
ch. superior (habenular) commissure ; *ck*, central canal of spinal cord ; *cp*, posterior commissure ;
cpa, anterior pallial (hippocampal) commissure ; *cpo*, posterior optic commissure ; *cpp*, posterior
pallial (aberrant) commissure ; *cs*, spinal commissure ; *cw*, swelling of optic chiasma ; *e¹*, paraphysis ; *hm*, cerebral hemisphere ; *hy*, hypophysis ; *in*, inter-orbital septum ; *J* (and *s*), ventricle
of infundibulum ; *opt*, optic chiasma ; *pa*, parietal organ ; *pch*, choroid plexus on medulla
oblongata ; *R*, 4th ventricle ; *ro*, optic recess ; *sl*, sulcus intraencephalicus posterior ; *tp*, tuberculum posterius superius ; *tr*, lamina terminalis ; *vb*, ventral flexure of medulla oblongata ;
vc, valvula cerebelli ; *vp*, posterior medullary velum ; *vt*, velum transversum ; *Z*, epiphysis.
(From Wiedersheim and Parker's *Comparative Anatomy*, after K. von Kupffer.)

The *cerebral nerves* resemble those of the Frog as regards their origin and
distribution in most respects, the principal difference being that a *spinal
accessory* is intercalated in front of the hypoglossal, and that the hypoglossal
arises from the medulla oblongata, not from the spinal cord, and is therefore a
cerebral nerve.

The *nasal cavities* (Fig. 334) open at the extremity of the snout by the
external nares, and into the cavity of the mouth by a pair of slit-like internal
nares situated near the middle line of the palate.   The external aperture opens

into a sort of vestibule, beyond which is the nasal or olfactory cavity proper, containing a convoluted *turbinal bone* over which the mucous membrane extends. Opening into each nasal cavity, near the internal opening, is *Jacobson's organ* (*J, J.*), an oval sac with strongly pigmented walls supported by cartilage.

The *eye* has a cartilaginous sclerotic having a ring of small bones (Fig. 335) supporting it externally. There is a cushion-like *pecten* or vascular pigmented process similar to the structure of the same name occurring in birds (see below, Class Aves), projecting into the inner chamber of the eye. In essential structure

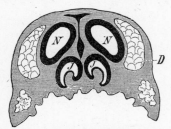

Fig. 334.—Transverse section of the nasal region of the head of **Lacerta** to show the relations of Jacobson's organs. *D,* nasal glands; *J, J.* Jacobson's organs; *N, N.* nasal cavities. (From Wiedersheim's *Comparative Anatomy.*)

Fig. 335.—Ring of ossicles in sclerotic of eye of **Lacerta.** (After Wiedersheim.)

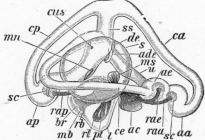

Fig. 336.—Membranous labyrinth of **Lacerta viridis**, viewed from the outer side. *aa.* anterior ampulla; *ac.* auditory nerve; *ade.* opening of the ductus endolymphaticus; *ae.* external ampulla; *ap.* posterior ampulla; *br.* basilar branch of nerve; *ca.* anterior semicircular canal; *ce.* external semicircular canal; *cp.* posterior semicircular canal; *cus.* canal connecting utriculus and sacculus; *de.* ductus endolymphaticus; *l.* cochlea; *mb.* basilar membrane; *raa, rae, rap, rl.* branches of auditory nerve; *s.* sacculus; *ss.* common canal of communication between anterior and posterior semicircular canals and utricle; *u.* utriculus. (From Wiedersheim's *Comparative Anatomy*, after Retzius)

the rest of the eye agrees with that of the Craniata generally as already described. Two glands lie in the orbit, the *lacrymal* and the *Harderian*.

The *ear* consists of two principal parts, the *internal ear* or *membranous labyrinth*, and the *middle ear* or *tympanum*. The latter is closed externally by the tympanic membrane, the position of which has been already mentioned. It communicates with the cavity of the mouth by the Eustachian passage, which is narrower and longer than in the Frog. The inner wall of the tympanic cavity is formed by the bony wall of the auditory region of the skull, in which there are two fenestræ—the *fenestra ovalis* and the *fenestra rotunda*. The columella stretches across the cavity from the tympanic membrane, and is fixed internally into the membrane covering over the fenestra ovalis.

The parts of the membranous labyrinth (Fig. 336) are enclosed by the bones of the auditory region : between the membranous wall of the labyrinth and the surrounding bone is a small space containing fluid, the *perilymph*. The labyrinth itself consists of the *utriculus* with the three *semicircular canals* and the *sacculus* with the *cochlea* (*lagena*). The *utriculus* (*u.*) is a cylindrical tube,

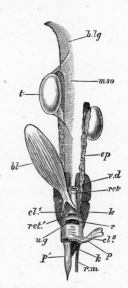

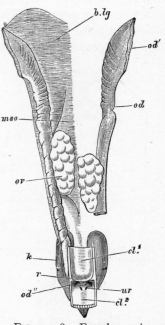

Fig. 337.—Male urinogenital organs of **Lacerta viridis.** The ventral wall of the cloaca is removed, the bladder is turned to the animal's right, and the peritoneal covering of the left testis and epididymis is dissected away. *bl.* urinary bladder ; *b. lg.* fold of peritoneum supporting epididymis ; *cl¹.* anterior and *cl².* posterior divisions of the cloaca ; *ep.* epididymis ; *k.* kidney ; *mso.* mesorchium ; *p.* copulatory organs, of which the right is shown retracted (*p′*) and the left everted (*p*) ; *r. m.* retractor muscle of latter ; *r.* ridge separating anterior and posterior divisions of cloaca ; *rct.* rectum ; *rct′.* its opening into the cloaca ; *t.* testis ; *u. g.* urinogenital papilla and aperture ; *v. d.* vas deferens. (From Parker's *Zootomy*.)

Fig. 338.—Female urinogenital organs of **Lacerta viridis.** The ventral wall of the cloaca, the urinary bladder, the posterior end of the left oviduct, and the peritoneal investment of the left ovary and oviduct are removed. *b. lg.* broad ligament ; *cl¹.* anterior and *cl².* posterior divisions of the cloaca ; *k.* kidney ; *mso.* mesoarium ; *od.* left oviduct ; *od′.* its peritoneal aperture ; *od″.* aperture of right oviduct into the cloaca ; *ov.* ovary ; *ur.* aperture of ureter. (From Parker's *Zootomy*.)

bent round at a sharp angle : the *semicircular canals* (*ca., ce., cp.*) are arranged as in vertebrates in general (p. 116). A narrow tube, the *ductus endolymphaticus*, leads upwards towards the roof of the skull and ends blindly in the dura mater. The *sacculus* is large and rounded. The *cochlea* (*l.*) forms a flattened, not very prominent, lobe, and is of simple form.

Urinary and Reproductive Systems.—The *kidneys* (Figs. 337 and 338, *k.*)

are a pair of irregularly shaped, dark red bodies, each consisting of two lobes, anterior and posterior, situated in close contact with the dorsal wall of the posterior portion of the abdominal cavity, and covered with peritoneum on their ventral faces only. Their posterior portions, which are tapering, are in close contact with one another. Each has a delicate duct, the *ureter*, opening posteriorly into the cloaca. A *urinary* (*allantoic*) *bladder* (*bl.*), a thin-walled sac, opens into the cloaca on its ventral side.

In the male the *testes* (Fig. 337, *t.*) are two oval white bodies, that on the right side situated just posterior to the right lobe of the liver, that on the left somewhat farther back. Each testis is attached to the body-wall by a fold of the peritoneum, the *mesorchium* (*mso.*). The *epididymis* (*ep.*) extends backwards from the inner side of each testis, and passes behind into a narrow convoluted tube, the *vas deferens* or spermiduct (*v. d.*), which opens into the terminal part of the corresponding ureter. A pair of vascular eversible *copulatory sacs* (*p, p'*), which when everted are seen to be of cylindrical form with a dilated and bifid apex, open into the posterior part of the cloaca.

In the female the *ovaries* (Fig. 338, *ov.*) are a pair of irregularly oval bodies having their surfaces raised up into rounded elevations, marking the position of the ova. They are situated a little farther back than the testes, and each is attached to the body-wall by a fold of the peritoneum, the *mesovarium* (*mso.*). The oviducts (*od.*) are thin-walled, wide, plaited tubes which open in front into the cavity of the body (*od'.*), while behind they communicate with the posterior part of the cloaca, their opening (*od''.*) being distinct from, and a little in front of, those of the ureters. A fold of the pertioneum, the *broad ligament* (*b. lg.*), attaches the oviduct to the body-wall.

INTERRELATIONSHIP OF THE REPTILIAN GROUPS.

One of the most important features of the reptiles is the evolution of the temporal region of their skulls, the structure of this region being of considerable help in their classification (Fig. 339).

The most primitive forms, the *Cotylosauria*, had a complete bony roofing in the temporal region, as did the early Amphibia from which the reptiles originated. This type of skulls is known as ANAPSID. According to most authorities it is still found in the living *Chelonia* (sometimes modified by emargination), which, together with the Cotylosaurs, form the sub-class *Anapsida*.

From this primitive skull there evolved two principal types. The first of these has a single vacuity in each side, and is known as SYNAPSID. The vacuity was bounded at first by the post-orbital and squamosal bones above, and the squamosal and jugal bones below, but later the parietal appeared within the opening owing to the enlargement of the vacuity and reduction in size of the post-orbital. Five orders of reptiles having this type of skull are therefore grouped as the sub-class *Synapsida*. They include the ancestors of mammals

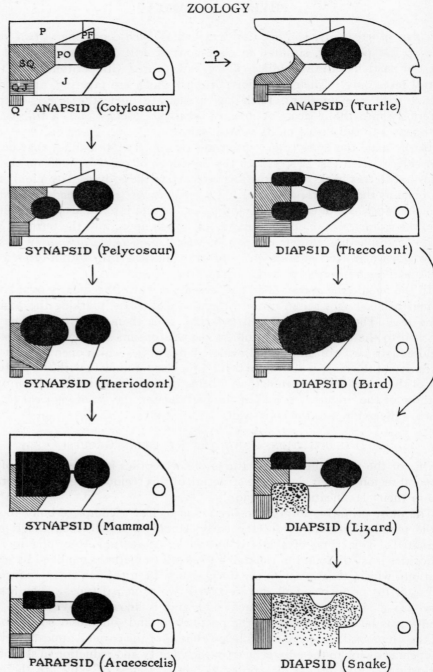

FIG. 339.—Diagrams showing the disposition of the vacuities and of certain bones in the types of reptilian skulls. *P.* parietal; *PF.* post-frontal; *PO.* post-orbital; *J.* jugal; *QJ.* quadrato-jugal; *Q.* quadrate; *S.* squamosal.

which themselves have this type of skull further modified by the loss of the post-orbital and quadratojugal bones and by the inclusion of the quadrate within the ear.

A later modification of the primitive type is known as DIAPSID. Here there are two vacuities in the temporal region, with the post-orbital and squamosal meeting between them. This condition is found in the majority of reptiles (e.g., Crocodilia, " Dinosaurs," Pterosaurs), and in a modified form in the lizards, snakes, and also the birds. The lizards lost the quadratojugal, thus opening the lower vacuity below, the snakes carried this modification still further by reducing or losing the post-orbital and losing the jugal. The birds lost the post-orbital with the result that the two vacuities and the orbital opening are confluent.

A few small reptiles (e.g., *Araeoscelis*) have a single temporal vacuity differing from the synapsid type in that the post-orbital and squamosal meet below the opening. Some authorities believe this vacuity is homologous with the upper vacuity of the diapsid skull, and that the vacuity of the synapsid skull is homologous with the lower vacuity of the diapsid skull, and so have given it another name—PARAPSID. The few forms known to have this type of skull are so problematical that they are not further discussed in this work, but it should be noted that it has been held that the lizards evolved from a form with a parapsid skull and a sub-class *Parapsida* has been constituted for them.

Two aquatic groups, the *Ichthyosauria* and *Plesiosauria*, have single temporal vacuities in the skull, and in both cases the post-orbital meets the squamosal below the opening. Their skulls, however, are peculiar, and there is little other evidence in the skeletons of these reptiles to ally them to the other orders, largely on account of the modifications for swimming, and it is probably best to leave them as isolated orders until primitive forms are found which indicate their relationships. It is possible that they may have arisen from independant amphibian stocks.

It appears therefore that the primitive reptiles with a completely roofed, or anapsid, skull gave rise to two major groups, the Synapsida and the Diapsida, and possibly to a third, the Parapsida.

CLASSIFICATION.

SUPER-ORDER I.—ANAPSIDA.

ORDER 1.—COTYLOSAURIA.

The most primitive reptiles, the Cotylosaurs, are also the oldest, ranging from the Upper Carboniferous to the Middle Trias when they became extinct. Much of their interest lies in the close resemblance many of them bear to the early Labyrinthodont Amphibia. They are to be distinguished from these only by their gastrocentrous vertebræ and a few minor features, but resemble them in general build and in their primitive " belly-crawling " mode of progression. The group is very likely mixed in origin, and the members composing it are held together chiefly by two characters : the complete roofing of the skull and the flattened, plate-like pelvis.

These reptiles show few specialisations, and varied in size from about a foot to the six or seven feet of the Parieasaurs. Three sub-orders are recognised. The Seymouriamorpha (e.g., *Seymouria*) (Fig. 340) include the most primitive forms, the Captorhinomorpha (e.g., *Captorhinus*, *Labidosaurus*) are small forms showing affinities with the Synapsida, and the Diadectomorpha (e.g., *Diadectes*,

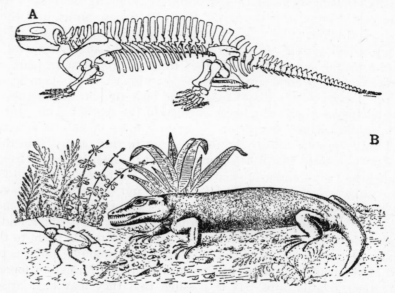

FIG. 340.—Skeleton and life restoration of Cotylosaurs : A. *Diasparactus*. (After Case.) B. *Seymouria*. This animal is about two feet long.

Parieasaurus, *Procolophon*) which survived into the Trias and include the majority and have some features in common with the Diapsida.

ORDER 2.—CHELONIA.

Reptilia in which the skull is without temporal vacuities. A condition which is regarded by some as primitive, by others as secondary (see pp. 375–76). The body is enclosed in a shell of bony plates, consisting of a dorsal carapace and a ventral plastron, partly of dermal partly of endoskeletal origin. There is usually on the surface an epidermal exoskeleton of horny plates. The vertebræ and ribs of the thoracic region are firmly fused with the body carapace, into the composition of which they enter. The shoulder and pelvic girdles have the unique position of being within the ribs. The limbs are sometimes terminated by clawed digits adapted for terrestrial locomotion, sometimes modified into the shape of flippers. There are no teeth, and the jaws have a horny investment. The lungs are compound sacs. In essentials the heart and brain

FIG. 341.—Skeleton and restoration of *Dimetrodon*, a Therapsid about eight feet long.
(After Williston.)

resemble those of the Squamata. There are no copulatory sacs, but a median penis.

This order includes the Land Tortoises, Soft Tortoises, River and Mud Tortoises, and the Turtles, besides a number of fossil forms of which *Eunotosaurus*, a species from the Middle Permian of South Africa which has teeth and broadened ribs, possibly the forerunners of the carapace, may be ancestral.

SUPER-ORDER II.—SYNAPSIDA (*Anomodontia, Therapsida*).

Reptiles with a single lateral temporal vacuity primitively lying below the post-orbital and squamosal. The brain-case is high and, as a result of the broad supraoccipital, the inner ear is placed low down. The teeth are usually heterodont, the lower jaw is flattened from side to side instead of being rounded in section, and except in the most primitive members, the dentary is relatively large. There are always two coracoids in the shoulder-girdle.

The group is important because it shows the various stages by which the mammals evolved from the earliest reptiles and because the Synapsids dominated the land fauna of the Permian and much of the Trias. They are found abundantly in some deposits in North America and South Africa, and are known also from South America, East Africa, India, Central Asia, Russia and Europe.

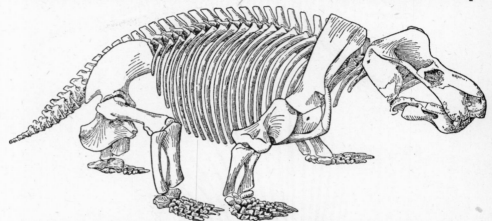

Fig. 342.—**Kannemeyeria**, a Dicynodont. (After Pearson. *Proc. Zool. Soc.*)

There are five orders, but two of them (Dromosauria, Deinocephalia) were unimportant and are not discussed here.

ORDER I.—PELYCOSAURIA.

The Pelycosaurs are the most primitive members of the Super-Order, and are confined almost entirely to the Lower Permian. Some members, such as *Varanosaurus*, differ from the captorhinomorph Cotylosaurs only in having the temporal vacuity. Others became specialised, *Dimetrodon* having enormously elongated neural spines to the vertebræ, which are believed to have been connected by skin and formed a huge sail (Fig. 341). The Pelycosaurs, like the Cotylosaurs, had relatively short limbs and a sprawling gait, but the remaining orders carried the body higher and were probably much more active.

ORDER II.—DICYNODONTIA.

The Dicynodontia were for a time the most successful order of the Synapsids, being found in extraordinary abundance from the Middle Permian to the

Lower Trias and surviving until the Middle Trias. Typically they were of a heavy build, varying in size from 1 to 7 or 8 feet in length (Fig. 342). Their skull was very specialised, having huge temporal fossæ, T-shaped squamosals and small quadrates. In the majority the dentition was reduced to a pair of canines (which were sometimes confined to the males) and the jaws were covered by a horny beak. The post-cranial skeleton was very mammal-like though clumsy. There was an acromion process on the scapula, the precoracoid was excluded from the glenoid cavity (Fig. 343), the ilium was considerably elongated and the number of phalanges had been reduced from the reptilian number of 2 3 4 5 3 to the mammalian 2 3 3 3 3. *Dicynodon* is the commonest genus with about seventy species. *Lystrosaurus*, which occurs abundantly in the

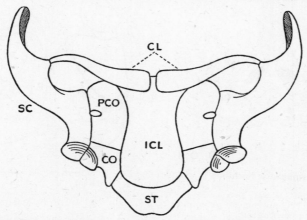

Fig. 343.—Dicynodont pectoral girdle, ventral aspect. *CL*. clavicle; *CO*. coracoid; *ICL*. interclavicle; *PCO*. precoracoid; *SC*. scapula; *ST*. sternum.

Lower Trias, had the snout elongated and turned down and was probably aquatic. Several genera, such as *Endothiodon* and *Esoterodon* kept post-canine teeth and one form, *Eumantellia* had incisors.

ORDER 3.—THERIODONTIA.

The Theriodontia are the most important order of the Synapsida, being almost certainly ancestral to the mammals. They are found from the Middle Permian to the Upper Trias, and are known from Africa, South America, and Russia.

The group shows considerable variation in size, some forms being less than a foot in length, others being the size of a lion. The majority were carnivorous or insectivorous, but some of the later members may have been herbivorous.

The evolutionary changes of the Theriodonts show the gradual appearance of those characters which are typical of the mammals. In the skull (Figs. 344 and 345) the temporal vacuity is enlarged by the reduction and loss of the pre-

frontals, post-frontals, and finally the post-orbitals.   A false palate is formed
by the outgrowth of a shelf from the maxillæ and palatines, the basioccipital

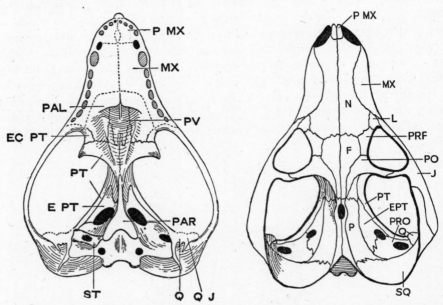

FIG. 344.—**Thrinaxodon liorhinus,** a cynodont.   *ECPT*. ectopterygoid; *EPT*. epipterygoid;
F. frontal; *J.* jugal; *L.* lachrymal; *MX.* maxilla; *N.* nasal; *P.* parietal; *PAL.* palatine;
PAR. parasphenoid; *PMX.* premaxilla; *PO.* postorbital; *PRF.* pre-frontal; *PRO.* pro-otic;
PT. pterygoid; *PV.* "prevomer" or vomer; *Q.* quadrate; *QJ.* quadrato-jugal; *ST.* stages; *SQ.*
squamosal.   (After Parrington.)

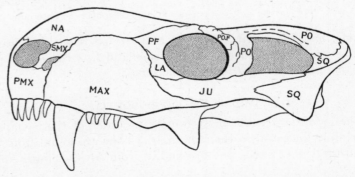

FIG. 345.—A gorgonopsid skull, based on specimens in the Museum of Zoology, Cambridge.
SMX ; Septo-maxillary.

is reduced and paired exoccipital condyles are formed.   Also the epipterygoid
(columella cranii) expands to form the mammalian alisphenoid.   In the lower
jaw the dentary increases steadily in size until the post-dentary bones are very

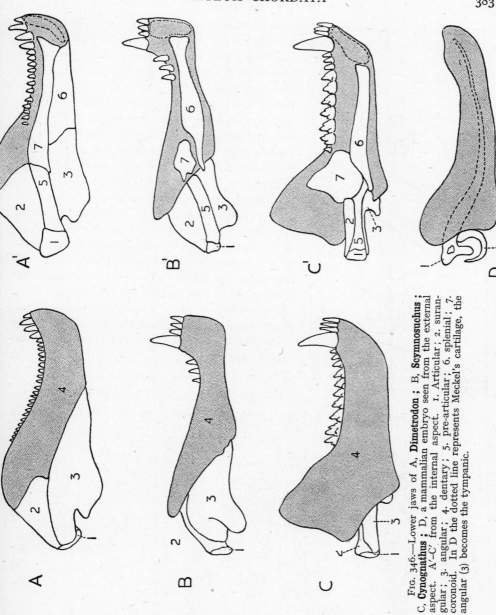

Fig. 346.—Lower jaws of A, **Dimetrodon**; B, **Scymnosuchus**; C, **Cynognathus**; D, a mammalian embryo seen from the external aspect. A'-C' from the internal aspect. 1. Articular; 2. surangular; 3. angular; 4. dentary; 5. pre-articular; 6. splenial; 7. coronoid. In D the dotted line represents Meckel's cartilage, the angular (3) becomes the tympanic.

small and almost hidden in outer view, and at the same time a mammal-like coronoid process is developed (Fig. 346). The teeth of the early members are simple, though there are enlarged canines, but the post-canine teeth of the later members become specialised in a variety of ways, and are often very mammal-like. The limb-girdles approach the mammalian condition in such characters as the formation of an acromion process on the scapula, the great expansion of the ilium, and the enlargement of the primitive pubic foramen to form the huge obturator foramen (Fig. 347). The form of the limb-bones approaches the mammalian condition, and the number of phalanges in the feet is reduced to the mammalian number of 2 3 3 3 3 by the reduction, and finally the loss, of one phalange in the third toe and two in the fourth (Fig. 348).

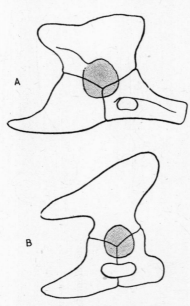

FIG. 347.—A. Right pelvic of **Lycænops** (a Gorgonopsian); B. of **Protacmon** (a Cynodont).

There are five sub-orders, and at least two major lines of evolution within the group. The Permian Gorgonopsia (e.g., *Scymnosuchus*, *Lycænops*) giving rise to the Triassic Cynodontia (e.g., *Thrinaxodon*, *Cynognathus*) and the Permian Therocephalia (e.g., *Lycosaurus*) giving rise to the Triassic Bauriamorpha (e.g., *Ericiolacerta*). In addition, some very mammal-like forms from the top of the Trias have been put into a separate sub-order, the *Ictidosauria*.

ORDER INCERTÆ SEDIS.—SAUROPTERYGIA.

Aquatic reptiles with a single temporal vacuity in the skull, which is

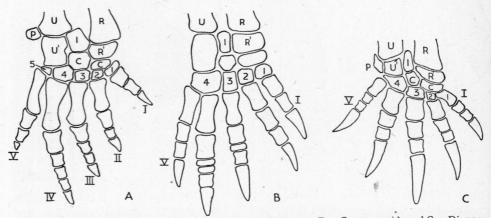

FIG. 348.—Diagrams of hands of A, a primitive Pelycosaur, B, a Gorgonopsid, and C, a Dicynodont, to show the reduction from the reptilian number of phalanges to the mammalian condition; *U*. ulna; *R*. radius; *U'*. ulnare; *R'*. radiale; *I*. intermedium; *C.C.* centralia; *P.* pisiform.

bounded below by a post-orbital-squamosal arch. The coracoids are single. There are three orders :—

NOTHOSAURIA, small and somewhat primitive forms, amphibious in habit, with webbed feet. The vertebræ are platycœlous. These forms are found in the Middle and Upper Trias.

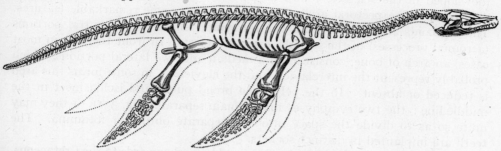

FIG. 349.—**Plesiosaurus macrocephalus.** Restored. (After Owen.) In the dotted outline the vertical tail-fin has been omitted.

PLACODONTIA. Forms with long limb bones and a specialised palate armed with massive crushing teeth on the palatine bones. The vertebræ are deeply amphicœlous. The body is covered with heavy bony scutes. Confined to the Middle Trias, e.g., *Placodus, Cyamodus.*

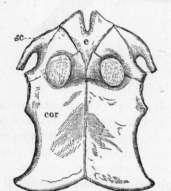

FIG. 350.—**Plesiosaurus,** pectoral arch. *cor.* coracoid ; *e.* interclavicle ; *sc.* scapula. (After Zittel.)

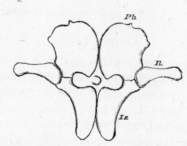

FIG. 351.—**Plesiosaurus,** pelvic arch. *Il.* ilium ; *Is.* ischium ; *Pb.* pubis. (After Huxley.)

PLESIOSAURIA. These are the typical representatives of the order (Fig. 349). They were aquatic reptiles, sometimes of large size (up to 40 feet), though many were quite small. They had a lizard-like body, a very long neck supporting a relatively small head, and a short tail ; the limbs were modified to form swimming-paddles. The spinal column of the Sauropterygia is characterised by the great length of the cervical and the comparative shortness of the caudal region. The vertebræ are usually amphicœlous. The sacrum consists of either one to five vertebræ. There is no sternum. In the skull there are large pre-maxillæ; a bony secondary palate is absent; an ectopterygoid is present. There is a well-marked parietal foramen. The ring of bony plates (developed in the sclerotic found in the orbit of some fossil reptiles) is not developed. The pectoral arch (Fig. 350) presents some remarkable features. The coracoids always meet in a ventral symphysis, and the ventral portions (acromial processes) of the scapulæ may also meet. In front there is, in most cases, an arch of bone, consisting of a median and two lateral portions, which probably represent the interclavicle and the clavicles: in some forms this arch is reduced or absent. In the pelvis the broad pubes and ischia meet in the middle line: the two symphyses may remain separate (Fig. 351), or they may unite so as to divide the space into two separate obturator foramina. The teeth are implanted in distinct sockets.

The Plesiosauria date from the Trias and extend onwards to the Cretaceous.

FIG. 352.—Skeleton of **Ichthyosaurus**. (After Dreverman.)

ORDER INCERTÆ SEDIS.—ICHTHYOPTERYGIA.

Fully marine reptiles having a skull with a single lateral temporal vacuity. The Ichthyopteryia, including *Ichthyosaurus* (Fig. 352) and its allies, were aquatic reptiles, some of very large size (30 or 40 feet in length), with somewhat fish-like body, large head produced into an elongated snout, no neck, and an elongated tail, and with the limbs in the form of swimming-paddles. The vertebræ are amphicœlous. A sacrum is absent, so that only pre-caudal and caudal regions are distinguishable. The ribs in the cervical region have two heads for articulation with the vertebræ: a sternum is absent, but there is a highly developed system of abdominal ribs. The skull is produced into an elongated rostum, formed chiefly of the pre-maxillæ, and with small nostrils situated far back. The orbits are large and contain a ring of bones developed in the sclerotic. A columella is present which articulates with the quadrate, and there is a large parietal foramen. The quadrate is immovably fixed to the skull. The pterygoids meet in the middle line and extend forwards to the vomers, so as to separate the palatines, as in Sphenodon. The pectoral arch contains only coracoid, scapula, and clavicle. There is no precoracoid. The coracoids are broad bones which meet ventrally for a short distance without overlapping. The bones of the pelvis are not strongly developed; there is no sacrum, *i.e.*, the ilia are not connected with the spinal column; the pubes and ischia of opposite sides meet in ventral symphyses; but there is no obturator foramen. Humerus and femur are both short, and the rest of the bones of the limb are disc-like or polyhedral. The phalanges are numerous, and are usually in more, sometimes in fewer, than the usual five series. The teeth are not in separate sockets, but set in a continuous groove. The tail vertebræ in the middle forms have a characteristic downward bend which in later forms becomes almost a right angle. The body thus extends into the lower lobe of a large vertical caudal fin.

The Ichthyopterygia are of Mesozoic age, ranging from the Middle Trias to the Upper Cretaceous. Geographically their remains have a very wide distribution, having been found not only in Europe and North America, but in the Arctic Regions, in India, Australia, New Zealand, and South America.

SUPER-ORDER III.—DIAPSIDA.

This super-order includes all Reptiles which have two lateral temporal vacuities in the skull (e.g., *Sphenodon*, Fig. 325, p. 361).

The orders are, some of them, large and important, and include the THECO-DONTIA, RHYNCHOCEPHALIA, DINOSAURIA, PTEROSAURIA, CROCODILIA, and, according to one view, the SQUAMATA as a derivative of an early Thecodont line.

ORDER I.—THECODONTIA.

These are the most primitive of the members of the super-order and the earliest reptiles to show a diapsid skull with the characteristic two lateral temporal vacuities. The most important specimen, of which little is as yet known beyond the skull, is *Youngina* from the Upper Permian of South Africa. This form has an interparietal and tabular bones in the skull and a parietal foramen, features which usually are not found in other orders of Thecodontia. The antorbital foramen is absent. As far as it is known, there is nothing in *Youngina* to prevent its being considered as a representative of the ancestral stage of the later orders of DIAPSIDA. Other families are the Phytosauridæ, aquatic, croco-dile-like reptiles but with a specialised snout formed by the elongated pre-maxillæ; Ornithosuchidæ; Aetosauridæ, etc.

ORDER 2.—RHYNCHOCEPHALIA.

Members of this order have lost the tabulars and interparietal of the Theco-dontia while retaining the large parietal foramen, in which, in the living form, traces of the median eye can still be made out. There is no antorbital foramen. The group, apparently never a large one, is known from the Middle Trias. e.g.

Hyperodapedon, Rhynchosaurus. The sole living representative of this group is *Sphenodon* (*Hatteria*), which is a lizard-like reptile with well-developed pentadactyle limbs adapted for walking. The anal opening is transverse. There are no copulatory sacs. The vertebræ are amphicœlous and intercentra are present. The ribs are single-headed and have uncinate processes. The rami of the mandible are united by ligament. There is a sternum and abdominal ribs. The teeth are acrodont. The lungs, heart, and brain resemble those of the Squamata.

ORDER 3.—SQUAMATA.

Reptiles in which the skull has secondarily lost either one (Lacertilia) or both temporal vacuities (Ophidia). The surface is covered with horny epidermal scales, sometimes with the addition of dermal ossifications. The opening of the cloaca is transverse in direction. There is a pair of eversible copulatory sacs in the male. The vertebræ are nearly always procœlous. The sacrum, absent in the Ophidia and Pythonomorpha, consists of two vertebræ in the Lacertilia. The ribs have simple vertebral extremities. The quadrate is movably articulated with the skull. There is no inferior temporal arch. The nasal apertures of the skull are separate. The limbs, when present, are sometimes adapted for terrestrial locomotion (Lacertilia), sometimes for swimming (Pythonomorpha). The teeth are acrodont or pleurodont (*see below*). The lungs are simple sacs. There is always a wide cleft between the right and left divisions of the ventricular cavity. The optic lobes are approximated, and the cerebellum is extremely small.

Sub-Order a.—Lacertilia.

Squamata in which, as a rule, the limbs are present and are adapted for walking. The mouth is capable of being opened to only a moderate extent. The maxillæ, palatines, and pterygoids are incapable of free movement. The rami of the mandible are firmly united at the symphysis. There are nearly always movable eyelids and a tympanum. A sternum and an episternum are present.

Including all the lizards, such as the Skincs, Geckos, Monitors, Iguanas, Amphisbænians, Chamæleons, and other groups.

Systematic Position of the Example (pp. 357–375).

There are twenty known species of the genus Lacerta, occurring in Europe, Asia, Africa, and North America. Lacerta is a member of the sub-order Lacertilia of the order Squamata. The flattened and elongated tongue with notched apex places it in the section Leptoglossæ of that sub-order. Among the Leptoglossæ the family Lacertidæ, which comprises Lacerta and a number of other genera, is characterised by the presence of dermal bony supra-orbital and supra-temporal plates, by the presence of small granular or wedge-shaped scales, and of pleurodont conical teeth, excavated at the base. The chief distinctive marks of the genus Lacerta are the presence of comparatively large shields on the head and on the ventral surface, the arrangement of the scales of the trunk in transverse rows which become circular zones or rings on the tail, the development of a collar-like band of larger scales round the neck, and the laterally-compressed falciform claws, grooved on the lower surface.

Sub-Order b.—Ophidia.

Squamata with long, narrow body, devoid of limbs. The mouth is capable of being opened to form a relatively very wide gape by the divarication of the jaws. The maxillæ, palatines, and pterygoids are capable of free movement. The rami of the mandible are connected together only by elastic fibres at the symphysis, so that they are capable of being widely separated. There is no

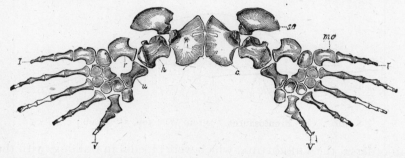

FIG. 353.—**Edestosaurus** (Pythonomorpha). Pectoral arch and fore-limbs. *c.* coracoid with pro-coracoid; *h.* humerus; *mc.* metacarpus; *r.* radius; *sc.* scapula; *u.* ulna; *I*, first digit; *V*, fifth digit. (From Zittel after Marsh.)

separate supra-temporal ossification. Sternum and episternum are absent. Movable eyelids and tympanum are absent.

Including all the Snakes—Vipers, Rattlesnakes, Sea Snakes, Fresh-water Snakes, Tree Snakes, Blind Snakes, Pythons, and Boas.

Sub-Order c.—Pythonomorpha.

Extinct Squamata with elongated snake-like body, provided with limbs which take the form of swimming-paddles (Fig. 353). The skull resembles that of the Lacertilia; a supra-temporal helps to suspend the quadrate. The union of the rami of the mandible was ligamentous. There is, as a rule, no sacrum, the ilia not articulating with the spinal column.

All the remaining orders of DIAPSIDA are without interparietal, tabular bones, or parietal foramen. They are usually grouped together as ARCHOSAURIA, and are probably all descendants of late, bipedal THECODONTS.

"Order" DINOSAURIA.—This well-known group of Reptiles is really divided by a series of clearly marked characters into two divisions which should rank as orders : these are the SAURISCHIA (= Theropoda and Sauropoda) and the ORNITHISCHIA (= Predentata or Orthopoda). In these two orders are to be found not only small forms but the largest animals which have ever existed on land, whose bulk has only been exceeded by the larger of the modern whales. The greatest variation of adaptation to various habits and extreme specialisation of shape and ornamentation can also be observed within the limits of these two orders.

ORDER 4.—SAURISCHIA.

In the pelvic girdle of members of this order the pubes and ischia are long, project downwards, and meet in a ventral symphysis. In the skull there are two, or one, antorbital vacuities, which are often very large. Teeth are present on the pre-maxillæ. Dermal bones are never present on the body. There are

FIG. 354.—**Brontosaurus.** (From Williston, after Lull.)

two sub-orders : the THEROPODA, which were bipedal in walking, with the front limbs more or less reduced, and which were carnivorous in habit, with large skulls, e.g., *Plateosaurus, Megalosaurus, Compsognathus*, etc. ; and the SAURO-PODA, which were quadrupedal, herbivorous, with small skulls and elongated necks and tails, e.g., *Brontosaurus* (Fig. 354), *Cetiosaurus, Diplodocus, Tornieria*, etc.

Each sub-order contains many families, genera, and species.

ORDER 5.—ORNITHISCHIA.

These Dinosaurs have a pelvis in which the pubes do not meet in a median symphysis, but which have an anterior bird-like pre-pubis which is expanded at its end, and a long posterior pubis which runs along the lower (anterior) border of the ischium. In the skull the antorbital vacuities are always small and may be obliterated. One of the most noticeable characters is the possession of a "predentary" bone in the mandible which may have supported a horny beak. As a result the teeth on the pre-maxillæ and on the front of the lower jaw become suppressed. All the Ornithischia were herbivorous. There are three sub-orders : ORNITHOPODA, bipedal, digitigrade forms with a complete slender post-pubis, a small antorbital vacuity ; examples, *Hypsilophodon*, a small form ;

Iguanodon (Fig. 355), 30 feet in length, one of the earliest described Dinosaurs ; *Trachodon*, etc. STEGOSAURIA, heavy quadrupedal forms, but with the anterior limbs shorter than the posterior, with small skulls and a heavy dermal armour,

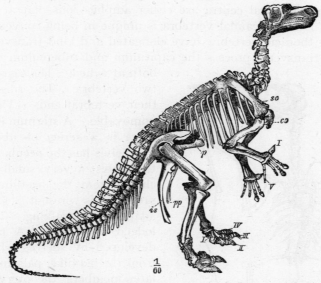

FIG. 355.—**Iguanodon bernissartensis.** One sixtieth natural size. *co.* coracoid ; *is.* ischium ; *p.* pre-pubis ; *pp.* post-pubic process (pubis) ; *sc.* scapula. *I—V, I—IV,* digits. (From Zittel, after Dollo.)

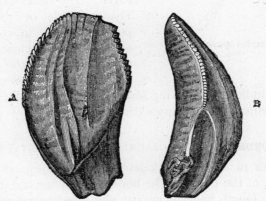

FIG. 356.—Teeth of **Iguanodon mantelli.** *A,* from the inner, *B,* from the outer side. (From Zittel, after Mantell.)

e.g., *Stegosaurus, Polacanthus* ; and CERATOPSIA, quadrupedal forms with large skulls and bony horns—a fringe of bone from the skull lying over the neck, e.g., *Triceratops.*

ORDER 6.—CROCODILIA.

Reptiles in which the dorsal surface, or both dorsal and ventral surfaces, are covered with rows of sculptured bony scutes. Epidermal scales are also present. The vertebral centra are either amphicœlous, flat at each end, or procœlous. The first caudal vertebra is unique in being convex at each end. The anterior thoracic vertebræ have elongated and bifid transverse processes, and to this transverse process the capitulum and tuberculum of the rib are both attached. The sacrum consists of two vertebræ. The ribs are bifid at their vertebral ends. The quadrate is immovable. A sternum is present, and there is a series of abdominal ribs. The pelvis has the peculiarity of having the pubis, a very small element, excluded from the acetabulum ; a long prepubis is present. The limbs are adapted for walking. The teeth are lodged in sockets. A false palate is developed by shelves which grow out from the maxillæ, palatines and, in the later members, the pterygoids so that the internal nares open into the throat. In life they are covered with a fleshy valve. The lungs are compound sacs. The ventricle of the heart is completely divided in recent forms. The opening of the cloaca is elongated in the direction of the long axis of the body. There is a median penis.

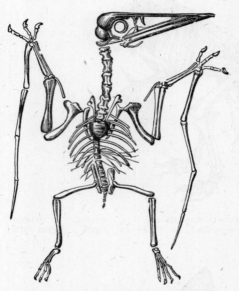

FIG. 357.—**Pterodactylus spectabilis.** Three-fourths of the natural size. (From Zittel, after H. v. Mayer.)

This order includes among living forms the true Crocodiles, the Gavials, the Alligators, and Caimans, and many extinct families.

ORDER 7.—PTEROSAURIA or PTERODACTYLA.

Flying Reptiles in which the skeleton has become modified in a manner analogous to that of the Birds. The bones are pneumatic, the fore-limb is a wing in which the fourth finger is greatly elongated to support a membranous patagium, the first three fingers are small and clawed, and the fifth is absent. The carpus is reduced but has a spur-like sesamoid bone added to it. Though the sternum is well ossified, the clavicles and interclavicle are absent.

The pelvis has pre-pubic bones which join one another. The hind limbs are pentadactyle and rather weak, the fibula being reduced or absent.

The skull is pointed and elongated, sometimes to an exaggerated degree; the external nares are placed far back; the antorbital vacuity is large and the

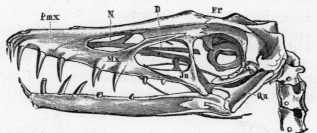

FIG. 358.—Skull of **Scaphognathus.** *D.* pre-orbital aperture; *Fr.* frontal; *Ju.* jugal; *Mx.* maxilla; *N.* nasal opening; *Pmx.* premaxilla; *Qu.* quadrate. (After Zittel.)

eye is bordered with sclerotic plates. There is no parietal foramen. The head is supported at a right angle on a long neck of eight or nine proccœlous vertebræ. The group flourished during the Jurassic and Cretaceous periods.

There are two sub-orders: the RHAMPHORHYNCHOIDEA, which are charac-

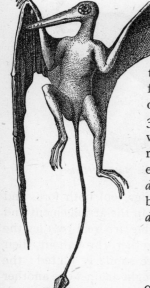

terised by a long tail which is dilated at the end, by free cervical ribs, and by the possession of a fifth toe on the hind foot: examples, *Rhamphorhynchus* (Fig. 359) *Dimorphodon*, etc.; and the PTERODACTYLOIDEA, which have an extremely reduced tail, no cervial ribs, and an incomplete fifth toe. Some forms are edentulous: Examples, *Scaphognathus* (Fig. 358), *Pterodactylus* (Fig. 357), *Pteranodon*, a form with a curious balancing backward prolongation of the head, *Ornithodesmus*, etc.

GENERAL ORGANISATION OF RECENT REPTILIA.

External Features.—In external form, as in some other respects, certain of the Lacertilia exhibit the least specialised condition to be observed among the living Reptilia. Lacerta is such a central type, and the general account of that Lizard which has just been

FIG. 359.—**Rhamphorhynchus**, restored. (After Zittel.)

given applies in all the points of cardinal importance to a large proportion of the Lacertilia. Modifications take place, however, in a variety of different

directions. Of such the following are a few of the chief. The tail region
is usually, as in the example, extremely long and tapering; but in some
groups of Lizards it is comparatively short and thick; and in others it is
depressed and expanded into a leaf-like form. In the Chamæleons (Fig. 360)
the long and tapering tail is used as a prehensile organ, the coiling of which
round branches of the trees in which the animal lives aids in maintaining the
balance of the body in climbing from branch to branch.

In the limbs there is likewise a considerable amount of variation in the
different groups of the Lacertilia. Moderately long pentadactyle limbs like

FIG. 360.—**Chamæleon vulgaris**, × ⅔. (From the *Cambridge Natural History*.)

those of Lacerta are the rule. In the Chamæleons (Fig. 360) both fore- and
hind-limbs become prehensile by a special modification in the arrangement and
mode of articulation of the digits. In these remarkable arboreal reptiles the
three innermost digits of the manus are joined together throughout their
length by a web of skin, and the two outer digits are similarly united: the
two sets of digits are so articulated that they can be brought against one another
with a grasping movement analogous to the grasping movement of a Parrot's
foot or of the hand of Man. A similar arrangement prevails in the pes, the
only difference being that the two innermost and three outermost digits are
united. In some groups of Lacertilia, on the other hand, such as the Blind-
Worm (*Anguis*), limbs are entirely absent, or are represented only by mere
vestiges; and numerous intermediate gradations exist between these and forms,

such as Lacerta, with well-developed limbs. The limbless lizards (Fig. 361) bear a very close resemblance to the snakes, not only in the absence of the limbs, but also in the general form of the body and the mode of locomotion.

The body of a snake is elongated, narrow, and cylindrical, usually tapering towards the posterior end, sometimes with, more usually without, a constriction behind the head. In the absence of limbs the beginning of the short caudal region is only indicated by the position of the cloacal opening. The fore-limbs are never represented even by vestiges ; in some Pythons there are inconspicuous vestiges of hind-limbs in the form of small claw-like processes. The mouth of the Snake is capable of being very widely opened by the free articulation of the lower jaw, and it is this which mainly distinguishes it from the snake-like lizards. But other, less conspicuous, points of distinction are the absence of movable eyelids in the Snake, and also the want of a tympanum.

FIG. 361.—**Pygopus lepidopus,** with scale-like vestiges of hind-limbs. (After Brehm.)

Sphenodon or *Hatteria*, the New Zealand Tuatara (Fig. 362), the only living representative of the Rhynchocephalia, is a lizard-like Reptile with a well-developed laterally-compressed tail, and pentadactyle extremities, very similar to those of a typical Lizard. The upper surface is covered with small granular scales, and a crest of compressed spine-like scales runs along the middle of the dorsal surface. The lower surface is covered with transverse rows of large squarish plates.

In the Chelonia (Fig. 363) the body is short and broad, enclosed in a hard " shell " consisting of a dorsal part or *carapace* and a ventral part or *plastron*. These are in most cases firmly united, apertures being left between them for the head and neck, the tail and the limbs. The neck is long and mobile ; the tail short. The limbs are fully developed though short. In some (land and fresh-water Tortoises) they are provided each with five free digits terminating in curved horny claws ; in the Turtles the digits are closely united together, and the limb assumes the character of a " flipper " or swimming-paddle. The cloacal aperture is longitudinal.

FIG. 362.—**Sphenodon punctatum**, × ⅓. (From the *Cambridge Natural History*.)

The Crocodilia, the largest of living reptiles, have the trunk elongated and somewhat depressed, so that its breadth is much greater than its height.   The snout is prolonged, the neck short, the tail longer than the body and compressed laterally. The limbs are relatively short and powerful, with five digits in the manus and four in the pes, those of the latter being partly or completely united by webs of skin. The eyes are very small, the nostrils placed close to the end of the snout and capable of being closed by a sphincter muscle. The cloacal aperture is a longitudinal slit. The dorsal and ventral surfaces are covered with thick, squarish horny scales, often pitted or ridged, those of the dorsal surface of the tail developed into a longitudinal crest.

Integument and Exoskeleton.—Characteristic of the Squamata is the development of horny plates which cover the entire surface, overlapping one another in an imbricating manner. These differ considerably in form and arrangement in different groups; sometimes they are smooth, sometimes sculptured or keeled. Sometimes they are similar in character over all parts of the surface; usually

FIG. 363.—Grecian **Tortoise** (*Testudo græca*). (After Brehm.)

there are specially developed scales—the *head-shields*—covering the upper surface of the head. In the majority of snakes the ventral surface is covered with a row of large transversly elongated scales, the *ventral shields*. In certain lizards (Chamæleons and Geckos) the scales are reduced and modified into the form of minute tubercles or granules. In some lizards special developments of the scales occur in the form of large tubercles or spines. Underlying the horny epidermal scales in some lizards (Skincoids) are series of dermal bony plates. In the integument of the Geckos are numerous minute hard bodies which are intermediate in character between cartilage and bone.

In the snake-like Amphisbænians there are no true scales, with the exception of the head-shields, but the surface is marked out into annular bands of squarish areas.

In addition to the modification of the scales, the integument of the Chamæleons is remarkable for the changes of colour which it undergoes, these changes being due to the presence in the dermis of pigment-cells which contract or expand under the influence of the nervous system, reminding one of the integument of the Cephalopoda. Less conspicuous and rapid changes of colour take place in Anguis and in some snakes.

In the Chelonia, scales, when developed, are confined to the head and neck, the limbs, and the tail; but in all of them, with the exception of the Soft Tortoises, both dorsal and ventral surfaces are covered by a system of large horny plates. A series of horny head-shields usually cover the dorsal surface of the head. Beneath the horny plates of the dorsal and ventral surfaces are the bony carapace and plastron, partly composed of dermal bones, but so intimately united with elements derived from the endoskeleton that the entire structure is best described in connection with the latter (*vide* p. 401).

In the Crocodilia, the whole surface is covered with horny plates or scales,

Fig. 364.—
Vertebra of **Sphenodon**, showing the amphicœlous centrum (*C.*). (After Headley.)

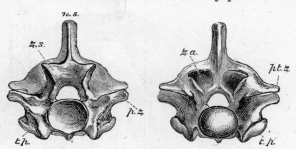

Fig. 365.—Vertebra of **Python**, anterior and posterior views. *n. s.* neural spine; *p. z.* pre-zygapophysis; *pt. z.* post-zygapophysis; *t. p.* transverse processes; *z. a.* zygantrum; *z.s.* zygosphene. (After Huxley.)

each usually marked with a pit-like depression about the centre, those on the dorsal surface ridged longitudinally. Underlying each of these, which are of epidermal derivation, is a thick pad of dermal connective-tissue which, in the case of the dorsal scales, is replaced by a bony scute. In the Caimans thin scutes also occur under the ventral scales.

A periodical *ecdysis* or casting and renewal of the outer layers of the horny epidermis takes place in all the reptilia with the exception of the Crocodiles. Sometimes this occurs in a fragmentary manner; but in snakes and many lizards the whole comes away as a continuous slough.

Endoskeleton.—The vertebræ are always fully ossified. Among recent forms the Geckos and Sphenodon (Fig. 364) are exceptional in having the centra amphicœlous with remnants of the notochord in the intercentral spaces. The rest of the recent groups for the most part have the centra procœlous. In many extinct forms the neural arches are not directly attached to the bodies by bone (*temnospondyly*): in recent forms there is a bony union (*stereospondyly*) either through a suture or by fusion. Intercentra may be represented by inter-

vertebral discs of fibrocartilage (Crocodilia) or by bony elements formed by ossification of the ventral portions of the discs (Geckos, Sphenodon).   In Lizards

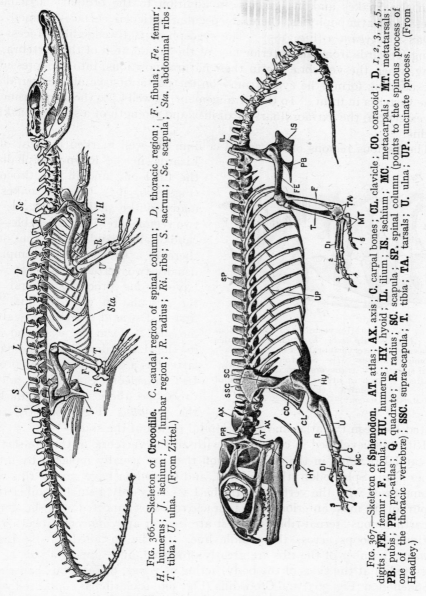

Fig. 366.—Skeleton of **Crocodile.** *C.* caudal region of spinal column; *D*, thoracic region; *F.* fibula; *Fe.* femur;
H. humerus; *J.* ischium; *L.* lumbar region; *R.* radius; *Ri.* ribs; *S.* sacrum; *Sc.* scapula; *Sta.* abdominal ribs;
T. tibia; *U.* ulna. (From Zittel.)

Fig. 367.—Skeleton of **Sphenodon. AT.** atlas; **AX.** axis; **C.** carpal bones; **CL.** clavicle; **CO.** coracoid; **D.** 1, 2, 3, 4, 5,
digits; **FE.** femur; **F.** fibula; **HU.** humerus; **HY.** hyoid; **IL.** ilium; **IS.** ischium; **MC.** metacarpals; **MT.** metatarsals;
PB. pubis; **PR.** pro-atlas; **Q.** quadrate; **R.** radius; **SC.** scapula; **SP.** spinal column (points to the spinous process of
one of the thoracic vertebræ); **SSC.** supra-scapula; **T.** tibia; **TA.** tarsals; **U.** ulna; **UP.** uncinate process. (From
Headley.)

in general and the Crocodiles there are inferior processes (*hypapophyses*),
perhaps representing intercentra, situated below the centra in the anterior

cervical region. Chevron bones (inferior arches) occur in the caudal region of many Reptiles (Sphenodon, Lacertilia, Crocodilia).

In the Snakes and in Iguanas, in addition to the ordinary articulating processes or zygapophyses, there are peculiar articular surfaces termed *zygosphenes* and *zygantra* (Fig. 365). The zygosphene is a wedge-like process projecting forwards from the anterior face of the neural arch of the vertebra, and fitting, when the vertebræ are in their natural positions, into a depression of corresponding form—the zygantrum—on the posterior face of the neural arch of the vertebra in front. To this arrangement, as well as to the deeply concavo-convex centra, the extraordinary flexibility and strength of a snake's backbone are due.

The various regions of the spinal column are well marked in most of the Lizards, in the Rhynchocephalia, in the Chelonia, and in the Crocodilia (Figs. 366, 367). In the snakes and many of the snake-like lizards only two regions are distinguishable—pre-caudal and caudal. In the others there is a sacral region comprising usually two vertebræ, both of which have strong processes (sacral ribs) for articulation with the ilia. The first and second vertebræ are always modified to form an atlas and axis: in the Lacertilia and Chelonia the latter has a distinct odontoid process. In Chamæleons, Sphenodon, and the Crocodiles there is a median bone, the *pro-atlas* (Fig. 368, *O*), inter-calated between the atlas and the occipital region of the skull.

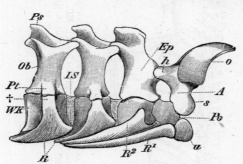

FIG. 368.—Anterior vertebræ of young **Crocodile.** *A.* atlas; *Ep.* axis; *h.* articulation of atlas with axis; *IS.* intervertebral discs; *o.* pro-atlas; *Ob.* neural arches; *Po.* odontoid bone; *Ps.* neural spines; *Pt.* transverse processes; *R*, *R¹*, *R².* ribs; *s.* arch of atlas; *u.* median piece of atlas; *WK.* centra. (From Wiedersheim's *Comparative Anatomy*.)

Ribs are developed in connection with all the vertebræ of the pre-sacral or pre-caudal region; in the caudal region they are usually replaced by inferior arches; but Sphenodon, the Chelonia, and Crocodilia have caudal ribs which become fused with the vertebræ. In the Lacertilia only a small number (three or four) of the most anterior of the thoracic ribs are connected with the sternum by cartilaginous sternal ribs; the rest are free, or are connected together into continuous hoops across the middle line. In the so-called Flying Lizards (*Draco*) a number of the ribs are greatly produced, and support a pair of wide flaps of skin at the sides of the body, acting as wings, or rather as parachutes. In Sphenodon (Fig. 367) and Crocodilia (Fig. 366) each rib has connected with it posteriorly a flattened curved cartilage, the *uncinate*.

In the Chelonia (Fig. 369) the total number of vertebræ is always smaller than in the members of the other orders. The cervical ribs are small and fused with the vertebræ. The cervical and the caudal are the only regions in which the vertebræ are movable upon one another. The vertebræ of the trunk, usually ten in number, are immovably united with one another by means of fibro-cartilaginous intervertebral discs. Each of the neural spines, from the second to the ninth inclusively, is flattened and fused with a flat plate of dermal origin, the *neural plate* (Fig. 370), and the row of plates thus formed constitutes the median portion of the carapace. The ribs are likewise immovable; a short

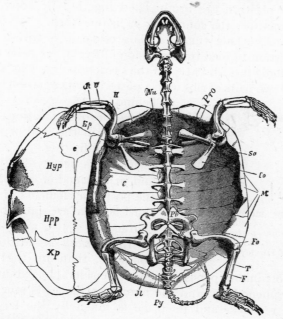

FIG. 369.—**Cistudo lutaria.** Skeleton seen from below; the plastron has been removed and is represented on one side. *C.* costal plate; *Co.* coracoid; *e.* entoplastron (episternum); *Ep.* epiplastron (clavicle?); *F.* fibula; *Fe.* femur; *H.* humerus; *Hyp.* hyoplastron; *Hpp.* hypoplastron; *Jl.* ilium; *Js.* ischium; *M.* marginal plates; *Nu.* nuchal plate; *Pb.* pubis; *Pro.* procoracoid or process of scapula; *Py.* pygal plates; *R.* radius; *Sc.* scapula; *T.* tibia; *U.* ulna; *Xp.* xiphiplastron. (From Zittel.)

distance from its origin each passes into a large bony dermal *costal plate*, and the series of costal plates uniting by their edges form a large part of the carapace on either side of the row of neural plates. The carapace is made up of the neural and costal plates supplemented by a row of *marginal* plates (Figs. 369 and 370) running along the edge, and *nuchal* and *pygal* plates situated respectively in front of and behind the row of neural plates. In some cases the neural plates (*Chelodina*) and even the costal plates and ribs (*Testudo loveridgii*) are absent.

The bony elements of the plastron of the Chelonia are an anterior and median plate (*entoplastron*) and four pairs of plates which are termed in their order from

before backwards *epiplastra, hyoplastra, hypoplastra,* and *xiphiplastra.* The median element probably corresponds to the interclavicle or episternum of other Reptiles, the first pair (epiplastra) to the clavicles, the others probably being of the same character as the abdominal ribs of the Crocodilia.

The carapace of the Luth or Leather-backed Turtle (*Dermatochelys* or *Sphargis*) is distinguished from that of the rest of the order in being composed of numerous polygonal discs of bone firmly united together, and in not being connected with the endoskeleton; in the plastron the median bone is absent.

Carapace and plastron are firmly fixed together by bony union in most instances, but sometimes the connection is ligamentous.

The *sternum* in the Lacertilia is a plate of cartilage with a simple or bifid posterior continuation formed by the fusion of five or six pairs of ribs. In the Ophidia and Chelonia it is absent. In the Crocodilia it is a broad plate bearing the coracoids and two pairs of ribs with a posterior continuation which bifurcates behind.

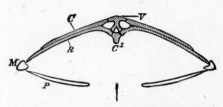

FIG. 370.—**Chelone midas.** Transverse section of skeleton. *C.* costal plate; *C¹.* centrum; *M.* marginal plate; *P.* lateral element of plastron; *R.* rib; *V.* expanded neural plate. (After Huxley.)

A series of ossifications—the *abdominal ribs*—lies in the wall of the abdomen in the Crocodilia (Fig. 366, *Sta.*), and similar ossifications occur also in the Monitors and in Sphenodon. As already noticed, the posterior elements of the plastron of the Chelonia are probably of a similar character.

In the *skull* ossification is much more complete than in the Amphibia, the primary chondrocranium persisting to a considerable extent only in some Lizards and in Sphenodon; and the number of bones is much greater. The parasphenoid is reduced, and its place is taken by the large basioccipital, basisphenoid, and presphenoid.

A fairly typical lacertilian skull has been described in the case of Lacerta. Its principal characteristic features are the presence of an inter-orbital septum, the presence of the epipterygoid, and the mobility of the quadrate. The last of these features it shares with that of the Ophidia. The epipterygoid is not universal in the Lacertilia, being absent in the Geckos, the Amphisbænians, and the Chamæleons. The quadrate is not always movable. The skull of the Chamæleons has a remarkable helmet-like appearance owing to the development of processes of the squamosal and occipital regions, which unite above the posterior part of the cranial roof. The skull of the Amphisbænians differs from that of other Lacertilia and approaches that of Snakes in the absence of an inter-orbital septum.

In the skull of the Ophidia (Fig. 371) orbitosphenoidal and alisphenoidal elements are absent, their places being taken by downward prolongations of the parietals and frontals.   In the substance of the mesethmoid are two cartilaginous tracts (Fig. 371, **B**, *T*) which are the persistent trabeculæ of the embryonic skull.   The inter-orbital septum is absent, and the cranial cavity is prolonged

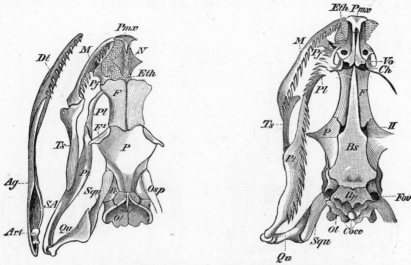

FIG. 371.—Skull of Colubrine Snake (**Tropidonotus natrix**).   **A,** from above; **B,** from below. *Ag.* angular; *Art.* articular; *Bp.* basi-occipital; *Bs.* basi-sphenoid; *Ch.* internal nares; *Cocc.* occipital condyle; *Dt.* dentary; *Eth.* ethmoid; *F.* frontal; *F'.* post-orbital; *Fov.* fenestra ovalis; *M.* maxilla; *N.* nasal; *Ol.* exoccipital; *Osp.* supra-occipital; *P.* parietal; *Pe.* periotic; *P. f.* pre-frontal; *Pl.* palatine; *Pmx.* permaxilla; *Pt.* pterygoid; *Qu.* quadrate; *SA.* supraangular; *Squ.* squamosal; *Ts.* transverse; *Vo.* vomer; *II,* optic foramen.   (From Wiedersheim's *Comparative Anatomy*.)

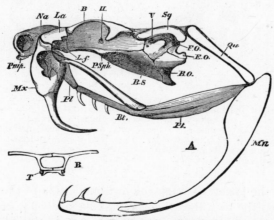

FIG. 372.—**A,** lateral view of skull of **Rattlesnake (Crotalus).**   *B. O.* basi-occipital; *B. S.* basi-sphenoid; *E. O.* exoccipital; *F. O.* fenestra ovalis; *La.* conjoined lacrymal and pre-frontal; *L. f.* articulation between lacrymal and frontal; *Mn.* mandible; *Mx.* maxilla; *Na.* nasal; *Pl.* palatine; *Pmp.* premaxilla; *P. Sph.* presphenoid; *Pt.* pterygoid; *Qu.* quadrate; *Sq.* squamosal; *II, V,* foramina of exit of the second and fifth cranial nerves.   **B,** transverse section at point lettered *B* in Fig. **A**; *T.* trabeculæ.   (After Huxley.)

forwards to the ethmoidal region. Neither upper nor lower temporal arches are present. The palatines (*Pl.*) are movably articulated with the base of the skull; as in the Lizards, they are widely separated from one another, and do not develop palatine plates. They are movably articulated behind with the ptery-

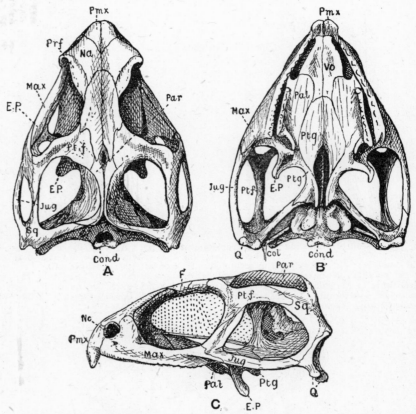

FIG. 373.—Skull of **Sphenodon.** *A*, dorsal; *B*, ventral; *C*, left-sided view of skull of Sphenodon, × ⅔. *Col.* Columella auris; *Cond.* occipital condyle; *E. P.* ectopterygoid; *F.* frontal; *Jug.* jugal; *Max.* maxilla; *Na.* nasal; *Nc.* anterior nasal opening; *Pal.* palatine; *Par.* parietal; *Pmx.* premaxilla; *Prf.* pre-frontal; *Pt. f.* post-frontal and post-orbital; *Ptg.* pterygoid or endopterygoid; *Q.* quadrate and quadrato-jugal (paraquadrate); *Sq.* squamosal; *Vo.* vomer. (From the *Cambridge Natural History*.)

goids (*Pt.*), and the latter, through the intermediation of the slender transverse bones (*Ts.*), with the maxillæ. The premaxillæ are very small (in some venomous Snakes entirely absent) and when present usually fused together. The maxillæ (*Mx.*), usually short, articulate by means of a movable hinge-point with the conjoined lacrymal and pre-frontal (*La.*), which, in turn, is movably connected with the frontal. The long and slender quadrate (*Qu.*) is freely articulated with the posterior end of the elongated squamosal. The rami of the mandible, likewise long and slender, are not united anteriorly in a symphysis, but are connected together merely by elastic ligamentous tissue, so that, when the mouth of the Snake is opened to allow of the entry of the relatively large prey, which it swallows whole, they are capable of being widely separated from one another. The Typhlopidæ differ from the rest of the Ophidia in having the maxillæ immobile, the quadrate more closely connected with the skull, and the rami of the mandible united by a fibro-cartilaginous symphysis.

The skull of Sphenodon (Fig. 373) differs very considerably from that of the Lizards. There is a large *supra-temporal fossa* bounded by the parietal, post-orbital (*Pt. f.*), and squamosal, and separated below by a bar of bone (*superior temporal arch*), formed of processes of the two last-mentioned bones

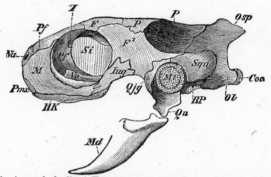

FIG. 374.—Lateral view of skull of **Emys europæa.** *Coc.* occipital condyle; *F.* frontal; *F*[1]. post-frontal; *I*, foramen by which the olfactory nerve enters the orbit; *Iug.* jugal; *M.* maxilla; *Md.* mandible; *Mt.* tympanic membrane; *Na.* external nares; *Ol.* exoccipital; *Osp.* supra-occipital; *P.* parietal; *Pf.* pre-frontal; *Pmx.* pre-maxilla; *Qjg.* quadrato-jugal; *Qu.* quadrate; *Si.* inter-orbital septum; *Squ.* squamosal; *Vo.* vomer. (From Wiedersheim's *Comparative Anatomy.*)

and of the post-frontal, from a still larger space—the *lateral temporal fossa*. The latter is bounded below by a slender bony bar (the *inferior temporal arch*), formed of the long narrow jugal (*Jug.*), with a small quadrato-jugal or para-quadrate, by which the jugal is connected with the quadrate (*Q.*). The lateral temporal fossa is separated from the orbit in front by a bar of bone formed of the jugal and post-orbital, and is bounded behind by a posterior temporal arch formed of the parietal and squamosal. The quadrate (*Q.*) is immovably fixed, wedged in by the quadrato-jugal, squamosal, and pterygoid. The premaxillæ (*Pmx.*) are not fused together, but separated by a suture. There is a broad palate formed by the plate-like vomers, palatines, and pterygoids.

In the Chelonia (Figs. 374, 375) all the bones, including the quadrate, are solidly connected together. Transverse bones (ectopterygoids), lacrymals, orbitosphenoids, and alisphenoids are absent. The place of alisphenoids is taken to a certain extent by vertical downward plate-like extensions of the parietals, the lower part of the plates perhaps representing the epipterygoids of Lizards. There may be open temporal fossæ, the inferior boundary of which (*inferior temporal arch*) may be incomplete owing to the absence of the quadrato-jugal (paraquadrate), or the entire temporal region may be covered over (Turtles, Fig. 375) by a sort of false roof formed of expansions of the post-

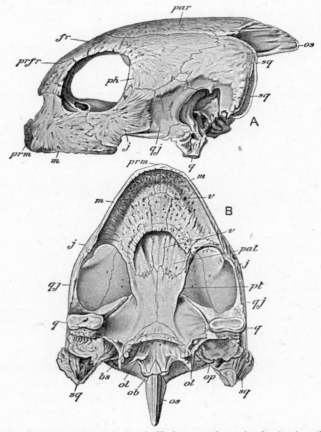

FIG. 375.—Ventral view of the skull of **Chelone mydas**. *bs.* basi-sphenoid; *fr.* frontal; *j.* jugal; *m.* maxilla; *ob.* basi-occipital; *ol.* exoccipital; *op.* opisthotic; *os.* supra-occipital; *pal.* palatine; *par.* parietal; *ph,* post-frontal; *prfr.* pre-frontal; *pt.* pterygoid; *prm.* pre-maxilla; *q.* quadrate; *qj.* quadrato-jugal; *sq.* squamosal; *v.* vomer. (After Hoffmann.)

frontals (*ph.*), parietals (*par.*), and squamosals (*sq.*) with the jugal (*j.*) and quadrato-jugal (*q.j.*). The immovably fixed quadrates (Fig. 374, *qu.*, and Fig. 375, *q.*) are modified to afford a part or the whole of the rim for the support of the tympanic membrane. The occipital condyle is sometimes trilobed. The vomer (*v.*) is unpaired. The palatines (*pal.*) are approximated and give off palatine plates, which for a short distance cut off a nasal passage from the cavity of the mouth. Nasals are usually absent as separate bones. The pre-maxillæ are very small. The rami of the mandibles are stout, and are firmly united together at the symphysis.

In the Crocodiles (Figs. 376, 377), as in the Chelonia, the quadrate (*Qu.*) is firmly united with the other bones of the skull. There is a membranous and

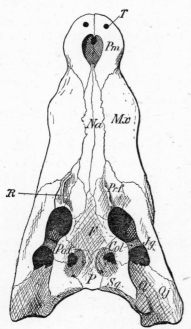

FIG. 376.—Skull of **Crocodilus porosus**, dorsal view, × about ⅓. *Col.* buttress connecting the post-frontal with the jugal and ectoptery-goid; *F.* frontal; *Jg.* jugal; *Mx.* maxilla; *Na.* nasal; *P.* parietal; *Pm.* premaxilla; *Po. f.* post-frontal; *Pr. f.* pre-frontal; *Q.* quadrate; *Qj.* quadratojugal; *R.* characteristic ridge on the pre-frontal bone; *Sq.* squamosal; *T.* perforation in the premaxilla caused by a pair of lower incisor teeth. (After Gadow.)

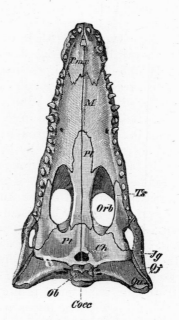

FIG. 377.—Ventral view of the skull of young **Crocodile.** *Ch,* posterior nares; *Cocc.* occipital condyle; *Jg.* jugal; *M.* maxilla (palatine process); *Ob.* basi-occipital; *Orb.* orbit; *Pl.* palatine; *Pmx.* pre-max-illæ; *Pt.* pterygoid; *Qj.* quadratojugal; *Qu.* quadrate. (From Wiedersheim's *Comparative Anatomy.*)

cartilaginous inter-orbital septum. There are no distinct orbitosphenoids, but alisphenoids are well developed. The orbit is separated from the lateral temporal fossa by a stout bar situated somewhat below the surface, and formed of processes from the post-frontal, jugal, and ectopterygoid. The lateral temporal fossa is bounded below, as in Sphenodon, by an inferior temporal arch composed of jugal and quadrato-jugal (paraquadrate). The frontals are early united into one, and the same holds good of the parietals.

Both palatine (*Pl.*) and pterygoid (*Pt.*), as well as maxillæ, develop palatine plates in the roof of the mouth, cutting off a nasal passage of great length from the cavity of the mouth, the posterior nares (*ch.*) being situated far back towards the posterior end of the cranial base. The nature of the articulation between the mandible and the quadrate is such that movement is restricted to the vertical plane, and lateral displacement is further provided against by the development of a broad process of the pterygoid against which the inner surface of the mandibular ramus plays, an arrangement which occurs also in most Lacertilia.

In accordance with their purely aerial mode of respiration, the *visceral arches* are much more reduced in the Reptilia than in the Amphibia in general. The only well-developed post-mandibular arch is the hyoid, and even this may undergo considerable reduction (Ophidia). The branchial arches are greatly reduced or aborted in the adult.

There is little variation in the structure of the limb-arches and skeleton of the limbs in the different groups of Lacertilia. The pelvic arch is distinguished in the Lacertilia in general by its slender character ; and the pubes and ischia are, as in fact is the case throughout the class, separated from one another by wide ischio-pubic foramina—a feature which markedly distinguishes the reptilian pelvis from that of the Amphibia. In limbless forms the pectoral arch may be present or may be absent. In the Ophidia all trace of limb is, as a rule, absent ; but in some Pythons vestiges of hind-limbs are to be detected in the form of two or three small bones which support a small horny claw.

In Sphenodon there is a foramen above the outer and one above the inner condyle of the humerus. There are eleven carpal elements, of which there are four, including a pisiform, in the proximal row, two centrals, and five in the distal row. The pubes are united in a symphysis, in front of which is a cartilaginous epipubis. A large oval foramen intervenes between the ischium and the pubis. A cartilaginous *hypo-ischium* is attached to the ischia behind. In the tarsus the tibial and fibular elements are distinct, though firmly united. The intermedium and the centrale are firmly fixed to the tibiale. There are three distal tarsal bones.

In the Chelonia (Fig. 369) the interclavicle (episternum) and clavicles are absent, unless, as is probable, the former be represented by the median element of the plastron and the latter by the first lateral pair. The entire pectoral arch is a tri-radiate structure of which the most ventral and posterior ray, ending in a free extremity, is the coracoid ; while the other two are the scapula and a process, sometimes regarded as representing the procoracoid, given off on the inner side of the scapula near its glenoid end. The bones of the carpus have nearly the typical arrangement, consisting, as in Lizards, of a proximal row of three, a distal row of five, and a centrale between the two. The pelvis resembles that of Lacertilia, except that it is broader and shorter. Both pubes and ischia meet in ventral symphyses, and epipubic and hypo-ischial cartilages may be present. In the tarsus (Fig. 378) there is usually a single proximal bone and four distalia. There are never more than two phalanges in any of the digits.

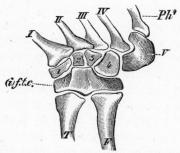

FIG. 378.—Tarsus of **Emys europæa** (right side) from above. *F.* fibula; *T.* tibia; (*i.*) *f. t. c.* the united tarsals of the proximal row; *Ph'*. first phalanx of the fifth digit; *1—4*, distal tarsals; *I—V*, metatarsals. (From Wiedersheim's *Comparative Anatomy*.)

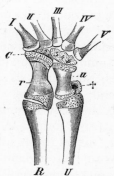

FIG. 379.—Carpus of young **Alligator.** *C.* centrale (?); *R.* radius; *U.* ulna; *r.* radiale; *u.* ulnare; *1—5*, the five distal carpals (not yet ossified); *1* and *2* united into one, and also *3, 4*, and *5*; †, pisiform; *I—V*, the five metacarpals. (From Wiedersheim's *Comparative Anatomy*.)

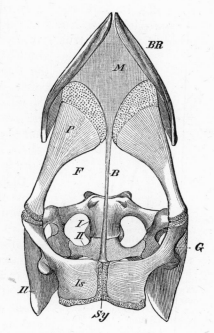

FIG. 380.—Pelvis of young **Alligator,** ventral aspect. *B*, fibrous band passing between the pubic and ischiatic symphyses; *BR.* last pair of abdominal ribs; *F.* obturator foramen; *G.* acetabulum; *Il.* ilium; *Is.* ischium; *M.* fibrous membrane between the anterior ends of the two innominate bones and the last pair of abdominal ribs; *P.* pubis; *Sy.* ischiatic symphysis; *I, II*, first and second sacral vertebræ. (From Wiedersheim's *Comparative Anatomy*.)

In the Crocodilia also the clavicle is absent, but there is an episternum. The number of carpal elements is reduced, the largest being two proximal bones, the radiale and the ulnare (Fig. 379, *r, u.*). On the ulnar side of the latter is a small accessory bone (*pisiform,*†). The pelvic arch (Fig. 380) differs somewhat widely from that of other living Reptiles, and the parts have been variously interpreted. Two bones (*P.*), which are usually regarded as the pubes, extend from the region of the acetabula forwards and inwards, but, though they become closely approximated anteriorly, do not meet in a symphysis. Between and in front of their anterior extremities, which are tipped with cartilage, extends a membrane (*M.*) with which are connected in front the last pair of abdominal ribs (*BR.*). The posterior ends of the pubes are cut off from the acetabulum by the interposition of a pair of bones which may be parts of the ilia, but are separately ossified. The ischia extend downwards and somewhat backwards from the acetabula and are fixed together ventrally (at *Sy.*), but there is no true symphysis, as their extremities remain cartila-

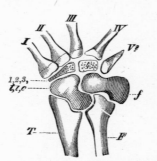

FIG. 381.—Tarsus of **Crocodile** (right side) from above. *F.* fibula ; *T.* tibia ; *t. i. c.* the astragalus, formed of the united tibiale, intermedium and centrale ; *f.* fibulare (calcaneum) ; *1—3,* united first, second and third distal tarsals ; *4,* fourth tarsal ; *I—IV,* first to fourth metatarsals ; *V*?, fifth distal tarsal and fifth meta-tarsal. (From Wiedersheim's *Comparative Anatomy.*)

ginous. A hypo-ischium is not present. In the tarsus (Fig. 381) there are two proximal bones—an *astragalo-scaphoid* and a *calcaneum*— the latter having a prominent calcaneal process and two distal tarsal bones, together with a thin plate of cartilage supporting the first and second metatarsals. The missing fifth digit is represented by a rudimentary metatarsal.

Digestive Organs.—The form and arrangement of the teeth already described in the account of Lacerta prevail in the majority of Lizards. In some of them the palatine teeth are absent. The teeth are sometimes fixed by their bases to the summit of the ridge of the jaw (*acrodont* forms), sometimes fixed by their sides to the lateral surface of the ridge (*pleurodont*) ; they are never embedded in sockets in any recent form. A Mexican Lizard, *Heloderma*, differs from all the rest in having teeth which are grooved for the ducts of poison-glands. In the Snakes (Figs. 371, 372) teeth are rarely developed on the premaxillæ, but are present on the maxillæ, palatines, and pterygoids, as well as the dentary of the mandible. They may be of the same character throughout, solid, elongated, sharp-pointed teeth, which are usually strongly recurved, so that they have the character of sharp hooks, their function being to hold the prey and prevent it slipping from the mouth while being swallowed—not to masticate it. Non-venomous Snakes possess only teeth of this character. In the venomous Snakes more or fewer of the maxillary teeth assume the character of poison-fangs. These are usually much larger than the ordinary teeth and either grooved or perforated by a canal for the passage of the duct of the poison-gland. In the Vipers (Fig. 372) there is a single large curved poison-fang with small reserve-fangs at its base, these being the only teeth borne by the maxilla, which

is very short ; in the venomous Colubrine Snakes the poison-fangs are either
the most anterior or the most posterior of a considerable range of maxillary
teeth. In the Vipers the large poison-fang is capable of being rotated through
a considerable angle, and moved from a nearly horizontal position, in which it
lies along the roof of the mouth embedded in folds of the mucous membrane,
to a nearly vertical one, when the Snake opens its mouth to strike its prey.
The rotation of the maxilla is brought about by the backward or forward movement of the pterygoid with the palatine and transverse. In Sphenodon (Fig.
373) there are pointed, triangular, laterally-compressed teeth, arranged in two
parallel rows, one along the maxilla, the other along the palatine. The teeth
of the lower jaw, which are of similar character, bite in between these two upper

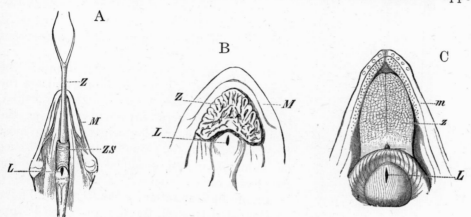

FIG. 382.—**A,** tongue of **Monitor indicus. B,** tongue of **Emys europæa. C,** tongue of
Alligator. *L*, glottis; *M*, mandible; *Z*, tongue; *ZS*, tongue-sheath. (From Wiedersheim's
Comparative Anatomy.)

rows, all the rows becoming worn down in the adult in such a way as to form
continuous ridges. Each premaxilla bears a prominent, chisel-shaped incisor,
represented in the young animal by two pointed teeth. In the young Hatteria
a tooth has been found on each vomer—a condition exceptional among Reptiles.
In the Chelonia, teeth are entirely absent, the jaws being invested in a horny
layer in such a way as to form a structure like a Bird's beak. The Crocodilia
have numerous teeth which are confined to the premaxillæ, the maxillæ, and the
dentary. They are large, conical, hollow teeth devoid of roots, each lodged in
its socket or alveolus (*thecodont*), and each becoming replaced, when worn out,
by a successor developed on its inner side.

A bifid tongue like that of Lacerta occurs in several families of Lacertilia.
Others have a thick, short tongue, undivided in front and often provided with
two long appendages behind. The Monitors (Fig. 382, **A**) have forked retractile tongues like those of Snakes. The tongue of the Chamæleons is an

extremely remarkable organ ; it is of sub-cylindrical form with an enlarged extremity, and is so extensile that it is capable of being darted out to a distance sometimes equalling, or even exceeding, the length of the trunk ; this protrusion can be effected with lightning-like rapidity ; and it is in this way that the animal catches the Insects which constitute its food. The tongue in Snakes is slender and bifid, capable of being retracted into a basal sheath, and highly sensitive, being used chiefly as a tactile organ. The tongue of the Crocodilia (**C**) is a thick, immobile mass extending between the rami of the mandible. In some of the Chelonia (**B**) the tongue is immobile ; in others it is protrusible, sometimes bifid.

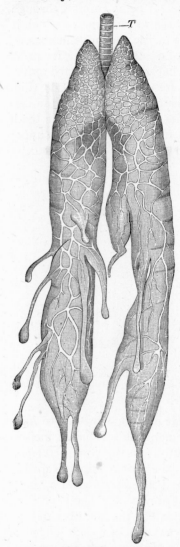

FIG. 383.—Lungs of **Chamæleon.** *T.* trachea. (From Wiedersheim's *Comparative Anatomy.*)

In the enteric canal of the Reptiles the principal special features to be noticed are the muscular gizzard-like stomach of the Crocodilia, the presence of a rudimentary cæcum at the junction of small and large intestines in most Lacertilia and in the Ophidia, and the presence of numerous large cornified papillæ in the œsophagus of the Turtles.

Organs of Respiration.—The Reptiles all have an elongated trachea, the wall of which is supported by numerous cartilaginous rings. The anterior part of this is dilated to form the *larynx*, the wall of which is supported by certain special cartilages—the *cricoid* and the *arytenoids*. The trachea bifurcates posteriorly to form two bronchi, right and left, one passing each lung. The lungs of the Lacertilia and Ophidia are of the simple sac-like character already described in the case of the Lizard. In some the lung is incompletely divided internally into two portions —an anterior respiratory part with sacculated walls, and a posterior part with smooth, not highly vascular, walls, having mainly the function of a reservoir. The only additional complication to be specially noted is the presence in the Chamæleons (Fig. 383) of a number of diverticula or *air-sacs* which are capable of being inflated, causing an increase in the bulk of the animal which doubtless has an effect on assailants. In the snake-like Lizards the right lung is larger than the left, and in the Amphis-bænians the latter is entirely aborted. In the Snakes a similar reduction or abortion of the left lung is observable. In the Crocodilia and Chelonia the lungs are of a more complex character, being divided internally by septa into a number of chambers.

Organs of Circulation.—In the heart (Fig. 384) the sinus venosus is always present, though not, except in Sphenodon, distinguishable externally; its aperture of communication with the right auricle is guarded by two valves. There are, as in the Amphibia, always two quite distinct auricles, the right

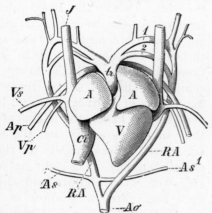

FIG. 384.—Heart of **Lacerta muralis,** ventral view. *A, A.* auricles; *Ap.* pulmonary artery; *As, As¹,* subclavian arteries; *Ci,* post-caval; *J.* jugular vein; *Ra,* aortic arches (made up on either side of two embryonic arches, *1* and *2*); *tr.* aortic root; *V.* ventricle; *Vp.* pulmonary vein; *Vs,* subclavian vein. (From Wiedersheim's *Comparative Anatomy.*)

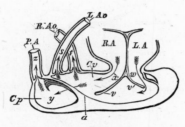

FIG. 385.—Diagram of heart of **Turtle.** *a,* incomplete ventricular septum; *C. p.* cavum pulmonale; *C. v.* cavum venosum; *L. A.* left auricle; *L. Ao.* left aortic arch; *P. A.* pulmonary artery; *R. A.* right auricle; *R. Ao.* right aortic arch; *s,* arrow showing the course of blood in left aorta; *t.* in right aorta; *v., v'.* auriculo-ventricular valves; *w,* arrow showing the course of blood in left auriculo-ventricular aperture; *x,* in right; *y,* between cavum venosum and cavum pulmonale; *z,* in pulmonary artery. (After Huxley.)

receiving the venous blood from the body, the left the oxygenated blood brought from the lungs by the pulmonary veins. But a vital point of difference between the heart of the Reptile and that of the Amphibian is that in the former the ventricle is always more or less completely divided into right and left portions. In all the Lacertilia, Ophidia, and Chelonia (Fig. 385) the structure is essentially what has been described in Lacerta, the ventricular septum being well developed, but not completely closing off the left-hand portion of the cavity of the ventricle from the right (*cavum pulmonale*). The left-hand portion, which is much the larger, is further imperfectly divided into two parts—the *cavum arteriosum* on the left and the *cavum venosum* on the right—by the two elongated flaps of the auriculo-ventricular valve, which project freely into the cavity of the ventricle. From the cavum pulmonale arises the pulmonary artery, and from the cavum venosum the right and left aortic arches. When the auricles contract, the cavum venosum becomes filled with venous blood from the right auricle, the cavum arteriosum with arterial blood from the left auricle ; the cavum pulmonale becomes filled with venous blood which flows into it past the edges of the incomplete septum. When the ventricle contracts, its walls come in contact with the edge of the septum, and the cavum pulmonale is thus cut off from the rest of the ventricle. The further contraction consequently results in the venus blood of the cavum pulmonale being driven out

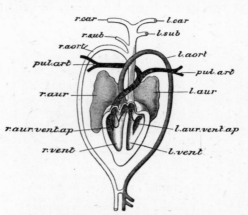

through the pulmonary artery to the lungs, while the blood which remains in the ventricle (arterial and mixed) is compelled to pass out through the aorta. But in the Crocodilia (Fig. 386) the cavity is completely divided, so that there we may speak of distinct right and left ventricles. From the right arise the pulmonary artery and the left aortic arch : from the left the right aortic arch only. The right and left arches cross one another, and where their walls are in contact is an aperture—the *foramen Panizzæ*—placing their cavities in communication.

FIG. 386.—Heart of **Crocodile** with the principal arteries (diagrammatic). The arrows show the direction of the arterial and venous currents. *l. aort.* left aortic arch ; *l. aur.* left auricle ; *l. aur. vent. ap.* left auriculo-ventricular aperture ; *l. car.* left carotid ; *l. sub.* left subclavian ; *l. vent.* left ventricle ; *pul. art.* pulmonary artery ; *r. aort.* right aortic arch ; *r. aur.* right auricle ; *r. aur. vent. ap.* right auriculo-ventricular aperture ; *r. car.* right carotid ; *r. sub.* right subclavian ; *r. vent.* right ventricle. (From Hertwig's *Lehrbuch*.)

The **brain** of Reptiles is somewhat more highly organised than that of the Amphibia. The brain-substance of the cerebral hemispheres exhibits a distinction into superficial grey layer or cortex containing pyramidal nerve-cells, and central white medulla, not observable in lower groups. The cerebral hemispheres are well developed in all, and there is a hippocampus (*see later* in the description of the brain of the Rabbit, and of that of the Mammals in general) in the shape of a specially modified region of the dorsal and mesial walls of each hemisphere, represented less distinctly in the Amphibia ; a commissure—the *hippocampal*—connects the hippocampi of opposite sides, and is dorsal to the chief cerebral commissure—the *anterior commissure*. The mid-brain consists dorsally usually of two closely-approximated oval optic lobes ; rarely it is divided superficially into four. The cerebellum is always of small size, except in the Crocodilia (Fig. 387), in which it is comparatively highly developed, and consists of a median and two lateral lobes.

Sensory Organs.—In most Lacertilia, but not in the Ophidia, the nasal cavity consists of two parts—an outer or vestibule, and an inner or olfactory chamber—the latter having the sense-cells in its walls, and containing a turbinal bone. In the Turtles each nasal chamber is divided into two passages, an upper

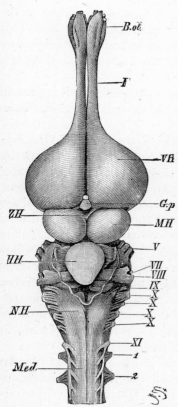

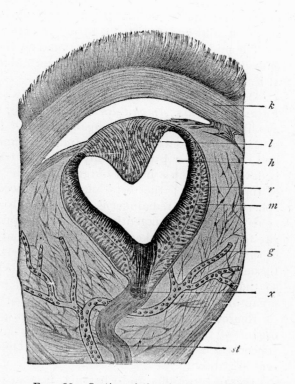

FIG. 387.—Brain of **Alligator,** from above. *B. ol.* olfactory bulb; *G. p.* epiphysis; *HH*, cerebellum; *Med*, spinal cord; *MH*, optic lobes; *NH*, medulla oblongata; *VH*, cerebral hemispheres; *I—XI*, cerebral nerves; *1, 2*, first and second spinal nerves. (From Wiedersheim's *Comparative Anatomy*.)

FIG. 388.—Section of the pineal eye of **Sphenodon punctatum.** *g*, blood-vessels; *h*, cavity of the eye filled with fluid; *k*, capsule of connective-tissue; *l*. lens; *m*. molecular layer of the retina; *r*. retina; *st*. stalk of the pineal eye; *x*, cells in the stalk. (From Wiedersheim's *Comparative Anatomy*, after Baldwin Spencer.)

and a lower, and the same holds good of the hinder part of the elongated nasal chamber of the Crocodilia.

Jacobson's organs (Fig. 334) are present in Lizards and Snakes, absent in Chelonia and Crocodilia in the adult condition.

The eyes are relatively large, with a cartilaginous sclerotic in which a ring of bony plates (Fig. 335) is developed in some cases. The muscular fibres of the iris are striated. A pecten is present in most. Most Reptiles have both upper and lower eyelids and a nictitating membrane. The greater number of the Geckos and all the Snakes constitute exceptions, movable eyelids being absent in both of these groups ; in the former the integument passes uninterruptedly over the cornea with a transparent spot for the admission of the light ; in the Snakes there is a similar modification, but the study of development shows that the transparent area is derived from the nictitating membrane which becomes drawn over the cornea and permanently fixed. In the Chamæleons there is a single circular eyelid with a central aperture.

The middle ear is absent in the Snakes, though a columella auris is present embedded in muscular and fibrous tissue and attached externally, in some cases at least, to the middle of the quadrate.

Developed in close relation to the epiphysis there is in many Lizards (*Lacerta*, *Varanus*, *Anguis*, *Amphibolurus* and others), and in Sphenodon, a remarkable eye-like organ—the *parietal organ* or *pineal eye* (Fig. 388), which is situated in the parietal foramen of the cranial roof immediately under the integument, and covered over by a specially modified, transparent scale. The pineal eye is developed from a hollow outgrowth of the roof of the diencephalon in front of the epiphysis ; the distal end of this becomes constricted off as a hollow sphere, while the remainder is converted into a nerve. The wall of the hollow sphere becomes divergently modified on opposite sides ; the distal side gives rise to a lens-like thickening (*l.*), the proximal forms a membrane several layers in thickness—the *retina* (*r.*) : the whole is enclosed in a capsule of connective-tissue (*k.*). The nerve usually degenerates before the animal reaches maturity, so that the organ would appear—though evidently, from its structure, an organ of sight—to have now entirely or nearly lost its function.

Reproductive Organs.—The description already given of the reproductive organs of the Lizard (p. 374) applies, so far as all the leading features are concerned, to all the Lacertilia and to the Ophidia ; in Hatteria the copulatory sacs are absent.

In the Crocodilia and Chelonia, instead of the copulatory sacs, there is a median solid *penis* attached to the wall of the cloaca, and a small process or *clitoris* occurs in a corresponding position in the female. Though fertilisation is always internal, most reptiles are oviparous, laying eggs enclosed in a tough, parchment-like or calcified shell. These are usually deposited in holes and left to hatch by the heat of the sun. In the Crocodiles they are laid in a rough nest and guarded by the mother. In all cases development has only progressed to a very early stage when the deposition of the eggs takes place, and it is only after a more or less prolonged period of incubation that the young, fully formed in every respect, emerge from the shell and shift for themselves.

Many Lizards, however, and most Snakes are viviparous, the ova undergoing development in the interior of the oviduct, and the young reaching the exterior in the completely-formed condition.

Development.—In all the Reptilia the segmentation is meroblastic, being confined to a germinal disc of protoplasm situated on one side of the yolk.

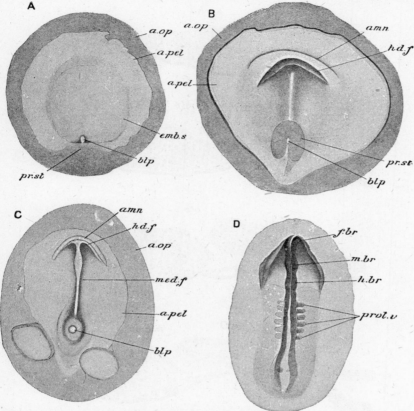

Fig. 389.—*A—D*, early stages in the development of the **Alligator.** *A*, stage with embryonic shield, primitive knot and blastopore; *B*, considerably later stage in which the medullary groove has become formed, together with the head-fold of the embryo and the head-fold of the amnion; *C*, somewhat later stage with well-developed medullary folds and medullary groove; *D*, later stage in which the medullary groove has become partly closed in by the medullary folds and in which six pairs of protovertebræ have become developed. *amn.* amnion; *a. op.* area opaca; *a. pel.* area pellucida; *blp.* blastopore; *emb. s.* embryonic shield; *f. br.* fore-brain; *h. br.* hind-brain; *hd. f.* head-fold; *m. br.* mid-brain; *med. f.* medullary folds; *prot.v.* protovertebræ; *pr. st.* primitive knot. (After S. F. Clarke.)

This divides to form a patch of cells which gradually extends as a two-layered sheet, the blastoderm, over the surface of the ovum. The upper of the two layers is the *ectoderm*, the lower the *yolk-endoderm*; the latter is the equivalent of the mass of yolk-cells of the Frog, and the shallow space between it and the yolk represents the segmentation-cavity. As the blastoderm extends (Fig. 389), it becomes distinguishable into a central clearer area—*area pellucida* (*a. pel.*)—and a peripheral whitish zone—*area opaca* (*a. op.*). On the former now appears an elliptical thickened patch—the *embryonic shield* (*emb. s.*)—which is formed by the ectoderm cells in this region assuming a cylindrical form while remaining flat elsewhere. Behind the embryonic shield appears

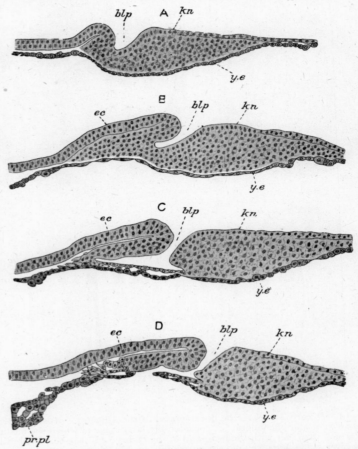

Fig. 390.—**Lacerta,** longitudinal sections through the embryonic area of blastoderms illustrating successive stages in the formation of the invagination-cavity (archenteron) and its communication with the segmentation-cavity. *blp.* blastopore ; *ec.* ectoderm of embryonic shield ; *kn.* primitive knot ; *pr. pl.* protochordal plate ; *y. e.* yolk-endoderm. In *D* the opening below and in front of *blp.* points to aperture of communication established between the invagination-cavity and the underlying space. (Modified after Wenckebach.)

a thickening, due to a proliferation of the ectoderm cells—the so-called *primitive knot* or *primitive plate* (*pr. st.*), and on this is formed an invagination opening on the surface by an aperture—the blastopore (*blp.*)—which subsequently takes the form of a narrow slit running in the direction of the long axis of the future embryo. The cavity of the invagination corresponds to the archenteron of the Frog, and the cells lining it are the endoderm (primitive endoderm). The latter subsequently (Fig. 390) coalesces with the yolk-endoderm below the floor of the archenteron, and in this position an aperture is formed through which the archenteron opens freely into the shallow space that lies between the yolk-endoderm and the yolk. It is from the common cavity thus formed that the lumen of the enteric canal is derived. At a some-what earlier stage a thickening (*pr. pl.*) has appeared in the yolk-endoderm in the region which will give rise to the head of embryo. This is the *protochordal plate* ; it enters into intimate relationship with the endoderm cells that roof over the archenteron, and, when the floor of the latter becomes opened out, forms with them a continuous plate. In this the notochord originates along the middle line, and the mesoderm of all the region in front of the blastopore grows out from it at the sides. The aperture of invagination becomes narrowed and is eventually closed by the approximation and coalescence of its edges. In the region in which the coalescence of the edges takes place there is for a time complete union of the layers, as in the region of the *primitive streak* of Birds and Mammals. The anterior part of the aperture, however, remains open for a time as the opening of the neurenteric canal.

In front of the blastopore a longitudinal depression bounded by a pair of longitudinal folds (Fig. 389, *med. f.*) is the beginning of the medullary groove. As this becomes closed, it encloses, in its posterior portion, the blastopore or dorsal opening of the neurenteric canal. At the sides of the medullary groove appear the protovertebræ (*prot. v.*) : the general history of these parts has already been sketched in the section on the Craniata, and further details will be given in the account of the development of Birds, which agrees with that of Reptiles in most essential respects. Under the head of Birds also will be found an account of the formation of the characteristic fœtal membranes, the *amnion* and the *allantois*, which applies in all essential respects to the Reptilia as well.

A species of the genus *Chalcides* or *Seps*, a lizard with vestigial limbs, which is viviparous, is apparently exceptional in the formation of a structure closely homologous with the *placenta* of Mammals, a structure by means of which an intimate connection is established between the embryo and its membranes and the wall of the special compartment of the oviduct in which it lies. As in the case of the Mammal, the intimate union thus brought about facilitates the transmission of nourishment from the blood of the parent to that of the fœtus.

Ethology.—The Lizards are, for the most part, terrestrial animals, usually extremely active in their movements and endowed with keen senses. The majority readily ascend trees, and many kinds are habitually arboreal ; but the Chamæleons are the only members of the group, which have special modi-fications of their structure in adaptation to an arboreal mode of life. The Skinks and the Amphisbænians are swift and skilful burrowers. The Geckos are enabled by the aid of the sucker-like discs on the ends of their toes to run readily over vertical or overhanging smooth surfaces. A few, on the other hand (Water-Lizards), live habitually in fresh water. The Flying Lizards (*Draco*, Fig. 391) are arboreal, and make use of their wings—or, to speak more accurately, aeroplane or parachute—to enable them to take short flights from branch to branch. *Chlamydosaurus* and *Amphibolurus* are exceptional in frequently running on the hind-feet, with the fore-feet entirely elevated from the ground. A tolerably high temperature is essential for the maintenance of the vital activities of Lizards, low temperatures bringing on an inert con-

FIG. 391.—**Draco volans**, × ⅔. (From the *Cambridge Natural History*.)

dition, which usually passes during the coldest part of the year into a state of suspended animation or hibernation. The food of Lizards is entirely of an animal nature. The smaller kinds prey on insects of all kinds, and on worms. Chamæleons, also, feed on insects, which they capture by darting out the extensile tongue covered with a viscid secretion. Other Lizards supplement their insect diet, when opportunity offers, with small reptiles of various kinds, frogs and newts, small birds and their eggs, and small mammals, such as Mice and the like. The larger kinds, such as the Monitors and Iguanas, prey exclusively on other vertebrates; some, on occasion, are carrion-feeders. Most Lizards lay eggs enclosed in a tough calcified shell. These they simply bury in the earth, leaving them to be hatched by the heat of the sun. Some, however, as already stated, are viviparous; in all cases the young are left to shift for themselves as soon as they are born.

Most of the Snakes also are extremely active and alert in their movements; and most are very intolerant of cold, undergoing a hibernation of greater or less duration during the winter season. Many live habitually on the surface of the ground—some kinds by preference in sandy places or among rocks, others among long herbage. Some (Tree-Snakes) live habitually among the branches of trees. Others (Fresh-water Snakes) inhabit fresh water; others (Sea-Snakes) live in the sea. The mode of locomotion of snakes on the ground is extremely characteristic, the reptile moving along by a series of horizontal undulations brought about by contractions of the muscles inserted into the ribs, any inequalities of the surface of the ground serving as fulcra against which the free posterior edges of the ventral shields (which are firmly connected

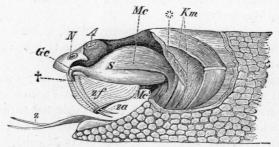

FIG. 392.—Poison apparatus of **Rattlesnake**. *A*, eye; *Gc*, poison-duct entering the poison-fang at †; *Km*, muscles of mastication partly cut through at *; *Mc*. constrictor (masseter) muscle; *Mc'*. continuation of the constrictor muscle to the lower jaw; *N*. nasal opening; *S*, fibrous poison sac; *z*, tongue; *za*, opening of the poison-duct; *zf*, pouch of mucous membrane enclosing the poison-fangs. (From Wiedersheim's *Comparative Anatomy*.)

with the ends of the ribs) are enabled to act. The burrowing Blind-Snakes and other families of small snakes feed on insects and worms. All the rest prey on vertebrates of various kinds, fishes, frogs, lizards, snakes, birds and their eggs, and mammals. The Pythons and Boas kill their prey by con-striction, winding their body closely round it and drawing the coils tight till the victim is crushed or asphyxiated. Some other non-venomous Snakes kill with bites of their numerous sharp teeth. The venomous Snake sometimes, when the prey is a small and weak animal such as a frog, swallow it alive; usually they first kill it with the venom of their poison-fangs.

When a venomous Snake strikes, the poison is pressed out from the poison-gland by the contraction of the masseter (Fig. 392, *Mc*.), one of the muscles which raise the lower jaw; it is thus forced along the duct (*Gc*) to the aperture (*za*), and injected into the wound made by the fang. The effect is to produce acute pain with increasing lethargy and weakness, and in the case of the venom of some kinds of Snakes, paralysis. According to the amount of the poison

injected (in relation to the size of the animal) and the degree of its virulence (which differs not only in different kinds of Snakes, but in the same Snake under different conditions) the symptoms may result in death, or the bitten animal may recover. The poison is a clear, slightly straw-coloured or greenish liquid ; it preserves its venomous properties for an indefinite period, even if completely desiccated. The poisonous principles are certain proteids not to be distinguished chemically from other proteids which have no such poisonous properties. Immunity against the effects of the poison, and relief of the symptoms after a bite has been inflicted, have been found to be conferred by injections of the serum of animals which have been treated with injections of increasing doses of the poison.

The majority of Snakes are viviparous. Some, however, lay eggs, which, nearly always, like those of the oviparous Lizards, are left to be hatched by the heat of the sun, some of the Pythons being exceptional in incubating them among the folds of the body.

Sphenodon lives in burrows in company with a Bird—the Shearwater (*Puffinus*)—and feeds on Insects and small Birds. It lays eggs enclosed in a tough, parchment-like shell.

Of the Chelonia some (Land Tortoises) are terrestrial ; others (Fresh-water Tortoises) inhabit streams and ponds, while the Sea-Turtles and Luths inhabit the sea. Even among Reptiles they are remarkable for their tenacity of life, and will live for a long time after severe mutilations, even after the removal of the brain ; but they readily succumb to the effects of cold. Like most other Reptiles, the Land and Fresh-water Tortoises living in colder regions hibernate in the winter ; in warmer latitudes they sometimes pass through a similar period of quiescence in the dry season. The food of the Green Turtle is exclusively vegetable ; some of the Land Tortoises are also exclusively vegetable-feeders ; other Chelonia either live on plant-food, together with Worms, Insects, and the like, or are completely carnivorous. All are oviparous, the number of eggs laid being usually very great (as many as 240 in the Sea-Turtles) ; these they lay in a burrow carefully prepared in the earth, or, in the case of the Sea-Turtles, in the sand of the sea-shore, and, having covered them over, leave them to hatch.

The Crocodiles and Alligators, the largest of living Reptiles, are in the main aquatic in their habits, inhabiting rivers and, in the case of some species, estuaries. Endowed with great muscular power, these Reptiles are able, by the movements of the powerful tail and the webbed hind-feet, to dart through the water with lightning-like rapidity. By lying in wait motionless, sometimes completely submerged with the exception of the extremity of the snout bearing the nostrils, they are often able by the suddenness and swiftness of their onset to seize the most watchful and timid animals. In the majority of cases the greater part, and in some the whole, of their food consists of Fishes ; but all the larger and more powerful kinds prey also on Birds and Mammals of all kinds, which they seize unawares when they come down to drink or attempt to cross the stream. On land their movements are comparatively slow and awkward, and they are correspondingly more timid and helpless.

The Crocodilia, as already mentioned, are all oviparous, and the eggs, as large in some species as those of a Goose, are brought forth in great numbers (sometimes 100 or more) and either buried in the sand, or deposited in rough nests.

Geographical Distribution.—The order Lacertilia, the most numerous of the orders of Reptiles living at the present day, is of very wide distribution, occurring in all parts of the earth's surface except the circumpolar regions ; but some of its larger sections are of limited range. The Geckos are numerous in all warm countries, their headquarters being Australia and the Oriental region. The snake-like Pygopidæ are entirely confined to the Australian region. The Agamidæ (a family which includes the Flying Lizards besides many others) are most abundantly represented in the Australian region, though extending to other regions of the Old World, except New Zealand and Madagascar. Of the Iguanas two genera occur in Madagascar and one in the Friendly Islands ; all the other members of this group, which is a large one, are confined to America. Three families occur exclusively in America—the Xenosauridæ, the Tejidæ, and the Helodermidæ, or poisonous Lizards. The Zonuridæ or Girdle-tailed Lizards are confined to Africa and Madagascar. The Anguidæ or Blind-worm Lizards are mostly American, but are represented in Europe and Asia. The family of the Monitors is distributed in Africa, Southern Asia, Oceania, and the Australian region. The snake-like Amphisbænians are most numerous in America, but are well represented in Africa, and occur also in the Mediterranean area. The Lacertidæ are most abundant in Africa, but occur in Europe and Asia. The family of the Skinks (Scincidæ) is of world-wide range, but is most abundant in Australia, Oceania, the Oriental region, and Africa. Sphenodon is confined to the New Zealand region, and at the present day only occurs on certain small islands off the N.E. coast and in Cook's Straits. The Chamæleons are most abundant in Africa and Madagascar, but there are representatives in various other parts of the Old World ; they do not occur in the Australian, New Zealand, or Polynesian regions, and are only represented in Europe by one species, which occurs in Andalusia.

Chelonia are widely distributed over the surface of the earth, by far the greater number being natives of tropical and temperate zones. The Sea-turtles, including the Hawk's-bills and the Luths, are for the most part, but not entirely, confined to the tropical seas. Giant Land-tortoises occur, or occurred in historic times, on islands of the Galapagos and Mascarene groups.

Of the Crocodilia the Caimans are confined to Central and South America. The Alligators are represented in North America by one species and in China by another.   The true Crocodiles occur widely distributed over Africa, Southern Asia, the northern parts of Australia and tropical America, while the Gavial occurs only in certain Indian and Burmese rivers.

Geological Distribution (Fig. 393).—The Squamata are geologically the most recent of the existing orders of Reptiles.   The earliest fossil remains of Lizards have been found in beds belonging to the Jurassic and Cretaceous periods ; but

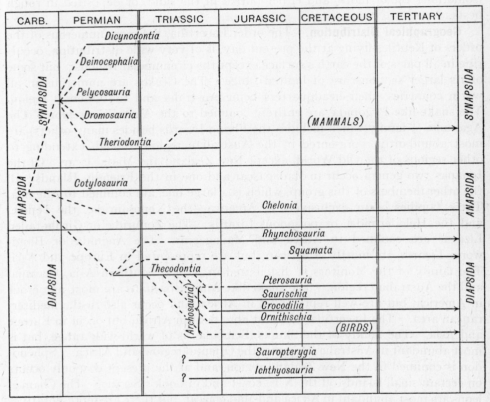

FIG. 393.—Geological distribution and relations of the orders of reptiles.

most of the families are not represented earlier than the Tertiary.   All the known fossil remains of Snakes, except one imperfectly known form from the Cretaceous, have been found in deposits of Tertiary age.   The Rhynchocephalia are much more ancient, being present in deposits as old as the Trias.   The order Chelonia (except for the still problematic form *Eunotosaurus*, see p. 379), was represented from the Triassic period onwards.   Of the extinct forms one group —the *Protostegidæ*—differs from the living Chelonia in having the carapace incompletely developed, entirely composed of dermal elements, and quite separate from the vertebræ and ribs, a condition which is probably secondary and specialised. *Archelon*, a member of this family, reached twelve feet or more in length. The Crocodilia date back as far as the Trias. The most primitive of the fossil forms had the internal nares situated in front of the palatines, while the external nares were situated towards the middle of the snout. Later forms (post-Triassic) had palatine plates developed from the premaxillæ, the maxillæ, and the palatines; and some resembled the living members of the order in having such plates developed also from the pterygoids; all had the external nares situated towards the end of the snout. Those in which the palatine plates of the pterygoids were absent had usually amphicœlous vertebræ. Some of the fossil Crocodiles reached an immense size. Some, as *Geosaurus*, which had a downwardly turned tail reminiscent of the Ichthyosaur condition and swimming paddles, was purely aquatic.

CLASS IV.—AVES.

In many respects Birds are the most highly specialised of Craniata. As a class they are adapted for aërial life; and almost every part of their organisation is modified in accordance with the unusual environment. The nonconducting covering of feathers; the modification of the fore-limbs as wings, of the sternum and shoulder-girdle to serve as origins of the great wing-muscles, and of the pelvic girdle and hind-limbs to enable them to support the entire weight of the body on the surface of the ground; the perfection of the respiratory system, producing a higher temperature than in any other animals: all these peculiarities are of the nature of adaptations to flight. Add to them the absence, in all existing Birds, of teeth, the loss of the left aortic arch, and of the right ovary and oviduct, the specialised character of the brain, the poorly developed olfactory organs, and the extraordinarily large and perfect eyes, and we have a series of strongly-marked characteristics such as distinguish hardly any other class. Moreover, the organisation of existing Birds is, in its essential features, singularly uniform, the entire class presenting less diversity of structure than many single orders of Fishes, Amphibians, and Reptiles.

EXAMPLE OF THE CLASS.—THE COMMON PIGEON (*Columba livia*, var. *domestica*).

The Common or Domestic Pigeon is known under many varieties, which differ from one another in size, proportions, coloration, details in the arrangement of the feathers, and in many points of internal anatomy. The Pouters, Carriers, Fantails, and Tumblers may be mentioned as illustrating extreme forms. All these varieties have, however, been produced by artificial selection, that is, by breeders selecting, generation after generation, the Birds which most nearly attained to some artificial standard of perfection, breeding from them alone, and killing off the inferior strains. The ancestral species from which the domestic breeds have in this way been evolved is the Rock Pigeon (*Columba livia*), which is widely distributed in the Palæarctic and Oriental regions. The following description refers especially to the common Dovecot Pigeon.

External Characters.—In the entire Bird (Fig. 394) the plump trunk appears to be continued insensibly into the small mobile head, with its rounded brain-case and prominent *beak*, formed of upper and lower jaws covered by horny

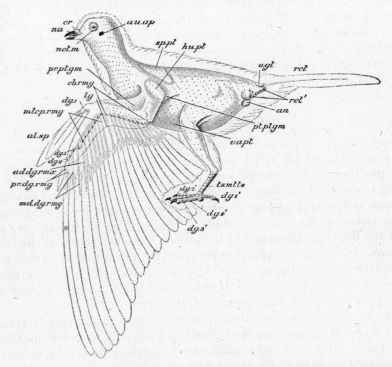

FIG. 394.—**Columba livia.** The entire animal from the left side with most of the feathers removed. *ad. dg. rmx.* ad-digital remex; *al. sp.* ala spuria; *an.* anus; *au. ap.* auditory aperture; *cb. rmg.* cubital remiges; *cr.* cere; *dg. 1, 2, 3,* digits of manus; *dg. 1′, 2′, 3′, 4′,* digits of pes; *hu. pt.* humeral pteryla; *lg.* ligament of remiges; *md. dg. rmg.* mid-digital remiges; *na.* nostril; *nct. m.* nictitating membrane; *o. gl.* oil-gland; *pr. dg. rmg.* pre-digital remiges; *pr. ptgm.* pre-patagium; *pt. ptgm.* post-patagium; *rct.* mesial rectrix of right side; *rct′.* sacs of left rectrices; *sp. pt.* spinal pteryla; *ts. mtts.* tarso-metatarsus; *v. apt.* ventral apterium.

sheaths. The head, neck, and trunk are invested in a close covering of *feathers*, all directed backwards and overlapping one another. Posteriorly the trunk gives origin to a number of outstanding feathers which constitute what is ordinarily called the tail. From the anterior region of the trunk spring the *wings*, also covered with feathers, and, in the position of rest, folded against the sides of the body. The legs spring from the hinder end of the trunk, but, owing to the thick covering of feathers, only the feet are to be seen in the living Bird, each covered with *scales* and terminating in four digits (*dg. 1'—dg. 4'*), three directed forwards and one backwards.

In order to make a fair comparison of the outer form with that of other Craniate types, it is necessary to remove the feathers. When this is done, the Bird is seen to have a long, cylindrical, and very mobile neck, sharply separated both from head and trunk. The true tail is a short, conical projection of the trunk, known as the *uropygium*, and giving origin to the group of large feathers (*rct.*) to which the word "tail" is usually applied. On the dorsal surface of the uropygium is a papilla bearing on its summit the opening of a large gland, the *oil-gland* (*o. gl.*), the secretion of which is used for lubricating or "preening" the feathers.

The wings show the three typical divisions of the fore-limb, upper arm, fore-arm, and hand, but the parts of the hand are closely bound together by skin, and only three imperfectly-marked digits, the second (*dg. 2*) much larger than the first (*dg. 1*) and third (*dg. 3*), can be distinguished. In the position of rest the three divisions of the wing are bent upon one another in the form of a Z; during flight they are straightened out and extended so that the axis of the entire wing is at right angles to that of the trunk. On the anterior or pre-axial border of the limb a fold of skin stretches between the upper arm and the fore-arm; this is the *alar membrane* or *pre-patagium* (*pr. ptgm.*). A similar but much smaller fold extends, post-axially, between the proximal portion of the upper arm and the trunk; this is the *post-patagium* (*pt. ptgm.*).

In the hind-limb the short thigh is closely bound to the trunk, not standing well out as in a Reptile, but directed downwards and forwards; the long shank extends from the knee downwards and backwards; and the foot is clearly divisible into a proximal portion, the *tarso-metatarsus* (*ts. mtts.*), and four digits, of which one, the hallux (*dg. 1'*), is directed backwards, the others, the 2nd, 3rd, and 4th of the typical foot, forwards. The entire hind-limb is in a plane parallel with the sagittal plane of the trunk.

The mouth is terminal, and is guarded by the elongated upper and lower beaks; it has, therefore, a very wide gape. On each side of the base of the upper beak is a swollen area of soft skin, the *cere* (*cr.*), surrounding the nostril (*na.*), which has thus a remarkably backward position. The *eyes* are very large, and each is guarded by an upper and a lower eyelid and a transparent nictitating membrane (*nct. m.*). A short distance behind the eye is the *auditory aperture* (*au. ap.*), concealed by feathers in the entire Bird, and leading into a short *external auditory meatus*, closed below by the tympanic membrane. The *anus* or cloacal aperture (*an.*) is a large, transversely-elongated aperture placed on the ventral surface at the junction of the uropygium with the trunk.

Exoskeleton.—The exoskeleton is purely epidermal, like that of the Lizard, which it also resembles in consisting partly of horny *scales*. These cover the tarso-metatarsus and the digits of the foot, and are quite reptilian in appearance and structure. Each digit of the foot is terminated by a *claw*, which is also a horny product of the epidermis; and the *beaks* are of the same nature. The rest of the body, however, is covered by *feathers*, a unique type of epidermal product found nowhere outside the present class.

A feather (Fig. 395) is an elongated structure consisting of a hollow stalk, the *calamus* or quill (*cal.*), and an expanded distal portion, the *vexillum* or *vane*. At the proximal end of the quill is a small aperture, the *inferior umbilicus* (*inf. umb.*), into which fits, in the entire Bird, a small conical prolongation of the skin, the *feather papilla*. A second, extremely minute aperture, the *superior umbilicus* (*sup. umb.*), occurs at the junction of the quill with the vane on the inner or ventral face of the feather, *i.e.*, the face adjacent to the body. A small tuft of down in the neighbourhood of the superior umbilicus represents the *after-shaft* of many Birds —including some Pigeons (*vide infra*).

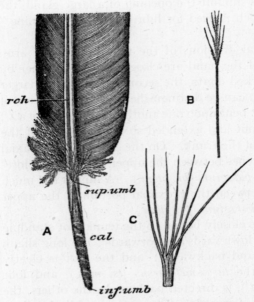

FIG. 395.—**Columba livia.** *A*, proximal portion of a remex. *cal.* calamus; *inf. umb.* inferior umbilicus; *rch.* rachis; *sup. umb.* superior umbilicus. *B*, filoplume. *C*, nestling-down. (*C.* from Bronn's *Thierreich*.)

The vane has a longitudinal axis or *rachis* (*rch.*) continuous proximally with the quill, but differing from the latter in being solid. To each side of the rachis is attached a kind of membrane forming the expanded part of the feather and composed of *barbs*— delicate, thread-like structures which extend obliquely outwards from the rachis. In an uninjured feather the barbs are closely con- nected so as to form a continuous sheet but a moderate amount of force separates them from one another, and it can readily be made out with the aid of a mag- nifying glass that they are bound together by extremely delicate oblique filaments, the *barbules*, having the same general relation to the barbs as the barbs themselves to the rachis.

The precise mode of interlocking of the barbs can be made out only by microscopic examination. Each barb (Fig. 396, *A*) is a very thin and long plate springing by a narrow base from the rachis, and pointed distally. From its upper edge—the edge furthest from the body of the Bird—spring two sets of barbules, a *proximal set* (*C*) directed towards the base of the feather, and a *distal set* (*D*) towards its tip. Owing to their oblique disposition the distal barbules of a given barb cross the proximal barbules of the next, each distal barbule being in contact with several proximal barbules of the barb immediately distal to it (*A*). The lower edge of the distal barbule is produced into minute *hooklets* (*D*) : in the entire feather the hooklets of each distal barbule hook over prominent *flanges* of the proximal barbules with which it is in contact (*A*, *B*). In this way the parts of the feather are so bound together that the entire structure offers great resistance to the air.

Among the *contour* feathers which form the main covering of the Bird and

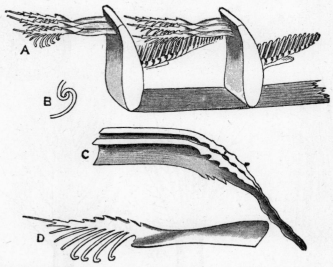

FIG. 396.—Structure of **Feather.** *A*, small portion of feather with pieces of two barbs, each having to the left three distal barbules, and to the right a number of proximal barbules, many of them belonging to adjacent barbs. *B*, hooklet of distal barbule interlocking with flange of proximal barbule. *C*, two adjacent proximal barbules. *D*, a distal barbule. (From Headley, after Pycraft.)

have the structure just described are found *filoplumes* (Fig. 395, *B*), delicate hair-like feathers having a long axis and a few barbs, devoid of locking apparatus at the distal end. Nestling Pigeons are covered with a temporary investment of *down-feathers* (*C*), in which also there is no interlocking of the barbs : when these first appear each is covered by a horny sheath like a glove-finger.

Feathers, like scales, arise in the embryo from papillæ of the skin (Fig. 397, **A**, *Pap.*), formed of derm with an epidermal covering. The papilla becomes sunk in a sac, the *feather-follicle* (**B**, *F*), from which it subsequently protrudes as an elongated *feather-germ* (*FK*), its vascular dermal interior being the *feather-pulp* (*P*). The Malpighian layer of the distal part of the feather-germ proliferates in such a way as to form a number of vertical radiating ridges (**C**, *Fal.* (SM^1)) : its proximal part becomes uniformly thickened, and in this way is produced the rudiment of a down-feather, having a number of barbs springing, at the same level, from the distal end of the quill. The horny layer of the epidermis (HS ($Sc.^1$)) forms the temporary sheath which is thrown off as the feather grows and expands. The pulp of the permanent feather (**D,** F^1) is formed from the lower or deep end of that of the down-feather, and its development is at first similar, but, instead of the ridges of the Malpighian layer remaining all of one size, two adjacent ones outgrow the rest and become the

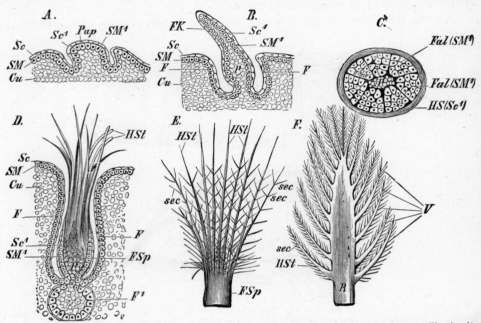

FIG. 397.—Six stages in the development of the feather. **A,** early feather-papilla in its follicle; **B,** feather-germ; **C,** transverse section of feather-germ; **D,** down-feather in its follicle; **E,** down-feather removed from follicle; **F,** early stage of permanent feather. *Cu,* dermis; *F.* follicle of down-feather; *F'.* follicle of permanent feather; *Fal.* (SM^1.), folds of Malpighian layer extending into feather-germ; *FK.* feather-germ; *FSp,* calamus of down-feather; *HS*(Sc^1.), feather-sheath; *HSt,* barbs; *P.* pulp; *Pap.* feather-papilla; *R.* rachis; *Sc.* stratum corneum; *Sc^1*. its extension into feather-papilla; *sec.* barbules; *SM.* stratum Malpighii; *SM^1*. its extension into feather-papilla; *V.* vexillum. (From Wiedersheim's *Comparative Anatomy,* after Studer.)

rachis; as the latter elongates it carries up with it the remaining ridges, which become the barbs.

The feathers do not spring uniformly from the whole surface of the body, but from certain defined areas (Fig. 398), the *feather tracts* or *pterylæ* (*sp. pt.,* *hu. pt.,* etc.), separated from one another by featherless spaces or *apteria* (v. apt., etc.), from which only a few filoplumes grow. The feathers are, however, long enough to cover the apteria by their overlap, and the body is thus completely covered with a thick, very light, and non-conducting investment.

In the wings and tail certain special arrangements of the feathers are to be distinguished. When the wing is stretched out at right angles to the trunk, twenty-three large feathers (Fig. 394) are seen to spring from its hinder or post-axial border : these are the *remiges* or wing-quills. Twelve of them are connected with the ulna and are called *cubitals* or *secondaries* (*cb. rmg.*). The rest are known as *primaries* : seven of these are attached to the metacarpal region, and are hence called *metacarpals* (*mtcp. rmg.*), the remaining four or *digitals* to the phalanges of the second and third digits. These are again distinguished into a single *ad-digital* (*ad. dg. rmx.*), connected with the single phalanx of the third digit (Fig. 402, *ph. 3*), two *mid-digitals* (*md. dg. rmg.*) with the proximal phalanx of the second digit (Fig. 402, *ph. 2*), and two *pre-*

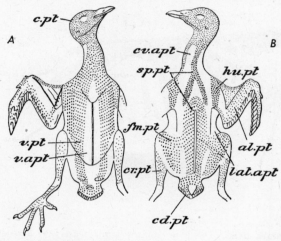

Fig. 398.—Pterylosis of **Columba livia.** *A*, ventral; *B*, dorsal. *al. pt.* alar pteryla or wing-tract; *c. pt.* cephalic pteryla or head-tract; *cd. pt.* caudal pteryla or tail-tract; *cr. pt.* crural pteryla; *cv. apt.* cervical apterium or neck-space; *fm. pt.* femoral pteryla; *hu. pt.* humeral pteryla; *lat. apt.* lateral apterium; *sp. pt.* spinal pteryla; *v. apt.* ventral apterium; *v. pt.* ventral pteryla. (After Nitzsch.)

digitals (*pr. dg. rmg.*) with its distal phalanx (Fig. 402, *ph. 2'*). A special tuft of feathers on the anterior border of the wing, arising from the pollex (Fig. 402, *ph. 1*), forms the *ala spuria* (*al. sp.*). The spaces which would otherwise be left between the bases of the remiges are filled in, both above and below, by several rows of *upper* and *under wing-coverts*. In the tail there are twelve long *rectrices* (Fig. 394, *rct.*) or tail-quills, springing in a semicircle from the uropygium ; their bases are covered, as in the wing, by *upper* and *under tail-coverts*. The whole feather-arrangement is known as the *pterylosis*.

Endoskeleton.—The *vertebral column* is distinguished from that of most other Craniata by the great length and extreme mobility of the neck, the rigidity of the trunk-region, and the shortness of the tail. As in Reptilia, the cervical passes almost insensibly into the thoracic region, and the convention is again adopted of counting as the first thoracic (Fig 398a, *th. v. 1*), the first vertebra having its ribs united with the sternum. There are fourteen cervical vertebræ, the last or last two of which have double-headed ribs (*cv. r.*), each having its proximal end divisible into the *head* proper articulating with the centrum of the vertebra, and a *tubercle* with the transverse process: their distal ends are free, not uniting with the sternum. In the third to the twelfth there are vestigial ribs (Fig. 398b, *rb.*), each having its head fused with the centrum, and its tubercle with the transverse process. The whole rib thus has the appearance of a short, backwardly-directed transverse process perforated at its base; the perforation transmits the vertebral artery, and is called the *vertebrarterial foramen (vrb. f.)*.

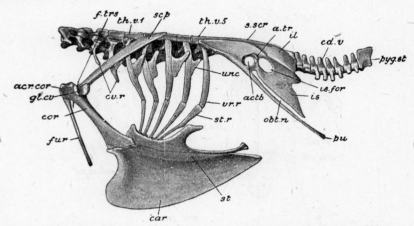

FIG. 398a.—**Columba livia.** The bones of the trunk. *acr. cor.* acrocoracoid; *a. tr.* antitrochanter; *actb.* acetabulum; *car.* carina sterni; *cd. v.* caudal vertebræ; *cor.* coracoid; *cv. r.* cervical ribs; *f. trs.* probe passed into foramen triosseum; *fur.* furcula; *gl. cv.* glenoid cavity; *il.* ilium; *is.* ischium; *is. for.* ischiadic foramen; *obt. n.* obturator notch; *pu.* pubis; *pyg. st.* pygostyle; *scp.* scapula; *s. scr.* syn-sacrum; *st.* sternum; *st. r.* sternal ribs; *th. v. 1*, first, and *th. v. 5*, last thoracic vertebra; *unc.* uncinates; *vr. r.* vertebral ribs.

The centra of the cervical vertebræ differ from those of all other Vertebrata in having saddle-shaped surfaces, the anterior face (Fig. 398b, A) being concave from side to side and convex from above downwards, the posterior face (B) convex from side to side and concave from above downwards. Thus the centrum in sagittal section appears opisthocœlous, in horizontal section procœlous. This peculiar form of vertebra is distinguished as *heterocœlous*. The centra articulate with one another by synovial capsules, each traversed by a vertical plate of cartilage, the *meniscus*, with a central perforation through which a *suspensory ligament* passes from one centrum to the other.

The first two vertebræ, the atlas and axis, resemble those of the Lizard, but have the various elements of which they are composed completely fused. The small size of the ring-like atlas is noticeable.

Between the last cervical vertebræ and the pelvic region come either four
or five thoracic vertebræ (Fig. 398a)—the first three, when four only are present,
the second, third, and fourth, when there are five, united into a single mass, the
last free.   The anterior thoracic as well as the posterior cervical vertebræ have
the centrum produced below into a compressed plate, the *hypapophysis*, for
the origin of the flexor muscles of the neck.   They all bear ribs, each consisting
of a vertebral (*vr. r.*) and a sternal (*st.r.*) portion, and articulating with the
vertebra by a double head.   The sternal, like the vertebral rib, is formed of
true bone, not of calcified cartilage as in Reptiles, and articulates with the verte-

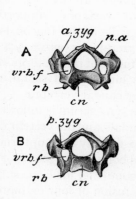

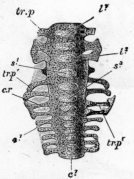

FIG. 398b.—**Columba
livia.** Cervical vertebra.
A, anterior, *B*, posterior
face.   *a. zyg.* anterior
zygapophysis;   *cn.* centrum;   *n. a.* neural arch;
p. zyg. posterior zygapophysis;   *rb.* rib;   *vrb. f.*
vertebrarterial foramen.

FIG. 398c.—**Columba
livia.** Sacrum of a nestling (about fourteen days
old), ventral aspect.   *c¹.*
centrum of first sacral
vertebra;   *c⁷.* centrum of
fifth caudal;   *c. r.* first
sacral rib;   *l¹.* centrum of
first lumbar;   *l³.* third
lumbar;   *s¹.* of fourth
lumbar;   *s³.* of sixth lumbar;   *tr. p.* transverse
process of first lumbar;
tr. p'. of fifth lumbar;
tr. p''. of first sacral.
(From Parker's *Zootomy*.)

bral rib by a synovial joint.   Springing from the posterior edge of the vertebral rib is an *uncinate* (*unc.*), resembling that of Sphenodon and the Crocodile,
but formed of bone and ankylosed with the rib.

Following upon the fourth or fifth thoracic are about twelve vertebræ, all
fused into a single mass (Fig. 398a, *s.scr.*), and giving attachment laterally to
the immense pelvic girdle.   The whole of this group of vertebræ has, therefore,
the function of a sacrum, differing from that of a Reptile in the large number of
vertebræ composing it.   The first of them bears a pair of free ribs, and is,
therefore, the fifth or sixth (last) thoracic (*th. v. 5*).   The next five or six
have no free ribs, and may be looked upon as lumbar (Fig. 398c, *l¹.*—*s³.*):

their transverse processes arise high up on the neural arch, and the ligament uniting them is ossified, so that the lumbar region presents dorsally a continuous plate of bone. Next come two sacral vertebræ (c^1.) homologous with those of the Lizard: besides transverse processes springing from the neural arch, one or both of them bears a second or ventral outgrowth (c. r.) springing from each side of the centrum and abutting against the ilium just internal to the acetabulum. These distinctive processes are ossified independently and represent sacral ribs. The remaining five vertebræ of the pelvic region are caudal. Thus the mass of vertebræ supporting the pelvic girdle in the Pigeon is a compound sacrum, or *syn-sacrum*, formed by the fusion of the posterior thoracic, all the lumbar and sacral, and the anterior caudal vertebræ.

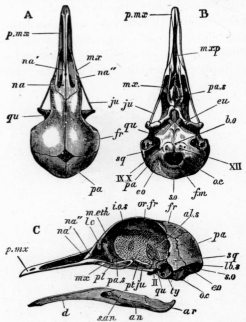

FIG. 398*d*.—**Columba livia.** Skull of young specimen. *A*, dorsal; *B*, ventral; *C*, left side. *al.s.* alisphenoid; *an.* angular; *ar.* articular; *b. o.* basi-occipital; *d.* dentary; *e.o.* exoccipital; *eu.* aperture of Eustachian tube; *f. m.* foramen magnum; *fr.* frontal; *i. o. s.* inter-orbital septum; *ju.* jugal; *lc.* lacrymal; *lb. s.* lamboidal suture; *m.eth.* mesethmoid; *mx.* maxilla; *mx. p.* maxillo-palatine process; *na. na'. na''.* nasal; *o. c.* occipital condyle; *or. fr.* orbital plate of frontal; *pa.* parietal; *pa.s.* parasphenoid (rostrum); *pl.* palatine; *p.mx.* premaxilla; *pt.* pterygoid; *qu.* quadrate; *s. an.* supra-angular; *s. o.* supra-occipital; *sq.* squamosal; *ty.* tympanic cavity; *II—XII*, foramina for cerebral nerves. (From Parker's *Zootomy*.)

The syn-sacrum is followed by six free caudals, and the vertebral column ends posteriorly in an upturned, compressed bone, the *pygostyle* or plough-share-bone (Fig. 398*a*, *pyg.st.*), formed by the fusion of four or more of the hindmost caudal vertebræ.

Thus the composition of the vertebral column of the Pigeon may be expressed in a *vertebral formula*.[1]

The *sternum* (Fig. 398*a*, *st.*) is one of the most characteristic parts of the Bird's skeleton. It is a broad plate of bone produced ventrally, in the sagittal plane, into a deep keel or *carina sterni* (*car.*), formed, in the young bird, from a separate centre of ossification. The posterior border of the sternum presents two pairs of notches, covered, in the recent state, by membrane; its anterior edge bears a pair of deep grooves for the articulation of the coracoids.

The *skull* (Fig. 398*d*) is distinguished at once by its rounded brain-case,

	Syn-sacrum.	Pyg.

[1] Cerv. 14. Thor. 4 or 5 + 1. Lumb. 5 or 6. Sacr. 2. Caud. 5 + 6 + 4 = 43.

immense orbits, and long, pointed beak. The foramen magnum (*f. m.*) looks downwards as well as backwards, so as to be visible in a ventral view, and on its anterior margin is a single, small, rounded occipital condyle (*o. c.*). Most of the bones, both of the cranial and facial regions, are firmly ankylosed in the adult, and can be made out only in the young birds.

The occipitals, parietals, frontals, and alisphenoids have the usual relations to the brain-case, the basi-occipital (*b. o.*), as in the Lizard, bearing the occipital condyle. The basisphenoid (Fig. 399, **B. SPH.**) is a large bone forming the greater part of the basis cranii and continued forwards, as in the Lizard, by a

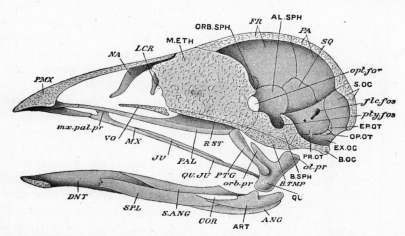

FIG. 399.—Sagittal section of a **Bird's** skull (diagrammatic). *Replacing Bones*—**AL.SPH.** alisphenoid; **ART.** articular; **B. OC.** basi-occipital; **B. SPH.** basi-sphenoid; **EP.OT.** epiotic; **EX.OC.** exocciptal; **M.ETH.** mesethmoid; **OP.OT.** opisthotic; **ORB. SPH.** orbito-sphenoid; **PR. OT.** pro-otic; **QU.** quadrate; **S. OC.** supra-occipital. *Investing bones*—*ANG.* angular; *B. TMP.* basi-temporal; *COR.* coronary; *DNT.* dentary; *FR.* frontal; *JU.* jugal; *LCR.* lacrymal; *MX.* maxilla; *NA.* nasal; *PA.* parietal; *PAL.* palatine; *PMX.* premaxilla; *PTG.* pterygoid; *QU.JU.* quadratojugal; *RST.* rostrum; *S. ANG.* supra-angular; *SPL.* splenial; *SQ.* squamosal; *VO.* vomer; *flc. fos.* floccular fossa; *mx. pal. pr.* maxillo-palatine process; *opt. for.* optic foramen; *orb. pr.* orbital process; *ot. pr.* otic process; *pty. fos.* pituitary fossa.

slender *rostrum* (Fig. 398*d*, *pa.s.*, Fig. 399, *RST.*), which represents the anterior portion of the parasphenoid. On the ventral aspect of the basisphenoid paired membrane bones, the *basi-temporals* (Fig. 399, *B. TMP*), are developed, and become firmly ankylosed to it in the adult: they probably represent the posterior portion of the parasphenoid. The tympanic cavity is bounded by the squamosal (Fig. 398*d*, *sq.*), which is firmly united to the other cranial bones. The main part of the auditory capsule is ossified by a large pro-otic (Fig. 399, **PR. OT.**): the small opisthotic of the embryo early unites with the exoccipital, the epiotic with the supra-occipital. The parasphenoid and mesethmoid together form the *inter-orbital septum* (Fig. 398*d*, *i. o. s.*), a vertical partition, partly bony, partly cartilaginous, which separates the orbits from one another. It is very characteristic of the bird's skull that the immense size of the eyes has produced a compression of this region of the skull. The ecto-ethmoids or turbinals are comparatively poorly developed, in correspondence with the small size of the olfactory organs. There are large lacrymals (Fig. 398*d*, *lc.*, Fig. 399, *LCR.*), and the nasals (*na*, *na'*, *na''*, *NA*) are forked bones, each furnishing both an inner and an outer boundary to the corresponding nostril.

The premaxillæ (*p.mx.*, *PMX.*) are united into a large triradiate bone which forms practically the whole of the upper beak. The maxillæ (*mx.*, *MX.*), on

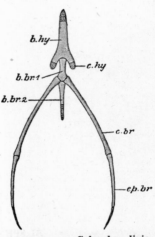

FIG. 400.—**Columba livia.**
Hyoid apparatus. The cartilaginous parts are dotted. *b. br. 1*, *b. br. 2*, basi-branchials; *b. hy.* basi-hyal; *c. br.* cerato-branchial; *c. hy.* hyoid cornu; *ep. br.* epi-branchial.

the other hand, are small, and have their anterior ends produced inwards into spongy *maxillo-palatine processes* (Fig. 398*d*, *mx. p.*, Fig. 399, *mx. pal. pr*). The slender posterior end of the maxilla is continued backwards by an equally slender jugal (*ju.*, *JU.*) and quadratojugal (*QU.JU.*) to the quadrate. The latter (*qu.*, **QU.**) is a stout, three-rayed bone articulating by two facets on its *otic process* (*ot. pr.*) with the roof of the tympanic cavity, sending off an *orbital process* (*orb. pr.*) from its anterior margin, and presenting below a *condyle* for articulation with the mandible ; it is freely movable upon its tympanic articulation, so that the lower jaw has a double joint as in Lizards and Snakes.

The palatines (*pl.*, *PAL.*) have their slender anterior ends ankylosed with the maxilla, their scroll-like posterior ends articulating with the pterygoids and the rostrum. The pterygoids (*pt.*, *PTG.*) are rod-shaped and set obliquely ; each articulates behind with the quadrate, and, at about the middle of its length, with the *basi-pterygoid process*, a small faceted projection of the base of the rostrum. There is no vomer in the Pigeon.

The *mandible* of the young Bird consists of a replacing bone, the articular (*ar.*, **ART.**), and four investing bones the angular (*an.*, *ANG.*), supra-angular (*s.an.*, *S. ANG.*), dentary (*d.*, *DNT.*), and splenial (*SPL.*), all having the same general relations as in the Lizard. The *hyoid apparatus* (Fig. 400) is of characteristic form, having an arrow-shaped body (*b. hy.*) with a short pair of anterior cornua (*c. hy.*) derived from the hyoid arch, and a long pair of posterior cornua (*c. br.*, *ep. br.*) from the first branchial. The *columella* (Fig. 401) is a rod-shaped bone ankylosed to the stapes, and bearing at its outer end a three-rayed cartilage, the *extra-columella* (*e. st.*, *i. st.*, *s. st.*), fixed to the tympanic membrane.

The *shoulder-girdle* (Fig. 398*a*) is quite unlike that of other Craniates. There is a pair of stout, pillar-like *coracoids* (*cor.*) articulating with deep facets on the anterior border of the sternum, and directed upwards, forwards, and outwards. The dorsal end of each is produced into a *acro-coracoid process* (*acr. cor.*), and below this, to the posterior aspect of the bone, is attached by ligament a sabre-shaped *scapula* (*scp.*) which extends backwards over the ribs, and includes, with the coracoid, an acute angle, the *coraco-scapular angle.* The glenoid cavity (*gl. cv.*) is formed in equal proportion by the two bones ; internal to it the scapula is produced into an *acromion process.*

FIG. 401.—**Columba livia.** The columella auris (magnified). The cartilaginous parts are dotted. *e. st.* extra-stapedial ; *i. st.* infra-stapedial ; *s. st.* supra-stapedial ; *st.* stapes. (From Parker's *Zootomy*.)

In front of the coracoids is a slender V-shaped bone, the *furcula* (*fur.*) or " merry-thought," the apex of which nearly reaches the sternum, while each of its extremities is attached by ligament to the acromion and acro-coracoid processes of the corresponding side in such a way that a large aperture, the *foramen triosseum* (*f. trs.*), is left between the three bones of the shoulder-girdle. The furcula is an investing bone and represents fused clavicles and interclavicle.

Equally characteristic is the skeleton of the fore-limb. The *humerus* (Fig. 402, *hu.*) is a large, strong bone, with a greatly expanded head and a prominent ridge for the insertion of the pectoral muscle. In it, as in all the other long bones, the extremities as well as the shaft are formed of true bone. The *radius* (*ra.*) is slender and nearly straight, the *ulna* stouter and gently curved. There are two large free carpals, a *radiale* (*ra'.*) and an *ulnare* (*ul'.*), and articulating with these is a bone called the *carpo-metacarpus* (*cp. mtcp.*) consisting of two rods, that on the pre-axial side strong and nearly straight, that on the post-axial side slender and curved, fused with one another

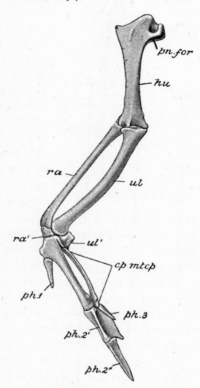

FIG. 402.—**Columba livia.** Skeleton of the left wing. *cp. mtcp.* carpo-meta-carpus; *hu.* humerus; *ph. 1*, phalanx of first digit; *ph. 2'*, *ph. 2''*, phalanges of second digit; *ph. 3*, phalanx of third digit; *pn. for.* pneumatic foramen. *ra.* radius; *ra'.* radiale; *ul.* ulna; *ul'.* ulnare.

at both their proximal and distal ends ; the proximal end is produced, pre-axially, into an outstanding step-like process. The study of development shows that this bone is formed by the union of the distal carpals with three metacarpals (Fig. 403), the second and third of which are the two rod-like

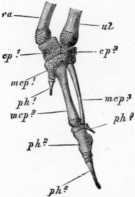

FIG. 403.—**Columba livia.** Left manus of a nestling. The cartilaginous parts are dotted. *cp. 1*, radiale; *cp. 2*, ulnare; *mcp. 1, 2, 3*, metacarpals; *ph. 1*, phalanx of first digit; *ph. 2, ph. 2'*, phalanges of second digit; *ph. 3*, phalanx of third digit; *ra.* radius; *ul.* ulna. (From Parker's *Zootomy*.)

portions of the bone, the first the step-like projection. Articulating with the first metacarpal is a single pointed phalanx (Fig. 402, *ph. 1*); the second metacarpal bears two phalanges, the proximal one (*ph. 2'*) produced post-axially into a flange, the distal one (*ph. 2''*) pointed; the third metacarpal bears a single pointed phalanx (*ph. 3*).

The *pelvic girdle* (Fig. 398a) resembles that of no other Vertebrate with the exception of some Dinosaurs. The *ilium* (*il.*) is an immense bone attached by fibrous union to the whole of the syn-sacrum and becoming ankylosed with it in the adult. It is divisible into *pre-acetabular* and *post-acetabular* portions of approximately equal size. As usual it furnishes the dorsal portion of the acetabulum, and on the posterior edge of that cavity is produced into a process, the *anti-trochanter* (*a. tr.*), which works against the trochanter, a process of the femur. The ventral portion of the acetabulum is furnished in about equal proportions by the pubis and ischium (Fig. 404): it is not completely closed by bone, but is perforated by an aperture covered by membrane in the recent state. Both pubis and ischium are directed sharply backwards from their dorsal or acetabular ends. The *ischium* (*is.*) is a broad bone, ankylosed posteriorly with the ilium, and separated from it in front by an *ischiatic foramen* (Fig. 398a, *is. for.*; Fig. 404, *i. s. f.*). The *pubis* (*pu.*) is a slender, curved rod, parallel with the ventral edge of the ischium, and separated from it by an *obturator notch* (Fig. 395, *obt. n.*; Fig. 404, *ob. f.*). Neither ischium nor pubis unites ventrally with its fellow to form a symphysis.

In the hind-limb the *femur* (Fig. 405, *fe.*) is a comparatively short bone. Its proximal extremity bears a prominent *trochanter* (*tr.*) and a rounded *head*

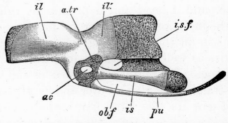

FIG. 404.—**Columba livia.** Left innominate of a nestling. The cartilage is dotted. *ac.* acetabulum; *a. tr.* anti-trochanter; *il.* pre-acetabular, and *il'.* post-acetabular portion of ilium; *is.* ischium; *i. s. f.* ischiadic foramen; *ob. f.* obturator notch; *pu.* pubis. (From Parker's *Zootomy*.)

(*hd.*), the axis of which is at right angles to the shaft of the bone; so that the femur, and indeed the whole limb, lies in a plane parallel with the sagittal plane of the trunk, and is not directed outwards as in Reptiles. Its distal end is produced into pulley-like *condyles*. There is a small sesamoid bone (*i.e.*, a bone developed in a tendon), the *patella* (*pat.*), on the extensor side of the knee-joint. Articulating with the femur is a very long bone, the *tibio-tarsus* (*ti. ts.*), produced on the anterior face of its proximal end into a large *cnemial process* (*cn. pr.*) for the insertion of the extensor muscle of the thigh. Its proximal articular surface is slightly hollowed for the condyle of the femur; its distal end is pulley-like, not concave like the corresponding extremity of the tibia of other Amniota. The study of development shows that the pulley-like distal end of the bone (Fig. 406, *tl. 1*) consists of the proximal tarsals—astragalus and calcaneum—which at an early period unite with the tibia and give rise to the compound shank-bone of the adult. The *fibula* (*fi.*) is very small, much shorter than the tibia, and tapers to a point at its distal end.

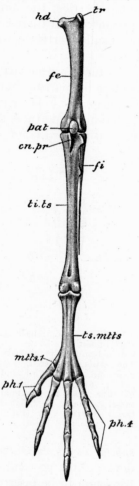

Following the tibio-tarsus is an elongated bone, the *tarso-metatarsus* (Fig. 405, *ts. mtts.*), presenting at its proximal end a concave surface for the tibio-tarsus, and at its distal end three distinct pulleys for the articulation of the three forwardly-directed toes. In the young bird the proximal end of this bone is a separate cartilage (Fig. 406, *tl. 2*), representing the distal tarsals, and followed by three distinct metatarsals, belonging respectively to the second, third, and fourth digits. Thus the ankle-joint of the bird is a *mesotarsal* joint, occurring, as in the Lizard, between the proximal and distal tarsals, and not, as in Mammals (*q.v.*), between the tibia and the proximal tarsals. To the inner or pre-axial side of the tarso-metatarsus, near its distal end, is attached by fibrous tissue a small irregular bone, the first metatarsal (Fig. 405, *mtts. 1*). The digits have the same number of phalanges as in the Lizard, the backwardly-directed hallux two, the second or inner toe three, the third or middle toe four, and the fourth or outer toe five. In all four

FIG. 405.—**Columba livia.** Bones of the left hind-limb. *cn. pr.* cnemial process; *fr.* femur; *fi.* fibula; *hd.* head of femur; *mtts. 1*, first metatarsal; *pat.* patella; *ph. 1*, phalanges of first digit; *ph. 4*, phalanges of fourth digit; *ti. ts.* tibio-tarsus; *ts. mtts.* tarso-metatarsus; *tr.* trochanter.

digits the distal or ungual phalanx is pointed and curved, and serves for the support of the horny claw.

It will be observed that every part of the bird's skeleton presents characteristic and indeed unique features. The vertebral column, the skull, the sternum, the ribs, the limb-girdles, and the limbs themselves are all so highly specialised that there is hardly a bone, except the phalanges of the toes and the free caudal vertebræ, which could possibly be assigned to any other vertebrate class.

A further peculiarity is the fact that the larger proportion of the bones contain no marrow, but are filled during life with air, and are therefore said to be *pneumatic*. The cavities of the various bones open externally in the dried skeleton by apertures called *pneumatic foramina* (Fig. 402, *pn. fr.*), by which, in the entire Bird, they communicate with the air-sacs (*vide* p. 445). In the Pigeon the bones of the fore-arm and hand, and of the leg, are non-pneumatic.

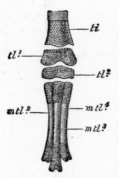

FIG. 406.—**Columba livia.** Part of left foot of an unhatched embryo (magnified). The cartilage is dotted. *mtl. 2*, second, *mtl. 3*, third, and *mtl. 4*, fourth metatarsal; *ti.* tibia; *tl. 1*, proximal tarsal cartilage; *tl. 2*, distal tarsal cartilage. (From Parker's *Zootomy.*)

Muscular System.—As might naturally be expected, the muscles of the fore-limb are greatly modified. The powerful downstroke of the wing by which the Bird rises into and propels itself through the air is performed by the *pectoralis* (Fig. 407, *pct.*), an immense muscle having about one-fifth the total weight of the body; it arises from the whole of the keel of the sternum (*car. st.*), from the posterior part of the body of that bone (*cp.st.*), and from the clavicle (*cl.*), filling nearly the whole of the wedge-shaped space between the body and the keel of the sternum and forming what is commonly called the " breast " of the bird. Its fibres converge to their insertion (*pct.''*) into the ventral aspect of the humerus (*hu., hu'.*) which it depresses. The elevation of the wing is performed, not, as might be expected, by a dorsally-placed muscle, but by the subclavius (*sb.clv.*), arising from the anterior part of the body of the sternum, dorsal to the pectoralis, and sending its tendon (*sb.clv'.*) through the foramen triosseum to be inserted into the dorsal aspect of the humerus. In virtue of this arrangement, the foramen acting like a pulley, the direction of action of the muscle is changed, the backward pull of the tendon raising the humerus. There are three *tensores patagii* (*tns. lg., tns. br., tns. acc.*), the action of which is to keep the pre-patagium tensely stretched when the wing is extended. A similar muscle (*tns. m. p.*) acts upon the post-patagium. The muscles of the digits are naturally much reduced.

The muscles of the neck and tail are well developed; those of the back are practically atrophied, in correspondence with the immobility of that region. In the leg certain of the muscles are modified to form the *perching mechanism*.

The toes are flexed by two sets of tendons and superficial. The deep tendons of the three forwardly-directed digits are formed by the trifurcation of the tendon of a single muscle, the *peronæus medius*; that of the hallux is derived from a separate muscle, the *flexor perforans*, which is joined by a slip from the peronæus medius. Thus a pull upon one tendon flexes all the toes. When the leg is bent, as the bird settles to roost, the flexion of the tarso-metatarsus on the shank puts the flexor tendons on the stretch as they pass over the mesotarsal joint, and by the pull thus exerted the toes are automatically bent round the perch by the simple action of flexing the leg. They are kept in this position

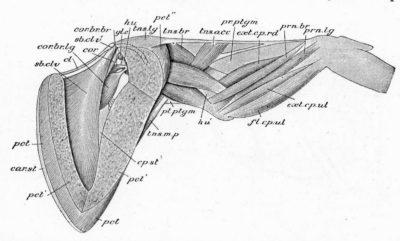

FIG. 407.—**Columba livia.** The principal muscles of the left wing; the greater part of the pectoralis (*pct.*) is removed. *car. st.* carina sterni; *cl.* furcula; *cor.* coracoid; *cor. br. br.* coraco-brachialis brevis; *cor. br. lg.* coraco-brachialis longus; *cp. st.* corpus sterni; *ext. cp. rd.* extensor carpi radialis; *ext. cp. ul.* extensor carpi ulnaris; *fl. cp. ul.* flexor carpi ulnaris; *gl. c.* glenoid cavity; *hu.* head of humerus; *hu'.* its distal end; *pct.* pectoralis; *pct'.* its cut edge; *pct''.* its insertion; *prn. br.* pronator brevis; *prn. lg.* pronator longus; *pr. ptgm.* pre-patagium; *pt. ptgm.* post-patagium; *sb.clv.* subclavius; *sb.clv'.* its tendon of insertion passing through the foramen triosseum, and dotted as it goes to the humerus; *tns. acc.* tensor accessorius; *tns. br.* tensor brevis; *tns. lg.* tensor longus; *tns. m. p.* tensor membranæ posterioris alæ.

while the bird is asleep by the mere weight of the body. The action is assisted by a small but characteristic muscle, the *ambiens*, which arises from the pubis, passes along the inner surface of the thigh, and is continued into a long tendon which comes round to the outer side of the knee, enclosed in a special sheath, and continuing down the leg, joins the superficial flexors of the digits.

Digestive Organs.—The *mouth* (Fig. 408) is bounded above and below by the horny beak, and there is no trace of teeth. The *tongue* (*tng.*) is large and pointed at the tip. The pharynx leads into a wide and distensible *gullet* (*gul.*) which soon dilates into an immense reservoir or *crop* (*crp.*) situated at the base of the neck, between the skin and the muscles, and immediately in front of the sternum. In this cavity the food, consisting of grain, undergoes a process of

maceration before being passed into the stomach.   From the crop the gullet is continued backwards into the *stomach*, which consists of two parts, the *proventriculus* (*prvn.*) and the *gizzard* (*giz.*).   The proventriculus appears extern-

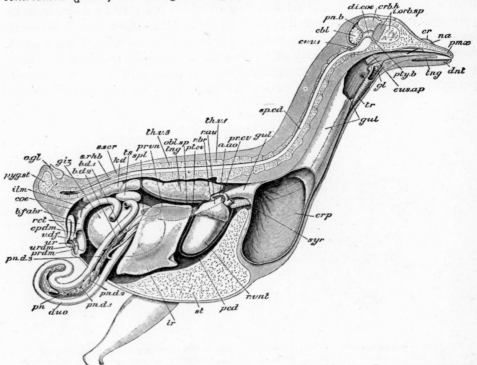

FIG. 408.—**Columbia livia**. Dissection from the right side. The body-wall, with the vertebral column, sternum, brain, etc., are in sagittal section ; portions of the gullet and crop are cut away and the cloaca is opened ; nearly the whole of the ileum is removed, and the duodenum is displaced outwards. *a. ao.* aortic arch ; *bd. 1, bd. 2*, bile-ducts ; *b. fabr.* bursa Fabricii ; *cbl.* cerebellum ; *cœ.* right cæcum ; *cpdm.* coprodæum ; *cr.* cere ; *crb. h.* left cerebral hemisphere ; *crp.* crop ; *cr. v. 1*, first cervical vertebra ; *di.cœ.* diacœle ; *dnt.* dentary ; *duo.* duodenum ; *eus. ap.* aperture of Eustachian tubes ; *giz.* gizzard (dotted behind the liver) ; *gl.* glottis ; *gul.* gullet ; *ilm.* ileum ; *i. orb. sp.* inter-orbital septum ; *kd.* right kidney ; *lng.* right lung ; *lr.* liver (right lobe) ; *na.* bristle passed from nostril into mouth ; *obl. sep.* oblique septum ; *o. gl.* oil-gland ; *pcd.* pericardium ; *pmx.* premaxilla ; *pn.* pancreas ; *pn. b.* pineal body ; *p. nd. 1—3*, pancreatic ducts ; *pr. cv.* right pre-caval ; *prdm.* proctodæum ; *prvn.* proventriculus (dotted behind liver) ; *pt. cv.* post-caval ; *pty. b.* pituitary body ; *pyg.st.* pygostyle ; *r. au.* right auricle ; *r. br.* right bronchus ; *rct.* rectum ; *r. vnt.* right ventricle ; *sp. cd.* spinal cord ; *spl.* spleen (dotted behind liver) ; *s. rhb.* sinus rhomboidalis ; *s. scr.* syn-sacrum ; *st.* carina sterni ; *syr.* syrinx ; *th. v. 1*, first, and *th. v. 5*, fifth thoracic vertebra ; *tng.* tongue ; *tr.* trachea ; *ts.* right testis ; *ur.* aperture of left ureter ; *urdm.* urodæum ; *v. df.* aperture of left vas deferens.

ally like a slight dilatation of the gullet ; but its mucous membrane is very thick, and contains numerous gastric glands so large as to be visible to the naked eye.   The gizzard has the shape of a biconvex lens : its walls are very thick and its lumen is small.   The thickening is due mainly to the immense development of the muscles which radiate from two tendons, one on each of the convex surfaces. The epithelial lining of the gizzard is very thick and horny, and of a yellow or green colour: its cavity always contains small stones, which are swallowed by the bird to aid the gizzard in grinding up the food.

The *duodenum* (*duo.*) leaves the gizzard quite close to the entrance of the proventriculus and forms a distinct loop enclosing the pancreas. The rest of the small intestine is called the *ileum* (*ilm.*): it presents first a single loop; then follows its greater part coiled into a sort of spiral; and lastly comes a single loop which passes without change of diameter into the *rectum* (*rct.*), the junction between the two being marked only by a pair of small blind pouches or *cæca* (*cœ.*). The *cloaca* is a large chamber divided into three compartments, the *coprodæum* (*cpdm.*), which receives the rectum, the *urodæum* (*urdm.*), into which the urinary and genital ducts open, and the *proctodæum* (*prdm.*), which opens externally by the anus.

There are small *buccal glands* opening into the mouth, but none that can be called salivary. The *liver* (*lr.*) is large, and is divisible into right and left lobes, each opening by its own duct (*b. d. 1, b. d. 2*) into the duodenum: there is no gall-bladder. The *pancreas* (*pn.*) is a compact reddish gland lying in the loop of the duodenum, into which it discharges its secretion by three ducts (*pn. d. 1-3*). A thick-walled glandular pouch, the *bursa Fabricii* (*b. fabr.*), lies against the dorsal wall of the cloaca in young birds and opens into the proctodæum: it atrophies in the adult.

Ductless Glands.—The spleen (*spl.*) is an ovoid red body, of unusually small proportional size, attached by peritoneum to the right side of the proventriculus. There are paired *thyroids* at the base of the neck; and, in young Pigeons, there is an elongated *thymus* on each side of the neck. The *adrenals* (Fig. 417, *adr.*) are irregular yellow bodies placed at the anterior ends of the kidneys.

Respiratory and Vocal Organs.—The *glottis* (Fig. 408, *gl.*) is situated just behind the root of the tongue, and leads into the *larynx*, which is supported by cartilages—a *cricoid* divided into four pieces, and paired *arytenoids*—but does not, as in other vertebrates, function as the organ of voice. The anterior part of the trachea (*tr.*) has the usual position, ventral to the gullet; but further back it is displaced to the left by the crop, becoming ventral once more as it enters the body-cavity, where it divides into the right (*r. br.*) and left *bronchi*. The rings supporting the trachea are not cartilaginous but bony, as also is the first ring of each bronchus, those of the trachea completely surrounding the tube, those of the bronchi incomplete mesially.

At the junction of the trachea with the bronchi occurs the characteristic vocal organ, the *syrinx* (*syr.*), found in no other class. The last three or four rings of the trachea (Fig., 409 *tr.*), and the first or bony half-ring of each bronchus (*br.*), are modified to form a slightly dilated chamber, the *tympanum*, the mucous membrane of which forms a cushion-like thickening on each side.

At the junction of the bronchi a bar of cartilage, the *pessulus*, extends dorso-ventrally and supports an inconspicuous fold of mucous membrane, the *membrana semilunaris*. The membranous inner walls of the bronchi form the *internal tympaniform membranes*. A pair of *intrinsic syringeal muscles* arise from the sides of the trachea and are inserted into the syrinx, and a pair of *sterno-tracheal muscles* arise from the sternum and are inserted into the trachea. The voice is produced by the vibration of the semilunar membrane : its pitch is altered by changes produced by the action of the muscles.

The *lungs* (Figs. 408, *lng.*, and 409) are very small in comparison with the

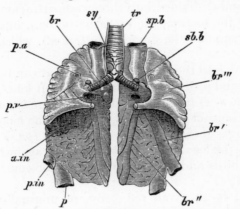

FIG. 409.—**Columba livia.** The lungs with the posterior end of the trachea, ventral aspect. *a. in.* aperture of anterior thoracic air-sac ; *br.* principal bronchus ; *br′, br″, br‴,* secondary bronchi ; *p.* aperture of abdominal air-sac ; *p. a.* pulmonary artery entering lung ; *p. in.* aperture of posterior thoracic air-sac ; *p. v.* pulmonary vein leaving lung ; *sb. b.* aperture of inter-clavicular air-sac ; *sp. b.* aperture of cervical air-sac ; *sy.* syrinx ; *tr.* trachea. (From Parker's *Zootomy*.)

size of the bird, and are but slightly distensible, being solid, spongy organs, not mere bags with sacculated walls as in amphibia and many reptiles. Their dorsal surfaces fit closely into the spaces between the ribs, and have no peritoneal covering : their ventral faces are covered by a strong sheet of fibrous tissue, the *pulmonary aponeurosis* or *pleura* (Fig. 410, *B, pul. ap.*), a special development of the peritoneum. Into this membrane are inserted small fan-like *costopulmonary muscles*, which arise from the junction of the vertebral and sternal ribs.

The bronchus, on entering the lung, is continued to its posterior end (Figs. 408 and 409), dividing into two branches, each of which enters a bladder-like air-sac, formed as a dilation of the mucous membrane of the bronchus. One of these, the *abdominal air-sac* (Fig. 410, *A, abd. a. s.*), lies among the coils of the intestine ; the other, or *posterior thoracic air-sac* (*post. th. a. s.*), is closely applied to the side-wall of the body. The bronchus also gives off, near its entrance into the lung, three short branches, one of which becomes connected with an *anterior thoracic air-sac* (*ant. th. a. s.*), situated just in front of the posterior thoracic ; another with an *interclavicular air-sac* (*int. clav. a. s.*), which is median and unpaired and connected with both lungs ; the third enters a *cervical air-sac* (*cerv. a. s.*) placed at the root of the neck. Each side of the interclavicular gives off an *axillary air-sac*, lying in the arm-pit. All these sacs are paired except the interclavicular, which is formed by the fusion of right and left moieties. The sacs are in communication with the pneumatic cavities of the bones.

The ventral or free walls of the thoracic air-sacs of each side are covered by a sheet of fibrous tissue, the *oblique septum* (*obl. sept.*), which is continued forwards to the pericardium, and is united with its fellow of the opposite side in the middle dorsal line: it divides the cœlome into two compartments—one containing the lungs with the interclavicular and thoracic air-sacs, the other (*abd. cav.*) the heart, liver, stomach, intestine, etc., with the abdominal air-sacs.

Besides the branches to the air-sacs, the main bronchus gives off secondary bronchii, and these branch again, sending off tubes which give rise to a system of fine branching and anastomosing tubules, the "lung-capillaries," which make up the main substance of the lung.

When the Pigeon is standing, the alternative elevation and depression of the sternum, produced partly by the abdominal, partly by the intercostal muscles, causes an alternate enlargement and diminution of the capacity of the cœlome, and thus pumps air in and out of the lungs. During flight, when the weight is supported by the wings, and the sternum is thus rendered relatively immovable, the same effect seems to be produced by the elevation and depression of the back. In either case the inspired air rushes through the lungs into the air-sacs and

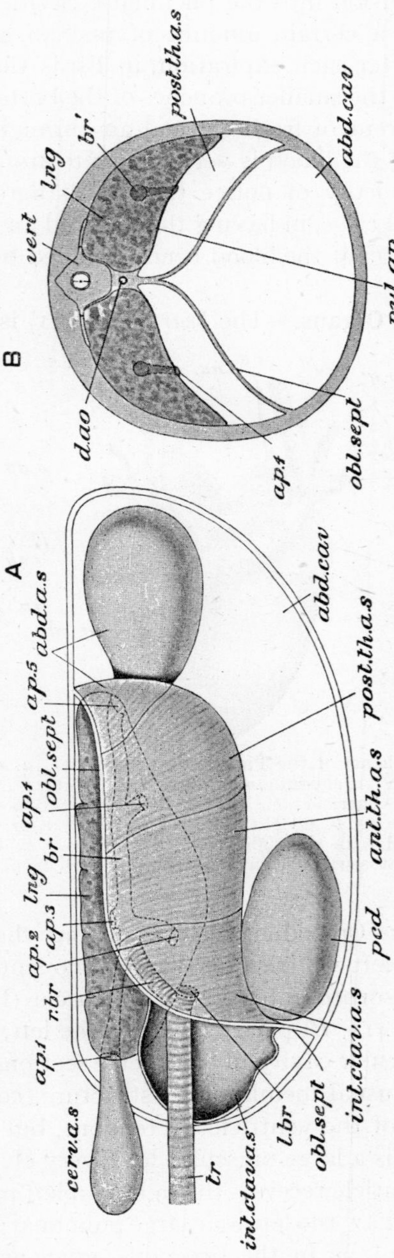

FIG. 410.—Diagrams showing the relations of the air-sacs of a **Bird**. *A*, from the left side; *B*, in transverse section. *abd. a. s.* right abdominal air-sac; *abd. cav.* abdominal cavity; *ant. th. a. s.* anterior thoracic air-sac; *ap. 1*, aperture of cervical air-sac; *ap. 2*, of interclavicular; *ap. 3*, of anterior thoracic; *ap. 4*, of posterior thoracic; *ap. 5*, of abdominal; *br′*, right bronchus passing through the lung (dotted); *cerv. a. s.* cervical air-sac; *d. ao.* dorsal aorta; *int.clav. a. s.* interclavicular air-sac; *int.clav. a. s′*, its anterior portion cut open; *l. br*, left bronchus cut off short; *lng*, right lung, the outline dotted where it is concealed by the air-sacs; *r. br*, right lung, cut off short; the cut edge in *A* shows the junction of the right and left moieties; *pcd*. pericardium; *post. th. a. s.* posterior thoracic air-sac; *pul. ap.* pulmonary aponeurosis; *r. br.* right bronchus; *tr.* trachea; *vert.* vertebra.

thence by diffusion into the pneumatic cavities of the bones. Thus, while in other animals a certain amount of unchanged or residual air is always left in the lungs after each expiration, in Birds the residual air is confined to the air-sacs and to the smaller branches of the bronchi, every respiratory movement drawing a current of fresh or tidal air through the lungs. As a result of this the aëration of the blood is very complete and its temperature correspondingly high. It is worthy of notice that Birds agree with Insects, the only other typically aerial class, in having the inspired air distributed all over the body, so that the aëration of the blood is not confined to the limited area of an ordinary organ.

Circulatory Organs.—The *heart* (Fig. 411) is of great proportional size, and,

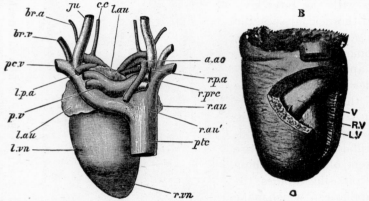

FIG. 411.—*A*, heart of the **Pigeon**, dorsal aspect. *a. ao.* arch of aorta ; *br. a.* brachial artery ; *br. v.* brachial vein ; *c. c.* common carotid ; *ju.* jugular ; *l. au.* left auricle ; *l. p. a.* left pulmonary artery ; *l. vn.* left ventricle ; *p.c. v.* left pre-caval ; *pt.c.* post-caval ; *p. v.* pulmonary veins ; *r. au*, *r. au'*, right auricle ; *r. p. a.* right pulmonary artery ; *r. pr. c.* right pre-caval ; *r. vn.* right ventricle. *B*, heart of a **Bird** with the right ventricle opened. *L. V.* septum ventriculorum ; *R. V.* right ventricle ; *V.* right auriculo-ventricular valve. (*A*, from Parker's *Zootomy* ; *B*, from Headley's *Birds*.)

like that of the Crocodile, consists of four chambers—right and left auricles, and right and left ventricles. There is no sinus venosus, that chamber being, as it were, absorbed into the right auricle (Fig. 411, *A, r. au.*). The right ventricle (Fig. 411, *B*) partly encircles the left, the former having a crescentic, the latter a circular cavity in transverse sections. The left auriculo-ventricular valve has the usual membranous structure, consisting of two flaps connected with the wall of the ventricle by tendons, but the corresponding valve of the right side (*V.*) is a large muscular fold, very characteristic of the class.

The right auricle receives the right and left precavals *(r. pr. c., p. c. v.)* and the post-caval (*p. tc.*) ; the left four large pulmonary veins (*p. v.*). The left ventricle (Fig. 412, *l. vn.*), as in the Crocodile, gives origin to the right aortic arch (*a. ao.*), but the right ventricle (*r. vn.*) gives off only one trunk, the pulmonary artery, which soon divides into two (*r. p. a., l. p. a.*). The left aortic arch is

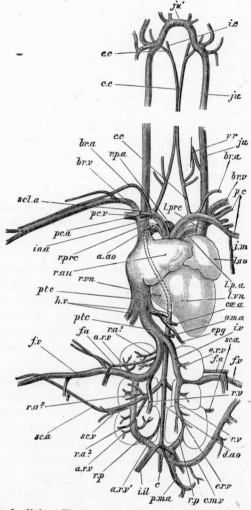

FIG. 412.—**Columba livia.** The heart and chief blood-vessels, ventral aspect. *a. ao.* arch of aorta; *a. m. a.* anterior mesenteric artery; *a. r. v.* afferent renal veins; *a. r. v'.* vein bringing blood from pelvis into renal portal system; *br. a.* brachial artery; *br. v.* brachial vein; *c.* caudal artery and vein; *c. c.* common carotid artery; *c. m. v.* coccygeo-mesenteric vein, displaced to the right; *cœ. a.* cœliac artery; *d. ao.* dorsal aorta; *e. c.* external carotid artery; *epg.* epigastric vein; *e. r. v.* efferent renal vein; *f. a.* femoral artery; *f. v.* femoral vein; *h. v.* hepatic vein; *i. c.* internal carotid artery; *i. il.* internal iliac artery and vein; *i. m.* internal mammary artery and vein; *in. a.* innominate artery; *i. v.* iliac vein; *ju.* jugular vein; *ju'.* anastomosis of jugular veins; *l. au.* left auricle; *l. p. a.* left pulmonary artery; *l. pr. c.* left pre-caval vein; *l. vn.* left ventricle; *pc.* left pectoral arteries and veins; *pc. a.* right pectoral artery; *pc. v.* right pectoral vein; *p. m. a.* posterior mesenteric artery; *pt. c.* post-caval vein; *ra.¹, ra.², ra.³,* renal arteries; *r. au.* right auricle; *r. p.* renal portal vein, on the left side of the figure, supposed to be dissected so as to show its passage through the right kidney; *r. p. a.* right pulmonary artery; *r. pr. c.* right pre-caval vein; *r. v.* renal vein; *r. vn.* right ventricle; *sc. a.* sciatic artery; *sc. v.* sciatic vein; *scl. a.* subclavian artery; *vr.* vertebral artery and vein. (From Parker's *Zootomy*.)

absent in the adult, and it is the right alone which is continued into the dorsal aorta. The result of this is that the systemic arteries receive pure arterial blood from the left side of the heart, and the only mingling of aërated and non-aërated blood is in the capillaries. This is perhaps the most important physiological advance made by Birds over Reptiles.

The aortic arch curves over the right bronchus to reach the dorsal body-wall, and then passes directly backwards as the dorsal aorta (*d. ao.*). Owing to the immense size of the pectoral muscles, the arteries supplying them are of corresponding dimensions, and the right and left *innominate arteries* (*in. a.*), from which the carotids (*c. c.*), subclavians (*br. a.*), and pectorals (*pc. a.*) arise, are actually larger than the aorta itself beyond their origin. In correspondence with the position of the legs, the femoral (*f. a.*) and sciatic (*sc. a.*) arteries arise very far forward : the caudal artery (*c.*) is naturally small.

The most characteristic feature in the disposition of the circulatory organs is the almost complete disappearance of the *renal portal system*. There are two renal portal veins (*r.p.*) formed by the bifurcation of the caudal ; but each, instead of breaking up into capillaries in the kidney, sends off only a few small branches (*a. r. v.*) which apparently carry blood to that organ, the main vein passing forwards, through the substance of the kidney, and joining the femoral vein (*f. v.*) from the leg to form the iliac vein (*i. v.*), which, uniting with its fellow of the opposite side, forms the post-caval (*pt. c.*). Thus the main part, at any rate, of the blood from the caudal and pelvic regions is taken directly to the heart, and not through the renal capillaries as in most Fishes and all Amphibians and Reptiles.

At the point of bifurcation of the caudal veins a large *coccygeo-mesenteric vein* (*c. m. v.*) comes off, and, running parallel with the rectum, from which it receives tributaries, joins the portal vein. The abdominal vein of Amphibians and Reptiles appears to be represented, in part at least, by the *epigastric vein* (*epg.*), which returns the blood, not from the ventral body-wall, but from the *great omentum*, a fold of peritoneum, loaded with fat, lying ventral to the intestine and gizzard : the epigastric discharges into the hepatic vein.

The red blood-corpuscles are oval and nucleated. The temperature of the blood is unusually high—over 38° C. (100° F.).

Nervous System.—The brain (Fig. 413) completely fills the cranial cavity, and is remarkable for its short, broad, rounded form. The *medulla oblongata* (*m. o.*) has a well-marked ventral flexure, as in the Lizard. The *cerebellum* (*cb.*) is of great size, and has a large median portion and two small lateral lobes or *flocculi* (*f.*) ; the surface of the middle lobe is marked by grooves passing inwards in a radiating manner and carrying with them the grey matter, the extent of which is thus greatly increased. The *metacœle* (Fig. 414, v^4.) is completely hidden by the cerebellum, and the latter is solid, having no epicœle. The *hemispheres* (*c. h.*) extend backwards to meet the cerebellum, and the *optic* *lobes* (*o. l.*) are thereby pressed outwards so as to take up a lateral instead of the usual dorsal position : these are of rounded form, and each contains an *optocœle* (Fig. 414, *o. v.*) opening from a narrow passage, the *iter*, which represents the original cavity of the mid-brain. A further result of the extension of the hemispheres and cerebellum respectively backwards and forwards is that no part of the diencephalon (*thc.*) appears externally except on the ventral surface : elsewhere it is seen only when the hemispheres are pressed aside. It

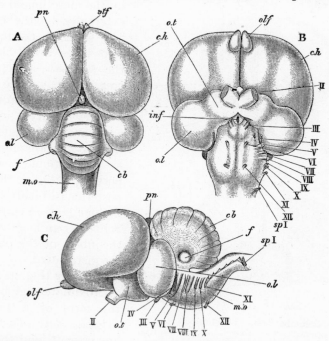

FIG. 413.—**Columba livia.** The brain. *A*, from above; *B*, from below; *C*, from the left side. *cb.* cerebellum ; *c. h.* cerebral hemispheres ; *f.* flocculus ; *inf.* infundibulum ; *m. o.* medulla oblongata ; *o. l.* optic lobes ; *olf.* olfactory bulbs ; *o. t.* optic tracts ; *pn.* pineal body ; *II—XII,* cerebral nerves ; *sp. I,* first spinal nerve. (From Parker's *Zootomy*.)

contains a narrow vertical cavity, the *diacœle* (*v³.*), bounded laterally by the optic thalami, and communicating on each side by the foramina of Monro (*f. m.*) with the *paracœles* or cavities of the hemispheres. The *corpora striata* (*c. s.*) are of immense size, and form the great mass of the hemispheres : the dorsal portions of the latter, forming the roofs of the paracœles, are very thin. Hippocampi are absent. The anterior commissure is, as in lower Vertebrates, the chief commissure of the fore-brain. The *olfactory bulbs* (*olf.*) are extremely small, in correspondence with the poorly developed olfactory organ : on the other hand the optic nerves and tracts are of unusual size.

The *spinal cord* (Fig. 408, *sp. cd.*) presents large brachial and lumbar enlargements from which the nerves of the fore- and hind-limbs respectively are given off. In the lumbar enlargement there is a divergence of the dorsal columns of the cord converting the central canal into a wide, diamond-shaped cavity, the *sinus rhomboidalis* (*s. rhb.*), bounded above only by the membranes of the cord.

Sensory Organs.—The *olfactory organs* are paired chambers in the base of the beak, separated from one another by the mesethmoid and bounded externally by the ecto-ethmoid. The latter is produced inwards into three scroll-like processes, the *turbinals*, which greatly increase the surface of mucous membrane. The anterior portion of the cavity, including the anterior turbinal, is covered by laminated epithelium and serves as a vestibule ; its posterior portion, including the middle and posterior turbinals, is invested by the one-layered epithelium of the Schneiderian membrane to which the fibres of the olfactory nerve are distributed.

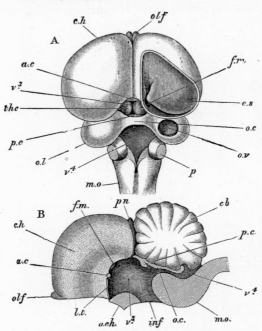

FIG. 414.—**Columba livia.** The brain. *A*, with the cavities opened from above ; *B*, in sagittal section. *a. c.* anterior commissure ; *cb.* cerebellum ; *c. h.* cerebral hemispheres ; *c. s.* corpus striatum ; *f. m.* foramen of Monro ; *inf.* infundibulum ; *m. o.* medulla oblongata ; *o. c.* optic commissure ; *o. ch.* optic chiasma ; *o. l.* optic lobes ; *olf.* olfactory bulbs ; *o. v.* optocœle ; *p.* peduncles of cerebellum ; *p. c.* posterior commissure ; *pn.* pineal body ; *thc.* diencephalon ; *v³.*, diacœle ; *v⁴.*, metacœle. (From Parker's *Zootomy*.)

The *eye* (Fig. 415) is not even approximately globular, but has the form of a biconvex lens. *Sclerotic bony plates* (*B*, *scl. pl.*) are present, and there is a large *pecten* (*pct.*) in the form of a plaited and strongly pigmented membrane projecting into the cavity of the eye from the entrance of the optic nerve. The pecten is stated to be of nervous character, and is in all probability a sensory organ having some function connected with the process of accommodation.

The *auditory organ* (Fig. 416) is chiefly distinguished from that of Reptiles by the great development of the *cochlea* (*lag.*). The anterior canal (*SB*) is of great size, and the whole membranous labyrinth is closely invested by a layer of dense ivory-like bone, which can be isolated by cutting away the surrounding spongy bone, and is then seen to form a sort of model of the contained organ, to

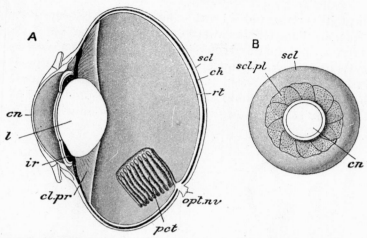

Fig. 415.—**Columba livia.** The eye. *A*, in sagittal section; *B*, the entire organ, external aspect. *cn.* cornea; *ch.* choroid; *cl. pr.* ciliary processes; *ir.* iris; *l.* lens; *opt. nv.* optic nerve; *pet.* pecten; *rt.* retina; *scl.* sclerotic; *scl. pl.* sclerotic plates. (After Vogt and Yung.)

which the name *bony labyrinth* is applied. The tympanic cavity and columella have the same arrangement as in the Lizard; the narrow Eustachian tubes open by a common aperture (Fig. 408, *eus. ap.*) in the roof of the pharynx.

Urinogenital Organs.—The *kidneys* (Figs. 408, *kd.*, Figs. 417 and 418, *k.*) have a very characteristic form. Each is a flattened organ divided into three main lobes and fitted closely into the hollows of the pelvis. It is formed from the metanephros, the large mesonephros or Wolffian body, which forms the embryonic kidney, undergoing atrophy. The *ureters* (*ur.*) are narrow tubes passing directly backwards to open into the urodæum or middle compartment of the cloaca.

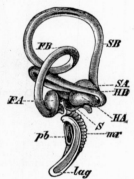

Fig. 416.—**Columba livia.** The right membranous labyrinth, outer aspect. *FA*, ampulla of posterior canal; *FB*, posterior canal; *HA*, ampulla of horizontal canal; *HB*, horizontal canal; *lag.* cochlea or lagena; *mr.* membrane of Reissner; *pb*, basilar part of cochlea; *S*, sacculus; *SA*, ampulla of anterior canal; *SB*, anterior canal. (From Wiedersheim, after Hasse.)

The *testes* (Figs. 408 and 417, *ts.*) are ovoid bodies, varying greatly in size according to the season, attached by peritoneum to the ventral surfaces of the anterior ends of the kidneys From the inner border of each goes off a convoluted *vas deferens* (*vd.*), which passes backwards, parallel with the ureter, to open into the urodæum on the extremity of a small papilla. The posterior end of the spermiduct is slightly enlarged to form a *vesicula seminalis* (*v. s.*). There is no copulatory organ.

The female organs (Fig. 418) are remarkable for the more or less complete atrophy of the right ovary and oviduct. The *left ovary* (*ov.*) is a large organ in

the adult bird, its surface studded with follicles or ovisacs, varying in size from
about 15 mm. in diameter downwards, and each containing a single ovum.
The *left oviduct* (*l. od.*) is long and convoluted ; its anterior end is enlarged to form
a wide membranous cœlomic funnel (*l. od''.*) into which the ripe ova pass on
their liberation from the ovisacs ; the rest of the tube has thick muscular walls,
lined with glandular epithelium, and opens into the urodæum.   A fair-sized
vestige of the *right oviduct* (*r. od.*) is found in connection with the right side of

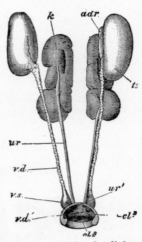

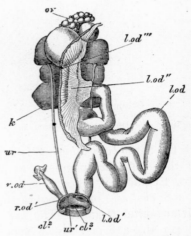

FIG. 417.—**Columba livia.** Male
urinogenital organs. *adr.* adrenal ;
cl². urodæum ; *cl³*. proctodæum ;
k. kidney ; *ts.* testis, that of the right
side displaced ; *ur.* ureter ; *ur'.*
aperture of ureter ; *vd.* vas deferens ;
vd'. its cloacal aperture ; *v. s.* vesicula
seminalis. (From Parker's *Zootomy*.)

FIG. 418.—**Columba livia.** Female
urinogenital organs in breeding season.
cl². urodæum ; *cl³*. proctodæum ; *k.* kidney ; *l. od.* left oviduct ; *l. od'.* its cloacal
aperture ; *l. od''.* its cœlomic funnel ;
l. od'''. its cœlomic aperture ; *ov.* ovary ;
r. od. right oviduct ; *r. od'.* its cloacal
aperture ; *ur.* ureter ; *ur'.* its cloacal
aperture. (From Parker's *Zootomy*.)

the cloaca, and a more or less extensive vestige of the *right ovary* is frequently
present.

Internal impregnation takes place.   As the ova or " yolks " pass down the
oviduct they are invested with the secretions of its various glands ; first with
layers of *albumen* or " white," next with a parchment-like double *shell membrane*,
and lastly with a white calcareous *shell*.   They are laid, two at a time, in a rough
nest, and are *incubated* or sat upon by the parents for fourteen days, the temperature being in this way kept at about 38° to 40° C. (100° to 103° F.).   At the
end of incubation the young bird is sufficiently developed to break the shell and
begin free life.   It is at first covered with fine down, and is fed by the parents
with a secretion from the crop, the so-called " Pigeon's milk."

Distinctive Characters and Classification.

Aves are Craniata in which the epidermal exoskeleton takes the form of feathers over the greater part of the body, of a *rhamphotheca* or horny sheath to the beak, and of claws on the digits of the foot and sometimes of the hand. In the standing position the body is entirely supported on the hind-limbs, the articulations of which are thrown forward. The fore-limbs are modified to form wings, usually provided with large feathers for the support of the body during flight. The cervical and free thoracic vertebræ are usually heterocœlous, but may be procœlous or amphicœlous. The sacral vertebræ are fused with the lumbar and with more or fewer of the posterior thoracic and anterior caudal to form a syn-sacrum for the support of the ilia. The posterior caudal vertebræ are usually fused to form a pygostyle around which the tail-quills are arranged in a semicircle. The bones of the skull undergo early ankylosis. There is a single, rounded, occipital condyle; the united premaxillæ form nearly the whole of the upper jaw; and the lower jaw is composed originally of five or six bones in each ramus, and is supported by a freely articulated quadrate. The vertebral ribs are double-headed, provided with bony uncinates, and articulate with the bony sternal ribs by synovial joints. The sternum is broad, and is typically produced into a longitudinal ventral keel, having a separate centre of ossification. The coracoid is usually more or less pillar-like, the scapula is sabre-shaped, and the clavicles and interclavicle unite to form a furcula. Except in one extinct species the distal carpals and the metacarpals are united to form a carpo-metacarpus. There are usually only three digits in the wing, which probably represent the first, second, and third of the typical hand. The ilium is of great size, having large pre- and post-acetabular portions. The acetabulum is perforated in the dry bone. The pubis and ischium are directed backwards and, except in one case of each, there is neither pubic nor ischiatic symphysis. The head of the femur is at right angles to the shaft. The proximal tarsals are fused with the tibia to form a tibio-tarsus; the fibula is much reduced. The distal tarsals are fused with the second, third and fourth metatarsals to form a tarso-metatarsus; the first metatarsal is free. The fifth digit of the typical foot is absent.

In all tertiary and recent Birds teeth are absent. The gullet is frequently dilated into a crop and the stomach is usually divided into proventriculus and gizzard. The junction between the large and small intestines is marked by a pair of cæca. The lungs are spongy and non-distensible. The bronchi give off branches which open on the surface of the lung into thin-walled air-sacs, and these in their turn usually communicate with pneumatic cavities in more or fewer of the bones. The voice is produced in a syrinx situated at or near the junction of the trachea with the bronchi. The heart is four-chambered, the right auriculo-ventricular valve is muscular, and the right aortic arch alone is present in the adult. The renal portal system is vestigial. The red blood-corpuscles are oval and nucleated. The temperature of the blood is high (about 38° C.). The optic lobes are displaced laterally owing to the meeting of the large cerebral hemispheres and cerebellum. The lumbar region of the spinal cord has a sinus rhomboidalis. The olfactory organ is usually poorly developed. The eye is usually large, and has sclerotic plates and a pecten. The auditory organ has a large curved cochlea. The kidney is three-lobed, and is developed from the metanephros, the mesonephros undergoing atrophy. There is no urinary bladder. The ovary and oviduct of the right side are more or less completely atrophied.

Birds are all oviparous, and the large ovum, containing much food-yolk, becomes invested with albumen, a double shell-membrane, and a calcareous shell, in its passage down the oviduct. The embryo has an amnion, an allantois, and a large yolk-sac. The newly-hatched young may be either well covered with down and able to run or swim and to obtain their own food, in which case they are said to be *precocious* ; or may be more or less naked and dependent for a time upon the parents for their food supply, when they are *non-precocious*.

There is no general agreement with regard to the classification of Birds. Owing to the singular uniformity of the class in essential matters of structure, the vast and bewildering diversity in detail, and the puzzling cross-relationships between group and group, the splitting up of the class into orders is a matter of great difficulty and one upon which hardly two ornithologists are agreed. The following scheme will probably answer the present purpose sufficiently well.*

Sub-Class I.—Archæornithes.

ORDER.—ARCHÆOPTERYGIFORMES.

Mesozoic Birds : have no ploughshare bone (pygostyle), but a long tail of many vertebræ, having the rectrices arranged in two rows, one on each side of it. The carpals and metacarpals are probably free, and the hand has three clawed digits. Teeth are present in both jaws.

Including only two genera each with a single species, *Archæopteryx litho-graphica* (Figs. 426, 427) and *Archæornis siemondsi* (Fig. 425), known only from two specimens found in the Jurassic rocks of Bavaria.

Sub-Class II.—Neornithes.

All other Birds in which the greatly shortened tail usually ends in a pygo-style, around which the rectrices, when present, are arranged in a semicircle. Except in a few extinct forms there are no teeth. The metacarpals are fused with the distal carpals to form a carpo-metacarpus. Except in one instance, not more than two digits of the hand bear claws, and in nearly all cases claws are absent in the manus.

* This classification is based on that of Lowe, Wetmore, and others.

SUPER-ORDER.—ODONTOGNATHÆ

Order I.—Hesperornithiformes.

Including *Hesperornis* (Fig. 419) a large diving and swimming Bird from the Cretaceous of North America. The jaws carry sharply pointed teeth.

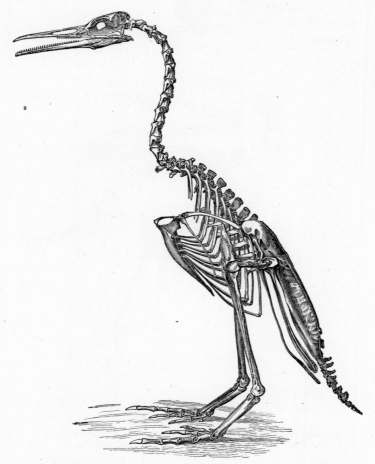

Fig. 419.—**Hesperornis regalis.** The restored skeleton. The posture is too erect.
(After Marsh.)

The body was elongated and the sternum lacked a keel. The shoulder-girdle was much reduced, and the Bird was unable to fly. *Baptornis* from the same aged deposits was a smaller but apparently similar form. *Enaliornis* from the Cambridge Greensand was an allied form.

ORDER 2.—ICHTHYORNITHIFORMES.

This order contains several species found in the Cretaceous of Kansas in North America—e.g., *Ichthyornis* (Fig. 420) and *Apatornis*. Small pointed teeth were present, recurved and set in sockets. The neck vertebræ show an

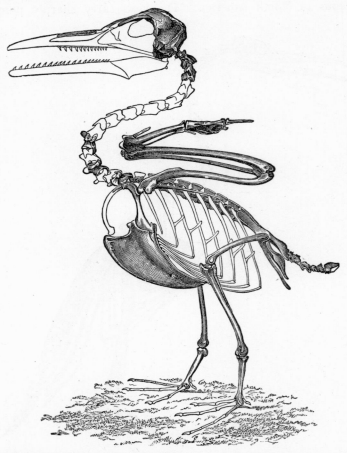

FIG. 420.—**Ichthyornis victor.** The restored skeleton. There is some doubt as to the correctness of this restoration and the jaws may not belong to the skeleton. (After Marsh.)

unusual feature for Birds in being biconcave. The sternum has a well developed keel and the Birds were strong flyers of tern-like habit.

SUPER-ORDER.—PALÆOGNATHÆ.

Flightless Neornithes, usually of large size, having no hooked barbules to the feathers, so that the barbs are free. Apteria are usually absent in the adult. The rectrices are absent or irregularly arranged, and the pygostyle is small or undeveloped. The sternal keel is vestigial or absent. The coracoid and scapula are comparatively small and completely ankylosed; the acro-coracoid process is vestigial, and the coraco-scapular angle approaches two right angles. The wing is reduced in size and may be vestigial or absent. There are large basi-pterygoid processes developed from the basi-sphenoid. The vomer is large and broad and separates the palatines. The quadrate articulates

FIG. 421.—**Apteryx australis,** with egg.
(From a specimen in the Royal College of Surgeons, London.)

with the skull by a single or partially divided facet. The male has a penis. The young are precocious.

ORDER 1.—CASUARIIFORMES.

Including the Emus (*Dromœus*) and Cassowaries (*Casuarius*).

ORDER 2.—APTERYGIFORMES.

Including only the Kiwis (*Apteryx*, Figs. 421, 422).

ORDER 3.—DINORNITHIFORMES.

Including the Moas (*Dinornithidæ*, Fig. 423).

ORDER 4.—RHEIFORMES.

Including the South American Ostriches (*Rhea*).

FIG. 422.—**Apteryx australis.** Skeleton.
(From a specimen in the British Museum, Natural History.)

ORDER 5.—STRUTHIONIFORMES.

Including the true Ostriches (*Struthio*).

ORDER 6.—ÆPYORNITHIFORMES.

Including only the post-pliocene Madagascan genera *Æpyornis* and *Mullerornis*.

ORDER 7.—TINAMIFORMES.

Including a single family, the Tinamous of South America and South Mexico.

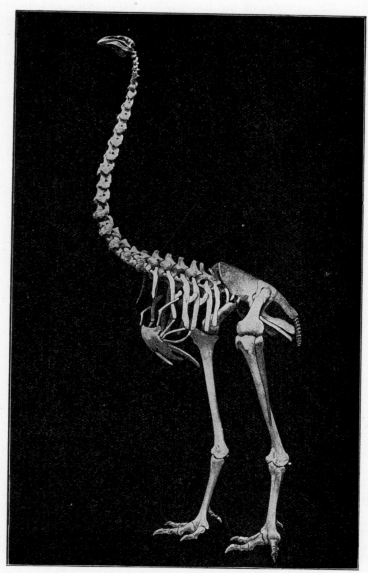

FIG. 423.—Skeleton of **Dinornis robustus,** one of the Moas : actual height 9 ft. 6 in. (From a specimen at the Royal College of Surgeons, London.)

SUPER-ORDER.—NEOGNATHÆ

Neornithes in which the sternum has a keel, the coracoid and scapula are not ankylosed, and usually the furcula and acrocoracoid are well developed and the coraco-scapular angle is less than a right angle. There is a pygostyle around which the rectrices or tail-feathers are arranged. The quadrate articulates with the skull by two facets. The vomer is smaller than in the

FIG. 424.—**Eudyptes antipodum.** (After Buller.)

Palæognathæ, and the palatines converge together behind it and are movably attached to it by a cup-and-ball joint. The barbs of the feathers are provided with hooklets.

The classification of the Neornithes, which include the great majority of living Birds, is into twenty-three orders, as follows :—

Sphenisciformes (Impennes).

Including the Penguins (*Aptenodytes*, *Eudyptes*) (Fig. 424, etc.).

Colymbiformes (Pygopodes).

Including the Divers (Colymbus).

Podicipiformes.

Including the Grebes (*Podicipes*).

Procellariiformes (Turbinares).

Including the Petrels (*Procellaria*), Shearwaters (*Puffinus*), Fulmars (*Fulmarus*), Storm Petrels (*Oceanites*), Albatross (*Diomedia*), etc.

Pelicaniformes (Steganopodes).

Including the Boatswain Bird (*Phaëthon*), Gannets (*Sula*), Cormorants or Shags (*Phalacrocorax*), Frigate Bird (*Fregata*), and the Pelicans (*Pelecanus*).

Ciconiiformes (Herodines).

Including the Herons (*Ardea*), Storks (*Ciconia*, etc.), Ibises (*Ibis*), Spoonbills (*Platalea*), Whale-headed Stork (*Balaeniceps*), and Flamingoes (*Phonicopterus*).

Anseriformes (Anseres).

Including the Ducks (*Anas*), Geese (*Anser*), Swans (*Cygnus*), Mergansers (*Mergus*).

Falconiformes (Accipitres).

Including the diurnal Birds of Prey, such as the Eagles (*Aquila*), Falcons (*Falco*), Vultures (*Vultur*, etc.), Secretary Bird (*Sagittarius*), and the American Vultures or Turkey-Buzzards (*Cathartes*).

Galliformes (Gallinæ).

Including the Fowls (*Gallus*), Pheasants (*Phasianus*), Grouse (*Tetrao*), and other Game Birds. Curassows (*Crax*), Megapodes (*Megapodius*), Peacock (*Pavo*), Guinea-fowl (*Numida*), Turkeys (*Meleagris*), Hoatzin (*Opisthocomus* *), etc.

Diatrymiformes.

An extinct order containing several species from the Eocene of North America. *Diatryma steini* was a gigantic Bird standing seven feet high, with reduced wings and incapable of flight.

Ralliformes.

Including the Rails (*Rallidæ*), the flightless Giant Rail (*Aptornis*), the Finfoots (*Heliornithidæ*).

Telmatomorphormes.

Including the Sub-order Gruæ, ? the Screamers (*Carimidæ*), Cranes (*Gruidæ*), Kagu (*Rhinochetidæ*), Sunbitterns (*Eurypygidæ*), Bustards (*Otidæ*), Lily Trotters (*Jacanidæ*), etc. The Sub-order Limicolæ with the Painted Snipe (*Rostratulidæ*), Waders (*Charadriidæ*), and Snipe (*Scolopacidæ*), and the Sub-order Laro-Limicolæ with Seedsnipe (*Thinocorythidæ*), Chionis (*Chionidæ*), Gulls and Terns (*Laridæ*), Auks (*Alcidæ*).

* The position of this bird is doubtful. It may be a primitive game bird.

Columbiformes (Columbæ).

>Including the Pigeons and Doves (*Columba, Turtur*, etc.), Crowned Pigeons (*Goura*), Sand Grouse (*Pteroclidæ*), the extinct Dodo and Solitaire (*Raphus* and *Pezophaps*), Hernipodes (*Turnicidæ*), etc.

Cuculiformes.

>An order of Birds including the Cuckoos (*Cuculidæ*), and ? Plantain Eaters (*Musophagidæ*).

Psatticiformes (Psittaci).

>Including the Parrots (*Psittacus*), Parrakeets (*Platycercus*), Cockatoos (*Cacatua*), Lories (*Lorius*), and Macaws (*Ara*).

Strigiformes (Striges).

>Including the Owls (*Strigidæ*).

Caprimulgiformes.

>Including the Night-jars (*Caprimulgi*).

Coliiformes.

>Including the Colies (*Coliidæ*), a small order found only in Africa.

Trogoniformes.

>Including only the single family of Trogons (*Trogonidæ*).

Coraciiformes.

>Including the Kingfishers (*Alcedinidæ*), Motmots (*Momotidæ*), Bee-eaters (*Meropidæ*), Rollers (*Coraciidæ*), Hoopoes (*Upupidæ*), and ? Hornbills (*Bucerotidæ*).

Piciformes.

>Including the Woodpeckers (*Picidæ*) and Toucans (*Rhamphastidæ*), Barbets (*Cepitonidæ*).

Passeriformes.

>A very large order of birds including about half the known species— *e.g.*, Swifts (*Micropodidæ*), Humming Birds (*Trochilidæ*), Broadbills (*Eurylæmidæ*), Lyre birds (*Menuridæ*), Swallows (*Hirudinidæ*), Thrushes (*Turdidæ*, etc.), Warblers (*Sylviidæ*), Sparrows (*Passer*), Finches (*Fringillidæ*), etc., etc.

Systematic Position of the Example.

The numerous species of Columba belongs to the family *Columbidæ*, of the order *Columbiformes*.

The following are the chief characters of the Columbæ : there are eleven primary remiges, the first very small ; the skull is schizognathous (see p. 472) ; the oil-gland has no tuft of feathers ; the vomer is vestigial ; there is a large crop ; the cæca are vestigial ; and the young are non-precocious.

Of the two families of Columbæ the *Columbidæ*, or Doves and Pigeons, are distinguished from the *Raphidæ*, including the Dodo and Solitaire, by the power of flight and the accompanying typical carinate characters of the sternum and shoulder-girdle.

In Columba there are twelve retrices; the second primary remex is longer than the sixth, and the proximal portion of the tarso-metatarsus is feathered.

General Organisation.

In respect of range of structural variations, the entire class of Birds is hardly the equivalent of a single order of Reptiles. Among existing Birds, the Emu and the Raven, which may be said to stand at opposite ends of the series, present nothing like the anatomical differences to be found between a common Lizard and a Chamæleon, or between a Turtle and a Tortoise. Hence in dividing the class into orders we find none of those striking distinctive characters which separate the orders of Fishes, Amphibia, and Reptiles, but have to be content with characters which in other groups would be considered insignificant, such as details in the structure of the skull and sternum, in the arrangement of the muscles of the wing and leg, in the form of the foot, and in the peculiarities of the newly-hatched young. It is for this reason that in the preceding classification no diagnoses of the orders are given: to define them adequately would involve a degree of anatomical detail quite beyond the scope of the present work.

The differences between the two avian sub-classes, the Archæornithes and the Neornithes, are, however, of a far more fundamental nature; and as Archæopteryx and Archæornis, sole representatives of the first of these groups, and perhaps the best examples of an undoubted link between two classes—Reptiles and Birds—it will be convenient to deal with them separately.

Sub-Class I.—Archæornithes.

Only two specimens of this sub-class which are placed in two genera, i.e., *Archæopteryx lithographica* (in the British Museum) and *Archæornis siemensi* (in the Berlin Museum), have hitherto been found, both in the finely-grained lithographic limestone of Solenhofen, Bavaria, belonging to the Jurassic period. The Birds (Fig. 425) were about the size of a Crow, and in the fossils not only are the bones preserved, but also many of the feathers.

The most striking feature in the organisation of this Bird is the fact that the *tail* is composed of about 18–20 free caudal vertebræ gradually tapering to the distal end as in a Lizard. The *rectrices* are arranged in two rows, one on each side of the caudal vertebræ, forming a long tail quite unlike that of any existing Bird. The centra probably had biconcave faces. In addition to cervical and thoracic ribs (which were apparently devoid of uncinates) there were *abdominal ribs*, like those of Sphenodon and Crocodiles.

The skull (Fig. 426) is proportionately large, with rounded brain-case and strong jaws, in each of which is a series of conical *teeth* lodged in sockets. There is no trace of sternum in either specimen, and the coracoids (*co.*) are only partially visible : the scapulæ (*sc.*) are slender, curved bones, and there is a U-shaped furcula (*cl.*).

The bones of the upper and fore-arm are of the normal avian character :

only one carpal is certainly known (Fig. 427, *c.*) : it apparently belongs to the distal row, and is closely applied to the first and second metacarpals. Three digits (*d. 1, 2, 3*) are clearly visible in one of the specimens—that in the Berlin Museum—the metacarpals are usually stated to be all free, in which case there is no carpo-metacarpus as in other Birds, and the hand approaches the normal reptilian type. The number of phalanges follows the usual reptilian rule, two in the first digit, three in the second, and four in the third, and the ungual phalanx of all three digits is claw-shaped and doubtless supported a horny claw.

The *remiges*, like the rectrices, are in a wonderful state of preservation (Fig. 425), and are divisible, as usual, into primaries or meta-carpo-digitals, and secondaries or cubitals. The primaries were probably attached to the second or to the second and third of the digits just described.

The *pelvis* and the *hind-limb* have the usual avian character. The tibia and fibula are separate. The foot consists of a slender

FIG. 425.—**Archæornis siemensi.** From the Berlin specimen. *c.* carpal ; *cl.* furcula ; *co.* coracoid ; *h.* humerus ; *r.* radius ; *sc.* scapula ; *u.* ulna ; *I—IV*, digits.

tarso-metatarsus and four digits, the hallux being small and directed backwards.

In addition to the wing and tail-quills already referred to, there are remains of contour feathers at the base of the neck and of wing-coverts. Moreover the rectrices are continued forwards by a series of large feathers which extend for some distance along the sides of the body, and a row of similar but smaller feathers is attached along both anterior and posterior faces of the tibio-tarsus.

Sub-Class II.—Neornithes.

External Characters.—In the general build of the body the Neornithes differ from Archæopteryx chiefly in the shorter and stouter trunk, and in the point of

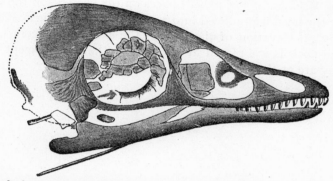

FIG. 426.—**Archæopteryx lithographica.** The skull, showing teeth and sclerotic plates.
(From Headley, after Dames.)

articulation of the hind-limbs being thrown forward, so as to be almost directly below the centre of gravity of the body : the animal is thus enabled without effort to support itself on the legs alone. In a word Birds are essentially bipedal, the only exception being the young of the Hoatzin (*Opisthocomus*), which uses its wings in climbing.

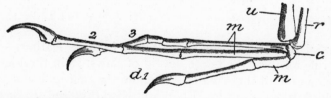

FIG. 427.—**Archæopteryx lithographica.** The left manus. *c.* carpal ; *d 1*, first digit ; *2*, second digit ; *3*, third digit ; *m, m.* metacarpals ; *r.* radius ; *u.* ulna. (From Headley, after Dames.)

The neck is always well developed, and is often, as in the Swan and Flamingo, of immense proportional length. The cranial portion of the head is usually not large, but the beak may attain extraordinary dimensions, and exhibits a wide range of form. It may be extremely short and wide for catching Moths and other flying Insects, as in Swifts and Nightjars ; short and conical for eating seed, as in Finches ; strongly hooked for tearing the bodies of animals, as in Birds of Prey, or for rending fruits of various kinds, as in

Parrots ; long, conical, and of great strength, as in Storks ; slender and elongated, as in Ibises and Curlews ; broad and flattened for feeding in mud, as in Ducks and Geese ; expanded at the end, as in Spoonbills ; immensely enlarged, as in Hornbills and Toucans. It is most commonly bent downwards at the tip, but may be straight or curved upwards, as in the Avocet, or bent to one side, as in the New Zealand Wry-billed Plover. It is sometimes, as in the Toucans, brilliantly coloured, and there may also be bright coloration of the cere as in the Macaws, and of naked spaces on the head, as in the Cassowaries. In the latter the head is produced into a great horny prominence or " casque," supported by an elevation of the roof of the skull. The cere is frequently absent. The nostrils are placed at the base of the beak, except in Apteryx, in which they are at the tip.

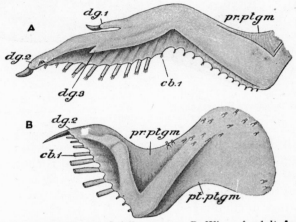

FIG. 428.—*A*, Wing of nestling of **Opisthocomus** ; *B*, Wing of adult **Apteryx** ; both from the inner (ventral) aspect. *cb. 1.* first cubital remex ; *dg. 1, dg. 2, dg. 3,* digits ; *pr. ptgm.* prepatagium ; *pt. ptgm.* post-patagium. (*A*, after Pycraft ; *B*, after T. J. Parker.)

The essential structure of the wing—apart from its feathers—is very uniform. As a rule all three digits are devoid of claws, as in the Pigeon, but the Ostrich has claws on all three digits ; Rhea on the first and sometimes on the second and third ; the Cassowary, Emu, and Kiwi (Fig. 428, *B*) on the second ; the Crested Screamer (*Chauna*) and two other species, and, as a rare abnormality, the Common Fowl and Goose, on the first. With these exceptions the hand of the adult bird has lost all the characters of a fore-foot ; but in the young cf the Hoatzin (*Opisthocomus*) claws are present on the first two digits (Fig. 428, *A*), which are sufficiently mobile to be used in climbing. Besides the true claws horny *spurs* are sometimes present on the carpo-metacarpus.

There is almost every gradation in the proportional length of the hind-limb, from Birds in which nothing but the foot projects beyond the contour feathers, and even the toes may be feathered, to the long-legged Storks and Cranes, in which the distal part of the tibio-tarsus is covered with scales as well as the foot. In aquatic forms a fold of skin or *web* is stretched between the toes, sometimes including all four digits, as in the Cormorants ; sometimes leaving the hallux free, sometimes forming a separate fringe to each digit, as in the Coots and Grebe. As to the toes themselves, the commonest arrangement is for the hallux to be directed backwards, and Nos. 2, 3, and 4 forwards, but in the Owls No. 4 is reversible, *i.e.*, can be turned in either direction, and in the Parrots, Woodpecker, etc., it, as well as the hallux, is permanently turned backwards. In the

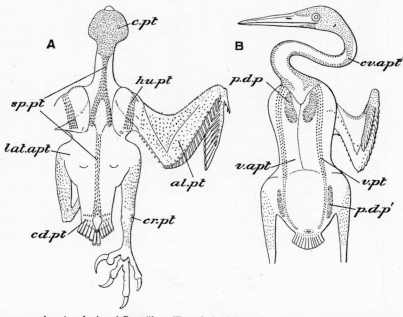

FIG. 429.—*A*, pterylosis of **Gypaëtus** (Bearded Vulture) ; *B*, of **Ardea** (Heron). *al. pt.* wing-tract ; *c. pt.* head-tract ; *cd. pt.* caudal tract ; *cr. pt.* crural tract ; *cv. apt.* cervical space ; *hu. pt.* humeral tract ; *lat. apt.* lateral space ; *p. d. p.*, *p. d. p'.*, powder-down patches ; *sp. pt.* spinal tract ; *v. apt.* ventral space ; *v. pt.* ventral tract.

Swifts, on the other hand, all four toes turn forwards. The hallux is frequently vestigial or absent, and in the Ostrich No. 4 has also atrophied, producing the characteristic two-toed foot of that bird.

Pterylosis.—With the exception of the Penguins, most Carinatæ have the feathers arranged in distinct feather-tracts or pterylæ, separated by apteria or featherless spaces. These are commonly much more distinct than in the Pigeon, and their form and arrangement are of importance in classification (Fig. 429). In the Ratitæ apteria are usually found only in the young, the adult having a uniform covering of feathers. The Ratitæ, also, have nothing more than the merest trace of hooklets on the barbules, so that the barbs do not interlock and the vanes of the feathers are downy or hair-like.   In the Penguins the wing-feathers are degenerate.

Many Birds are quite naked when hatched, but in most cases the body is more or less completely covered by a temporary crop of feathers, the *nestling-downs*, of various forms, but always having a short axis, soft loose barbs, devoid of interlocking apparatus, and, except in ·the Emu, having no after-shaft (*vide* p. 428).   They are succeeded, as already described, by the permanent feathers.

Many Birds, such as the Swan, possess *down-feathers* or *plumulæ* throughout life, interspersed among and hidden by the contour feathers or *pennæ*.   In the Heron and some other Carinatæ are found *powder-down patches* (Fig. 429, *B, p. d. p., p. d. p'.*), areas of downs, the ends of which break off and make a fine dust.   *Semi-plumes* are downs with a well-developed axis : *filoplumes*, as we have seen (Fig. 305, *B*), have an elongated axis and vestigial vexillum.

In many Birds there springs from the under side of the quill, near the superior umbilicus, a second vane, the *after-shaft* (Fig. 430), usually smaller than the main shaft, but sometimes of equal size.   Both among Carinatæ and Ratitæ we find genera with double-shafted feathers and allied forms in which the after-shaft is rudimenatry or absent.

The feathers are always shed or " moulted " at regular intervals, as a rule annually.   The old feathers drop out and new ones are formed from the same pulps.

The *colours* of feathers present great variety.   Black, brown, red, orange, and yellow colours are due to the presence of definite pigments, *i.e.*, are absorption colours. White, and in some cases yellow, are produced by the total reflection of light from the spongy air-containing substance of the feather, there being, as in nearly all other natural objects, no such thing as a white pigment.   Blue, violet, and in some cases green are produced by the light from a brown pigment becoming broken up as it passes through the superficial layer of the feathers in its passage to the eye : no blue or violet pigments occur in feathers, and green pigments are very rare.   The beautiful metallic tints of many birds are entirely the result of structure, owing their existence to a thin, transparent, superficial layer, which acts as a prism : in such feathers the colour changes according to

Fig.   430.—Feather   of   **Casuarius** (Cassowary),   showing aftershaft   and   disconnected   barbs. (From Headley.)

the relative position of the bird and of the eye of the observer with regard to the source of light.

There is also infinite variety in the general coloration of Birds. In many the colouring is distinctly concealing, harmonising with the environment, and even changing with the latter—as in the Ptarmigan, which is greyish-brown in summer, white in winter, the former hue helping to conceal the bird among herbage, the latter on snow. Frequently, as in Pheasants and Birds of Paradise, the female alone is protectively coloured, while the male presents the most varied and brilliant tints, enhanced by crests, plumes or tufts of feathers on the wings, elongated tail, lappets of skin, etc. These have been variously explained as " courtship colours " for attracting the female ; as due simply to the exuberant vitality of the male bird ; or as helping to keep the number of males within proper limits by rendering them conspicuous to their enemies. Such ornaments as the bars and spots on the wings and tail of many gregarious Birds, such as Plovers, fully exposed only during flight, and often widely different in closely allied species, have been explained as " recognition marks," serving to enable stragglers to distinguish between a flock of their own and of some other species.

Skeleton.—The vast majority of birds have saddle-shaped or heterocœlous cervical and thoracic vertebræ, but the thoracic vertebræ are opisthocœlous in the Impennes (Penguins), the Gaviæ (Gulls), and the Limicolæ (Plovers, etc.), while in the Ichthyornithes alone they are biconcave. The spaces between adjacent centra are traversed by a meniscus with a suspensory ligament, as in the Pigeon (p. 432). The number of vertebræ is very variable, especially in the cervical region, where it rises to twenty-five in the Swan and sinks to nine in some Song-birds. There is very commonly more or less fusion of the thoracic vertebræ, and the formation of a syn-sacrum by the concrescence of the posterior thoracic, lumbar, sacral, and anterior caudal vertebræ is universal. The posterior cervical and anterior thoracic vertebræ commonly bear strong *hypapophyses* or inferior processes for the origin of the great flexor muscles of the neck. The number of true sacral vertebræ varies from one to five. A pygostyle, formed by the fusion of more or fewer of the caudal vertebræ, is of general occurrence, but is small and insignificant or absent in the Ratitæ.

The *ribs* are always double-headed, the sternal ribs are ossified, not merely calcified, and are united with the vertebral ribs by synovial joints. Ossified uncinates are nearly always present, and usually become ankylosed to the vertebral ribs.

What may be considered as the normal type of *sternum* is a broad plate, concave dorsally from side to side, and produced ventrally into an anteroposterior keel which is ossified from a distinct centre (Fig. 431, *A, os. 1*). The posterior edge of the bone is either entire (*D*), or presents on each side of the keel one or two more or less deep notches (*A, B*) or foramina (*C*). In the

Ratitæ (E) the keel is either absent or reduced to the merest vestige, and there is no trace of the carinal ossification in the young. External to the coracoid grooves the anterior edge of the sternum is produced into larger or smaller antero-lateral processes (*ant. lat. pr.*); in the Emu these are of great size and are closely applied to the pericardium.

It was upon the characters of the raft-like sternum that the group Ratitæ was founded, but the difference between them and the Carinatæ in this respect

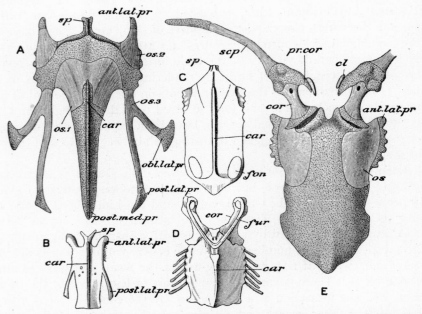

FIG. 431.—Sterna of various Birds. *A*, **Gallus** (common Fowl, young); *B*, **Turdus** (Thrush); *C*, **Vultur** (Vulture); *D*, **Procellaria** (Petrel); *E*, **Casuarius** (Cassowary). *ant. lat. pr.* anterior lateral process; *car.* carina; *cl.* clavicle; *cor.* coracoid; *fon.* fontanelle; *fur.* furcula; *obl. lat. pr.* oblique lateral process; *os.* paired ossification of sternum in *E*; *os. 1*, carinal ossification in *A*; *os. 2, os. 3*, lateral ossifications; *post. med. pr.* posterior median process; *post. lat. pr.* posterior lateral process; *pr. cor.* pro-coracoid; *scp.* scapula; *sp.* spina sterni. (*A* and *E*, after W. K. Parker; *B*, *C*, and *D*, from Bronn's *Thierreich*.)

is not absolute, the ratite condition having been acquired by many Carinatæ which have lost the power of flight. The keel is very small in *Ocydromus*, *Notornis*, and *Aptornis*, three flightless Rails—the last extinct—from New Zealand, and is practically absent in the Dodo (*Raphus*) and Solitaire (*Pezophaps*), two gigantic extinct Pigeons from Mauritius and Rodriguez; in the Kakapo or Ground-parrot (*Stringops*) of New Zealand; in the extinct Giant-Goose (*Cnemiornis*) from the same country; and in Hesperornis. The absence of the carina may therefore be considered as an adaptive modification of no significance as indicating affinity.

The entire order of Penguins (*Impennes*) and the extinct Great Auk (*Penguinus impennis*) are also flightless, but their wings, instead of being functionless, are modified into powerful swimming paddles (Fig. 432). There has therefore, in these cases, been no reduction either of the pectoral muscles or of the carina.

The *skull* of Birds is generally remarkable for its huge orbits separated by a thin inter-orbital septum, and for the comparatively small size of the ethmoid bone and its turbinals. The most striking exception is afforded by the Kiwi

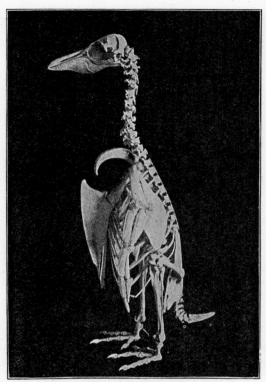

FIG. 432.—**Eudyptes pachyrhynchus** (Penguin). Skeleton.
(From a photograph by A. Hamilton.)

(*Apteryx*), in which the orbits (Fig. 433) are small and indistinct, while the olfactory chambers (*Ec. Eth.*) extend backwards between the eyes ; the orbits being therefore separated from one another by the whole width of the organ of smell. The same thing occurs, to a less degree, in the Moas.

In its essential features the skull is remarkably uniform throughout the class. The rounded form of the brain-case, more or less concealed externally by ridges for the attachment of muscles ; the upper beak, composed mainly of great tri-radiate pre-maxillæ ; the single, small, rounded occipital condyle ;

the slender maxillo-jugal arch ; the large parasphenoidal rostrum ; the freely articulated quadrate, with its otic, orbital, and articular processes ; the absence of the reptilian post-frontals ; and the early ankylosis of the bones—all these characters are universal among birds.   There are, however, endless differences in detail , some of which, connected with the bones of the palate, are of importance in classification.

In the Ratitæ and the Tinamous (*Crypturi*) there are large basi-pterygoid processes (Fig. 434, *B, ptg. pr.*) springing, as in Lizards, from the basi-sphenoid, and articulating with the pterygoids near their posterior ends.   The vomer (*Vo.*) is large and broad, and is usually connected posteriorly with the palatines (*Pal.*), which do not articulate with the rostrum.   The maxillo-palatine pro-

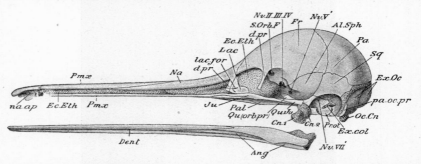

FIG. 433.—**Apteryx mantelli.**   Skull of a young specimen, side view.   The cartilaginous parts are dotted.   *Al. Sph.* alisphenoid ; *Ang.* angular ; *Cn. 1, cn. 2,* condyle of quadrate ; *Dent.* dentary ; *d. pr. d. pr.* descending processes of nasal and frontal ; *Ec. Eth.* ectoethmoid ; *Ex. col.* extra-columella ; *Ex. Oc.* ex-occipital ; *Fr.* frontal ; *Ju.* jugal ; *Lac.* lacrymal ; *lac. for.* lacrymal foramen ; *Na.* nasal ; *na. ap.* nasal aperture ; *Nv. II, III, IV,* optic foramen, transmitting also the 3rd and 4th nerves ; *Nv. V',* foramen for orbito-nasal nerve ; *Nv. VII',* for facial ; *Pa.* parietal ; *Pal.* palatine ; *pa. oc. pr.* par-occipital process ; *P. mx.* pre-maxilla ; *Pr. ot.* pro-otic ; *Qu.Ju.* quadratojugal ; *Qu. (orb. pr.)* orbital process of quadrate ; *S. Orb. F.* supra-orbital foramen ; *Sq.* squamosal.   (After T. J. Parker.)

cesses are comparatively small, and do not unite with one another or with the vomer.   This arrangement of the bones of the palate is called *dromæognathous.*

In many Carinatæ, *e.g.,* the Pigeon and the Fowl, the basi-pterygoid processes are either absent or spring from the base of the rostrum. The vomer is small and pointed, or may be absent, and the palatines articulate posteriorly with the rostrum. The maxillo-palatines do not unite with one another. These peculiarities characterise the *schizognathous* arrangement. In the Passeres a similar arrangement obtains, but the vomer is broad and truncated instead of pointed in front. This gives the *ægithognathous* arrangement. Lastly in the Storks, Birds of Prey, Ducks, and Geese, etc., the maxillo-palatines (Fig. 435, *mx. p.*) fuse with one another in the middle line, often giving rise to a flat, spongy palate and producing the *desmognathous* arrangement.

The most specialised form of skull is found in the Parrots (Fig. 436).   In many Birds the nasals and the ascending process of the premaxillæ are very

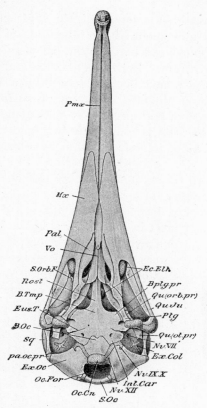

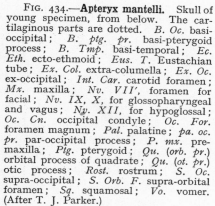

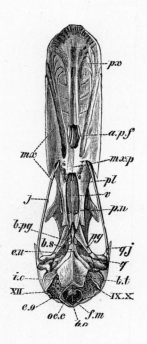

FIG. 434.—**Apteryx mantelli.** Skull of young specimen, from below. The cartilaginous parts are dotted. *B. Oc.* basioccipital; *B. ptg. pr.* basi-pterygoid process; *B. Tmp.* basi-temporal; *Ec. Eth.* ecto-ethmoid; *Eus. T.* Eustachian tube; *Ex. Col.* extra-columella; *Ex. Oc.* ex-occipital; *Int. Car.* carotid foramen; *Mx.* maxilla; *Nv. VII'*, foramen for facial; *Nv. IX, X,* for glossopharyngeal and vagus; *Nv. XII,* for hypoglossal; *Oc. Cn.* occipital condyle; *Oc. For.* foramen magnum; *Pal.* palatine; *pa. oc. pr.* par-occipital process; *P. mx.* premaxilla; *Ptg.* pterygoid; *Qu. (orb. pr.)* orbital process of quadrate; *Qu. (ot. pr.)* otic process; *Rost.* rostrum; *S. Oc.* supra-occipital; *S. Orb. F.* supra-orbital foramen; *Sq.* squamosal; *Vo.* vomer. (After T. J. Parker.)

FIG. 435.—**Anas boschas** (Duck). Ventral view of Skull. *a. p. f.* anterior palatine foramen; *b. o.* basi-occipital; *b. pg.* basi-pterygoid. process; *b. s.* basi-sphenoid; *b. t.* basi-temporal; *e. o.* ex-occipital; *eu.* aperture of Eustachian tube; *f. m.* foramen magnum; *i. c.* internal carotid foramen; *j.* jugal; *mx.* maxilla; *mx. p.* maxillo-palatine process; *oc. c.* occipital condyle; *pl.* palatine; *p. n.* posterior nares; *px.* premaxilla; *q.* quadrate; *qj.* quadratojugal; *v.* vomer; *IX, X,* foramen for ninth and tenth nerves; *XII,* for twelfth nerve. (From Wiedersheim's *Vertebrata.*)

thin and elastic where they join the skull, and there is an unossified space in the mesethmoid, so that the upper beak is capable of a considerable amount of movement in the vertical plane. In Parrots there is a true joint between the upper beak and the skull, allowing of that movement of the former which is so striking in the living Bird.   When the mandible is depressed, the contraction of the digastric muscle causes a forward movement of the lower end of the quadrate, which pushes forwards the maxillo-jugal bar and the palatines and pterygoids, the latter sliding upon the rostrum.   Both the maxillæ and the palatines are articulated in front with the premaxilla, and together push it upwards ; in this way depression of the lower produces an automatic raising of the upper jaw.   The great size and strength of both premaxilla and mandible are remarkable, as also is the fact that the orbit is completely surrounded by bone, a backward process of the lacrymal being joined beneath it by a forward process of the frontal.

The *mandible* contains in the young bird the six bones on each side characteristic of reptiles ; the coronary is, however, often absent.   As a rule the head of the *quadrate* articulates with the roof of the tympanic cavity by a single facet in Ratitæ, by a double facet in Carinatæ.   The *hyoid* always agrees in essential respects with that of the Pigeon ; in the Woodpecker the posterior cornua are curved round the head and attached to the skull in the neighbourhood of the right nostril, a very flexible and protrusible tongue being produced.

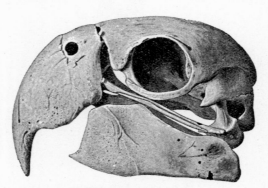

FIG. 436.—Skull of **Ara** (Macaw).   (From a photograph by A. Hamilton.)

The structure of the *shoulder-girdle* furnishes one of the most fundamental distinctive characters between Ratitæ and Carinatæ, but, as with the sternum, the differences are adaptive and not of phylogenetic significance.   In most Carinatæ both coracoid and scapula are large and united with one another by ligament ; the coracoid has an acrocoracoid and the scapula an acromion process ; the coraco-scapular angle is acute ; and there is a furcula.   In the Ratitæ the coracoid (Fig. 437, *cor.*) and scapula (*scp.*) are much reduced in proportional size and are ankylosed with one another ; the acrocoracoid (*acr. cor.*) and acromion (*acr.*) processes are reduced or absent ; the coraco-scapular angle approaches two right angles ; and there is no furcula, although separate vestiges of clavicles are present in the Emu and Cassowary.   In some of the Moas (*Pachyornis*, etc.) the shoulder-girdle is wholly absent.   But, as in the case of the sternum, the distinction is not absolute.   In Hesperornis, the Dodo, the Solitaire, Aptornis, Notornis, Ocydromus, and Cnemiornis the bones of the shoulder-girdle are proportionally small, the coraco-scapular angle exceeds 90° and in some cases, such as certain Parrakeets and Owls, the furcula is feeble, or represented by paired vestiges, or absent. Curiously enough, considering that increase in the coraco-scapular angle is usually correlated with diminished powers of flight, it also slightly excedes 90° in the Albatross and some of its allies.

In most adult Birds the procoracoid is reduced to a process on the dorsal end of the coracoid, but in the Ostrich and in the embryo of Apteryx it is well developed and separated by a fenestra from the coracoid. A small bone, the *accessory scapula*, is sometimes found on the outer side of the shoulder-joint.

The variations in the structure of the wing are mostly matters of proportion, but a remarkable flattening of all the bones is very characteristic of Penguins

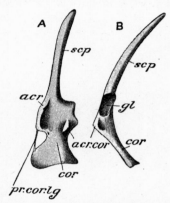

FIG. 437.—**Apteryx mantelli.** The left shoulder-girdle. *A*, anterior ; *B*, lateral (outer) surface. *acr.* acromion ; *acr. cor.* acrocoracoid ; *cor.* coracoid ; *gl.* glenoid cavity ; *pr. cor. lg.* procoracoid, reduced to a ligament ; *scp.* scapula. (After T. J. Parker.)

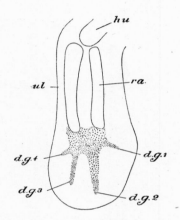

FIG. 438.—**Sterna wilsoni** (Tern). Fore-limb of embryo. *dg. 1—4*, digits ; *hu.* humerus ; *ra.* radius ; *ul.* ulna. (After Leighton.)

(Fig. 432), which are further distinguished by the presence of a sesamoid bone, the *patella ulnaris*, taking the place of the olecranon process. In the Emu and Kiwi the first and third digits of the normal wing have atrophied during development, the middle one alone remaining. In the Moas (Fig. 423) no trace of a wing has been found, and in one species only is there even a trace of the glenoid cavity. In the embryos of several Birds an additional digit has been found on the ulnar or post-axial side (Fig. 438, *dg. 4*) : this brings the total number of digits up to four, the fifth of the pentadactyle hand alone being unrepresented.

The simplest type of *pelvic girdle* is found in Apteryx (Fig. 439) and the Tinamous, in which both pubis and ischium are free along their whole length, as in Dinosaurs. In the Emu and Cassowary the pubis and ischium unite by cartilage or bone at their posterior end with the ilium, and in most Birds the union between the two last is extensive, the deep ischiatic notch being replaced by a small foramen. In the embryonic condition (Fig. 440) the ilium has a very small pre-acetabular portion, the pubis and ischium are nearly vertical, and there is a distinct pectineal process (*pp*)—retained in Apteryx (Fig. 439, *p*)—the whole pubis being singularly like that of a Dinosaur. In the Ostrich alone the pubes unite in the middle ventral line to form a symphysis: Rhea presents the unique peculiarity of a dorsal symphysis of the ischia, just below the vertebral column : in the Emu the posterior end of the pubis gives off a slender process, which extends forwards close to the ventral edge of that bone and probably represents the *epi-pubis* of reptiles.

The bones of the *hind-limb* are very uniform throughout the class, but the form of the tarso-metatarsus of Penguins is worthy of notice. It is short and

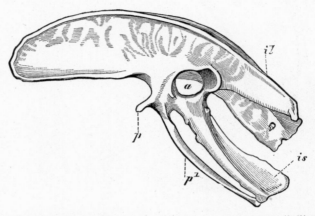

FIG. 439.—**Apteryx australis.** Left innominate. *a.* acetabulum ; *il.* ilium ; *is.* ischium ; *p.* pectineal process ; *p¹.* pubis. (From Wiedersheim, after Marsh.)

wide, its three constituent metatarsals, though fused, are clearly distinguishable throughout their whole length, and the resemblance to the homologous part in Iguanodon is very striking. In the embryo (Fig. 441) a vestige of the fifth digit (*mt. tsl. 5*) has been found in the form of a small rod of cartilage on the post-axial or fibular side. One or two free centralia may occur in the mesotarsal joint.

The skeleton is always more or less pneumatic, but there is no definite relation between pneumaticity and power of flight. A very usual arrangement is for all the bones to contain air except those of the fore-arm and hand, shank and foot. But in Apteryx, Penguins, and some Song-birds the skull alone is pneumatic, while in the Hornbill every bone in the body contains air.

Myology.—As might be inferred from a study of the skeleton, the muscles of flight undergo a great reduction, often amounting to complete atrophy, in the Ratitæ ; and to a less degree in the flightless Carinatæ. The presence or absence of an ambiens and of certain other muscles in the leg and in the wing furnish characters of considerable classificatory importance.

Digestive Organs.—In all existing Neornithes the jaws are covered by a horny beak and there are no *teeth*. But that teeth were present in the more primitive birds, and have gradually been lost during the evolution of the recent orders, seems certain from the fact that the cretaceous birds were toothed. In Hesperornis (Fig. 420) there are long conical teeth in both jaws, set in a continuous groove. In Ichthyornis (Fig. 419) the teeth are thecodont, like those of the Crocodile, each being placed in a distinct socket. In Gastornis and in Odontopteryx, an extinct carinate form allied to the Anseres, the margins of the bony jaws are produced into strong, pointed, tooth-like prominences.

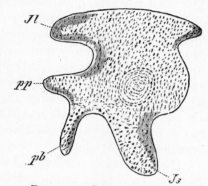

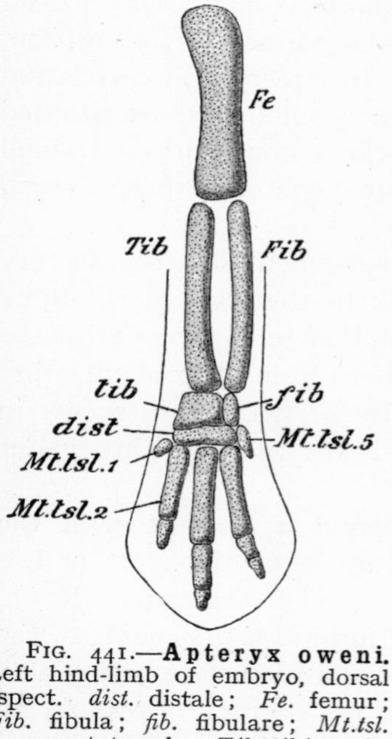

FIG. 440.—**Gallus bankiva** (common Fowl). Innominate of a six days' embryo. *Jl.* ilium; *Js.* ischium; *pb.* pubis; *p. p.* pectineal process. (From Wiedersheim, after Johnson.)

FIG. 441.—**Apteryx oweni.** Left hind-limb of embryo, dorsal aspect. *dist.* distale; *Fe.* femur; *Fib.* fibula; *fib.* fibulare; *Mt.tsl.* *1—5*, metatarsals; *Tib.* tibia; *tib.* tibiale. (After T. J. Parker.)

In the *enteric canal* the chief variations have to do with the size of the crop and of the cæca, with the gizzard, and with the coiling of the intestine. In grain-eating Birds the gizzard has thick muscular walls and is lined by a thickened horny epithelium, as in the Pigeon: in flesh-eaters, such as Gulls, Petrels, Hawks, and Owls, it is thin-walled and lined with epithelium of the ordinary character. In the Common Fowl and many other birds the cæca are of great length. A *gall-bladder* is usually present : the *spleen* is always small. The *tongue* may be pointed, as in the Pigeon ; very long and protrusible, as in Woodpeckers ; short and thick, as in Parrots ; or modified for honey-sucking by the tip being produced either into a brush-like organ or into paired sucking tubes. There are variously situated *buccal glands*, to some of which the name *salivary* is often applied.

Respiratory and Vocal Organs.—The rings of the *trachea* are always ossified : the tube is frequently deflected to one side by the crop, as in the Pigeon, and may undergo such an increase in length as to extend beneath the skin of the abdomen, or even into the keel of the sternum. The *syrinx* is either *tracheo-bronchial*, as in the Pigeon, *i.e.*, formed by the distal end of the trachea and the proximal ends of the bronchi, or is exclusively *tracheal* or exclusively *bronchial*. In singing birds it is complex, and is provided with numerous muscles—five or seven pairs.

The *lungs* are always firmly fixed to the dorsal body-wall by a pulmonary aponeurosis, and are but slightly distensible. The general arrangement of the air-sacs has been described in the Pigeon (p. 444) : in Apteryx the abdominal air-sacs are small, and are completely enclosed by the oblique septum, so as not to extend into the abdominal cavity among the viscera. The bronchi send off branches at right angles.

The **Circulatory Organs** agree in all essential respects with those of the Pigeon : their most characteristic features are the large size of the heart, the muscular right auriculo-ventricular valve, the atrophy of the left aortic arch, and the vestigial character of the renal portal system. The red blood-corpuscles are always oval and nucleated.

Nervous System and Sense Organs.—The *brain* is also very uniform in structure, being characterised by its short, rounded hemispheres, large folded cerebellum produced forwards to meet the hemispheres, and laterally placed optic lobes. In the embryo the optic lobes have the normal dorsal position, and the whole brain resembles that of a Reptile. In Apteryx, in correlation with the reduction of the eyes, the optic lobes are very small, and are situated on the under side of the brain. Above the anterior commissure is a small bundle of fibres which has been considered as the homologue of the *hippocampal commissure* of Mammals.

Apteryx is also distinguished by the high development of the olfactory chamber, which extends from the tip of the beak to the level of the optic foramina : the turbinals are large and complex, and there is a vestige of the cartilage of Jacobson's organ. The small eye differs from that of all other birds in the absence of a pecten, although a vestige of that organ occurs in the embryo. The structure of the *auditory organ* is very uniform throughout the class.

Urinogenital Organs.—In these, also, the general agreement with the Pigeon is very close, the most characteristic feature being the more or less complete atrophy of the right ovary and oviduct. The Megistanes, Rheæ, Anseres, and some other Birds have a penis in the form of a thickening of the ventral wall of the cloaca : it has a groove on the dorsal surface acting as a sperm-channel, and its distal end is invaginated, in the position of rest, by an elastic ligament. In the Ostrich there is a solid penis, like that of Chelonia and Crocodiles : it can be retracted into a pouch of the cloaca.

Development.—The process of development in Birds has been most thoroughly worked out in the Common Fowl, but enough is known of the embryology of other Birds to show that the differences are comparatively unimportant.

The *ovum* is always large owing to the great quantity of food-yolk ; the protoplasm forms a small *germinal disc* at the upper pole. Impregnation is internal, and as the oosperm passes down the oviduct it is coated by successive secretions from the oviducal glands. It first receives a coat of thick, viscid *albumen* (Fig. 442, *alb.*), which, as the egg rotates during its passage, becomes coiled at either end into a twisted cord, the *chalaza* (*ch.*). Next, more fluid albumen (*alb'.*) is deposited layer by layer, then a tough, parchment-like *shell-membrane* (*sh. m.*), and finally a calcareous *shell* (*sh.*). The shell-membrane is double, and, at the broad end of the egg, the two layers are separate and enclose an air-cavity (*a.*). The shell may be white or variously coloured by special pigments : it consists of three layers, and is traversed by vertical pore-canals, which are unbranched in the Carinatæ and in Apteryx, branched in the other Ratitæ.

The eggs may be laid on the bare ground or on the rocks by the sea-shore, as in Penguins and Auks, or on the ledges on inaccessible cliffs, as in the Sooty Albatross (*Diomedea fuliginosa*) ; but as a rule a *nest* is constructed for their reception by the parent Birds. This may simply be a hole in the sand, as in the Ostrich ; a mere clearing on the hill-side surrounded by a low wall of earth, as in the Wandering Albatross (*Diomedea exulans*) ; or a cylinder with excavated top, built of grass, earth, and manure, as in the Mollymawks (*Diomedea melanophrys*, etc.). It may take the form of a burrow, as in many Petrels, Kingfishers, and Sand-martins, or it may be more or less elaborately built or woven of sticks, moss, leaves, hair, or feathers, showing every stage of constructive skill, from the rude contrivance of sticks of the Pigeon and Eagle to the accurately constructed cap- or dome-shaped nests of many familiar Passeres. In the Tailor-bird (*Orthotomus*) it is formed of leaves sewn together, the beak acting as needle : in a Malayan Swift (*Collocalia*) it is largely built of the secretion of the Bird's buccal glands.

The number of eggs laid varies from 15–18 in the Partridge to a single one in many Sea-birds and in the Kiwi. As a rule the size of the eggs bears some proportion to that of the Bird, the smallest being those of Humming-birds, the largest those of the Moas and of Æpyornis : but in Apteryx the egg is of disproportionate size—as large as a Swan's or an Albatross's, the Kiwi itself being no larger than a barndoor Fowl.

Segmentation takes place during the passage of the egg down the oviduct, and results, as in Reptiles, in the formation of a *blastoderm* (Fig. 442, *bl.*) occupying a small area on the upper pole of the yolk. After the egg is laid, the process of development is arrested unless the temperature is kept up to about 37° to 40° C. : this is usually done by the heat of the body of the parent Birds, one or both of which sit upon, or *incubate*, the eggs until the young are hatched ;

but in the Australian mound-makers (*Megapodius*) the eggs are buried in heaps of decaying vegetable matter, the decomposition of which generates the necessary heat.

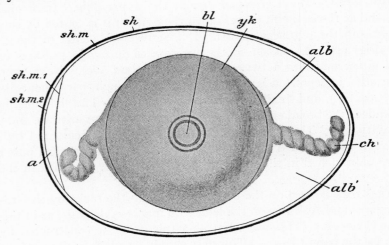

FIG. 442.—**Gallus bankiva** (domestic Fowl). Semi-diagrammatic view of the egg at the time of laying. *a.* air-space; *alb.* dense layer of albumen; *alb'.* more fluid albumen; *bl.* blastoderm; *ch.* chalaza; *sh.* shell; *sh. m.* shell-membrane; *sh. m. 1, sh. m. 2,* its two layers separated to enclose air-cavity. (From Marshall's *Embryology*, slightly altered.)

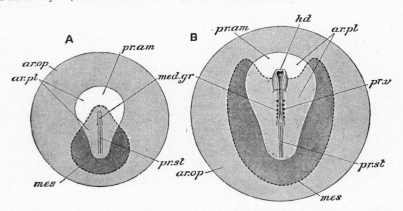

FIG. 443.—**Gallus bankiva.** Two stages in the development of the blastoderm: diagrammatic. *ar. op.* area opaca; *ar. pl.* area pellucida; *hd.* head; *med. gr.* medullary groove; *mes.* mesoderm, indicated by dotted outline and deeper shade; *pr. am.* pro-amnion; *pr. st.* primitive streak; *pr. v.* protovertebræ. (From Marshall's *Embryology*, in part after Duval.)

In the newly-laid egg the blastoderm is divisible, as in Reptiles, into two parts, a central, clear *area pellucida* (Fig. 443, *ar. pl.*) and a peripheral *area opaca* (*ar. op.*), and is formed of a superficial ectoderm having below it a somewhat irregular aggregation of cells not yet forming a definite layer.

On the surface of the area pellucida, as in the Reptiles, appears an *embryonic shield*, the formation of which is due to the elongation of the ectoderm cells in a ventral direction. A primitive knot (p. 418) is absent as a distinct structure, and there is no invagination. In the posterior part of the area pellucida behind the embryonic shield appears a longitudinal opaque band, the *primitive streak* (*pr. st.*), and along the middle of this is formed a groove, the *primitive groove*. The latter represents the blastopore of the reptiles, and there is no archenteric cavity. It is by active proliferation of cells along the course of the primitive streak, which represents the coalescent lips of the blastopore, leading to the

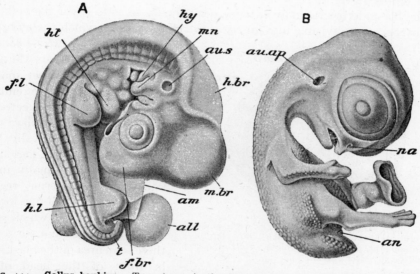

FIG. 444.—**Gallus bankiva.** Two stages in the development of the embryo. *all.* allantois; *am.* cut edge of amnion; *an.* anus; *au. ap.* auditory aperture; *au. s.* auditory sac; *f. br.* fore-brain; *f. l.* fore-limb; *h. br.* hind-brain; *h. l.* hind-limb; *ht.* heart; *hy.* hyoid arch; *m. br.* mid-brain; *mn.* mandibular arch; *na.* nostril; *t.* tail. (After Duval.)

formation of masses of new cells that grow out laterally and forwards into the space between the ectoderm and yolk-endoderm, that the foundations of the mesoderm are formed. In the anterior primitive streak-region the primitive knot of the reptiles is represented by a close union, for a short space, of all three layers. In front the primitive streak becomes free from the ectoderm and unites below with the endoderm : this anterior extremity of the primitive streak is known as the *head-process*.

As there is no invagination in birds in general, there is no primitive endoderm, and the definitive endoderm is formed solely from cells underlying the embryonic shield. The notochord is formed by an axial modification of the endoderm cells along the anterior primitive streak-region and the head-process. In the latter is formed the anterior of head-part of the notochord, and from it are derived also the mesoderm of the head and the endodermal lining of the head-part of the enteric canal.

Immediately in front of the primitive streak the *medullary groove* (*med. gr.*) appears, and the *medullary folds* which bound it on the right and left diverge posteriorly, so as to embrace the anterior end of the primitive streak, in just the same way as they embrace the blastopore in Amphioxus. In some Birds there is an invagination at the anterior end of the primitive groove, resulting in the formation of a neurenteric canal. Both primitive streak and medullary groove lie at right angles to the long axis of the egg, the broad end of the latter being to the embryo's right.

The blastoderm gradually extends peripherally so as to cover the yolk, and thereby becomes divisible into an *embryonic portion*, from which the embryo is formed, and an *extra-embryonic portion*, which invests the yolk-sac and takes no direct share in the formation of the embryo. The extension of the ectoderm and endoderm takes place regularly and symmetrically, but the extra-embryonic mesoderm, while extending equally in the lateral and posterior regions, grows forwards in the form of paired extensions, which afterwards unite, so that for a time there is an area of the blastoderm in front of the head of the embryo, formed of ectoderm and endoderm only : this is called the *proamnion* (*pr. am.*).

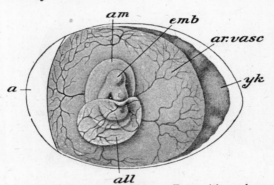

FIG. 445.—**Gallus bankiva.** Egg with embryo and fœtal appendages. *a.* air-space; *all.* allantois; *am.* amnion; *ar. vasc.* area vasculosa; *emb.* embryo; *yk.* yolk-sac. (After Duval.)

At an early period the *vertebral plate* or dorsal portion of mesoderm bounding the medullary groove becomes segmented into proto-vertebræ (Fig. 443, *B*, *pr. v.*), and the *lateral plate* or ventral portion of the same layer splits into somatic and splanchnic layers with the cœlome between (Fig. 446, *B*).

Gradually the embryo becomes folded off from the yolk-sac, as in other large-yolked eggs ; but, owing apparently to the confined space in which it is enclosed, it soon turns over so as to lie with its left side against the yolk and its right side facing the shell (Fig. 445). The body (Fig. 444, *A*) becomes strongly flexed so as to bring the head and tail almost into contact, and the head soon acquires a proportionally immense size, with very large projecting eyes. At first the head is quite like that of one of the lower vertebrate embryos, with protuberant brain-swellings (*f. br., m. br., h. br.*), large square mouth, ventrally placed nostrils connected by grooves with the mouth, and three or four pairs of gill-slits. As in Reptiles, there is never any trace of gills. In the Ostrich and Apteryx, as well as in some Carinatæ, an opercular fold grows backwards from the hyoid arch, and covers the second and third branchial clefts. Soon the margins of the mouth grow out into a beak (Fig. 444, B), the clefts close, with the exception of the first, which gives rise to the tympano-eustachian passage, and the head becomes characteristically avian. The limbs are at first alike in form and size (A, f. l., h. l.), and the hands and feet have the character of paws, the former with three, the latter with four digits; but gradually the second digit of the hand outgrows the first and third, producing the characteristic avian manus (B), while the metatarsal region elongates and gives rise to the equally characteristic foot. At the same time feather-papillæ make their appearance, arranged in narrow and well-defined pterylæ.

At an early period capillaries appear in the extra-embryonic blastoderm between the opaque and pellucid areas, and give rise to a well-defined *area vasculosa* (Fig. 445, *ar. vasc.*): they are supplied by *vitelline arteries* from the dorsal aorta, and their blood is returned by *vitelline veins* which join the portal vein and take the blood, through the liver, to the heart. The vascular area gradually extends, until it covers the whole of the yolk-sac: its vessels take an important share in the absorption of the yolk by the embryo.

Before the embryo has begun to be folded off from the yolk the rudiment of one of the two characteristic *embryonic membranes*, the *amnion*, has appeared. A crescentic *amniotic fold* arises (Fig. 446, A, *am. f.*), in front of the head-end of the embryo, from the region of the pro-amnion: it consists at first of ectoderm only, the mesoderm not having yet spread into the pro-amnion. The fold is soon continued backwards along the sides of the body (B) and round the tail (A), but in these regions (*am. f'.*) it consists from the first of ectoderm *plus* the somatic layer of mesoderm, *i.e.*, it is a fold of what may be called the extra-embryonic body-wall. The cavity is a prolongation of the space between the somatic and splanchnic layers of mesoderm, *i.e.*, is an extension of the extra-embryonic cœlome.

The entire amniotic fold gradually closes in above (C), forming a double-layered dome over the embryo. Its inner layer, formed of ectoderm internally and mesoderm externally, is the *amnion* (*am.*), the cavity of which becomes filled with a watery *amniotic fluid*, serving as a protective water-cushion to the enclosed embryo. Its outer layer, formed of ectoderm externally and mesoderm internally, is the *serous membrane* (*sr. m.*): it comes to lie just beneath the vitelline membrane, with which it subsequently fuses.

The second of the embryonic membranes, the *allantois*, is developed as an outpushing of the ventral wall of the mesenteron at its posterior end (C, *all.*), and consists, therefore, of a layer of splanchnic mesoderm lined by endoderm. It has at first the form of a small ovoid sac having the precise anatomical relations of the urinary bladder of Amphibia (Fig. 446, A, *all.*). It increases

484

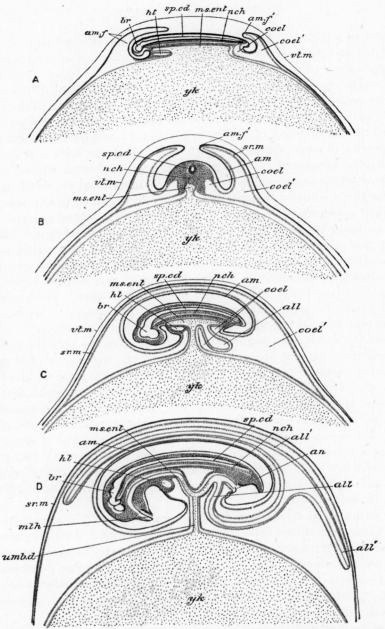

FIG. 446.—Diagrams illustrating the development of the fœtal membranes of a **Bird.** *A,* early stage in the formation of the amnion, sagittal section ; *B,* slightly later stage, transverse section ; *C,* stage with completed amnion and commencing allantois ; *D,* stage in which the allantois has begun to envelop the embryo and yolk-sac. The ectoderm is represented by a blue, the endoderm by a red line ; the mesoderm is grey. *all.* allantois ; *all'.* the same growing round the embryo and yolk-sac ; *am.* amnion ; *am. f., am. f'.* amniotic fold ; *an.* anus ; *br.* brain ; *cœl.* cœlome ; *cœl'.* extra-embryonic cœlome ; *ht.* heart ; *ms. ent.* mesenteron ; *mth.* mouth ; *nch.* notochord ; *sp. cd.* spinal cord ; *sr. m.* serous membrane ; *umb. d.* umbilical duct ; *vt. m.* vitelline membrane ; *yk.* yolk-sac.

rapidly in size (Fig. 446, *all.*), and makes its way backwards and to the right, into the extra-embryonic cœlome, between the mnion and the serous membrane (Fig. 446, *C*, *D*). Arteries pass to it from the dorsal aorta, and its veins, joining with those from the yolk-sac, take the blood through the liver to the heart. Next, the distal end of the sac spreads itself out and extends all round the embryo and yolk-sac (*D*, *all'.*), fusing, as it does so, with the serous and vitelline membranes, and so coming to lie immediately beneath the shell-membrane. It finally encloses the whole embryo and yolk-sac together with the remains of the albumen, which has by this time been largely absorbed. The allantois serves as the embryonic respiratory organ, gaseous exchange readily taking place through the porous shell; its cavity is an embryonic urinary bladder, excretory products being discharged into it from the kidneys.

At the end of incubation the embryo breaks the shell, usually by means of a little horny elevation or *caruncle* at the end of the beak. By this time the remainder of the yolk-sac has been drawn into the cœlome, and the ventral body-walls have closed round it. On the shell being broken respiratory movements begin, the aperture is enlarged, and the young bird is hatched and begins a free life.

In the Ratitæ, Anseres, Gallinæ, and some other Birds the young when hatched are clothed with a complete covering of down or of feathers, and are able from the first to run about and feed themselves; such Birds are called *Præcoces* or *Nidifugæ*. In the higher types, such as the Rapacious Birds, Pigeons, and Passeres, the young are at first either quite naked, blind and helpless, or covered with mere patches of soft down, so that they require to be fed and kept warm by the parents; these forms are called *Altrices* or *Nidicolæ*. In many Sea-birds, such as Petrels, Gulls, and Penguins, the young have a complete covering of woolly down, but remain in the nest for a prolonged period, sometimes until the full size is attained.

Distribution.—The Ratitæ furnish an interesting case of discontinuous distribution. Struthio occurs in Africa and South-western Asia, Rhea in South America, Dromæus in Australia, Casuarius in Australia, New Guinea, and some of the other Austro-Malayan islands, and Apteryx in New Zealand. Thus, taking recent forms only, each of the great Southern land-masses contains one order of Ratitæ not found elsewhere; the Struthiones are Ethiopian, but extend also into the adjacent part of the Palæarctic region, the Rheæ Neotropical, and the Megistanes Australasian. Æpyornis, the affinities of which appear to be with the Megistanes, occurs only in Madagascar, where it has become extinct within—geologically speaking— comparatively recent times. When we take the scattered distribution of the above-mentioned Ratitæ into consideration, one of the most remarkable facts in distribution is the occurrence, in the limited area of New Zealand, of no fewer than six genera and between twenty and thirty species of Dinornithidæ or Moas, some of which became extinct so short a time ago that their skin, flesh, feathers, dung, and egg-shells are preserved.

Among the Carinatæ the Penguins are exclusively southern, occurring only in the South Temperate and Arctic Oceans. They may be said to be represented in the Northern Hemisphere by the Puffins and Auks, one of which, the Great Auk or Gare-fowl (*Alca impennis*), was actually impennate, its wings being converted, as in the Penguins, into paddles. The Crypturi (Tinamous) are exclusively Neotropical, the Humming-birds American, the Birds of Paradise and Bower-birds Australian and Austro-Malayan. Amongst negative facts, the Psittaci or Parrots are characteristically absent in the Palæarctic and most of the Nearctic region, the Finches in the Australasian region, as well as in New Zealand and Polynesia, and the Starlings in both regions of the New World.

Birds are comparatively rare in the fossil state : their powers of flight render them less liable to be swept away and drowned by floods and so imbedded in deposits at the mouths of rivers or in lakes. Up to the Cretaceous period, Archæopteryx and Archæornis, from the Jurassic, are the only Birds known. In the Cretaceous of North America toothed Birds of the orders Odontolcæ and Ichthyornithes make their appearance, while in the Eocene numerous interesting forms occur, including the Gastornithes and the Stereornithes.

Ethology.—It is impossible here to do more than allude, in the briefest way, to the immense and fascinating group of facts relating to the instincts, habits, and adaptations found in the present class. Their social instincts, their song, their courtship-customs, the wonderful advance in the parental instinct, leading to diminished mortality in the young, are all subjects for which the reader must be referred to the works on general Natural History mentioned in the Appendix.

CLASS V.—MAMMALIA.

The class Mammalia, the highest of the Vertebrata, comprises, among living animals, the sub-classes Prototheria (Monotremata), Metatheria (Marsupialia), and Eutheria (Placentalia). In addition to a number of extinct orders and families that can be placed in one or other of the above sub-classes, there are also several other sub-classes which arose and became entirely extinct at a much earlier period of time. These are loosely known as the " Mesozoic Mammals," and are divided into the groups Multituberculata, Triconodonta, Symmetrodonta, and Pantotheria.

Although no definite " missing link " has as yet been found, there is enough evidence from certain extinct forms, both Reptiles and Mammals, for the universal acceptance of the view that the Mammals had a reptilian ancestry, and this view is further supported by certain anatomical features found in the still-living Monotremes.

The Mammalia as a class have some characters that can be termed diagnostic, as long as it is remembered that at some time there must have been animals with a mixture of the ancestral reptilian and the beginnings of the modern mammalian characters. Indeed, the Monotremata are still in some respects in this position.

A typical modern Mammal, as compared with a modern Reptile, can be recognised by

1. The possession of a covering of hair. This, as a secondary adaptation, may largely be but never is entirely, lost. The scales of the reptilian ancestry are not fully dispensed with, but may remain on some parts of the body, as, for instance, on the tail of a rat.

2. The diaphragm, a partition of muscular fibres with a tendinous centre separating the lungs and pericardium from the other viscera, is a universal feature of Mammals, and occurs nowhere else.

3. There are always three auditory ossicles in the ear, which now consists of three parts : the outer, middle, and inner ear (see page 497).

4. The bones of the lower jaw are now reduced to one, the *dentary*.

5. The vertebræ are gastrocentrous (see page 337), and each vertebra consists of a centrum and neural arch, and, in addition, thin, plate-like discs of bone—the *epiphyses*—at each end which on the cessation of growth fuse with the body of the vertebra.

6. The heart is completely four-chambered, and the left aortic arch alone persists.

7. The young are nourished for some time after birth on milk, the secretion of the female mammary glands, a production peculiar to Mammals.

In addition to these seven diagnostic characters, there can be given a further list which can be divided into two categories—viz., those characters which are found in a primitive condition in the reptilian ancestors and which become increasingly perfected in Mammals from the earlier to the later types, as, for instance, the gradual growth of the brain leading up to the highly complex type with neopallium and numerous convolutions ; the gradual perfection of the larynx and epiglottis, which in the Amphibia and Reptilia are represented only by rudiments ; the gradual acquisition of a hard palate and so on. In the other category are those reptilian characters that are disappearing, such, for instance, as the loss of several bones of the skull and lower jaws ; the gradual reduction of the elements of the shoulder-girdle, accompanied by a greater mechanical perfection of the parts that remain ; the loss of the polyphyodont sets of teeth and their reduction to the milk and permanent sets only, together with the modification of the individual teeth into incisors, canines, premolars, and molars.

EXAMPLE OF THE CLASS—THE RABBIT (*Lepus cuniculus*).

External Characters.—The Rabbit (Fig. 447) is a four-footed or quadrupedal animal, having the whole surface of its body covered with soft fur. The head bears below its anterior extremity the mouth, in the form of a transverse slit bounded by soft lips. The upper lip is divided by a longitudinal cleft, running backwards to the nostrils, and exposing the chisel-shaped *incisor teeth*. Behind the incisor teeth the hairy integument projects on each side into the cavity of the mouth. At the end of the snout, above the mouth, are the

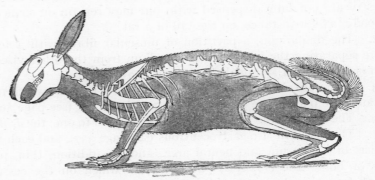

FIG. 447.—**Lepus cuniculus.** Lateral view of skeleton with outline of body.

nostrils, in the shape of two oblique slits. The large eyes, situated at the sides of the head, have each three eyelids, an upper and lower hairy lid, and an anterior hairless third eyelid or *nictitating membrane*, supported by a plate of cartilage. *Vibrissæ*—very long stiff hairs—are scattered above and below the eyes and on the snout. Behind the eyes, and a little nearer the summit of the head, are a pair of very long flexible and movable external ears or *pinnæ*. These are somewhat spout-shaped, expanding distally, and are usually placed vertically with the concavity directed laterally and somewhat forwards, leading to the external auditory opening. The *neck* is a distinct constriction, but relatively short as compared with the neck of the Pigeon. The *trunk* is distinguishable into *thorax* in front and *abdomen* behind. On the ventral surface of the abdomen in the female are four or five pairs of little papillæ—the *teats*. At its posterior end, below the root of the tail, is the *anal opening*, and in front of this in the male is the *penis*, with a small terminal *urinogenital aperture*, and with the *testes*, each in a prominent *scrotal sac*, at the sides ; and in the female the opening of the *vulva*. In the space (*perinæum*) between anus and penis or vulva are two bare, depressed areas of skin into which open the ducts of certain glands—the *perinæal glands*—with a secretion having a strong and characteristic odour. The *tail* is very short and covered with a tuft of fluffy fur.

The *fore-* and *hind-limbs*, both of which take part in locomotion and in supporting the weight of the animal, differ considerably in size—the fore-limbs being much shorter than the hind-limbs. Both have the same general divisions as in the Lizard. The upper arm is almost completely hidden by the skin, being applied closely against the side of the body. The *manus* is provided with five digits, each terminating in a horny claw. The thigh is also almost hidden by the skin ; the *pes* has four digits only, all provided with claws.

Skeleton.—The *spinal column* of the Rabbit is divisible, like that of the Pigeon and the Lizard, into five regions—the cervical, the thoracic, the lumbar, the sacral, and the caudal. In the *cervical* region there are seven vertebræ,

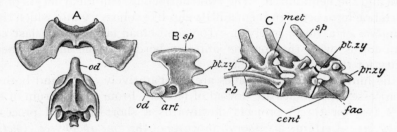

FIG. 448.—**Lepus cuniculus.** *A*, atlas and axis, ventral aspect. *od.* odontoid process of axis. *B*, lateral view of axis. *art.* articular facet for atlas ; *od.* odontoid process ; *pt. zy.* post-zygapophysis ; *sp.* neural spine. *C*, thoracic vertebræ, lateral view. *cent.* centrum ; *fac.* facet for rib ; *met.* metapophysis ; *pr. zy.* pre-zygapophysis ; *pt. zy.* post-zygapophysis ; *rb.* rib ; *sp.* spinous process.

in the *thoracic* twelve, or sometimes thirteen, in the *lumbar* seven, or sometimes six, in the *sacral* four, and in the *caudal* about fifteen.

The centra of the vertebræ in a young Rabbit consist of three parts—a middle part which is the thickest, and two thin discs of bone—the *epiphyses*—anterior and posterior, applied respectively to the anterior and posterior faces of the middle part or centrum proper. Between successive centra in an un-macerated skeleton are thin disc-like plates of fibro-cartilage—the *inter-vertebral discs*.

The transverse processes of all the cervical vertebræ, except the seventh or last, are perforated by a canal, the *vertebrarterial canal*, for the passage of the vertebral artery. The first vertebra or *atlas* (Fig. 448, *A*) resembles the corres-ponding vertebra of the Pigeon in being of the shape of a ring without any solid centrum like that of the rest. On the anterior face of its lateral portions are two concave articular surfaces for the two condyles of the skull. The second vertebra or *axis* (*A* and *B*) bears on the anterior face of its centrum a peg-like process—the *odontoid process* (*od.*)—which fits into the ventral part of the wing of the atlas : it has a compressed spine (*sp.*), produced in the antero-posterior direction ; its transverse processes are short and perforated by a canal for the vertebral artery. All the cervical vertebræ except the last have their transverse process bifurcated into dorsal and ventral lamellæ. The seventh differs from the others in having a more elongated neural spine, in having its transverse processes simple and without perforation for the vertebral artery, and in the presence on the posterior edge of the centrum of a little concave semi-lunar facet.

The thoracic vertebræ (C) have elongated spines which are mostly directed backwards as well as upwards. The transverse processes are short and stout ; each bears near its extremity a small smooth articular surface or *tubercular facet* for the tubercle of a rib. On the anterior and posterior borders of each vertebra is a little semi-lunar facet, the *capitular facet* (*fac.*), situated at the junction of the centrum and the neural arch. The two contiguous semi-lunar facets of successive vertebræ form between them a little cup-like concavity into which the head or *capitulum* of a rib is received. The semi-lunar facet on the last cervical vertebra forms, with that on the anterior border of the first thoracic, the concavity for the head of the first rib.

In the lumbar region the spines are comparatively short, and both transverse processes and bodies are devoid of facets. From the centrum of each of the first two (or three) projects downwards a short flattened process—the *hypapophysis*. Certain accessory processes—the *metapophyses* (*met.*) and *anapophyses*—are well-developed, the former being extremely long in the posterior lumbar region. The metapophyses are situated in front, projecting forwards and outwards over the pre-zygapophyses ; and the anapophyses are situated below the post-zygapophyses and project backwards The transverse processes are long, and are directed forwards and outwards ; that of the last lumbar is bifurcated.

The sacral vertebræ are firmly ankylosed together to form a single composite bone, the *sacrum*. The vertebræ bear a close resemblance to those of the lumbar region, but the hypophyses and anapophyses are wanting, and the metapophyses are comparatively small. The first and second bear great expanded lateral processes, or sacral ribs, with roughened external surfaces for articulation with the ilia. These are the only sacral vertebræ in the strict sense of the term, the following two being in reality anterior caudal.

Of the caudal vertebræ the more anterior resemble those of the sacral region, and have similar processes ; but as we pass backwards in the caudal region all the processes gradually diminish in size, the most posterior vertebra being represented merely by nearly cylindrical centra.

There are twelve pairs of *ribs*, of which the first seven are known as true ribs, *i.e.*, are connected by their cartilaginous sternal parts with the sternum ; while the remaining five, the so-called false or floating ribs, are not directly connected with the sternum. All, except the last four, bear two articular facets, one on the vertebral extremity or *capitulum*, and the other on a little elevation or *tubercle* situated at a little distance from this—the former for the bodies, the latter for the transverse processes of the vertebræ.

The sternum consists of six segments or *sternebræ* : the first, the *manubrium sterni* or *presternum*, is larger than the rest, and has a ventral keel. With the last is connected a rounded cartilaginous plate, the *xiphisternum*.

The *skull* (Figs. 449, 450), if we leave the jaws out of account, is not at all unlike that of the Pigeon in general shape. The length is great as compared with either the breadth or the depth ; the maxillary region, or region of the snout (corresponding to the beak of the Pigeon), is long in proportion to the rest, the orbits closely approximated, being separated only by a thin inter-orbital partition, and the optic foramina united into one. But certain important differences are to be recognised at once. One of these is in the mode of union of the constituent bones. In the Pigeon, as we have seen, long before maturity is attained, the bony elements of the skull, originally distinct, become completely fused together so that their limits are no longer distinguishable. In the Rabbit, on the other hand, such fusion between elements only takes place in a few instances, the majority of the bones remaining more or less distinct throughout life. The lines along which the edges of contiguous bones are united—the *sutures* as they are termed—are sometimes straight, sometimes wavy, sometimes zigzagged serrations of the edges of the two bones interlocking ; in some cases the edges of the bones are bevelled off and the bevelled edges overlap, forming what is termed a *squamous* suture.

Another conspicuous difference between the skull of the Rabbit and that of the Pigeon is in the mode of connection of the lower jaw, which in the former articulates directly with the skull—the quadrate, through which the union is effected in the Pigeon, being apparently absent. Certain large apertures which are distinguishable are readily identified with the large openings in the skull of the Pigeon. In the posterior wall of the skull is a large rounded opening, the *foramen magnum*, flanked with a pair of smooth rounded elevations or *condyles* for articulation with the first vertebra, these obviously corresponding to the single condyle situated in the middle below the foramen in the Pigeon. A large opening, situated at the end of the snout and looking forwards, obviously takes the place of the *external nares* of the Pigeon ; and a large opening in the roof of the mouth, leading forward to the external nasal opening, plainly represents, though much wider and situated farther back, the *external* or *posterior nares* of the Pigeon ; while the rounded tubular opening (*aud. me.*) situated at the side of the posterior part of the skull, some distance behind the orbit, is evidently the same as the *auditory aperture* of the Pigeon.

Surrounding the large opening of the foramen magnum are the bones of the *occipital* region of the skull, the *supra-, ex-* and *basi-occipitals*. The first of these (*s. oc.*) is a large plate of bone whose external surface is directed backwards

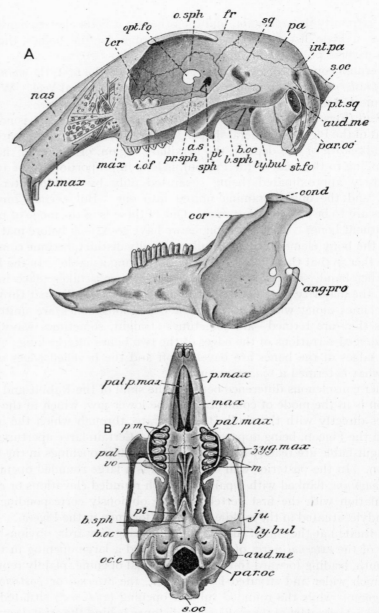

FIG. 449.—**Lepus cuniculus.** Skull. *A*, lateral view; *B*, ventral view. *ang. proc.* angular process of mandible; *a. s.* alisphenoid (external pterygoid process); *aud. me.* external auditory meatus; *b. oc.* basi-occipital; *b. sph.* basi-sphenoid; *cond.* condyle. *fr.* frontal; *int. pa.* interparietal; *i. o. f.* infra-orbital foramen; *ju.* jugal; *lcr.* lacrymal; *m.* molars; *max.* maxilla; *nas.* nasal; *opt. fo.* optic foramen; *o. sph.* orbito-sphenoid; *pa.* parietal; *pal.* palatine; *pal. max.* palatine plate of maxilla; *par.oc.* paroccipital process; *pal. p. max.* palatine process of premaxilla; *p.m.* premolars; *p. max.* pre-maxilla; *pr. sph.* pre-sphenoid; *pt.* pterygoid; *p. t. sq.* post-tympanic process of squamosal; *s. oc.* supra-occipital; *sph.* points to position of sphenoidal fissure, not clearly visible in a lateral view; *sq.* squamosal; *st. fo.* stylomastoid foramen; *ty. bul.* tympanic bulla; *vo.* vomer; *zyg. max.* zygomatic process of maxilla.

and upwards, and elevated in the middle into a shield-shaped prominence. The *ex-occipitals* lie at the sides of the opening, and each bears the greater part of the somewhat oval prominence or *condyle* with which the corresponding surface of the atlas or first vertebra articulates. Each is produced below into a process called the *par-occipital* (*par. oc.*), closely applied to the tympanic bulla. At the end of this, imbedded in the tendon of a muscle, the *styloglossus*, is a small bony rod, the *stylo-hyal*. A small aperture, the *condylar foramen*, situated below the condyle, is for the passage of one of the cerebral nerves, the hypoglossal. The *basi-occipital* is a median plate of bone, almost horizontal in position, which forms the floor of the most posterior part of the cranial cavity; it bears the lower third of the occipital condyles. All these four bones of the occipital region are in the adult Rabbit united together to form the single *occipital bone*. Articulating in front with the basi-occipital, but separated from it by a plate of cartilage, is a plate of bone, also horizontal in position, which forms the middle part of the floor of the cranial cavity. This is the *basi-sphenoid*; it is perforated at about its middle by an oval foramen—the *pituitary foramen*—and on its upper surface is a depression, the *sella turcica*, or *pituitary fossa* (Fig. 450, *s. t.*), in which the pituitary body rests. In front of it is another median bone of laterally compressed form, the *pre-sphenoid*, with which it is connected by cartilage, the removal of which leaves a gap in the dried skull; the pre-sphenoid forms the lower boundary of the single large *optic foramen* (Fig. 449, *opt. fo.*). Connected laterally with the basi-sphenoid and pre-sphenoid are two pairs of thin irregular plates, the *ali-sphenoids* (*sa.*) behind and the *orbito-sphenoids* (*o. sph.*) in front. The ali-sphenoids are broad wing-like bones, each produced below into a bilaminate process, the *pterygoid* process. A large foramen, the *sphenoidal fissure* (*sph.*), situated between the basi-sphenoid and the ali-sphenoid of each side, transmits from the interior of the skull the third and fourth cerebral nerves, the first and second divisions of the fifth, and the sixth nerves.

The boundary of the anterior part of the brain-case is completed by a narrow plate of bone, the *cribriform plate* of the *ethmoid* (Fig. 450, *eth.*), perforated by numerous small foramina for the passage of the olfactory nerves. This cribriform plate forms a part of a median vertical bone, the *mesethmoid*, the remainder of which, or *lamina perpendicularis*, forms the bony part of the partition (completed by cartilage in the unmacerated skull) between the nasal cavities. Fused with the mesethmoid are two lateral, thin, twisted bones, the *ethmo-turbinals* (*e. tb.*), and with its inferior edge articulates a long median bone, with a pair of delicate lateral wings, the *vomer* (*vo.*). None of these, with the exception of the cribriform plate, takes any share in the bounding of the cavity of the cranium. Roofing over the part of the cranial cavity the walls and floor of which are formed by the sphenoid elements, is a pair of investing bones, the *parietals* (Fig. 449, *pa.*), and farther forwards is another pair, the *frontals* (*fr.*). The parietals are plate-like bones, convex externally, concave internally, which articulate with the supra-occipital behind by a transverse serrated *lambdoidal suture*. The right and left parietals articulate together by means of a somewhat wavy suture, the *sagittal* ; in front a transverse serrated suture, the *coronal*, connects them with the frontals. Between the supra-occipital and the parietals is a median ossification or *inter-parietal* (*int. pa.*). The frontals are intimately united along the middle by means of the *frontal* suture. Laterally their orbital plates form an important part of the upper portion of the inner wall of the orbit ; above this, over each orbit, is a curved, somewhat crescentic process, the *supra-orbital process*. Between the ali-sphenoid below, the parietal and frontal above, the frontal and orbito-sphenoid in front, and the parietal behind, is a broad bone (*sq.*), the superior margin of which is bevelled off : this is the *squamosal*. It is produced in front into a strong *zygomatic process*, which curves outwards, then downwards, and finally forwards, to unite, with the jugal in the formation of the zygomatic arch. Below the root of the process is a hollow, the *glenoid fossa*. Posteriorly the squamosal gives off a slender process, the *post-tympanic process* (*p. t. sq.*), which becomes applied to the outer surface of the periotic.

Between the occipital and parietal bones, below and behind the squamosal, are the *tympanic* and *periotic* bones. The tympanic forms the bony part of the wall of the external auditory meatus ; below it is dilated to form a process (*ty. bul.*) projecting on the under surface of the skull—the *bulla tympani*. The periotic is a bone of irregular shape, its internal (*petrous*) portion (Fig. 450, *peri.*) enclosing the parts of the membranous labyrinth of the internal ear, and externally presenting two small openings—the *fenestra ovalis* and *fenestra rotunda*—visible only when the tympanic is removed ; internally it bears a depression, the *floccular fossa*, for the lodgment of the flocculus of the cerebellum. Part of the periotic (*mastoid* portion) is seen on the exterior of the skull between the tympanic and exoccipital. The periotic and tympanic are not ankylosed together, and are loosely connected with the surrounding bones, being held in position by the post-tympanic processes of the squamosal. Between the tympanic and periotic are two foramina of importance—the *stylomastoid*, which transmits the seventh cerebral nerve, and the *Eustachian aperture*, at which the Eustachian tube opens.

Roofing over the olfactory cavities are two flat bones—the *nasals* (*nas.*)—each having on its inner surface a very thin hollow process, the *naso-turbinal*. In front of the nasals are the premaxillæ (*p.max.*)—large bones which form the anterior part of the snout, bear the upper incisor teeth, and give off three processes—a nasal, a palatine (*pal. p.max.*), and a maxillary. The *maxillæ* (*max.*), which form the greater part of the upper jaw, and bear the premolar and molar teeth, are large, irregularly-shaped bones, the outer surfaces of which are spongy. They give off internally horizontal processes—the palatine processes (*pal. max.*)—which unite to form the anterior part of the bony palate.

Between the premaxillæ and maxillæ and the palatines on the lower surface of the skull is a large triangular opening divided into two—the *anterior palatine foramina*—by the palatine processes of the pre-maxillæ. On the outer surface of each maxilla, above the first premolar tooth, is a foramen—the *infra-orbital (i. o. f.)*—through which the second division of the fifth nerve passes. A strong process which is given off from the outer face of each maxilla, and turns outwards and then backwards to unite with the zygomatic process of the squamosal and thus complete the zygomatic arch, is a separate bone in the young, the *malar* or *jugal (ju.)*.

The maxillæ help to bound the nasal cavities externally, and with each is connected on its inner aspect a pair of thin scroll-like bones—the *maxillo-*

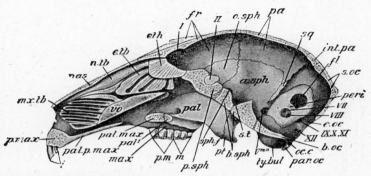

FIG. 450.—**Lepus cuniculus.** Skull in longitudinal vertical section. The cartilaginous nasal septum is removed. *a. sph.* ali-sphenoid; *e.oc.* exoccipital; *e. tb.* ethmo-turbinal; *eth.* ethmoid; *fl.* fossa for flocculus of brain; *i.* incisors; *mx. tb.* maxillary turbinal; *n. tb.* naso-turbinal; *pal'.* palatine portion of the bony palate; *peri.* periotic (petrous portion); *p. sph.* pre-sphenoid; *sph. f.* sphenoidal fissure; *s. t.* sella turcica, or depression in which the pituitary body lies; *I.* point at which the olfactory nerves leave the skull; *II.* optic foramen; *V. mn.* foramen for mandibular division of trigeminal; *VII.* for facial nerve; *VIII.* for auditory nerve; *IX, X, XI,* for glossopharyngeal, vagus, and spinal accessory; *XII.* for hypoglossal. Other letters as in Fig. 449. (From Parker's *Practical Zoology*.)

turbinals (Fig. 450, *mx. tb.*). The rest of the narrow bony palate, forming the roof of the mouth and the floor of the nasal cavities, is formed by the *palatine plates* of the *palatine bones (pal.)*. The so-called *pterygoids (pt.)* are small irregular bones, each of which articulates with the palatine in front and with the pterygoid process of the ali-sphenoid behind: these are probably not the equivalents of the pterygoids of other Vertebrates, but of the part of the para-sphenoid. The *lacrymals (lcr.)* are small bones, one situated in the anterior wall of each orbit, perforated by a small aperture—the *lacrymal foramen*.

In the interior of the skull (Fig. 450) are three cavities, the two olfactory or nasal cavities, right and left, in front, and the cranial cavity behind. The former are separated from one another by a median partition or septum, partly cartilaginous, partly bony, formed, as above described, by the *mesethmoid*.

Each contains the turbinals or turbinated bones of its side; it opens on the exterior by the large external nasal aperture, and behind it communicates with the cavity of the mouth by the posterior nasal aperture.

The cranial cavity has its walls moulded to a considerable extent on the surface of the contained brain, and, in consequence, there are to be recognised concavities in the former corresponding with the prominent portions of the latter. These concavities are termed the *fossæ*, and they consist of the *cerebellar fossa* behind and the *cerebral fossa* in front, with the inconspicuous *olfactory fossa* in the frontal region.

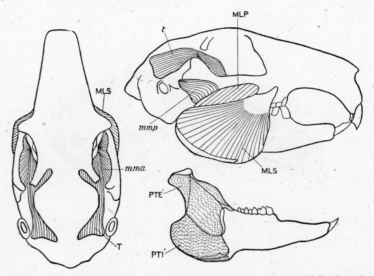

FIG. 451.—Jaw muscles of the rabbit. *MLS*. lateral superficial, *MLP*. deep lateral, *mma* anterior medial, *MMP*. posterior medial, of masseter; *PTE'*. insertion of external pterygoid. *PTI'*. insertion of internal pterygoid; *t*. temporal; *t'*. insertion of temporal. (Redrawn after Tullberg.)

The *mandible*, or lower jaw, consists of two lateral halves or rami, which are connected with one another in front by a rough articular surface or *symphysis*, while behind they diverge like the limbs of a letter V. In each ramus is a horizontal portion (anterior), which bears the teeth, and a vertical or ascending portion, on which is the articular surface or *condyle* (*cond.*) for articulation with the glenoid cavity of the squamosal; in front of the condyle is the compressed *coronoid process*. The angle where the horizontal and ascending processes meet gives off an inward projection or *angular process* (*ang. pro.*) (Fig. 449).

The jaw-muscles in the Rabbit are somewhat specialised for the action of gnawing, though to a less extent than in many other Rodents (see Fig. 451). The muscles chiefly concerned are the temporal, masseter, and digastric. The temporal has its origin from a long and rather irregular area on the reduced temporal fossa, and is inserted on the medial side of the coronoid process of the lower jaw. The masseter is a large mass, and is divided into three sections, deep and superficial lateral and medial. The origin is along the whole border of the jugal arch (the medial and deep lateral) and on the lower border of the maxilla (superficial lateral). The insertion of all three sections is on the outer face and border of the angle of the lower jaw. The internal and external pterygoid muscles arising from the pterygoid region are inserted on the inner side of the jaws at the angle and coronoid, respectively. The digastric muscles which open the jaws arise from the paroccipital process, and are inserted on the medial lower surface of the ramus. In the front part of the jaws are inserted other smaller muscles, such as the buccinator, which moves the lips, the genio- hyoglossus for the tongue, etc.

The *hyoid* consists, in addition to the separate vestigial stylo-hyals already mentioned (p. 493), of a stout thick body or *basi-hyal*, a pair of small anterior cornua or *cerato-hyals*, and a pair of long backwardly directed cornua or thyrohyals.

The *auditory ossicles*, contained in the cavity of the middle ear and cut off from the exterior in the unmacerated skull by the tympanic membrane, are extremely small bones, which form a chain extending, like the columella auris of the Pigeon, from the tympanic membrane externally to the fenestra ovalis internally. There are three of these auditory ossicles—the *stapes*, which corresponds to the columella of the Pigeon; the *incus*, and the *malleus*, the latter with a slender process (*processus gracilis*) : these are derived respect- ively from the quadrate and articular elements (*q.v.*) of lower vertebrates. In addition there is a small disc-like bone, the *orbicular*, which is attached to the incus.

The elements of the *pectoral arch* are fewer than in the Lizard. There is a broad, thin, triangular scapula, the base or vertebral edge of which has a thin strip of cartilage (the *supra-scapular* cartilage) continuous with it. Along the outer surface runs a ridge—the *spine*; the spine ends below in a long process— the *acromion process*—from which a branch process or *metacromion* is given off behind. The part of the outer surface of the scapula in front of the spine is the *pre-spinous* or *pre-scapular fossa*, the part behind is the *post-spinous* or *post-scapular fossa*. At the narrow lower end of the scapula is a concave surface—the *glenoid cavity*—into which the head of the humerus fits, and immediately in front of this is a small inwardly curved process—the *coracoid process*—which is represented by two separate ossifications in the young Rabbit. A slender rod—the *clavicle*—lies obliquely in the region between the pre-sternum and the scapula, but only extends a part of the distance between the two bones, and in the adult is only connected with them through the intermediation of fibrous tissue.

The skeleton of the fore-limb is more readily comparable with that of the

Lizard than that of the Bird ; but there is a difference in the position of the parts owing to the rotation backwards of the distal end of the humerus, all the segments being thus brought into a plane nearly parallel with the median vertical plane of the body, with the pre-axial border directed outwards, and the original dorsal surface backwards. The radius and ulna are fixed in the position of *pronation*, i.e., the distal end of the radius is rotated inwards, so that, while the proximal end is external to the ulna, the distal end becomes internal, and the digits of the manus are directed forwards.

At the proximal end of the humerus, are to be recognised : (1) a rounded *head* for articulation with the glenoid cavity of the scapula ; (2) externally a

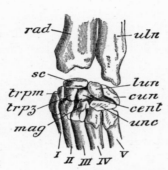

Fig. 452.—**Lepus cuniculus.** Distal end of fore-arm and carpus, dorsal view, the bones bent towards the dorsal side so as to be partly separated. *cent.* centrale ; *cun.* cuneiform ; *lun.* lunar ; *mag.* magnum ; *rad.* radius ; *sc.* scaphoid ; *trpz.* trapezoid ; *trpm.* trapezium ; *uln.* ulna ; *unc.* unciform ; *I—V*, bases of metacarpals. (After Krause.)

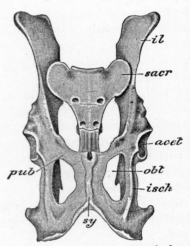

Fig. 453.—**Lepus cuniculus.** Innominate bones and sacrum, ventral aspect. *acet.* acetabulum ; *il.* ilium ; *isch.* ischium ; *obt.* obturator foramen ; *pub.* pubis ; *sacr.* sacrum ; *sy.* symphysis.

greater and (3) internally a *lesser tuberosity* for the insertion of muscles ; (4) a groove, the *bicipital groove*, between the two tuberosities. On the anterior surface of the proximal portion of the shaft is a slight ridge, the *deltoid ridge.* At the distal end are two articular surfaces, one large and pulley-like—*trochlea*—for the ulna ; the other smaller—*capitellum*—for the radius : laterally are two prominences or *condyles*, an internal and an external.

The radius and ulna are firmly fixed together so as to be incapable of movement, but are not actually ankylosed. The radius articulates proximally with the humerus, distally with the scaphoid and lunar bones of the carpus. The ulna presents on the anterior aspect of its proximal end a deep fossa, the *greater sigmoid cavity*, for the trochlea of the humerus ; the prominent process on the proximal side of this is the *olecranon* process. Distally it articulates with the cuneiform.

The carpal bones (Fig. 452), nine in number, are all small bones of irregular shape. Eight of these are arranged in two rows—a proximal and a distal; the ninth, *centrale* (*cent.*), lies between the two rows. The bones of the proximal row are—taken in order from the inner to the outer side—*scaphoid* (*sc.*), *lunar* (or *semi-lunar*) (*lun.*), *cuneiform* (*cun.*), and *pisiform*. Those of the distal row are reckoned in the same order, *trapezium* (*trpm.*), *trapezoid* (*trpz.*), *magnum* (*mag.*), and *unciform* (*unc.*).[1]

The five metacarpals are all small but relatively narrow and elongated bones, the first being smaller than the rest. Each of the five digits has three phalanges, except the first, which has only two. The distal (ungual) phalanges are grooved dorsally for the attachment of the horny claw.

The pelvic arch (Fig. 453) contains the same elements as in the Pigeon, but the union of the ilium with the sacrum is less intimate, the acetabulum is not perforated, and the pubes and ischia of opposite sides unite ventrally in a symphysis (*sy.*). The three bones of the pelvis—ilium, pubis, and ischium—are separate ossification in the young Rabbit; but in an adult animal complete fusion takes place between the bones. The ilium and ischium meet in the acetabulum or articular cavity, which they contribute to form, for the head of the femur; but the remainder of the cavity is bounded, not by the pubis, but by a small intercalated ossification—the *cotyloid* bone. The ilium (*il.*) has a rough surface for articulation with the sacrum. Between the pubis (*pub.*) in front and the ischium (*isch.*) behind is a large aperture—the *obturator foramen* (*obt.*). The femur is rotated forwards when compared with that of the Lizard, so that the limb is nearly in the same plane as the fore-limb, and the pre-axial border is internal and the originally dorsal surface anterior. The femur has at its proximal end a prominent *head* for articulation with the acetabulum, external to this a prominent process—the *great trochanter*, and internally a much smaller —the *lesser trochanter*, while a small process or *third trochanter* is situated on the outer border a little below the great trochanter. At its distal end are two prominences or *condyles*, with a depression between them. Two small sesamoids or *fabellæ* are situated opposite the distal end on its posterior aspect; and opposite the knee-joint, or articulation between the femur and the tibia, is a larger bone of similar character—the knee-cap or *patella*. The tibia has at its proximal end two articular surfaces for the condyles of the femur; distally it has also two articular surfaces, one, internal for the astragalus, the other for the calcaneum. The fibula is a slender bone which becomes completely fused distally with the tibia.

---

[1] The homologies of these bones are not quite certain, but are very probably as follows :— scaphoid = radiale; lunar = 1st centrale; cuneiform = intermedium; pisiform = ulnare; centrale = 2nd centrale; trapezium = 1st distale; trapezoid = 2nd distale; magnum = 3rd distale; unciform = 4th and 5th distalia.

The tarsus (Fig. 454) consists of six bones of irregular shape, arranged in two rows, one of the bones—the *navicular* (*nav.*)—being intercalated between the two rows. In the proximal row are two bones—the *astragalus* (*ast.*) and the *calcaneum* (*cal.*)—both articulating with the tibia; the calcaneum presents behind a long *calcaneal process*. The distal row contains three bones, the *meso-cuneiform*, *ecto-cuneiform*, and *cuboid* (*cub.*); the *ento-cuneiform*, which commonly forms the most internal member of this row in other Mammals, is not present as a separate bone.[1]

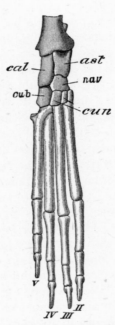

Fig. 454.—**Lepus cuniculus.** Skeleton of pes. *ast.* astragalus; *cal.* calcaneum; *cub.* cuboid; *cun.* cuneiforms; *nav.* navicular.

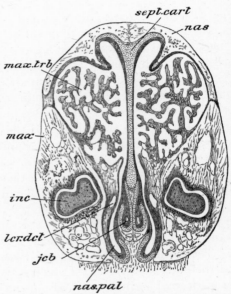

Fig. 455.—**Lepus cuniculus.** Vertical section through the anterior part of the nasal region of the head. *inc.* section of larger incisor tooth; *jcb.* lumen of Jacobson's organ, surrounded by cartilage; *lcr. dct.* lachrymal duct; *max.* maxilla; *max. trb.* maxillary turbinals; *nas.* nasal bone; *nas. pal.* naso-palatine canal; *sept. cart.* cartilaginous nasal septum. (After Krause.)

There are four metatarsals, the hallux or first digit being vestigial and fused with the second metatarsal in the adult. The proximal end of the second is produced into a process which articulates with the navicular. Each of the digits has three phalanges, which are similar in character to those of the manus.

The **cœlome** of the Rabbit differs from that of the Pigeon and Lizard in being divided into two parts by a transverse muscular partition, the *diaphragm*.

---

[1] In all probability the homologies of these bones are as follows:—astragalus = tibiale + intermedium; calcaneum = fibulare; navicular = centrale; ento-cuneiform = 1st distale; meso-cuneiform = 2nd distale; ecto-cuneiform = 3rd distale; cuboid = 4th and 5th distalia.

The anterior part, or *thorax*, contains the heart and the roots of the great vessels, the lungs and bronchi, and the posterior part of the œsophagus. The posterior part, or *abdomen*, contains the stomach and intestine, the liver and pancreas, the spleen, the kidneys, ureters and urinary bladder, and the organs of reproduction.

Digestive Organs.—The teeth (Fig. 449) are lodged in sockets or *alveoli* in the premaxillæ, the maxillæ, and the mandible. In the premaxillæ are situated four teeth—the four *upper incisors*. Of these the two anterior are very long, curved, chisel-shaped teeth, which are devoid of roots, growing throughout life from persistent pulps. Enamel is present, and forms a thick layer on the anterior convex surface, which accounts for the bevelled-off character of the distal end—the layer of enamel being much harder than the rest, which therefore wears more quickly away at the cutting extremity of the tooth. Along the anterior surface is a longitudinal groove. The second pair of incisors of the upper jaw are small teeth which are lodged just behind the larger pair. In the lower jaw are two incisors, which correspond in shape with the anterior pair of the upper jaw, the main difference consisting in the absence of the longitudinal groove. The remaining teeth of the upper jaw are lodged in the maxillæ. *Canines*, present in most Mammals as a single tooth on each side, above and below, are here entirely absent, and there is a considerable space, or *diastema*, as it is termed, between the incisors and the teeth next in order—the *premolars*. Of these there are three in the upper jaw and two in the lower. They are long, curved teeth with persistent pulps like the incisors. The first of the upper jaw is smaller than the others and of simple shape, the rest have each a longitudinal groove on the outer side and a transverse ridge on the crown. The first premolar of the lower jaw has two grooves; the second is similar to those of the upper jaw. Behind the premolars are the *molars*, three on each side both in the upper and lower jaws. These are similar to the upper premolars, except the last, which is small and of simple shape.

Opening into the cavity of the mouth, or *buccal cavity*, are the ducts of four pairs of salivary glands—the *parotid*, the *infraorbital*, the *sub-maxillary* (Fig. 456, *s. mx. gl.*), and the *sub-lingual* (*s. gl.*). On the floor of the mouth is the muscular tongue, covered with a mucous membrane which is beset with many papillæ, on certain of which the *taste-buds* (p. 111) are situated. The roof of the mouth is formed by the *hard palate*, which is crossed by a series of transverse ridges of its mucous membrane. Posteriorly the hard palate passes into the *soft palate*, which ends behind in a free pendulous flap in front of the opening of the *posterior nares*. At the anterior end of the palate is a pair of openings—the *naso-palatine* or *anterior palatine canals*, leading into the nasal chambers, and into them open a pair of tubular structures—the *organs of Jacobson* (Fig. 455, *jcb.*)—enclosed in cartilage and situated on the floor of the nasal cavities. Behind the mouth or buccal cavity proper is the *pharynx*, which in the Rabbit

is not sharply marked off from the buccal cavity, but begins where the hard palate ends. The pharynx is divided into two parts, an upper or *nasal* division and a lower or *buccal* division, by the soft palate. The passage of the posterior nares is continuous with the nasal division, at the sides of which are the openings of the *Eustachian tubes*. The nasal division is continuous with the buccal division round the posterior free edge of the soft palate. From the buccal division leads ventrally the slit-like opening of the glottis [1] into the larynx and trachea; overhanging the glottis is a leaf-like movable flap (Fig. 456, *ep.*) formed of a plate of yellow elastic cartilage covered with mucous membrane; this is the *epiglottis*. Behind, the pharynx becomes continuous

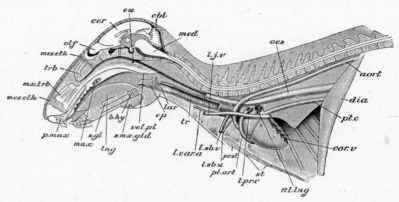

Fig. 456.—**Lepus cuniculus.** Lateral dissection of the head, neck, and thorax. The head and spinal column are represented in mesial vertical section; the left lung is removed; the greater part of the nasal septum is removed so as to show the right nasal cavity with its turbinals. *aort.* dorsal aorta; *b. hy.* basi-hyal; *cbl.* cerebellum; *cer.* cerebral hemispheres; *cor. v.* coronary vein; *dia.* diaphragm; *ep.* epiglottis; *eu.* opening of Eustchian tube into pharynx; *lar.* larynx; *l. j. v.* left jugular vein; *l. sb. a.* left subclavian artery; *l. sb. v.* left subclavian vein; *max.* maxilla; *med.* medulla oblongata; *mes.eth.* mesethmoid; *mx. trb.* maxillo-turbinal; *œs.* œsophagus; *olf.* olfactory bulb; *pl. art.* pulmonary artery; *p.max.* premaxilla; *pr.st.* presternum; *pt. c.* post-caval vein; *rt. l. lng.* root of left lung with bronchus and pulmonary veins and artery cut across; *s. gl.* sub-lingual salivary glands; *s. mx. gld.* sub-maxillary salivary gland; *st.* sternebræ; *tng.* tongue; *tr.* trachea; *trb.* ethmo-turbinals; *vel. pl.* soft palate.

with the *œsophagus* or gullet (*œs.*). The latter is a narrow but dilatable muscular tube which runs backwards from the pharynx through the neck and thorax to enter the cavity of the abdomen through an aperture in the diaphragm, and opens into the *stomach*.

The stomach (Fig. 457) is a wide sac, much wider at the *cardiac* end, at which the œsophagus enters, than at the opposite or *pyloric* end, where it passes into the small intestine. The small intestine is an elongated, narrow, greatly coiled tube, the first part of which, or *duodenum* (*du.* and *du'.*), forms a U-shaped loop. The large intestine is a wide tube, the first and greater part

[1] The term glottis is more strictly applied not to this slit, but to the slit-like aperture between two folds of the mucous membrane within the larynx—the *vocal cords*—which consitute the chief parts of the vocal apparatus.

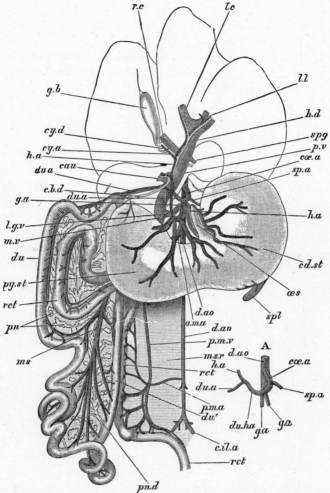

FIG. 457.—**Lepus cuniculus.** The stomach, duodenum, posterior portion of rectum and liver (in outline) with their arteries, veins and ducts. *A*, the cœliac artery of another specimen (both × ⅔). The gullet is cut through and the stomach somewhat displaced backwards to show the ramifications of the cœliac artery (*cœ. a.*); the duodenum is spread out to the right of the subject to show the pancreas (*pn.*); the branches of the bile-duct (*c. b. d.*), portal vein (*p. v.*), and hepatic artery (*h. a.*) are supposed to be traced some distance into the various lobes of the liver. *a. m. a.* anterior mesenteric artery; *cau.* caudate lobe of liver with its artery, vein and bile-duct; *c. b. d.* common bile-duct; *cd. st.* cardiac portion of stomach; *c. il. a.* common iliac artery; *cœ. a.* cœliac artery; *cy. a.* cystic artery; *cy. d.* cystic duct; *d. ao.* dorsal aorta; *du.* proximal, and *du'.* distal limbs of duodenum; *du. a.* duodenal artery; *du. h. a.* (in *A*), duodeno-hepatic artery; *g. a.* gastric artery and vein; *g. b.* gall-bladder; *h. a.* hepatic artery; *h. d.* left hepatic duct; *l. c.* left central lobe of liver, with its artery, vein and bile-duct; *l. g. v.* lieno-gastric vein; *l. l.* lateral lobe of liver with its artery, vein and bile-duct; *ms.* branch of mesenteric artery and vein to duodenum; *ms. r.* mesorectum; *m. v.* chief mesenteric vein; *œs.* œsophagus; *p. m. a.* posterior mesenteric artery; *p. m. v.* posterior mesenteric vein; *pn.* pancreas; *pn. d.* pancreatic duct; *p. v.* portal vein; *py. st.* pyloric portion of stomach; *rct.* rectum; *r. c.* right central lobe of liver, with artery, vein and bile-duct; *spg.* Spigelian lobe of liver with its artery, vein and bile-duct; *spl.* spleen; *sp. a.* splenic artery. (From Parker's *Zootomy*.)

of which, termed the *colon*, has its walls sacculated, and is continued into a narrow, smooth-walled posterior part or *rectum* (*rct.*). At the junction of the small with the large intestine is a very wide blind tube, the *cæcum*, which is of considerable length and is marked by a spiral constriction, indicating the presence in its interior of a narrow spiral valve. At its extremity is a small, fleshy, finger-like *vermiform appendix*.

The intestine, like that of the Pigeon, is attached throughout its length to the dorsal wall of the abdominal cavity by a *mesentery*, or fold of the lining membrane or peritoneum.

The *liver* is attached to the diaphragm by a fold of the peritoneum. Its

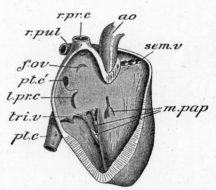

FIG. 458.—**Lepus cuniculus.** Heart, seen from the right side, the walls of the right auricle and right ventricle partly removed so as to expose the cavities. *ao.* aorta; *f. ov.* fossa ovalis; *l. pr. c.* opening of left pre-caval; *m. pap.* musculi papillares; *pt. c.* post-caval; *pt. c'.* opening of post-caval, with Eustachian valve below; *r. pr. c.* right pre-caval; *r. pul.* right pulmonary artery; *sem. v.* semilunar valves; *tri. v.* tricuspid valve.

substance is partly divided by a series of fissures into five lobes. A thin-walled *gall-bladder* lies in a depression on its posterior surface. The *common bile-duct* (*c. b. d.*), formed by the union of the *cystic duct* from the gall-bladder and *hepatic ducts* from the various parts of the liver, runs to open into the duodenum near the pylorus.

The *pancreas* (*pn.*) is a diffused gland in the fold of mesentery passing across the loop of the duodenum. Its single duct, the *pancreatic duct* (*pn. d.*), opens into the distal limb of the loop.

Circulatory Organs.—The *heart* (Fig. 458) is situated in the cavity of the thorax, a little to the left of the middle line, and lies between the two pleural sacs enclosing the lungs. Between the pleural sacs is a space, the *mediastinum* (Fig. 461). This is divisible into four parts, the anterior, the dorsal, the middle, and the ventral. In the anterior part lie the posterior part of the trachea, the neighbouring parts of the œsophagus and of the thoracic duct of the lymphatic system, the roots of the great arteries and the veins of the pre-caval system, and the phrenic, pneumogastric, and other nerves. In the dorsal part are situated the posterior part of the œsophagus, the thoracic part of the dorsal aorta, the pneumogastric nerve, the azygos vein, and the thoracic duct. The middle part is the widest, and lodges the heart and roots of the aorta and pulmonary artery enclosed in the pericardium, the posterior portion of the pre-caval veins, the phrenic nerves, the terminal part of the azygos vein, and the roots of the lungs. The ventral part contains only areolar tissue with the thymus gland. The pericardial membrane enclosing the heart consists of two layers, a *parietal*, forming the wall of the pericardial cavity, and a *visceral*, immediately investing the heart. Between the two is a narrow cavity containing a little fluid—the *pericardial fluid*. In general shape the heart resembles the heart of the Pigeon, with the apex directed backwards and slightly to the left, and the base forwards. Like that of the Pigeon, it contains right and left auricles and right and left ventricles, the right and left sides of the heart having their cavities completely separated off from one another by inter-auricular and inter-ventricular partitions.

Into the right auricle open three large veins—the *right* and *left pre-caval* veins and the single *post-caval*—the first into the anterior part, the second into the left-hand side of the posterior portion, and the third into the dorsal surface (Fig. 458). Projecting forwards from it is an ear-like *auricular appendix*, the inner surface of which is raised up into numerous cords of muscular fibres, the *musculi pectinati*. A membranous fold, the remnant of the fœtal *Eustachian valve*, extends from the opening of the post-caval forwards towards the auricular septum. The opening of the left pre-caval is bounded behind by a crescentic fold, the *valve of Thebesius*. On the septum is an oval area where the partition is thinner than elsewhere; this is the *fossa ovalis* (*f. ov.*): it marks the position of an aperture, the *foramen ovale*, in the fœtus. The crescentic anterior rim of the aperture is known as the *annulus ovalis*. The cavity of the right auricle communicates with that of the right ventricle by the wide right auriculo-ventricular opening. This is guarded by a valve, the *tricuspid* (*tri. v.*), composed of three membranous lobes or cusps, so arranged and attached that while they flap back against the walls of the ventricle to allow the passage of blood from the auricle to the ventricle, they meet together across the aperture so as to close the passage when the ventricle contracts. The lobes of the valve are attached to muscular processess of the wall of the ventricle, the *musculi papillares* (*m. pap.*), by means of tendinous threads called the *chordæ tendineæ*. The right ventricle, much thicker than the auricle, forms the right side of the conical apical portion, but does not extend quite to the apex. Its walls are raised up into muscular ridges called *columnæ carneæ*. It gives off in front, at its left anterior angle, the pulmonary artery, the entrance to which is guarded by three pouch-like *semilunar valves* (*sem. v.*).

The left auricle, like the right, is provided with an auricular appendix. Into its cavity on its dorsal aspect open together the right and left pulmonary veins. A large left auriculo-ventricular opening leads from the cavity of the left auricle into that of the left ventricle: this is guarded by a valve, the *mitral* consisting of two membranous lobes or cusps with chordæ tendineæ and musculi papillares. In the walls of the ventricle are columnæ carneæ, rather more strongly developed than in the right. At the basal (anterior) end of the left ventricle is the opening of the aorta, guarded by three *semilunar valves* similar to those at the entrance of the pulmonary artery. The *coronary* arteries, which supply the muscular substance of the heart, are given off from the aorta just beyond the semilunar valves. The corresponding vein opens into the terminal part of the left pre-caval. The pulmonary artery divides into two, a right and a left, each going to the corresponding lung.

The aorta gives origin to a system of arterial trunks by which the arterial blood is conveyed throughout the body. It first runs forwards from the base of the left ventricle, then bends round the left bronchus, forming the *arch of the aorta* (Fig. 459), to run backwards through the thorax and abdomen, in close contact with the spinal column, as the *dorsal aorta* (*d. ao.*). From the arch of the aorta are given off two large arteries, the *innominate* (*in.*) and the *left subclavian*. The innominate divides to form the *right subclavian* (*s.cl. a.*) and the *right* (*r. c. c.*) and *left* (*l. c. c.*) *common carotid* arteries. The right subclavian passes to the fore-limb as the *brachial* artery, giving origin first to the *vertebral* artery, which, after passing up through the vertebrarterial canal, enters the cranial cavity, having first supplied branches to the spinal cord ; and then to the *anterior epigastric* or *internal mammary*, which supplies the side of the chest behind the root of the fore-limb. The right carotid divides opposite the angle of the jaw into *internal* and *external carotids*. The left carotid and left sub-clavian correspond in their distribution and branching to the right carotid and right subclavian respectively. The aorta, in passing through the thorax, gives off a series of small paired *intercostal* arteries (*i.cs.*). In the abdomen its first large branch is the *cœliac artery* (*cœ.*), which supplies the liver, stomach, and spleen. Behind this it gives origin to the *anterior mesenteric* (*a. m.*), which supplies the intestine and the pancreas. Opposite the kidneys it gives off the two renal arteries (*r.*) for the supply of these organs, and a good deal farther back the *spermatic* (*spm.*) or *ovarian* arteries for the testes or ovaries as the case may be. Just in front of the origin of the spermatic arteries is given off a *posterior mesenteric* (*p. m.*), which supplies the hinder part of the rectum. A series of small *lumbar* arteries supply the side-walls of the abdominal cavity. Posteriorly the dorsal aorta divides to form the two common iliac arteries (*c. il. a.*) which supply the pelvic cavity and hind-limbs, a small *median sacral* (*caudal*) artery (*ms. c.*) passing backwards in the middle line to supply the caudal region.

The system of *caval* veins which open into the right auricle consists of the *right* and *left pre-cavals* and of the single *post-caval*. The right pre-caval is formed by the union of the *right jugular* (*e. ju.*) vein and *right subclavian* (*scl. v.*). The *azgyos vein* (*az. v.*), the *right anterior intercostal* (*i.cs.*), and the *right anterior epigastric* or *internal mammary* also opens into it. The left pre-caval receives a series of veins similar to those forming the right, except that there is no azygos on the left side.

The post-caval vein (*pt. c.*) is formed in the hinder part of the abdominal cavity by the union of the *internal iliacs* (*i. il. v.*) bringing the blood from the

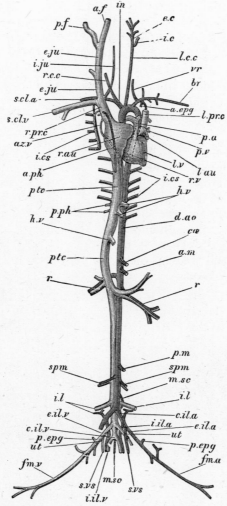

FIG. 459.—**Lepus cuniculus.** The vascular system. The heart is somewhat displaced towards the left of the subject ; the arteries of the right and the veins of the left side are in great measure removed. *a. epg.* internal mammary or anterior epigastric artery ; *a. f.* anterior facial vein ; *a. m.* anterior mesenteric artery ; *a. ph.* anterior phrenic vein ; *az. v.* azygos vein ; *br.* brachial artery ; *c. il. a.* common iliac artery ; *c. il. v.* hinder end of post-caval ; *cœ.* cœliac artery ; *d. ao.* dorsal aorta ; *e. c.* external carotid artery ; *e. il. a.* external iliac artery ; *e. il. v.* external iliac vein ; *e. ju.* external jugular vein ; *fm. a.* femoral artery ; *fm. v.* femoral vein ; *h. v.* hepatic veins ; *i. c.* internal carotid artery ; *i.cs.* intercostal vessels ; *i. ju.* internal jugular vein ; *i. l.* ilio-lumbar artery and vein ; *in* innominate artery ; *l. au.* left auricle ; *l. c. c.* left common carotid artery ; *l.pr.c.* left pre-caval vein ; *l. v.* left ventricle ; *m. sc.* median sacral artery ; *p. a.* pulmonary artery ; *p. epg.* posterior epigastric artery and vein ; *p. f.* posterior facial vein ; *p. m.* posterior mesenteric artery ; *p. ph.* posterior phrenic veins ; *pt. c.* post-caval vein ; *p. v.* pulmonary vein ; *r. renal* artery and vein ; *r. au.* right auricle ; *r. c. c.* right common carotid artery ; *r. pr. c.* right pre-caval vein ; *r. v.* right ventricle ; *scl. a.* right subclavian artery ; *scl. v.* subclavian vein ; *spm.* spermatic artery and vein ; *s. vs.* superior vesical artery and vein ; *ut.* uterine artery and vein ; *vr.* vertebral artery. (From Parker's *Zootomy*.)

back of the thighs.   Shortly after its origin it receives the two *external iliacs* (*e. il. v.*) coming from the hind-limb.   In front of this a pair of *ilio-lumbar* (*i. l.*) veins join it ; a little farther forward a pair of *spermatic* (*spm.*) or *ovarian* veins ; and opposite the kidneys a pair of *renal* veins (*r.*).   From the liver the blood is carried to the post-caval by the *hepatic* veins.   A pair of small *posterior phrenic* veins (*p. ph.*) bring the blood from the diaphragm and open into the post-caval as it passes through the substance of the latter.

The *hepatic portal system* consists, as in other Vertebrates, of a system of veins conveying blood from the various parts of the alimentary canal to the liver, the trunks of the system uniting to form the single large *portal vein* (Fig. 457, *p. v.*).   The principal veins of the portal system are the *lieno-gastric, duodenal, anterior mesenteric,* and *posterior mesenteric*.   There is no trace of a renal portal system.   The red blood corpuscles are circular, biconcave, non-nucleated discs.

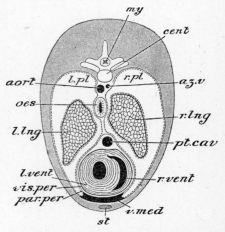

FIG. 461—**Lepus cuniculus.**   Diagram of a transverse section of the thorax in the region of the ventricles to show the relations of the pleuræ, mediastinum, etc.   The lungs are contracted.   *aort.* dorsal aorta ; *az. v.* azygos vein ; *cent.* centrum of thoracic vertebra ; *l. lng.* left lung ; *l. pl.* left pleural sac ; *l. vent.* left ventricle ; *my.* spinal cord ; *œs.* œsophagus ; *par. per.* parietal layer of pericardium ; *pt. cav.* post-caval, close to its entrance into right auricle ; *r. lng.* right lung ; *r. pl.* right pleural cavity ; *r. vent.* right ventricle ; *st.* sternum ; *v. med.* ventral mediastinum.

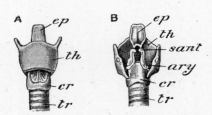

FIG. 460.—**Lepus cuniculus.** Larynx.   *A*, ventral view ; *B*, dorsal view.   *ary.* arytenoid ; *cr.* cricoid ; *ep.* epiglottis ; *sant.* cartilage of Santorini ; *th.* thyroid ; *tr.* trachea.   (From Krause, after Schneider.)

Respiratory Organs.—The *larynx* (Fig. 460) is a chamber with walls supported by cartilage, lying below and somewhat behind the pharynx, with which it communicates through a slit-like aperture.   The cartilages of the larynx are, in addition to the *epiglottis*, which has been already referred to (p. 502), the large *thyroid* (*th.*), which forms the ventral and lateral walls, the ring-like *cricoid* (*cr.*), the two small *arytenoids* (*ary.*), and a pair of small nodules, the *cartilages of Santorini* (*sant.*), situated at the apices of the arytenoids.   The *vocal cords* extend across the cavity from the thyroid below to the arytenoids above.   Leading backwards from the larynx is the *trachea* or wind-pipe (Fig. 460, *tr.*), a long tube the wall of which is supported by cartilaginous rings which are incomplete dorsally. The trachea enters the cavity of the thorax, and there divides into the two *bronchi*, one passing to the root of each lung.

The *lungs* (Fig. 461) are enclosed in the lateral parts of the cavity of the thorax. Each lung lies in a cavity, the *pleural sac*, lined by a *pleural membrane*. The right and left pleural sacs are separated by a considerable interval owing to the development in the partition between them of a space, the mediastinum, in which, as already explained, lie the heart and other organs. The lung is attached only at its root, where the pleural membrane is reflected over it. In this respect it differs widely from the lung of the bird. It differs also in its minute structure. The bronchus, entering at the root, divides and subdivides to form a ramifying system of tubes, each of the ultimate branches of which, or *terminal bronchioles*, opens into a minute chamber or *infundibulum*, consisting of a central passage and a number of thin-walled *air-vesicles* or *alveoli* given off from it. A group of these infundibula, supplied by a single bronchiole, which divides within it to form the terminal bronchioles, is termed a *lobule* of the lung.

In shape the lung may be roughly described as conical, with the apex directed forwards. The base, which is concave, lies, when the lung is distended, in contact with the convex anterior surface of the diaphragm. The outer or costal surface is convex in adaptation to the form of the side-wall of the thorax; the internal surface is concave.

Ductless Glands.—The *spleen* is an elongated, compressed, dark-red body situated in the abdominal cavity in close contact with the stomach, to which it is bound by a fold of the peritoneum. The *thymus*, much larger in the young Rabbit than in the adult, is a soft mass, resembling fat in appearance, situated in the ventral division of the mediastinal space below the base of the heart. The *thyroid* is a small, brownish, bilobed, glandular body situated in close contact with the ventral surface of the larynx.

Nervous System.—The neural cavity, as in the Pigeon, contains the central organs of the cerebro-spinal nervous system—the *brain* and *spinal cord*. The brain (Figs. 462, 463, 464) of the Rabbit contains the same principal parts as that of the Pigeon, with certain differences, of which the following are the most important.

The surface of the cerebral hemispheres or parencephala (Fig. 462, *f. b.*, Fig. 463, *c. h.*), which are relatively long and narrow, presents certain depressions or sulci, which, though few and indistinct, yet mark out the surface into lobes or convolutions not distinguishable in the case of the Pigeon or the Lizard. A slight depression—the *Sylvian fissure*—at the side of the hemisphere separates off a lateral portion, or *temporal lobe* (Fig. 464, *c. h.*,[2]), from the rest. There are very large club-shaped olfactory bulbs at the anterior extremities of the cerebral hemispheres, and behind each on the ventral surface of the hemisphere is the corresponding olfactory tract leading back to a slight rounded elevation, the *tuberculum olfactorium*.   Connecting together the two hemispheres is a commissural structure—the *corpus callosum* (Figs. 463, 464, *cp. cl.*)—not present in the Pigeon ; this runs transversely above the level of the lateral ventricles.   Examined in transverse section, *i.e.*, in a longitudinal section of the brain (Fig. 464), the corpus callosum is seen to bend slightly downwards,

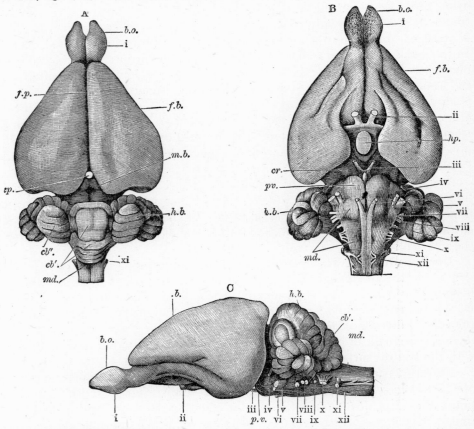

FIG. 462.—**Lepus cuniculus.**   Brain.   *A*, dorsal, *B*, ventral, *C*, lateral view.   *b. o.* olfactory bulb ; *cb'.* median lobe of cerebellum (vermis) ; *cb''.* lateral lobe of cerebellum ; *cr.* crura cerebri ; *ep.* epiphysis ; *f. b.* parencephala ; *f. p.* longitudinal fissure ; *h. b.* cerebellum ; *hp.* hypophysis ; *m. b.* mid-brain (corpora quadrigemina) ; *md.* medulla oblongata ; *pv.* pons Varolii, the transverse fibres of which are here not indicated ; *i–xii*, cerebral nerves.   (From Wiedersheim.)

forming what is termed the *genu* ; posteriorly it bends downwards and forwards, forming the *splenium*, which passes forwards and is united with the fornix. Below the corpus callosum is another characteristic structure of a commissural nature—the *fornix* (*b. fo.*)—a narrow median strand of longitudinal fibres, which bifurcates both anteriorly and posteriorly to form the so-called *pillars* of the fornix—anterior (Figs. 463 and 464, *a. fo.*), and posterior (Fig. 463, *p. fo.*).

Below the corpus callosum, between it and the fornix, the thin inner walls of the hemispheres (*septum lucidum, sp. lu.*) enclose a small, laterally compressed cavity, the so-called *fifth ventricle* or *pseudocœle*, this is not a true brain-ventricle, but merely a space between the closely-apposed hemispheres.

The lateral ventricles of the cerebral hemispheres are much more extensively developed than in the brain of the Pigeon, and of somewhat complex shape.

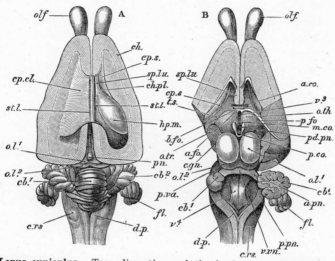

FIG. 463.—**Lepus cuniculus.** Two dissections of the brain from above (nat. size). In *A* the left parencephalon is dissected down to the level of the corpus callosum: on the right the lateral ventricle is exposed. In *B* the cerebral hemispheres are dissected to a little below the level of the genu of the corpus callosum; only the frontal lobe of the left hemisphere is retained; of the right a portion of the temporal lobe also is left; the velum interpositum and pineal body are removed, as well as the greater part of the body of the fornix, and the whole of the left posterior pillar; the cerebellum is removed with the exception of a part of its right lateral lobe. *a. co.* anterior commissure; *a. fo.* anterior pillar of fornix; *a. pn.* anterior peduncles of cerebellum; *b. fo.* body of fornix; *cb¹.* superior vermis of cerebellum; *cb².* its lateral lobe; *c. gn.* corpus geniculatum; *c. h.* cerebral hemisphere; *ch. pl.* choroid plexus; *cp. cl.* corpus callosum; *cp. s.* corpus striatum; *c. rs.* corpus restiforme; *d. pl.* dorsal pyramid; *fl.* flocculus; *hp.m.* hippocampus; *m. co.* middle commissure; *o. l¹.* anterior, and *o. l².* posterior lobes of corpora quadrigemina; *olf.* olfactory bulb; *o. th.* optic thalamus; *o. tr.* optic tract; *p. co.* posterior commissure; *p. fo.* posterior pillar of fornix (tænia hippocampi); *pn.* pineal body; *pd. pn.* peduncle of pineal body; *p. pn.* posterior peduncles of cerebellum; *p. va.* fibres of pons Varolii forming middle peduncles of cerebellum; *sp. lu.* septum lucidum; *st. l.* stria longitudinalis; *t. s.* tænia semicircularis (narrow band of white matter between corpus striatum and optic thalamus); *v. vn.* valve of Vieussens; *v³*, third ventricle; *v⁴*, fourth ventricle. (From Parker's *Zootomy*.)

Each consists of a middle portion of *body* roofed over by the corpus callosum, a narrow anterior prolongation, or *anterior cornu*, a *posterior cornu*, which runs backwards and inwards, and a *descending cornu*, which passes at first almost directly outwards, then downwards, and finally inwards and forwards. On the floor of the body of the ventricle, and continued along the whole extent of the descending cornu, is a prominent ridge of nearly semicircular transverse section—the *hippocampus* (*hp. m.*); this corresponds in position with a groove,

the *hippocampal sulcus,* on the inner surface of the temporal lobe. Internally the two hippocampi merge in a median commissural area—the *psalterium* or *lyra* (*ly.*).

Running along the anterior edge of the hippocampus is a ridge of fibres—the *tænia hippocampi* or *fimbria*—which passes down into the descending cornu. The union of the two tæniæ forms a median longitudinal strand, the *body of the fornix,* which, as already explained, lies below the corpus callosum, continuous with the splenium of the latter behind, but diverging from it anteriorly by dipping down towards the base of the brain. In the angular space between the corpus callosum and the fornix below is the septum lucidum with the " fifth ventricle." The tæniæ hippocampi are the *posterior pillars* of the fornix (Fig. 463, *p. fo.*) ; the *anterior pillars* (*a. fo.*) are a pair of vertical bands which

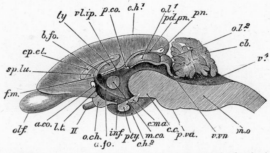

FIG. 464.—**Lepus cuniculus.** Longitudinal vertical section of the brain (nat. size). Letters as in preceding figure; in addition—*cb.* cerebellum, showing arbor vitæ ; *c. c.* crus cerebri ; *c. h*[1]. parencephalon ; *c. h*[2]. temporal lobe ; *c. ma.* corpus mammillare ; *f. m.* foramen of Monro ; *inf.* infundibulum ; *ly.* psalterium or lyra ; *m. o.* medulla oblongata ; *o. ch.* optic chiasma ; *olf.* olfactory bulb ; *pty.* pituitary body ; *p. va.* pons Varolii ; *vl. ip.* velum interpositum ; *v. vn.* valve of Vieussens ; *II,* optic nerve. (From Parker's *Zootomy.*)

pass from the anterior end of the body downwards to the corpus mammillare (*see below*) at the base of the diencephalon.

Lying immediately in front of the hippocampus is a vascular membrane, the *choroid plexus* (*ch. pl.*) ; this passes inwards to join its fellow of the opposite side through a transverse passage, the *foramen of Monro* (*f. m.*), which opens behind into the diacœle. The floor of the anterior cornu is formed of an eminence of grey matter—the *corpus striatum* (*cp. s.*). The right and left corpora striata are connected together by a narrow transverse band of white fibres—the *anterior commissure* (*a. co.*)—situated in front of the anterior pillars of the fornix.

The diacœle (*v*[3],) is a laterally compressed cavity, the roof of which is formed by a delicate vascular membrane, the *velum interpositum* (*vl. ip.*), in which there is a network of blood-vessels (*choroid plexus* of the diacœle) continuous with the choroid plexuses of the lateral ventricles. From the posterior part of the roof of the diacœle rise the peduncles of the pineal body. The *optic thalami* (*o. th.*) are large masses of mixed grey and white matter forming the lateral portions of the diencephalon; they are connected together by a thick mass of grey matter, the *middle* or *soft commissure* (*m. co.*), not represented in lower vertebrates, passing across the diacœle. A rounded elevation near the anterior end of the external surface of each thalamus is the *corpus geniculatum* (*c. gn.*). The anterior boundary of the diacœle is a thin vertical lamina—the *lamina terminalis*—of which the septum lucidum is a mesial anterior prolongation. The floor of the diencephalon is produced downward into a mesial process, the *tuber cinereum* or *infundibulum* (*inf.*), to which the pituitary body is attached. In front of this, on the ventral aspect of the brain, is a thick transverse band of nerve-fibres, the united *optic tracts*, from the anterior border of which the optic nerves are given off. Behind the tuber cinereum, and formed as a thickening of its posterior wall, is a rounded elevation, the *corpus mammillare* (*c. ma.*).

In the mid-brain the dorsal part is remarkable for the fact that each *optic lobe* is divided into two by a transverse furrow, so that two pairs of lobes (*o. l*^{1}*., o.l*^{2}*.*), the *corpora quadrigemina*, are produced. Between the anterior lobes passes the delicate *posterior commissure* (*p. co.*). On the ventral region of the mid-brain the *crura cerebri* are far more prominent than in the lower groups. In the hind-brain the *cerebellum* (Fig. 462, *cb'., cb''.*) is very large; it consists of a *central lobe* or *vermis* and two *lateral lobes*, divided by very numerous fissures or sulci into a large number of small convolutions. Each lateral lobe bears an irregularly-shaped prominence, the *flocculus*. On section (Fig. 464, *cb.*) the cerebellum exhibits a tree-like pattern (*arbor vitæ*) brought about by the arrangement of the white and grey matter. On the ventral aspect of the hind-brain a flat band of transverse fibres—the *pons Varolii*—connects together the lateral parts of the cerebellum. The cerebellum is attached to the other parts of the brain by three pairs of peduncles, the *anterior*, connecting it with the posterior optic lobes, the *middle*, passing on each side into the pons Varolii, and the *posterior*, connecting it with the dorsal portion of the medulla oblongata. Between the anterior peduncles extends a transverse band, the *valve of Vieussens* (Fig. 464, *v. vn.*), connected by its anterior edge with the corpora quadrigemina. Behind this is a short tract of transverse fibres—the *corpus trapezoideum*—and behind this again is a slightly elevated area marking the position of the *olivary body*. The floor of the fourth ventricle presents a median groove which ends posteriorly in a pointed depression—*calamus scriptorius*—leading into the central canal of the spinal cord.

The Rabbit, like most other vertebrates, possesses a *sympathetic nervous system*, consisting of a series of ganglia united together by commissural nerves, and giving off branches to the various internal organs. Two sympathetic ganglia are situated on each side in the neck—the *anterior* and *posterior cervical ganglia*. From the anterior nerve-branches pass forwards to enter the cranial cavity; from the posterior a nerve-cord passes backwards to the first thoracic ganglion. Of the *thoracic ganglia* there are twelve on each side. From one of the more posterior of these originates the *splanchnic nerve*, which passes backwards into the abdomen, ending in a ganglion—the *cœliac*—connected with an extensive nerve-plexus, the *cœliac plexus*. In the abdomen there are, on each side, twelve ganglia, the chain ending behind in a single *ganglion impar*.

In the **organs of special sense** the following special features are to be seen when a comparison is made with the Pigeon or Lizard. In the eye, the sclerotic is composed entirely of dense fibrous tissue; the pecten is absent. In the internal ear the principal point of difference is in the special development of the *cochlea*. This part of the membranous labyrinth, instead of retaining the simple

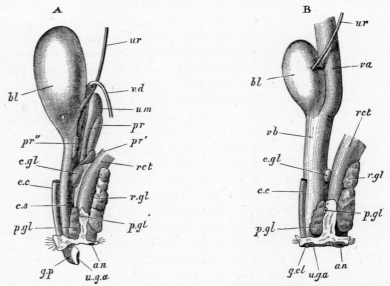

FIG. 465.—**Lepus cuniculus.** The urinogenital organs; *A*, of male; *B*, of female; from the left side (half nat. size). The kidneys and proximal ends of the ureters, in *A* the testes, and in *B* the ovaries, Fallopian tubes and uteri, are not shown. *an.* anus; *bl.* urinary bladder; *c. c.* corpus cavernosum; *c. s.* corpus spongiosum; *c. gl.* Cowper's gland; *g. cl.* apex of clitoris; *g. p.* apex of penis; *p. gl.* perineal gland; *p. gl'.* aperture of its duct on the perineal space; *pr.* anterior, *pr'.* posterior, and *pr''.* lateral lobes of prostate; *rct.* rectum; *r. gl.* rectal gland; *u. g. a.* urinogenital aperture; *u. m.* uterus masculinus; *ur.* ureter; *va.* vagina; *vb.* vestibule; *v. d.* vas deferens. (From Parker's *Zootomy*.)

curved form which it presents in the Bird, is coiled on itself in a close spiral of two-and-a-half turns. The spiral channel in the substance of the bone, in which this cochlear spiral runs, contains three passages; the middle one, much the smallest, being the *membranous cochlea*, the uppermost the *scala vestibuli*, and the lowermost the *scala tympani*.

The special features of the middle ear with its auditory ossicles, and of the external ear, have been already referred to (p. 497).

Urinogenital Organs.—The *kidneys* are of somewhat compressed oval shape, with a notch or *hilus* on the inner side. They are in close contact with the dorsal wall of the abdominal cavity, the right being somewhat in advance of the left. Towards the hilus the tubules of the kidney converge to open into a wide chamber—the *pelvis*—which forms the dilated commencement of the ureter. When the kidney is cut across, its substance is seen to be divided into a central mass or *medulla* and a peripheral portion or *cortex*. An *adrenal* (*suprarenal*) *body* lies in contact with the anterior end of each kidney. The *ureter* (Fig. 465, *ur.*) runs backwards to open, not into a cloaca, but directly into the *urinary bladder* (*bl.*). The latter is a pyriform sac with muscular walls which vary in thickness according as the organ is dilated or contracted. In the male the openings of the ureters are situated nearer the posterior narrower end or neck than in the female.

In the male Rabbit the *testes* are oval bodies, which, though in the young animal occupying a similar position to that which they retain throughout life in the Pigeon, pass backwards and downwards as the animal approaches maturity, until they come to lie each in a *scrotal sac* situated at the side of the urinogenital opening. The cavity of each scrotal sac is in free communication with the cavity of the abdomen by an opening—the *inguinal canal*. The sperms have an oval compressed " head " 0·005 mm. in length and a slender " tail " 0·045 mm. long. A convoluted *epididymis*, closely adherent to the testis,

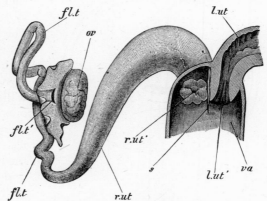

FIG. 466.—**Lepus cuniculus.** The anterior end of the vagina, with the right uterus, Fallopian tube and ovary (nat. size). Part of the ventral wall of the vagina is removed, and the proximal end of the left uterus is shown in longitudinal section. *fl. t.* Fallopian tube ; *fl. t'.* its peritoneal aperture ; *l. ut.* left uterus ; *l. ut'.* left os uteri ; *ov.* right ovary ; *r. ut.* right uterus ; *r. ut'.* right os uteri ; *s.* vaginal septum ; *va.* vagina. (From Parker's *Zootomy*.)

forms the proximal part of the *vas deferens*. The *vasa deferentia* (*v.d.*) terminate by opening into a urinogenital canal, or *urethra*, into which the neck of the urinary bladder is continued. A *prostate gland* (*pr.*) surrounds the commencement of the urethra, the neck of the bladder, and the terminal part of the vasa deferentia. A diverticulum of the urethra—the *uterus masculinus* (*u. m.*)— lies embedded in the prostate gland close to the neck of the bladder. A small pair of ovoid glands, *Cowper's glands* (*c. gl.*), lie just behind the prostate close to the side of the urethra.

The terminal part of the urethra traverses a cord of vascular tissue, the *corpus spongiosum* (*c. s.*), which forms the dorsal portion of the penis. The greater part of the penis is formed of two closely approximated firm cores of vascular tissue—the *corpora cavernosa* (*c. c.*), which are attached proximally to the ischia, and terminate in a pointed apex (*g. p.*). A loose fold of skin, the *prepuce*, encloses the penis. A pair of glands with an odorous secretion, the *perineal glands* (*p. gl.*), open on the perineal space at the base of the penis : two similar glands, the *rectal glands* (*r. gl.*), lie on either side of the rectum.

In the female the *ovaries* (Fig. 466 *ov.*) are small ovoid bodies attached to the dorsal wall of the abdomen behind the kidneys. The *Graafian follicles* enclosing the ova form only very small rounded projections on their outer surface.

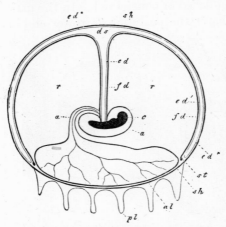

FIG. 467.—Diagrammatic longitudinal section of a Rabbit's embryo at an advanced stage of pregnancy. *a.* amnion ; *a.* stalk of allantois ; *al.* allantois with blood-vessels ; *c.* embryo ; *ds.* cavity of yolk-sac (umbilical vesicle) ; *ed.* endodermal layer of yolk-sac ; *ed'.* inner portion of endoderm ; *ed''.* outer portion of endoderm lining the compressed cavity of the yolk-sac ; *fd.* vascular layer of yolk-sac ; *pl.* placental villi ; *r.* space filled with fluid between the amnion, the allantois and the yolk-sac ; *sh.* subzonal membrane ; *st.* sinus terminalis. (From Foster and Balfour, after Bischoff.)

The *oviducts* in the anterior part of their extent (*Fallopian tubes, fl. t.*) are very narrow and slightly convoluted. They open into the abdominal cavity by wide funnel-shaped openings (*fl. t'.*) with fimbriated or fringed margins. Posteriorly each passes into a thick-walled *uterus* (*r. ut.*). The two uteri open separately into a median tube, the *vagina* (*va.*). The *vestibule* (Fig. 465 *B, vb.*), or *urinogenital canal*, is a wide median passage, into which the vagina and the bladder open. On its ventral wall is a small, hard, rod-like body, the *clitoris* (*c. c.*), with a pointed apex (*g. cl.*), corresponding to the penis of the male, and composed of two very short *corpora cavernosa* attached anteriorly to the ischia, and invested internally by a soft, grooved *corpus spongiosum*. The *vulva*, or external opening of the vestibule, is bounded laterally by two prominent folds—the *labia majora*.

Development.—The Rabbit is viviparous. The ovum, which is of relatively small size, after it has escaped from its Graafian follicle, passes into the Fallopian tube, where it becomes fertilised, and then reaches the uterus, in which it develops into the *fœtus*, as the intra-uterine embryo is termed. The young animal escapes from the uterus in a condition in which all the parts have become fully formed, except that the eyelids are closed and the hairy covering is not yet completed. As many as eight or ten young are produced at a birth, and the period of gestation, *i.e.*, the time elapsing between the fertilisation of the ovum and the birth of the young animal, is thirty days. Fresh broods may be born once a month throughout a considerable part of the year, and as the young

Rabbit may begin breeding at the age of three months, the rate of increase is very rapid.

The segmentation is of the holoblastic type. An amnion and an allantois are developed much as in the case of the Bird (p. 483). But the later history of these fœtal membranes is widely different in the Rabbit, owing to the modifications which they undergo, in order to take part of the formation of the *placenta*—the structure by whose instrumentality the fœtus receives its nourishment from the walls of the uterus. The placenta is formed from the *serous membrane* or *chorion*—the outer layer of the amniotic folds—in a limited disc-shaped area, in which the distal portion of the allantois coalesces with it (Fig. 467). The membrane thus formed develops vascular process—the *chorionic villi*—which are received into depressions (the *uterine crypts*) in the mucous membrane of the uterus. The completed placenta with its villi is supplied with blood by the allantoic vessels. The placenta of the Rabbit is of the type termed *deciduate*, the villi of the placenta being intimately united with the uterine mucous membrane, and a part of the latter coming away with it at birth in form of a *decidua*, or after-birth.

Systematic Position of the Example.

The genus Lepus, to which the common Rabbit belongs, comprises a number of other species, the common Hare being among the number, distinguished from one another by slight differences in the proportions of the parts and in other general features. Lepus is the only genus of the family *Leporidæ*, which is associated with the family *Lagomyidæ* or Picas under the designation *Duplicidentata*, owing to the presence in these two families, and in these two alone of the entire order Rodentia to which they belong, of a second pair of incisors in the upper jaw. The chief distinctive features of the family Leporidæ are the elongated hind-limbs, the short recurved tail, the long ears, and the incomplete clavicles.

CLASSIFICATION OF THE MAMMALIA

Sub-classes [1]
- I.   Allotheria (Multituberculata.)
- II. Triconodonta.
- III. Symmetrodonta.
- IV. Pantotheria.
- V.   Prototheria (Monotremata).
- VI. Metatheria (Marsupialia. Didelphia).
- VII. Eutheria (Placentalia. Monodelphia).

[1] The second, third, and fourth sub-classes are still uncertain as to their true rank. The Pantotheria, and perhaps the Symmetrodonta, are rather nearer the Metatheria and Eutheria, and might all be grouped together as a class, the Theria.

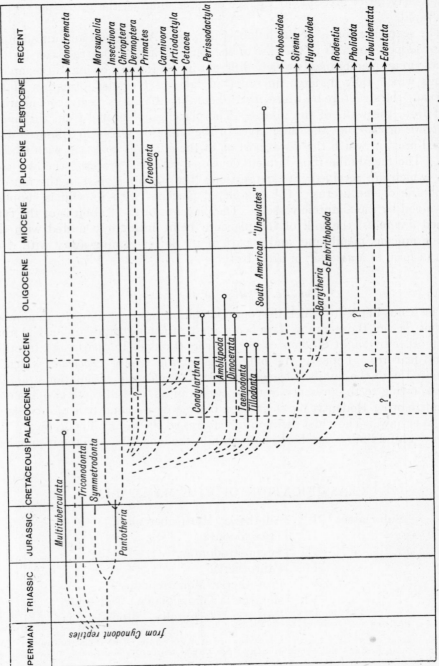

FIG. 468.—The appearance in time and probable relationship of the mammalian sub-classes and orders.

Sub-class Allotheria (Multituberculata).

Of the beginnings of mammalian history very little is known. During the whole of the Triassic period there was an expansion of the mammal-like Reptiles, the Cynodontia (p. 384), with their foreshadowing of several mammalian characters and, although no absolutely transitional specimens have as yet been discovered, it must have been from this stock that the Mammals evolved.

There was an expansion of Mammals, all of rather small size, during the

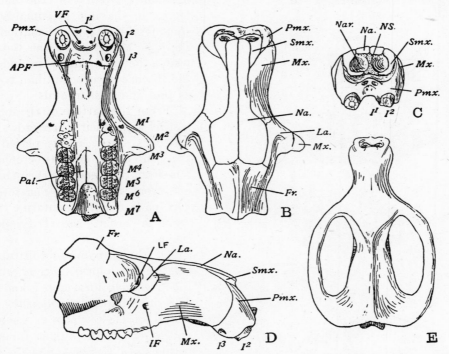

FIG. 469.—**Tritylodon longævus.** *A.* Palatal view. *B.* Dorsal view. *C.* Anterior view. *D.* Right lateral view. *E.* Hypothetical reconstruction of the entire dorsal surface. *APF.* anterior palatal foramen; *Fr.* frontal; *IF.* infra-orbital foramen; *La.* lachrymal; *LF.* lachrymal foramen; *Mx.* maxilla; *Na.* nasal; *Nar.* anterior nares; *NS.* nasal septum; *Pal.* palatine; *Pmx.* premaxilla; *Smx.* septomaxilla; *VF.* vascular foramen. (After Simpson.)

Mesozoic periods, of which only a few fragmentary specimens have been found in a few localities scattered over a great interval of geological time (see Fig. 468).[1]

The earliest animal accepted as a Mammal is the classic specimen, a frag-

[1] When it is realised that Mesozoic Mammals have been found in no more than a dozen localities in the whole world and then, with a few very rare skulls and parts of limbs, as mere fragments of jaws or teeth and, moreover, that between the few formations in which these fragments occur there are series of deposits representing great stretches of time in which no remains occur, it becomes clear that our knowledge of early mammalian life is strictly limited. For an account of the Mesozoic Mammals see G. G. Simpson (nos. 109, 110, 111), in Appendix on Literature.

mentary skull from the Upper Triassic (Stormberg beds) of South Africa corresponding to the Rhætic beds in age, known as *Tritylodon longævus*. All

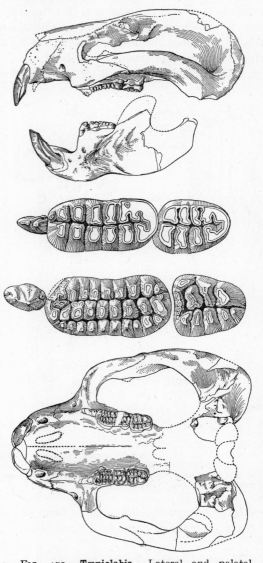

that can be said of this specimen (Fig. 489) is that it shows definitely mammalian characters in having typically mammalian infra-orbital and lachrymal foramina, in the division of roots of the molar teeth, in having presumably a squamosal-dentary articulation of the jaws as shown by the way in which the teeth are worn and by the absence of such reptilian bones as pre- and post-frontals.

From the pattern of the molar teeth, with their three rows of tubercles, *Tritylodon* is placed in the sub-class Multituberculata, but, from differences in their shape and from some other characters, it is made the representative of a separate order, the Tritylodon-toidea.

Of the remaining Multituber-culates, which form a second order, the Plagiaulacoidea, more is known. This order had an enormously long period of existence from its first appearance in the Upper Jurassic period until the beginning of the Tertiary period, when the group finally became extinct. The most noticeable character, and the one from which the name of the sub-class is taken, is the structure of the molar teeth. These have from two to three longitudinal rows of tubercles with from two to five, or more, cusps in each row. There is but a single lower incisor and

FIG. 470.—**Tæniolabis**. Lateral and palatal view of skull. The lower and upper (the lower of the two figures) molars. (After Simpson.)

three upper, of which the central one becomes much enlarged. Canines are entirely absent. In more advance forms the anterior lower cheek-teeth become much enlarged and very specialised, in a manner analogous to that of some living Marsupials, such as the " Rat kangaroo," *Bettongia*. The zygomatic arch arises far forward at the level of the anterior cheek-teeth, and extends back almost to the occiput. The lower jaw is stout, but has no angular process, a character held in common with the Triconodonta and Symmetrodonta.

The Multituberculata seem to have held a position analogous to that of the Rodentia of the present time.

Representative genera are *Plagiaulax, Bolodon, Tæniolabis* (Fig. 470), *Neoplagiaulax, Ptilodus, Ctenacodon* (Fig. 471), etc.

Sub-class Triconodonta.

Except for doubtful specimens in the Upper Triassic (Rhætic) beds, these small Mammals occur first in the Middle Jurassic (Stonesfield beds) of England and again at the top of the Jurassic in England (Purbeck beds) and North

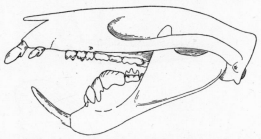

FIG. 471.—**Ctenacodon.** (After Simpson.)

America (Morrison beds). The period of this group therefore appears to have been comparatively short.

Little is known beyond the dentition. There were three or four incisors in each jaw, well-developed canines, four premolars, and up to five molars. The pattern of the molars is distinctive. There were three cusps arranged in an antero-posterior line; the central cusp in earlier forms was larger than the other two, but in later forms the three cusps became subequal.

Representative genera are *Amphilestes, Triconodon* (Fig. 472), *Phascolotherium, Trioracodon*, etc.

Sub-class Symmetrodonta.

This sub-class appears to have been confined to the Upper Jurassic period, and to have had an even shorter extension in time. The teeth are characteristic in being triangular, with one larger cusp and two smaller ones. In the lower molars the base of the triangle is on the inner or lingual side, and the large cusp is placed at the apex of the triangle on the outer, or labial, side. The upper molars are the reverse of this. The lower jaw is without an angular process.

Representative genera are *Spalacotherium* (Fig. 472), *Peralestes*, etc.

Sub-class Pantotheria.

While the preceding two sub-classes seem to have had no very close connection with one another, nor to have left any successors after the end of the
Jurassic period, the Pantotheria are quite possibly related, if only distantly, to

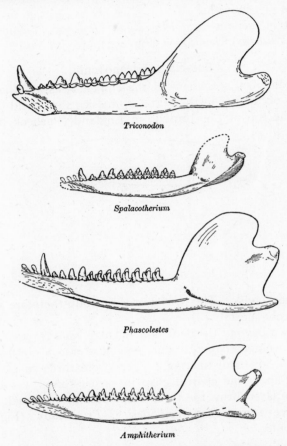

FIG. 472.—Lower jaws of **Triconodon** (Triconodonta), **Spalacotherium** (Symmetrodonta),
Phascolestes and **Amphitherium** (Pantotheria). (After Simpson.)

the stock which gave rise some time during the Cretaceous period to the
Metatheria and Eutheria. There is at least no known character in members of
the group which makes this view untenable. Like the preceding two sub-
classes, the Pantotheria themselves seem confined to the upper part of the
Jurassic.

The dental formula shows a large number of teeth. There are four incisors, a canine which may be bifanged, four premolars, and as many as eight molars. The lower molars are triangular, with one principal labial cusp and two smaller lingual ones. Small additional cusps may be present. The lower molars also show a posterior prolongation of the tooth, a foreshadowing of the trituberculo-sectorial type of later mammals. The upper molars are plain triangles with one principal lingual and two or three smaller labial ones. The contour of the lower jaw is not unlike that of a primitive Insectivore with a high coronoid and a well-marked angular process.

Representative genera are *Amblotherium*, *Peraspalax*, *Peramus*, *Phascolestes* (Fig. 472), *Amphitherium* (Fig. 472), etc.

Sub-class Prototheria (Monotremata).

Although the past history of this group is practically unknown, a study of the anatomy of its living representatives is enough to suggest that it is one of the greatest antiquity. While the two families of the group, the Ornithorhynchidæ and Tachyglossidæ, differ somewhat widely from one another in appearance and in some minor anatomical characters, all of which can be explained as adaptations to different modes of life, they are, on the other hand, bound together as a single sub-class by the possession in common of many deep-seated characters which are found in no other mammals.

While the essential mammalian characters, such as hair, diaphragm, four optic lobes to the brain, and so on, are all present, there are nevertheless some features which indicate a wide cleft between the Prototheria and all other mammals. The facts that eggs are laid and that there is no uterine gestation are pre-mammalian features, as is the structure of the urogenital organs, which are still in the reptilian condition (p. 375). In the skeleton the shoulder-girdle not only has the pre-coracoids well developed, which in other mammals become reduced to vestiges, but also retains an interclavicle. Milk is produced, but the mammary glands are unspecialised, are without nipples, and the marsupial pouch is temporary (Figs. 593, 594). The vertebræ are without epiphyses except in the tail region of *Ornithorhynchus*, and the position of the exit of the spinal nerves in the middle of the vertebra, instead of between adjacent vertebræ, is peculiar. The cervical vertebræ bear ribs. In the hind leg the proximal end of the fibula is prolonged in a manner analogous to the olecranon process of the ulna, and in the male there is a hollow tarsal spur which is connected with a small crural gland, the secretion of which appears to be poisonous.

The skull, though very different in shape in the two families (Figs. 477–478), is in each made up in the same general way. The chondrocranium is typically mammalian, but differs from other mammals in some respects, such as the absence of an alisphenoid bone and the presence of a bone in addition to the usual mammalian pterygoid known as the " Echidna pterygoid." This bone is to be homologised with the epipterygoid of reptiles.

The differences in the shape of the skull and body, and many of the external features shown by the two families, are the result of their different environment and habits.

Ornithorhynchus anatinus (Fig. 473), the " Duckbilled Platypus," is the sole species of the genus *Ornithorhynchus* and family Ornithorhynchidæ. Its distribution is in Eastern Australia and Tasmania, where it lives in the pools of rivers and creeks, in the banks of which it makes its burrows and nest.

The body is flattened and covered with a close, soft fur. The upper jaw is produced into a depressed muzzle, not unlike the beak of a duck, a feature that provided the specific name. This beak is covered by a smooth, hairless integument, which forms a free fold or flap at the base. The eyes are very

A

FIG. 473.—**Duck-Bill** (*Ornithorhynchus anatinus*). (After Vogt and Specht.)

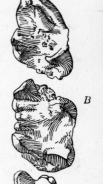

B

small, and rather close together on the top of the head. The openings of the external ear, likewise small, lie just behind the eyes, and lack the ear-flap or pinna. The forelegs are short but powerful, and the five digits end in strong claws which are set in a web which joins them together and then projects below and beyond the nails. This flap can be folded back at will, so that the limb can be used either for digging or swimming. The hind limb is less specialised. The tail is elongated, depressed, and is a powerful swimming-organ, which some-what resembles that of the Beaver.

FIG. 474.— Crown views of *A*, upper and *B*. lower teeth of **Ornithorhynchus.** (From Green after Simpson.)

The teeth are most peculiar (Fig. 474). In the young stages calcified teeth are formed in each half of the upper and lower jaws. They are very brittle, clearly degenerate, and are soon shed and replaced by under-lying horny plates, in depressions of which the teeth were originally set. In structure the teeth show some rather irregular tubercles arranged in a pattern that has given rise to a view that the Prototheria are descended from, or distantly related to, the Multituberculata, a view that cannot strongly be upheld on this evidence.

The dental formula is peculiar (Fig. 475). There appear to be no upper

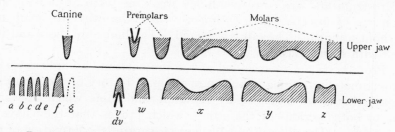

FIG. 475.—Dental formula of **Ornithorhynchus.** The absence of upper incisors and the presence of an upper and lower replacing tooth should be noticed. *A—e* lower incisors; *f.* lower canine; *g.* ? second canine; *vw.* premolars; *dv.* replacing tooth; *x. y. z.* molars. (After Green.)

incisors formed, but there are five in the lower jaw. A canine is present in both jaws. The lower canine is followed by a problematic calcification which it is suggested is a second canine. The rest of the series consists of two premolars, of which the anterior is replaced and three molars in both jaws. These teeth are not present together at any one time, and most of them are non-functional

FIG. 476.—**Spiny Ant-eater** (*Tachyglossus aculeata*). (After Vogt and Specht.)

and abort as mere calcifications. At eleven weeks old there remain only two teeth in the upper and three in the lower jaw.[1]

The Tachyglossidæ (Echidnidæ) (Fig. 476) are represented by two closely allied genera *Zaglossus*, confined to New Guinea and *Tachyglossus* (*Echidna*)

[1] See H. L. H. H. Green, " The Development and Morphology of the Teeth of *Ornithorhynchus*," *Trans. Royal Soc.*, 1937.

aculeata, which ranges from New Guinea to Tasmania. These animals are land-living, nocturnal, insect-eating, and capable burrowers. The body is covered above with strong pointed spines, between which are coarse hairs. The lower surface of the body has hair only. The jaws are produced into a pointed rostrum and are correspondingly weak, as teeth are absent and the food consists of insects. Like *Ornithorhynchus*, the eyes are small and the ears without a pinna. The tail is vestigial. The limbs are short and the feet provided with strong claws.

The Prototheria are represented at the present time by only three species and, unfortunately, nothing is known of the past history of the group. They have some characters undoubtedly reptilian, and some which appear to be peculiar to both sections of the group, which proves that they have had a common origin. The differences sufficient to warrant the formation of the two separate families are adaptive, and due to the very different environments of water and land life.

Skeleton of Prototheria.—In the Prototheria (Fig. 477) the epiphyses of the vertebræ are not well developed in Ornithorhynchus, being represented only in the caudal region, and they appear to be absent in Tachyglossus. In both genera there is the normal number of vertebræ in the cervical region. The odontoid process long remains separate from the centrum of the axis. The cervical transverse processes are separately ossified, and only completely unite with the vertebræ at a late period, sutures being traceable in all but very old animals. Zygapophyses are absent in the cervical region. There are nineteen thoraco-lumbar vertebræ in both genera. The transverse processes are short, and the ribs do not articulate with them, but only with the sides of the centra. In the sacrum of Tachyglossus there are three or four, in that of Ornithorhynchus two, united vertebræ. The caudal region differs considerably in its development in the two genera. In Tachyglossus the tail is very short, the vertebræ depressed, with no inferior spines, but with about five subvertebral bones, which differ from ordinary chevron bones in being mere flat nodules. In Ornithorhynchus the tail is long, and the number of caudal vertebræ is twenty or twenty-one. Each has a distinct inferior spinous process (*infr. proc.*). The sternum consists of a presternum and three keeled sternebræ : in Tachyglossus but not in Ornithorhynchus there is a xiphisternum. The most remarkable feature of the sternal apparatus in the Prototheria is the presence of a T-shaped *episternum* (interclavicle, *epist.*) corresponding to that of reptiles. The sternal ribs are ossified, and are connected with the vertebral ribs by imperfectly ossified intermediate ribs (*int. rbs.*).

The *skull* of the Monotremes differs widely from that of other Mammals. The bones early become fused together, so that it is difficult to trace their exact boundaries. The brain-case is larger and more rounded in Tachyglossus than in the Ornithorhynchus, in accordance with the larger size of the brain in the

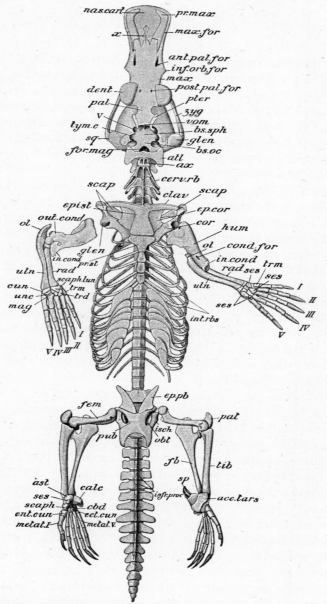

Fig. 477.—Skeleton of male **Ornithorhynchus**. Ventral view. The right fore-limb has been separated and turned round so as to bring into view the dorsal surface of the manus; the lower jaw is removed. *acc. tars.* accessory tarsal bone supporting the spur; *ant. pal. for.* anterior palatine foramen; *atl.* atlas; *ast.* astragalus; *ax.* axis; *bs. oc.* basi-occipital; *bs. sph.* basisphenoid; *calc.* calcaneum; *cbd.* cuboid; *cerv. rb.* cervical rib; *clav.* clavicle; *cond. for.* foramen above inner condyle of humerus; *cor.* coracoid; *cun.* cuneiform of carpus; *dent.* position of horny teeth; *ect. cun.* ecto-cuneiform; *ent. cun.* ento-cuneiform; *ep. cor.* epicoracoid; *epist.* episternum; *ep. pb.* epipubis; *fb.* fibula; *fem.* femur; *for. mag.* foramen magnum; *glen.* glenoid cavity of shoulder-joint and glenoid cavity for mandible; *hum.* humerus; *in. cond.* inner condyle of humerus; *inf. orb. for.* points to position of infra-orbital foramen; *infr. proc.* inferior processes of caudal vertebræ; *int. rbs.* intermediate ribs; *isch.* ischium; *mag.* magnum of carpus; *max.* maxilla; *max. for.* maxillary foramen; *metat. I,* first metatarsal; *metat. V,* fifth metatarsal; *nas. cart.* nasal cartilage; *obt.* obturator foramen; *ol.* olecranon; *out. cond.* outer condyle of humerus; *pal.* palatine; *pat.* patella; *post. pal. for.* posterior palatine foramen; *pr.max.* premaxilla; *pr. st.* presternum; *pter.* pterygoid; *pub.* pubis; *rad.* radius; *scap.* scapula; *scaph.* scaphoid of tarsus; *scaph. lun.* scapho-lunar; *ses.* sesamoid bones of wrist and ankle; *sp.* tarsal horny spur; *sq.* squamosal; *tib.* tibia; *trd.* trapezoid; *trm.* trapezium; *tym. c.* tympanic cavity; *uln.* ulna; *unc.* unciform; *vom.* vomer; *x,* dumb-bell shaped bone; *zyg.* zygomatic arch; *I—V,* digits of manus.

former genus. In both genera there is a pterygoid (investing) bone not separately represented in higher mammals, corresponding to the pterygoid of lower Vertebrates. The parasphenoid represents the lateral parts of the parasphenoid of lower Vertebrates and the inner lamella of the pterygoid process (usually regarded as the pterygoid) of higher mammals. Perforating the posterior root of the zygomatic arch is a canal, comparatively wide in the full-grown Ornithorhynchus, narrow in Tachyglossus—the *temporal canal*—which is not present in higher Mammals, and apparently represents the post-temporal fossa of reptiles.

In Tachyglossus (Fig. 478) the squamosal extends farther forwards and the posterior root of the zygomatic arch is more anterior than in mammals in general. The zygoma is very narrow, and there is no rudiment of post-orbital processes : the jugal is absent as a separate ossification. The alveolar border of the maxilla (*max.*) is narrow and devoid of teeth. The nasal and premaxillary region of the skull is drawn out into a long, narrow rostrum. Near the anterior end of this is a rounded opening, the external nasal opening, which is entirely bounded by the premaxillæ—the nasals not extending so far forwards. An aperture in the nasal septum corresponds to an actual perforation by which the nasal cavities are in direct communication in the living animal. The pterygoids (*pt.*) are in the form of flat plates continuous with the bony palate ; they extend back so as to form a part of the walls of the tympanic cavities. The tympanic (*ty.*) is an imperfect ring which does not become united with the periotic. The mandible consists of very narrow styliform rami, which are not firmly united at the symphysis. The condyle (*cond.*) is narrow, rather more elongated antero-posteriorly than transversely. There are very slight rudiments of the angle and of the coronoid process (*cor.*).

In the Ornithorhynchus (Fig. 477) the zygoma is stouter than in Tachyglossus, and there is a post-orbital process which is formed by the jugal. The maxillary root of the zygoma develops a process which supports the horny tooth (*dent.*) of the upper jaw. The nasal and premaxillary is expanded into a rostrum which is much broader than in Tachyglossus. The premaxillæ (*pr.max.*) diverge from one another anteriorly, and then curve inwards again, partly enclosing a large space in which the nostrils are situated, and which is covered over in the recent state by the tough but sensitive hairless integument investing the cartilage of the rostrum, the latter being continuous with the nasal septum. In this space between the premaxillæ is situated a dumb-bell-shaped bone (*x.*) which appears to arise from processes of the premaxilla. The pterygoid (*pter.*) is much smaller than in Tachyglossus, and does not extend as far back as the tympanic cavity. The mandible has its rami stouter than in Tachyglossus ; they meet for a short distance anteriorly, and then again diverge slightly. The condyle is much larger than in Tachyglossus, and is elongated transversely. In front of it is a broad process bearing the horny tooth.

It is in the shoulder-girdle that we find perhaps the most striking peculiarities of the skeleton of the Prototheria. There is a T-shaped episternum (*epist.*), as already stated, similar to that of Reptiles, the median limb articulating behind with the presternum and the cross-piece closely applied to the clavicles. There are two short and broad coracoids (*cor.*) articulating internally and behind with the presternum, and, externally, uniting with the scapula to form the

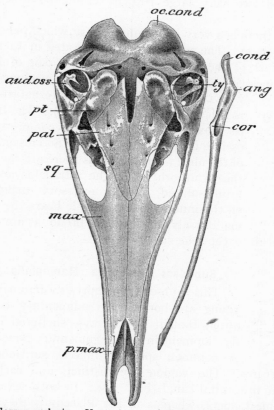

FIG. 478.—**Tachyglossus aculeata.** Ventral view of skull and right ramus of mandible. *ang.* angle of mandible; *aud. oss.* auditory ossicles; *cond.* condyle of mandible; *cor.* coronoid process; *max.* maxilla; *oc. cond.* occipital condyle; *pal.* palatine; *p.max.* premaxilla; *pt.* pterygoid; *sq.* squamosal; *ty.* tympanic ring.

glenoid cavity. In front of the coracoid is a flat plate, the epicoracoid (*ep. cor.*). The scapula (Fig. 479) is very unlike that of other Mammals. There is a well-developed acromion process (*acr.*) with which the clavicle articulates; this terminates the anterior border, so that the latter would appear to correspond to the spine of the scapula of other Mammals: this is confirmed by the arrangement of the scapular muscles. The anterior part of the inner surface is in reality the pre-spinous fossa; the anterior portion of the outer surface the post-spinous fossa; and the part behind this, separated from it by a slight ridge, together with the posterior portion of the inner surface, is the sub-scapular fossa.

The humerus is of remarkable shape, with greatly expanded extremities—especially in Tachyglossus—and prominent tuberosities and condyles. In the carpus the scaphoid and lunar are united; there is no separate centrale. There are a radial and two very large palmar sesamoids, which are sometimes united.

In the pelvis there is a very long symphysis in which pubes and ischia take an almost equal share. The acetabulum is perforated in Tachyglossus. With the anterior border of the pubes are articulated a pair of large epipubic or "marsupial" bones (Fig. 477, *ep. pb.*). The femur has expanded extremities with prominent external and internal trochanters. There is a large ossified patella (*pat.*). The fibula (*fb.*) has at its proximal end a remarkable compressed process which ossifies from a separate centre, and resembles the olecranon of the ulna. In the tarsus there are the usual bones. In the Ornithorhynchus the astragalus and calcaneum are firmly united, and an accessory ossification (*acc. tars.*) on the inner side in the male bears the tarsal spur. The metatarsals are short and broad, as are all the phalanges except the last.

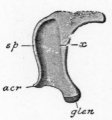

Fig. 479.—Outer surface of left scapula of **Ornithorhynchus**. *acr.* process corresponding to acromion; *glen.* glenoid articular surface; *sp.* anterior border, corresponding to the spine; *x*, slight ridge which bounds the surface of origin of the sub-scapularis muscle anteriorly.

Sub-class Metatheria (Marsupialia or Didelphia).

This sub-class comprises Mammals in which the young are born in a rudimentary condition and are often, though not always, sheltered during their later development in an integumentary pouch, the *marsupium*.

A common sphincter-muscle surrounds the anal and urogenital apertures. The vaginæ are distinct, and each has a separate opening into the urogenital canal (Fig. 48). In both sexes the ureters pass between the genital ducts, whereas in the Placentals they pass outside the ducts. A placenta is almost always absent, and in the rare instances in which it occurs, as in the Peramelidæ, it is simple in structure and functions for only a short period. The brain lacks a corpus callosum.

In the skull the tympanic chamber is often open, so that the tympanic ring is clearly visible, a primitive feature shared with some Placentals. There is, however, a number of forms in which the tympanic chamber is covered and the ring is hidden. When this occurs, the cover is always formed by the ali-sphenoid bone, and not by an extension of the tympanic itself or by a mixture of bones, as occurs in various Placentals. The optic foramina are confluent from side to side, and the internal carotid artery enters the skull through a foramen in the basi-sphenoid, and not through the foramen lacerum medium. The jugal bone extends far back, so as to take a share in the glenoid cavity for the articulation of the lower jaw, a feature universal in the sub-class, but one which occurs sporadically in the Placentals (e.g., *Hyrax* and many Rodents). An inward inflection of the ventral posterior border of the lower jaw, the " inflected angle," is practically a diagnostic feature, since it is found nowhere else except in a few Rodents. It occurs in all Marsupials with the sole exception of the degenerate, thread-like jaw of *Tarsipes*. The seventh cervical vertebra in a large number of instances is pierced by a foramen for the vertebral artery, but this is also a feature found occasionally in Placentals (some Rodents, *Hyrax*, *Hippopotamus*, etc.). Well-developed epipubic bones are frequently, but not always, present.

The dentition is peculiar, in that there is only one set of teeth functional throughout life, with the exception that one tooth, which is considered to be a milk-molar, is replaced by the last premolar. The pattern of the molar teeth varies according to function in much the same general directions as in the Placentals. Carnivorous, rodent, insectivorous, and herbivorous adaptations are all found.

While there is almost no absolutely constant difference between Marsupials and Placentals, the Marsupials in general may be said to be at a somewhat lower grade of organisation than the Placentals. They retain and share a number of primitive characters with the more primitive Placentals, such as many of the Insectivora, as, for example, the small brain, which occupies but a comparatively small portion of the skull. The olfactory part of the brain is proportionally large; the palate is deficient in ossification; an entepicondylar foramen is very frequently present in the humerus.

Metatheria were widely distributed over many parts of the world during the Eocene period, but are now confined to the Australasian region (with the exception of New Zealand), to South America, where during the Tertiary period they had a wide expansion and, for a few species, to North America. The earliest known forms are from the Cretaceous of Canada.

The usual method of classification is based on the dentition, whereby two groups are recognised : the Polyprotodontia, with more than three incisors in each half of the upper jaw, and the Diprotodontia, with never more than three incisors above and one pair in the lower jaws. Another method of classification, and in some ways a truer one, is based on certain peculiarities in the foot-structure. Some Marsupials have the second and third toes of the hind foot united by a common sheath, while others have the toes all separate. These conditions are known as *syndactyly* and *didactyly*, respectively. Most Polyprotodonts are didactylous and all Diprotodonts are syndactylous, but one series, the Peramelidæ (" Bandicoots "), are polyprotodont and syndactylous, and this fact prevents the use of the dentition as a diagnostic character.

If the primitive condition be presumed to be polyprotodont and didactylous,

it would appear that this stock evolved along two lines, of which one, Didactyla, retained the simple foot-structure, and the other, the Syndactyla, acquired the modification of the second and third toes. This second line underwent a further division in that some—in fact, the great majority—reduced the number of incisors and became diprotodont, while the Peramelidæ, although becoming syndactylous, remained conservative as to their polyprotodont teeth.

A tabular classification may, on these lines, be drawn up as follows but being based on a single unit character, must be considered as a working classification for living forms only.[1]

Sub-order Didactyla.

Insectivorous or carnivorous animals.

The pouch may be rudimentary or absent, when present the opening is ventrally or caudally directed.

Families Didelphidæ, the " Opossums " of America—

e.g., *Marmosa*; *Didelphys* (Fig. 480); *Peramys*; *Chironectes*, etc.

Dasyuridæ. All Australasian—

e.g., *Dasyurus* (Native " Cats "), (Fig. 481); *Sarcophilus* (the " Tasmanian Devil "); *Phascogale*; *Sminthopsis* (Marsupial " Mice "); *Antechinomys* (Jerboa " Mice "); *Thylacinus* (the Marsupial " Wolf "); *Myrmecobius* (the Banded " Ant-eater "), etc.

Notoryctidæ—

Notoryctes (Fig. 482) (the " Marsupial Mole ").

Cænolestidæ, South America—

An aberrant form with a polyprotodont upper dentition and the median pair of the five lower incisors enlarged. *Cænolestes*.

Sub-order Syndactyla.

Section Polyprotodonta.

Omnivorous. The marsupium opens downwards.

Family Peramelidæ (the Bandicoots of Australia)—

e.g., *Perameles*; *Thylacomys*; *Choeropus*.

Section Diprotodontia.

Herbivorous. Well-developed pouch opening forwards. The most completely specialised Marsupials.

Families Phalangeridæ—

e.g., *Phalanger*; *Tarsipes*; *Phascolarctos* (Fig. 483 (Native " Bear "); *Phascolomys* (Fig. 484) (Wombat);

[1] See F. Wood Jones (no. 98 in Appendix on Literature).

Petaurus ; Acrobates (Flying " Squirrels ") ; *Pseudo-chirus* (Ring-tailed Opossum), and other genera.

Macropodidæ—

e.g., *Macropus* (Fig. 485) ; *Dendrolagus* ; and other genera (the Kangaroos, Wallabies, etc.).

The first Marsupials are found in the Upper Cretaceous—i.e., *Eodelphis cutleri* of Canada. *Peratherium* is a genus of small animals found in both Europe and America from the Eocene to the Miocene, which hardly differ (as far as can be told from fragments) from living small Didelphids. *Diprotodon* (Fig. 487), *Nototherium* (Fig. 488), *Thylacoleo* (Fig. 489), are large diprotodonts of the Australian Pleistocene.

Various species have been described from tertiary deposits both of Europe and the Americas, but, on the whole, the past history of the Metatheria is not well known.

FIG. 480.—**Virginian Opossum** (*Didelphys virginiana*). (After Vogt and Specht.)

The Opossums (*Didelphyidæ*, Fig. 480) are arboreal rat-like Marsupials, with elongated naked muzzle, with well-developed, though nailless, opposable hallux, and elongated prehensile tail. A marsupium is sometimes present, but

FIG. 481.—**Dasyure** (*Dasyurus viverrinus*). (After Vogt and Specht.)

is absent or incomplete in the majority. One species—the Water Opossum—has the toes webbed. The Dasyuridæ (Australian Native Cats, Tasmanian Devil, Thylacine, etc.) often have the pollex rudimentary, the foot four-toed, the hallux, when present, small and clawless, and the tail non-prehensile.

There is a well-developed marsupium. The Native Cats (Figs. 481) and their near allies are cat-like animals, the largest equal in size to a domestic Cat, some no larger than Rats or Mice; the Tasmanian Devil has a more thickset body; the Thylacine has a remarkable resemblance in general shape, as well as size, to a Wolf. The Banded Ant-eater (*Myrmecobius*) is devoid of the marsupium.

FIG. 482.—**Marsupial Mole** (*Notoryctes typhlops*). (From the *Cambridge Natural History*.)

The Bandicoots (*Peramelidæ*) are burrowing Marsupials, ranging in size from that of a large rat to that of a rabbit. They have an elongated pointed muzzle, and, in some cases, large auditory pinnæ. The tail is usually short, sometimes long. The first and fifth digits of the fore-feet are vestigial or

FIG. 483.—**Koala** (*Phascolarctos cinereus*). (After Vogt and Specht.)

absent, the remaining three nearly equally developed. In the hind-foot the fourth toe is much longer and stouter than the others, while the second and third are small and slender, and united together by a web of skin, and the first is vestigial or absent. The marsupium has its opening directed backwards.

Notoryctes, the Marsupial Mole (Fig. 482), is a small burrowing Marsupial, with short and powerful limbs, each with five toes, the third and fourth of the fore-foot provided with remarkable, large, flat, triangular claws. The tail is short and covered with bare skin. An auditory pinna is absent, and the eyes are vestigial. The pouch opens backwards.

The Wombats (*Phascolomyidæ*, Fig. 484) are large, heavy, thick-bodied, burrowing animals, with short, flattened heads, short thick limbs, provided with strong claws on all the digits except the hallux, and with the second and third toes of the hind-foot partly connected together by skin. The tail is very short. The Kangaroos and their allies (Macropodidæ, Fig. 485) are adapted, as regards their limbs, for swift terrestrial locomotion. They have a relatively small head and neck, the fore-limbs small, and each provided with five digits ; the hind-legs

FIG. 484.—**Wombat** (*Phascolomys mitchelli*). (From the *Cambridge Natural History*.)

long and powerful ; rapid progression is effected by great springing leaps, with the body inclined forwards and the fore-limbs clear of the ground. The foot is narrow and provided with four toes, the hallux being absent ; the two inner (second and third) small and united together by integument, while the middle toe is very long and powerful. The tail is very long, and usually thick. There is a large marsupium. The Tree-Kangaroos differ from the ordinary Kangaroos in their shorter and thicker hind-limbs, in which the second and third toes are nearly as large as the fourth.

The Phalangers (*Phalangeridæ*) are climbing Marsupials which have both fore- and hind-feet prehensile ; the second and third toes of the hind-foot slender and united by a web, as in the Kangaroo, but the hallux, which is nailless, opposable to them ; the fourth and fifth nearly equal. The tail is well developed and prehensile. A number of Phalangers (Flying Phalangers) are provided with lateral folds of skin extending from the fore- to the hind-limbs and, acting as a parachute, enable the animal, as in the Flying Squirrels, to

perform flying leaps from tree to tree. The Koalas (Fig. 483) differ from
the Phalangers mainly in the relatively thicker body and the vestigial tail.

Skeleton of Metatheria.—In the Marsupials the inferior arch of the atlas

FIG. 485.—**Rock Wallaby** (*Petrogale xanthopus*).   (After Vogt and Specht.)

(Fig. 486) is often incompletely ossified, a gap being left in the prepared
skeleton ; sometimes the gap becomes closed in by the ingrowths of the lateral
parts of the arch, sometimes a small separate ossification is developed, filling up

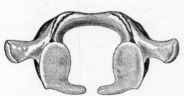

FIG. 486.—Atlas of Kangaroo.

the opening.   In the trunk there are always
nineteen vertebræ. The transverse processes
of the thoracic vertebræ are always well developed, and the ribs articulate with them as
well as with the bodies.   Prominent metapophyses and anapophyses are developed ;
these are largest in the lumbar region. Only one
sacral vertebra is present in most Marsupials ;
in some a second is ankylosed with it.   The caudal region varies greatly in
length.   It is short in the Koala and the Wombat, long in the Opossums,
Dasyures, Phalangers and Kangaroos (Fig. 490).   Chevron bones are generally
present, except in the Koala and the Wombat.

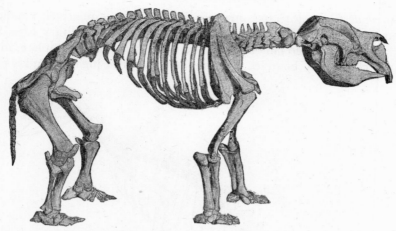

FIG. 487.—**Diprotodon australis.** (From a restoration of the skeleton by Prof. E. C. Stirlin in the Adelaide Museum.)

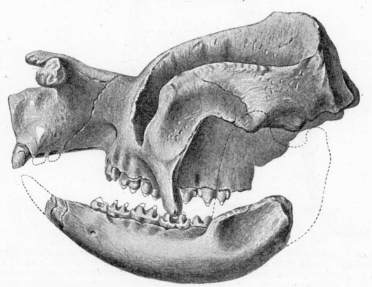

FIG. 488.—**Nototherium mitchelli.** Side view of skull. (After Owen.)

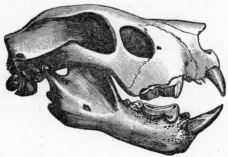

FIG. 489.—**Thylacoleo carnifex.** Side view of skull. (After Flower.)

In the *skull* (Figs. 491, 492, 493) the brain-cavity is relatively small, with the cerebellar fossa entirely behind the cerebral. The pituitary fossa is not distinct, and there are no clinoid processes. The zygoma is complete, but the orbit is not completely bounded by bone behind. The jugal extends beneath

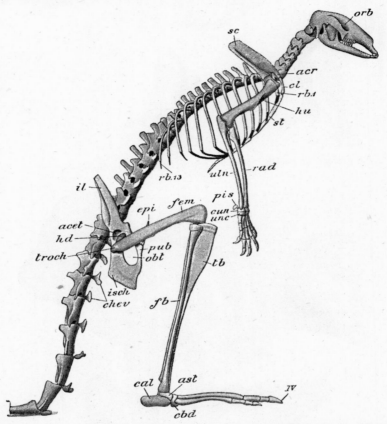

FIG. 490.—Skeleton of **Wallaby** (*Halmaturus ualabatus*). The scapula is represented as raised somewhat higher than it would be in the natural relations of the parts. The head of the femur has been separated from the acetabulum. *acet.* acetabulum; *acr.* acromion process; *ast.* astragalus; *calc.* calcaneum; *cbd.* cuboid; *chev.* chevron bones; *cl.* clavicle; *cun.* cuneiform of carpus; *epi.* epipubis; *fb.* fibula; *fem.* femur; *hd.* head of femur; *hu.* humerus; *il.* ilium; *isch.* ischium; *obt.* obturator foramen; *orb.* orbit; *pis.* pisiform; *pub.* pubis; *rad.* radius; *rb. 1,* first rib; *rb. 13,* last rib; *sc.* scapula; *st.* sternum; *tb.* tibia; *troch.* great trochanter of femur; *uln.* ulna; *unc.* unciform; *IV.* fourth toe.

the squamosal root of the zygoma to form part of the outer wall of the glenoid fossa. The lachrymal foramen is usually on the anterior margin of the orbit, sometimes on the face. The palate usually presents vacuities in its posterior portion. The pterygoid is always small. The ali-sphenoid is large, and forms the anterior boundary of the tympanic cavity; in the Kangaroos (Fig. 493, *ali.*) it extends backwards so as to join the paroccipital process, which is greatly elongated. When an auditory bulla is developed, it is formed by this bone, the tympanic being always small, and never ankylosed to neighbouring bones.

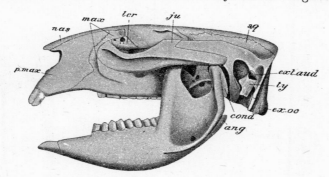

FIG. 491.—Skull of **Wombat** (*Phascolomys wombat*) (lateral view). Letters as in Figs. 492–493. In addition, *ext. aud.* opening of bony auditory meatus; *cond.* condyle of mandible.

The internal carotid artery perforates the basi-sphenoid. The optic foramen is not separate from the sphenoidal fissure. In all except *Tarsipes* the angle of the mandible sends inwards a remarkable process (*ang.*), and is said to be *inflected*.

In the *pectoral arch* of the Marsupials the coracoid process is, as usual,

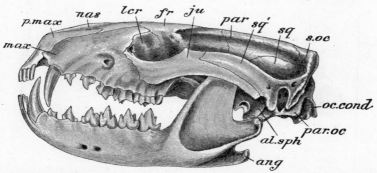

FIG. 492.—Skull of **Dasyurus** (lateral view). *al.sph.* ali-sphenoid; *ang.* angular process of mandible; *fr.* frontal; *ju.* jugal; *lcr.* lacrymal; *max.* maxilla; *nas.* nasal; *oc. cond.* occipital condyle; *par.* parietal; *par. oc.* par-occipital process; *p.max.* premaxilla; *s. oc.* supra-occipital; *sq.* squamosal; *sq'.* zygomatic process of squamosal.

developed from a special bony centre, and a distinct suture is often recognisable between it and the scapula until a comparatively late stage. In the young condition (when the fœtus is attached to the teat) the coracoid is comparatively extensive and reaches the pre-sternum ventrally. A clavicle is always present, except in the Bandicoots, but may be incomplete. There is never a distinct centrale in the carpus. In the Opossums the ilium has the primitive form of a straight, three-sided rod. In the Kangaroos (Fig. 490, *il.*) it is still simple and three-sided, but somewhat curved outwards; in the rest it is more or less compressed. In nearly all the Marsupials there is a pair of epipubic or marsupial bones (Fig. 490, *epi.*)—elongated and compressed bones which

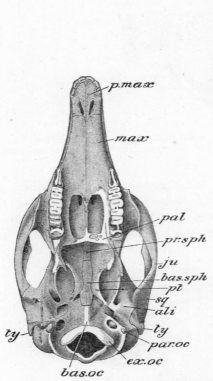

FIG. 493.—Skull of **Rock Wallaby** (*Petrogale penicillata*) (ventral view). Letters as in Fig. 492, except *ali.* alisphenoid. In addition, *bas. oc.* basi-occipital; *bas. oph.* basi-sphenoid; *ex. oc.* ex-occipital; *pal.* palatine; *pt.* pterygoid; *ty.* tympanic.

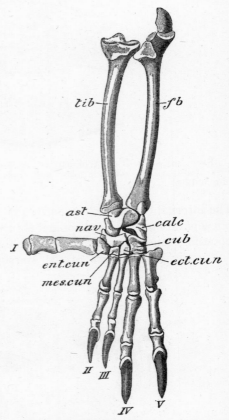

FIG. 494.—Bones of leg and foot of **Phalanger.** *ast.* astragalus; *calc.* calcaneum; *cub.* cuboid; *ect. cun.* ecto-cuneiform; *ent. cun.* ento-cuneiform; *fb.* fibula; *mes. cun.* meso-cuneiform; *nav.* navicular; *tib.* tibia; *I—V*, digits. (After Owen.)

articulate posteriorly with the anterior edge of the pubes: in the Thylacine they are represented only by small unossified fibro-cartilages. In the leg the fibula is always well developed. In the young condition of some Marsupials there is an accessory element situated outside the fibula at its proximal end: this apparently corresponds to a bone known as the *parafibula* which occurs in some Lacertilia. In the Phalangers (Fig. 494) and the Koala there is always a considerable range of movement between the fibula and the tibia, comparable in some degree to the movements of pronation and supination of the radius and ulna. The foot (Figs. 494, 495), as already stated in the account of the external characters, presents a much greater range of modification than the manus.

Eutheria (Placentalia Monodelphia)

The Eutheria and Metatheria are presumed to have arisen from some, as yet untraced, branch of the Jurassic Pantotheres and, since undoubted eutherians and metatherians are known in the Upper Cretaceous, they must have diverged along their separate lines of evolution during the early part of the Cretaceous period. In the succeeding Palæocene[1] there was a gradual expansion of Eutheria, and by the dawn of the Eocene most of the *orders* of the sub-class had become established (Fig. 496).

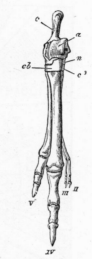

FIG. 495.—Bones of right foot of **Kangaroo** (*Macropus*). *a.* astragalus; *c.* calcaneum; *cb.* cuboid; *e³*. ento-cunei-form; *n.* navicular; *II—V*, digits. (After Flower.)

The characters common to the sub-class, which has radiated into a vast number of different forms, are naturally few. Although a simple form of placenta occurs, as has already been mentioned, in certain Marsupials, the chief eutherian character is nevertheless the highly organised placenta, whereby the young are nourished in the uterus for a comparatively long time, and are born in a more advanced stage of growth than the " larvæ " of the Marsupials. The uterus gradually loses its original double formation (uterus duplex) and becomes a single structure (uterus simplex). The urinary ducts now pass to the bladder outside the genital ducts. A common sphincter is not present except rarely, and then only as a remnant, so that there is no longer a cloaca. In the skull of the more primitive forms the palate may still be somewhat fenestrated, as in Metatheria, but the internal carotid now enters the skull either through the foramen posterius or through the bulla. The tympanic region in all but the most primitive forms is protected by a bony covering, or bulla, in the composition of which various surrounding bones may take part or, as is more usual, only one—namely an outgrowth of the petrous bone to which the tympanic bone becomes attached in various ways to form a true *tympanic bulla*, as opposed to the *ali-sphenoid bulla* of those Marsupials that have the ear region protected. In a very few cases—e.g., *Hyrax* and some Rodents—

[1] See G. G. Simpson (111); W. D. Matthew (102) in Appendix on Literature.

the jugal takes part in the formation of the glenoid cavity, and in some Rodents there is an inflection of the angle of the lower jaw, but otherwise these features and such other purely metatherian features as the epipubic bones and marsupial pouch are never found.

In the brain a new structure appears, the *corpus callosum* (p. 510), and the brain in the course of evolution from primitive to recent forms becomes more and more highly developed, especially by the perfection of the neopallial region of the cerebral hemispheres (pp. 487, 671).

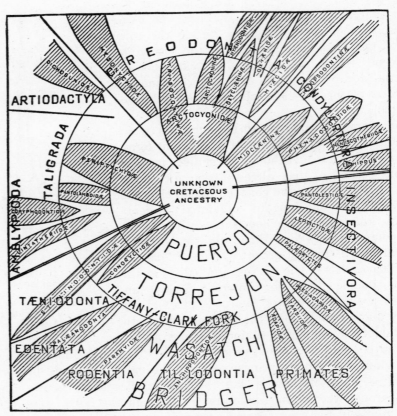

Fig. 496.—Relationship of the mammals of the Cretaceous and Basal Eocene. (From Matthew's " Paleocene Faunas of the San Juan Basin, New Mexico ".)

THE EARLY EVOLUTION OF THE PLACENTAL MAMMALS

A reference to the table of classification of Placental Mammals (Fig. 468) shows that during the long Palæocene period a number of Placental orders became established. Some of these, known loosely as the "Archaic Mammals", such as the Condylarthra, Amblypoda, Dinocerata, Tæniodonta, etc., had a comparatively short career, and did not survive beyond the Eocene. Of *orders* which still exist, the Insectivora, Dermoptera, Primates, Chiroptera, Rodentia, and Edentata had all started in the Palæocene, though, of course, no modern *families* were at that time represented.

While, as might be expected from the theory of evolution, all these early mammals are primitive in their general organisation, side lines with various specialisations were continually being evolved, and as a result it is not always easy, on the material available, to decide the actual affinity of many of them. The early Condylarthra, Insectivora, and Creodonta still show many characters in common which are reminiscent of their common origin from some still earlier stock. Of these three somewhat allied groups only the Insectivora and their derivatives, the Primates, Dermoptera, and Chiroptera, have persisted. The Creodonta and Condylarthra became extinct, but not before important orders had arisen as branches from them. From the Creodonta arose the modern Carnivora and in all probability the Artiodactyla and Cetacea, and from the Condylarthra the Perissodactyla and a number of orders which did not persist, such as the Amblypoda, Tillodontia, Dinocerata, Tæniodontia, and the important and interesting South American evolution of mammals the Notoungulata and other orders which persisted as late as the Pleistocene.

The Proboscidea and Sirenia appear in the Eocene, followed by the Hyracoidea in the Oligocene. These three orders together with the little-understood Barytheria and Embrithopoda, seem to come from a stock of African origin.[1] Of the remaining orders the Rodentia and Edentata are old groups of Palæocene origin, the Pholidota are Oligocene, and the Tubulidentata Eocene. These four orders are separate, and their origin and connections still a matter of doubt.[2]

ORDER INSECTIVORA.

The Insectivora may be considered the nearest living representatives of the Cretaceous stock from which all placental mammals have arisen. Although in the course of time different lines of Insectivora have acquired numerous and varied specialisations of their own, these specialisations are superimposed on a distinctly generalised and primitive foundation. Many features, both in the skeleton and in the anatomy of the soft parts, some of them shared in common with the metatheria, can be cited as evidence of their low grade of organisation. The skull, for instance, is typically rather long, and is con-

---

[1] There is still some doubt as to the place of origin of the Sirenia (see page 610).

[2] Properly to understand the relationships, whether proved or only suggested, of these early Placental orders requires the consideration of much more detail than can be presented in a general text-book. It must be remembered that in many instances the material on which judgment has to be passed is fragmentary, and that the conclusions based upon it are always subject to revision as fresh evidence occurs. Such a group as the Condylarthra, to give only one instance, may possibly represent several lines of very slightly related animals, of which only a small proportion has as yet been discovered.

stricted in the middle, owing to the smallness of the brain. The palate is often
fenestrated and the tympanic ring uncovered and unprotected by a bulla.
The brain is primitive in its lack of cerebral convolutions, in the large size
of the olfactory part (macrosmatism), and in that the cerebrum is not sufficiently
large to cover the corpora quadrigemina. The dentition in its general aspect
approaches near to the primitive trituberculo-sectorial condition (see p. 654).
The os centrale is often present in the carpus, and an entepicondylar foramen
in the humerus. The feet are pentadactyle and plantigrade. In the vertebral
column there may occur pairs of small bony nodules between the vertebræ
on the ventral side which appear to be remnants of chevron bones. The
uterus is bicornuate (uterus duplex) and the testes are abdominal.

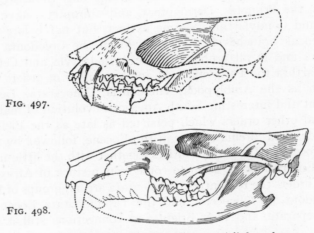

FIG. 497.

FIG. 498.

FIG. 497.—**Deltatheridium pretrituberculare.**
FIG. 498.—**Zalambdalestes lechei.**   (Both after Gregory and Simpson.)

The more noticeable specialisations are the great secondary lengthening,
in some forms, of the snout—*e.g.*, in the moles, shrews, and tenrecs—the frequent
reduction or absence of the zygomatic arch; the weakness of the pelvis, which
may be without a pubic symphysis; the peculiar incisors of the shrews; the
spines of the hedgehogs; the occasional presence of scent glands—*e.g.*, the
tail of *Desmana moschata*—and the adaptation of the limbs and girdles for
digging as in the different types of Moles, etc.

The order Insectivora is divided into several sub-orders which have long
and separate histories from as far back as the Eocene, or even farther. Some
of them have so little real connection with the others that they might really
rank as separate orders. It follows that a diagnosis and classification of so
polymorphic a group is difficult, and the Insectivora are recognised as a
" group " chiefly by their generalised structure and by their lack of the various

diagnostic characters of other orders. The sub-orders are to be recognised by their particular specialisations of structure and by distinguishing characters in their dentition.

The following is a list of the sub-orders.

Deltatheroidea.
Deltatheriidæ. *Deltatheridium.* Cretaceous. (Fig. 497).
Didelphodus. Eocene.
Centetoidea.
Centetidæ. *Centetes.* The Tenrecs of Madagascar (Fig. 502).
Solenodontidæ. *Solenodon.* Cuba and Hayti.
Potamogalidæ. *Potamogale.* The " Otter Shrew ", West Africa.

FIG. 499.—**Chrysochloris trevelyani.** Golden mole. A. Sole of front foot.
(From *Cambridge Natural History*.)

Chrysochloroidea.
Chrysochloridæ. *Chrysochloris.* " Golden Moles." South Africa (Fig. 499).

The Centetoidea and Chrysochloroidea have triangular upper molars, and are sometimes known as the Zalambdodont insectivores.

Erinaceoidea.
Zalambdalestidæ. *Zalambdalestes* (Fig. 498). Upper Cretaceous.
Leptictidæ. *Diacodon, Leptictis.* Upper Cretaceous to Oligocene.
Erinaceidæ. The Hedgehogs, *Erinaceus, Gymnura,* etc.
Soricoidea.
Soricidæ. The Shrews.
Talpidæ. The Moles.

These two groups have square upper molars with a **W** outer border, and are known as the Dilambdodont insectivores.

Menotyphla.

       Tupaiidæ.   The Oriental Tree Shews *Tupaia*, *Ptilocercus* (Fig. 500). Eocene to present day.

       Macroscelidæ.   African Elephant Shrews. *Macroscelides*, *Rhynchocyon* (Fig. 501).

FIG. 500.—**Ptilocercus lowi.**   The Pen-tailed Tree Shrew.

    The first five sub-orders are often placed together as the Lipotyphla to balance the Menotyphla.   The characters on which this division is based are that the Menotyphla have a long pubic symphysis, a tympanic bulla formed by the petrous bone which grows round and ensnares the tympanic ring as in the Lemurs, a complete jugal arch, and a cæcum in the alimentary canal. It does not, however, follow that the sub-orders of the Lipotyphla, in not having these characters, are so much to be considered as a closely allied group, as that the Menotyphla are on a definite and more progressive line of evolution. Nor are the two families of the Menotyphla very closely allied, and their anatomical resemblances are perhaps of less weight than their differences.   The

Macroscelidæ are specialised as hopping forms, while the Tupaiidæ, in some respects more primitive, show a transition towards the Lemurs.

Skeleton of the Insectivora.—The neural spine of the axis is usually well

FIG. 501.—**Rhynchocyon chrysopygus.** (From *Cambridge Natural History*.)

developed, that of the remaining cervical vertebræ small or obsolete. The number of trunk-vertebræ varies in the different families from eighteen to twenty-four, and there is also great variation in the development of the various processes. The caudal region varies in its length; frequently it has chevron

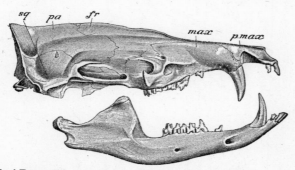

FIG. 502.—Skull of **Tenrec** (*Centetes ecaudatus*). *fr.* frontal; *max.* maxilla; *pa.* parietal; *p.max.* premaxilla; *sq.* squamosal. (After Dobson.)

bones. The presternum is expanded, the mesosternum composed of distinct, narrow sternebræ.

The *skull* (Figs. 502, 503) varies greatly in the different families, in the higher forms approaching that of the Lemurs, with comparatively large cerebral fossæ, large orbits with complete or nearly complete bony rims, well-developed zygoma, and a tympanic bulla and tubular auditory meatus. In the others the cranial capacity is less, and the orbits and temporal fossæ are completely continuous; the zygoma is incomplete, and the tympanic does not usually form a bulla.

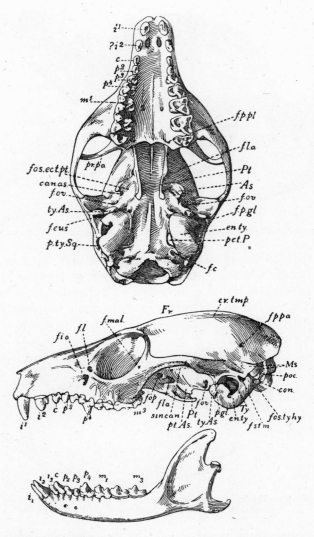

FIG. 503.—Skull of **Ptilocercus lowii.** *i.*[1] *i.*[2] incisors; *c.* canine; *p.*[2, 3, 4,] premolars; *M.*[1-3] molars. *As.* alisphenoid; *can. as.* alisphenoid canal; *con.* condyle; *cr. tmp.* temporal crest; *en. ty.* entotympanic; *f. c.* carotid foramen; *f. eus.* eustachian opening; *fr.* frontal; *f. l. a.* foramen lacerum anterius; *f. mal.* malar foramen; *f. op.* optic foramen; *f. or.* foramen orale; *f. os. ect. pt.* ectopterygoid fossa; *f. os. ty. hy.* tympano-hyoid fossa; *fo. pl.* palatine foramen; *f. st. m.* stylomastoid foramen; *Ms.* mastoid; *Pt.* pterygoid; *Ty.* tympanic. (After Gregory.)

The *pectoral arch* also varies a good deal in the different families of the Insectivora. In the true Moles (Fig. 504) and their allies there is a remarkable bone of cuboid shape articulating ventrally with the presternum and dorsally with the humerus, and only connected by a ligamentous band with the scapula. Its mode of formation from a mass of cartilage—to the anterior face of which the clavicle, formed as usual in membrane, becomes applied—proves that this bone represents a pro-coracoid as well as a clavicle. In other Insectivora this bone is not developed, and the clavicle is a distinct, long and slender bone, but vestiges of the inner or ventral ends of the coracoid and pro-coracoid

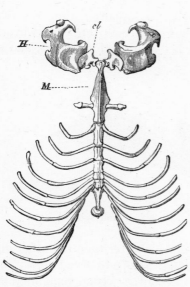

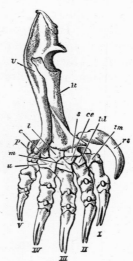

FIG. 504.—Sternum and shoulder girdle of **Talpa**. *cl.* clavicle; *H.* humerus; *M.* manubrium. (From *Cambridge Natural History*.)

FIG. 505.—Fore-arm and manus of **Talpa**. *c.* cuneiform; *ce.* centrale; *l.* lunar; *m.* magnum; *p.* pisiform; *R.* radius; *rs.* radial sesamoid; *td.* trapezoid; *s.* scaphoid; *tm.* trapezium; *U.* ulna; *u.* unciform; *I–V.* digits.

may be recognisable. Sometimes the " mesoscapular segment " (p. 643) is represented by a distinct bone intervening between the outer end of the clavicle proper and the acromion process.

The humerus usually has a supracondylar foramen. In the Moles this is absent, and their humerus is remarkable in other respects, being short, greatly expanded at the extremities, with a prominent deltoid ridge, and with two synovial articular surfaces at the proximal end, one for the glenoid cavity of the scapula, the other for the coraco-clavicle. The radius and ulna are completely developed in all and are usually distinct, but sometimes fused distally. In the carpus the scaphoid and lunar sometimes coalesce, sometimes remain distinct ; an os centrale is usually present. In the Moles (Fig. 505) the manus is extremely broad, the breadth being increased by the presence of a large, curved, radial sesamoid.

In the *pelvis* the symphysis pubis is in some cases elongated, in others short, and sometimes absent, the pubes remaining separated by a wide median ventral cleft. A third trochanter is sometimes represented by a ridge. The fibula usually, though not always, fuses distally with the tibia.

ORDER CHIROPTERA.

The Chiroptera (Fig. 506) are the only Mammals which are capable of active flight. The fore-limbs have the segments greatly elongated, especially the fore-arm and the four ulnar digits, and these support a thin fold of the integument which stretches to the hind-limbs and constitutes the wing. A fold (inter-femoral membrane) also extends between the hind-limbs, and may

FIG. 506.—Bat (*Synotus barbastellus*). (After Vogt and Specht.)

or may not involve the tail. The pollex is much shorter than the other digits, is directed forwards, and terminates in a well-developed curved claw ; in the Megachiroptera, but not in the Microchiroptera, the second digit also has a claw ; the other digits are always clawless. The position of the hind-limbs is peculiar, and the knee is directed backwards instead of forwards as in other Mammals ; the five digits of the foot are all provided with claws. So complete is the adaptation of the limbs to the purpose of flight that Bats are only able to shuffle along with great difficulty on the ground ; though with the aid of their claws they are able to climb and to suspend themselves from branches of trees by the hind-feet. In the Megachiroptera the muzzle is nearly always elongated, and the pinna of the ear simple, while in the Microchiroptera the muzzle is short, the pinna usually complicated by the presence of an inner lobe or tragus, and often produced into remarkable arborescent appendages, and the nose also often provided with elaborate leaf-like or arborescent lobes. The surface is usually covered with soft fur, except in one group of Micro- chiroptera in which the integument is practically naked. The tail is sometimes short, sometimes well developed; in the latter case it may or may not be involved in the tail-membrane.

Eutheria in which the pectoral limbs are modified to form wings, the bones, more especially those of the second to the fifth digits, being greatly elongated so as to support a broad web of skin extending back to the hind-limbs. The sternum has a keel for the attachment of the pectoral muscles, which play an important part in bringing about the movements of flight. The ulna is vestigial; the pollex is small, the remaining digits greatly elongated. The hind-limb is rotated outwards, so that the knee is directed backwards. There is a cartilaginous rod (*calcar*) attached to the inner side of the ankle-joint and helping to support a fold of skin (inter-femoral membrane) which extends from the hind-limbs to the tail or caudal region of the body. The cerebral hemispheres are smooth and do not overlap the cerebellum. The dentition is complete, heterodont and diphyodont. The penis is pendent; the testes abdominal or situated in the groin. The uterus is simple or two-horned (bicornuate); the placenta deciduous and discoidal.

Sub-order a.—*Megachiroptera*.

Large frugivorous Chiroptera with elongated snout, without foliaceous appendages to the nose and ears, the second digit of the manus terminating in a claw. The tail, when present, is not enclosed in the inter-femoral membrane, but lies below it. The crowns of the molar teeth are devoid of sharp cusps.

This sub-order comprises the so-called Flying Foxes (*Pteropus*) of tropical and sub-tropical parts of the Eastern Hemisphere.

Sub-order b.—*Microchiroptera*.

Small, mostly insectivorous, Chiroptera with short snout, frequently with foliaceous appendages of the nose and ears, the second digit of the manus never provided with a claw. The tail when present is enclosed in the inter-femoral membrane. The crowns of the molar teeth are provided with sharp cusps.

This sub-order includes all the ordinary Bats (*Vespertilio* and other genera).

Although so highly specialised for flying, it is surprising to find that the order is so old. *Palæochiropteryx*, one of several genera from the Eocene of Europe, is already as fully developed as any of the Microchiroptera; and *Zanycteris*, which, however, is known only by its teeth, may carry the sub-order as far back as the Palæocene.

Skeleton of the Chiroptera (Fig. 507).—The cervical region of the vertebral column is characterised by the absence of any distinct neural spines, and the same holds good to a less extent of the trunk-vertebræ; the transverse processes of the lumbar region are also rudimentary. The tail varies in development: when it is elongated the component vertebræ are long, cylindrical centra with-

out processes. Sagittal and occipital crests are developed in the skull of some species. The facial region is rather elongated, especially in the Megachiroptera (Fig. 508). Post-orbital processes of the frontal are present or absent: the zygoma is long and slender: the malar is small and applied to the outer surface of the zygoma. The long and narrow nasals are in some cases united; the pre-maxillæ are small. The mandible has an angular process in the Microchiroptera, not in the Megachiroptera. The segments of the sternum are sometimes distinct, sometimes united; the presternum has a mesial keel developed in co-ordination with the great size of the pectoral muscles. The sternal ribs are ossified.

The *scapula* is large and oval in shape: the spine is near the anterior margin: the post-scapula fossa has ridges for the origin of the muscular fibres: the spine has a well-developed acromion. The coracoid is elongated and in some cases bifurcated. The clavicle is long. The pro-coracoid is represented by a separate ossification; there are rudiments of the sternal end of the coracoid between the clavicle and the first rib. The humerus and radius are both elongated. The ulna is reduced, and is sometimes only represented by the proximal end, ankylosed with the radius. A large sesamoid is developed in the tendon of the triceps muscle near the

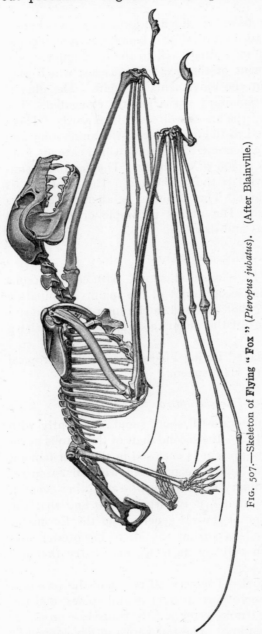

FIG. 507.—Skeleton of **Flying "Fox"** (*Pteropus jubatus*). (After Blainville.)

olecranon process of the ulna. In the carpus the scaphoid and lunar are united : sometimes also the cuneiform is united with these : the pisiform is small. There is no centrale. The ungual phalanges are absent in the nailless digits. The pelvis is small, and the symphysis pubis often imperfect. The fibula is sometimes well-developed, sometimes rudimentary. The tuber calcanei is an inwardly curved process of the calcaneum, attached to which by means of ligamentous fibres is a slender rod of bone or cartilage, the *calcar*, which supports the inter-femoral membrane.

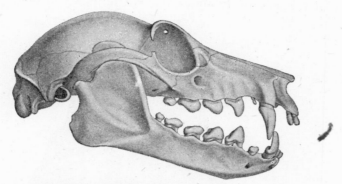

FIG. 508.—Skull of **Pteropus fuscus**.   (After Blainville.)

ORDER DERMOPTERA.

Two closely allied Oriental genera, *Cynocephalus* (Fig. 509) (*Galeopithecus*) and *Galeopterus*, each with only one species, together form the family of Cynocephalidæ (Galæopithecidæ) or " Flying Lemurs." These animals show such peculiarities of anatomical structure that they have to be placed in a separate order of the Mammalia, and the unfortunate lack in our knowledge of their past history makes any suggestions as to the relationship for the most part speculative. The most noticeable character of *Cynocephalus* is the hairy, muscular parachuting membrane or *patagium*, which extends from the neck to the wrist and down the sides of the body to the ankle, and thence to the tip of the moderately long tail. It may be compared to the similar, but not identical, structures in the parachuting Marsupials and Rodents. The brain, like that of the Insectivora, is primitive in being macrosmatic, and in having the corpora quadrigemina uncovered by the cerebrum. The dentition is peculiar. The lower incisors are procumbent and comb-like, the molars multicuspidate. The bulla is formed by the tympanic ring, which also forms the lower border of the spout-like external auditory meatus. There are several characters in which the Dermoptera agree with the Fruit Bats, the Tupaiidæ, and the Lemurs, but the extent to which these characters are convergent or not cannot be decided in the present state of knowledge. The order has presumably had a separate line of evolution from the Eocene, if *Plagiomene*, known only by the upper and lower dentition from the Lower Eocene, is rightly placed in the order. The affinities of this form, as of its older ally, *Planetetherium*, is still very uncertain.

ORDER PRIMATES.

There is still a considerable lack of knowledge as to many details of the structure of the earliest Primates, due to the rarity of their preservation as

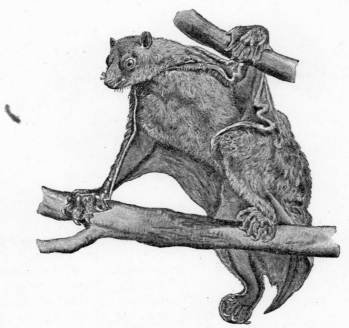

FIG. 509.—**Cynocephalus.** (After Vogt and Specht.)

fossils, a consequence, probably, of their forest-living habits. There is, however, enough evidence to show the great antiquity of the group. Tarsioids and Lemuroids occur first in the Palæocene, Anthropoids do not appear until the late Oligocene.

Absolutely diagnostic characters of a Primate are not easy to find, and the most primitive species still bear traces of their origin from the centralised Cretaceous "insectivore" stock. There are, however, definite trends of evolution within the group, of which the beginning can be seen even in the earliest forms. The dentition, for instance, never has the full eutherian formula of three incisors, a canine, four premolars, and three molars in each half of the upper and lower jaws, but from the first is reduced to two incisors, and, except in some early forms with four, to three premolars, and reduction may eventually proceed further by the loss of another premolar and a molar. The pattern of the molar teeth is at first trituberculo-sectorial, and in many later forms becomes quadri- or quinque-tubercular. The diet of Primates being either insectivorous, frugivorous, or omnivorous, no very great specialisation of tooth-pattern has been evolved.

The most important evolutionary trend is the increase in size and complexity of the brain, especially in the neopallium of the cerebral lobes, which grows so as ultimately to cover a large area of the cerebellum. This increase may be attributed largely to the possession of an opposable thumb and a grasping hand, which enables objects to be brought before the face and examined. This ability to pass the hand over and around objects is associated with the acquirement of an appreciation of tridimensional space, and finally with the acquisition of stereoscopic vision. The face gradually becomes more and more subcerebral as it becomes bent down on the basi-cranial axis, which becomes more inclined to the vertebral axis. Concurrently with the evolution of a grasping hand, the rounded articulation of the head of the radius with the humerus and of the distal extremity with the ulna allows the hand to have a very free movement of supination, a characteristic primate feature, the primitive position of the mammalian hand being, of course, one of pronation.

While the brain has become highly organised, with resulting modification of the skull, the rest of the body has retained a larger number of unspecialised features than is shown by many of the other orders of mammals. Progression is still plantigrade, and even in Man the number of digits remains the primitive five. Flat nails are characteristic of most primates, although claws occur on at least some of the fingers and toes of the Lemuroids. The skull always has a complete orbital ring, and the eye-socket may either be confluent with the temporal fossa or separated by a bony partition, according to the grade of evolution. There is always a tympanic bulla formed by a flange from the petrosal with which the tympanic ring takes part in various ways, so as to have some value in classification.

Primates were originally, and for the most part still are, arboreal. A return to a land habitat is a secondary and rare feature.

The order is divided into three sub-orders : the Lemuroidea, Tarsioidea, and Anthropoidea. The Lemuroidea, although showing special adaptations of their own, are the most primitive in general structure, and the Anthropoidea the most advanced. The Tarsioidea, from an anatomical point of view, occupy an intermediate position. The Lemuroids have a number of primitive characters in common with the Tupaiidæ (p. 546), with which group the Lemurs seem to have had a common origin. The actual relationship of the three sub-orders to one another is still a matter of debate, and considerable differences of opinion exist.[1]

[1] See LeGros Glark, Wood Jones, Gregory, Elliot Smith, in appendix on literature.

Compared with the Anthropoidea, the Lemuroidea show a number of distinguishing features, some explicable as persistent and primitive characters, others as specialisations peculiar to the Lemuroid line of evolution. Of the former the low brain-case, with its macrosmatic brain and uncovered cerebellum ; the confluence under the post-orbital rim of the orbital and temporal fossæ ; the lateral instead of forward direction of the orbits ; the presence of four or even five ethmoturbinal bones instead of the usual three ; the backward extension of the jugal ; the thickened hind border of the palate ; the large nasal bones, wide at the back, instead of narrow and pointed ; the uterus duplex, non-deciduous placenta and occasional inguinal mammæ ; an entepicondylar foramen in the humerus and a third trochanter in the femur. The dentition is on the primitive trituberculo-sectorial plan, but subject to considerable specialisation in various forms. The procumbent lower incisors and

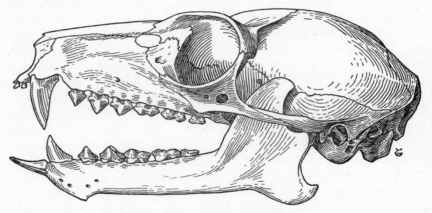

FIG. 510.—Skull of **Lemur**.

incisiform lower canines are specialisations that have arisen within the group. The hands and feet are also specialised, in that the second toe of the hind foot at least is always furnished with a sharp claw. In the hand the second finger is likewise always clawed. At least some of the fingers and toes have flat nails. The tympanic ring is enclosed inside the bulla, where either it lies free, as in the Tupaiidæ, or, as in the Lorisine Lemurs, is attached to the inner side of the outer wall of the bulla in the position of the external auditory meatus (Fig. 596).

There are numerous extinct groups of Lemuroids from as far back as the middle of the Palæocene period, where species of the families Plesiadapidæ and Anaptomorphidæ are first known to occur. The Adapidæ, with many described genera, are an important Eocene family. Modern Lemurs fall into two groups : the family Lemuridæ, confined to the island of Madagascar, where they have undergone a radiation into four separate sub-families, the Lemurinæ or true Lemurs with long skulls (Fig. 510) ; the Chirogalinæ (*Chirogale, Micro-*

cebus, Opolemur), with short skulls and elongated tarsus; the Indrisinæ (*Indris* and *Propithecus*) with short skulls and quadri- instead of tri-tubercular molars; and the Chiromyinæ (*Daubentonia* (*Chiromys*)), an aberrant form with short skull, a single pair of enlarged rodent-like incisors, and reduced premolars (Fig. 511). Of the second family, the Lorisidæ, none occurs in Madagascar, but they are found mostly in Africa, with two genera (*Loris* and *Nycticebus*) in the East Indies. The Lorisidæ fall into two sub-families, the Lorisinæ (*Perodicticus*, the Potto. of West Africa, *Arctocebus*, also of West Africa and *Loris* and *Nycticebus*, the Oriental genera), and the Galaginæ, characterised by a long calcaneum and astragalus in the tarsus (*Galago* and *Otolemur* of East Africa and (*Galagoides* (*Hemigalago*)) of West and Central Africa).

The sub-order Tarsioidea starts also in the Palæocene with the family of

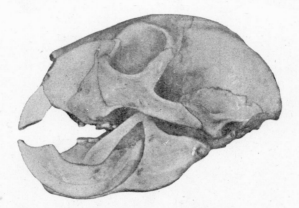

FIG. 511.—Skull of **Daubentonia**. The lower jaw has been partially cut to show the extent of the rodent-like incisor.

Anaptomorphidæ (*Tetonius* and *Anaptomorphus*), and a considerable number of families and genera have been described from the early tertiaries both of the Old and the New Worlds. At the present time there is only one genus and species, *Tarsius spectrum* (Figs. 512, 513), a small forest-living animal found in certain islands of the farther East, such as Borneo, Java, Celebes, and as far as the Philippines.

Tarsius from the anatomical point of view is an animal of considerable interest, and its zoological position with respect to the Lemurs on the one hand and to the Anthropoids on the other is still in dispute. It has been considered as a Lemur, and as the surviving member of a line from which man has directly sprung. The more usual view is that it represents a separate line of evolution which at a very early period branched off the stock which eventually produced the anthropoids.

From the Lemurs it differs in having an orbit directed forwards and almost completely separated from the temporal fossa; by the microsmatic brain; by single olfactory foramina; by the arrangement of the tympanic ring, which remains outside the bulla and forms the tubular external auditory meatus.

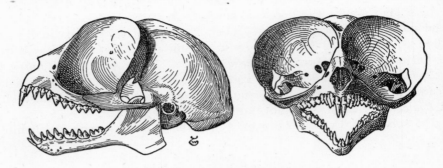

FIG. 512.—Skull of **Tarsius spectrum**.

The structure of the nostrils and upper lip is nearer that of the Anthropoids than of the Lemurs, the jugal does not extend so far back, and the carotid artery enters the bulla wall.

FIG. 513.—**Tarsius spectrum**.

There are specialised features which are sufficient to separate the Tarsioids from the Anthropoids. In the first place, the hind foot has a greatly elongated navicular and calcaneum, a feature which occurs in all the early forms (in which this structure is known), and one which alone is sufficient to prevent the line from being considered as directly ancestral. The digits of the hand have nails as do all the toes except the second and third, which are clawed. The tibia and fibula are fused. The great enlargement of the eyes—a specialisation for nocturnal habits—has caused considerable modification in the shape of the skull, and there are indications of a macula lutea and of the origin of stereo-scopic vision.

The sub-order Anthropoidea comprises the higher forms of Primates, including Man. Here the brain reaches its highest development. The eyes are forwardly directed and set close together. The nose differs from that of the Lemurs, where the muzzle, or rhinarium, has the primitive naked form and the nostrils have on each side the lateral cleft, typical of most mammals, which separates a central from lateral portions. The rhinarium itself is hairless, and runs on to the upper lip, and the lip is held down by a ligament, and is not pro-trusible. In the Anthropoids the nostrils are completely ringed round by naked skin, the moist muzzle is absent, and the upper lip is without a ligament, and so is free to protrude. With the exception of the rather primitive Hapalidæ, the fingers and toes are all provided with flat nails.

The Anthropoidea fall into two groups : the Platyrrhini, or New-World Monkeys, and the Catarrhini from the Old World. The former are characterised by a broad, as against a narrow, nasal septum. There are always three pre-molars, and the tympanic ring forms a bony canal to the external auditory meatus. In some forms the tail is prehensile, a character which occurs in no other Primates. There are two families : the Hapalidæ, or Marmosets, which are the most primitive Monkeys, with claws on all digits except the hallux. The third molar is lacking and the tail is non-prehensile. The genera are (*Callithrix* = *Hapale*) and (*Leontocebus* = *Midas*). The second family is that of the Cebidæ, containing the genera *Cebus*, the Capuchins (*Suimiri* = *Chryso-thrix*) Squirrel Monkeys ; *Pithecia*, the Sakis ; *Ateles*, Spider Monkeys ; *Alouatta* or *Mycetes*, the Howlers, etc.

The Old-World Monkeys and Apes are characterised by the loss of the first premolars and the presence of a bony external auditory meatus. Ischial callosities are often present, and there are cheek-pouches in all except the Langurs, Guerezas, and Apes. There are three families : the Cercopithecidæ, which comprise all forms except Man and the Apes such as *Macaca*, the Macaques ; *Papio*, the Baboons ; *Colobus*, the Guerezas ; *Cercopithecus* (*Presbytis* = *Semnopithecus*), the Langurs ; *Nasalis*, the Proboscis Monkey, etc. The second family, the Simiidæ, (or Anthropomorpha) contains *Hylobates*, the Gibbons ; *Ponge* = *Simia*, the Orang Utan ; *Pan* = *Anthropopithecus*, the Chimpanzee ; and *Gorilla*, the Gorilla. The third family is that of the Homi-nidæ, with three extinct genera in *Pithecanthropus*, *Sinanthropus*, and *Eoanthropus* and the single living genus *Homo*.

In the Lemurs and their allies the body is slender, and the limbs are adapted for an arboreal existence. The hallux is divergent from the other digits of the foot and opposable to them, and the same holds good, in some cases, of the pollex. In some all the digits are provided with claws, in others all but one hallux. More commonly all the digits have flat nails, except the second of the pes, which always has a claw. The eyes are very large. The muzzle is sometimes elongated, sometimes short; the nostrils are slit-like. The tail is sometimes absent or short; more usually it is greatly elongated, but it is never prehensile. The surface is always covered with soft fur.

Of the Anthropoidea the Hapalidæ or Marmosets are small squirrel-like animals with all the digits except the hallux provided with pointed claws, with the pollex incapable of opposition, the tail non-prehensile, and without cheek-pouches or callous patches over the ischia. The Cebidæ resemble the Hapalidæ in the negative characters of the absence of ischial callosities and of cheek-pouches, and of the power of opposition in the hallux. But the limbs are much longer, the digits are all provided with flat nails, and the tail is frequently prehensile. The Cercopithecidæ all have brightly-coloured, bare, callous patches of skin (*callosities*) over the ischia, and most of them have cheek-pouches for the storage of food. All the digits are provided with flat nails. The tail may be long, or short, or absent; when present it is never prehensile. The pollex, when developed, is always opposable to the other digits. In the Simiidæ or Man-like Apes (Fig. 516 A) a tail is never developed, and there are no cheek-pouches; ischial callosities are present only in the Gibbons. The Gibbons can walk in an upright position, without the assistance of the fore-limbs; in the others, though, in progression on the surface of the ground, the body may be held in a semi-erect position with the weight resting on the hind-limbs, yet the assistance of the long fore-limbs acting as crutches is necessary to enable the animal to swing itself along.

Skeleton of the Primates.—The atlas is ring-like, the odontoid sub-conical. The spines of the cervical vertebræ are usually well-developed and simple: in Man they are short—with the exception of the seventh—and bifid: in some they are trifid. The number of thoraco-lumbar vertebræ is usually nineteen, but only seventeen in Man, the Gorilla, and Chimpanzee, sixteen in the Orang; in some Lemurs it may be twenty-three or twenty-four. The number of sacral vertebræ varies from two to five. The sacral region of Man, which comprises five ankylosed vertebræ, differs from that of other Primates in its greater relative breadth and in its backward curvature; it forms a well-marked angle where it joins the lumbar region—the *sacro-vertebral angle*—scarcely recognisable in other Mammals. The number of caudal vertebræ varies with the length of the tail—from four to about thirty-three. In Man there are only four vestigial caudal vertebræ, ankylosed together to form the *coccyx*. In all those forms in which the tail is well developed chevron bones are present.

The human *skull* (Fig. 514) presents a marked contrast in certain respects

to that of other Mammals, but in many points is approached by that of the other Primates, more especially by that of the Simiidæ. One of the most important characteristics of the human skull is the large size of the brain-case, the cubic content of the cranial cavity averaging 1500 cubic centimetres in the male of white races. This great development is most marked in that part of the cavity which lodges the cerebral hemispheres, in adaptation to the large dimensions of which the cranium bulges out both anteriorly and posteriorly to

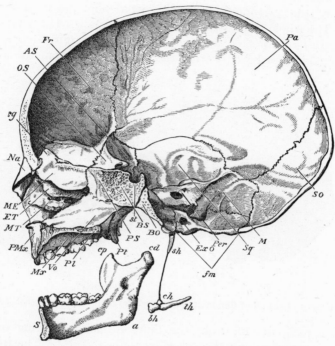

FIG. 514.—Skull of **Man**. Letters as in Fig. 595. In addition, *a.* angle of mandible; *c. g.* crista galli, a process of the mesethmoid; *f. m.* foramen magnum; *M.* mastoid; *s. t.* sella turcica. (After Flower.)

such an extent that the entire length of the cavity greatly exceeds that of the basi-cranial axis. A result of the posterior bulging of the brain-case is that the foramen magnum (*f. m.*) is no longer situated at the posterior extremity of the skull as in other Mammals, but assumes a position farther forwards towards the middle of the base. The anterior expansion, causing a strong arching forwards of the frontal region, brings about an alteration in the position of the ethmoidal plane, which, instead of being perpendicular or inclined to the basi-cranial axis, becomes horizontal, and the cribriform plate forms the middle part of the floor of the anterior extension of the cranial cavity. The fossa for lodgment of the

cerebellum lies entirely beneath the posterior portion of the cerebral fossa; the olfactory fossa is comparatively small (see Fig. 597, *D*.)

The outer surface is smooth and rounded, devoid of any prominent ridges or crests. The occipital crest of lower Mammals is represented merely by a rough raised line—the *superior curved line* of the occiput. The paroccipital processes are only represented by slight eminences—the *jugular eminences*. There is no auditory bulla; the mastoid portion of the periotic projects downwards as a prominent *mastoid process*. The periotic, tympanic, and squamosal early fuse into one bone—the *temporal bone*. The post-glenoid process is very slightly developed. The whole facial region is relatively small. The orbits, which are of moderate size, are directed forwards; the bony margin is complete, and a plate of bone, developed partly from the jugal, partly from the ali-sphenoid,

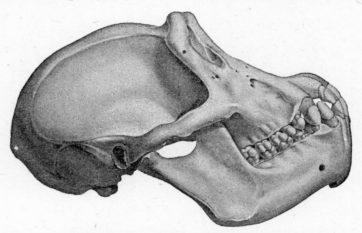

FIG. 515.—Skull of **Chimpanzee** (*Pan troglodytes*).   (After Blainville.)

almost completely cuts off from the temporal fossa, leaving only a small aperture of communication—the *spheno-maxillary fissure*. The frontal suture usually early disappears. The nasals are rarely fused. The suture between the premaxillæ and the maxillæ becomes obliterated at an early stage, so that the entire upper jaw appears to consist of a single bone. A peculiar spine, the *nasal spine*, is developed in the middle line below the nasal opening. The most marked feature of the mandible is the presence of a prominence, the *mental prominence*, in the lower part of the symphysial region (*S.*). The stylo-hyal nearly always becomes fused—together with the tympano-hyal—to the periotic and tympanic, giving rise to a slender process—the *styloid process* (*sh.*)—projecting downwards from the base of the skull.

None of the other Primates has a cranial capacity approaching that of Man; and those modifications in the shape of the skull which are the concomitants of the great development of the brain in the human species are accordingly not recognisable, or are much less strongly marked. The various fossæ of the cranium, however, as a rule occupy the same relative positions as in Man ; the cerebellar fossa is entirely beneath the cerebral ; and the ethmoidal plane, and that of the foramen magnum (occipital plane), are usually both horizontal or nearly so. In all the Simiidæ, with the exception of the Orang, the frontals meet in the middle line below, over the pre-sphenoid. In many Monkeys the outer surface of the cranium is smooth and free from prominent ridges ; but in the Baboons, the Orangs, the Gorilla, and the Chimpanzee (Fig. 515) there are strongly developed occipital, sagittal, and supra-orbital ridges, usually much more prominent in the male than in the female, and increasing in size with age. The paroccipital processes are always rudimentary, but there are well-marked post-glenoid processes. The mastoid does not form a distinct mastoid process. In the Cebidæ and Hapalidæ alone is there a tympanic bulla. The entire facial region is relatively larger than in Man ; the premaxillo-maxillary region is always more prominent, and in the Baboons projects forwards as a distinct muzzle. The orbit is separated from the temporal fossa as in Man. The nasals are usually ankylosed in the adult. The nasal spine is never developed. The suture between the premaxilla and the maxilla only becomes obliterated, if at all, in old individuals. The mental prominence of the mandible is never developed, the anterior surface of the symphysial region sloping backwards and downwards from the bases of the incisor teeth. The stylo-hyal never gives rise to an ossified styloid process.

In the skull, as in many other respects, the Lemurs occupy an intermediate position between the higher Primates and the lower orders of Mammals. The occipital and ethmoidal planes are usually vertical. The tympanic forms a large bulla. The orbits, which are large, are usually separated from the temporal fossæ only by a narrow rim of bone. The lachrymal foramen is situated on the face outside the margin of the orbit. The facial region is usually elongated, and may form a prominent muzzle.

In all the Primates the *clavicle* is present and complete, and in the *scapula* the spine, acromion, and coracoid process are well developed. In Man and the higher Apes the glenoid border of the scapula is much longer than the coracoid border. In the lower Monkeys, on the other hand, these borders are nearly equal. The humerus is comparatively long and slender ; the tuberosities and ridges are not, as a rule, very strongly developed. In Man and the Simiidæ the bone is twisted around its long axis ; in the lower forms this torsion is absent. In Man and the higher Apes the foramen above the inner condyle is absent ; it is present in many of the American Monkeys and in most Lemurs. Characteristic of the ulna of Man and the higher Apes is the small upward extension of the olecranon process. The radius and ulna are distinct in all ; in the higher forms the shafts of the two bones are bent outwards, so that there is a wide interosseous space, and there is considerable freedom of movement in pronation

FIG. 516 A.—**Gorilla.**   (From the *Cambridge Natural History*.)

FIG. 516 B.—Skeleton of **Orang** (*Ponge satyrus*).   (After Blainville.)

and supination.   In the carpus (Fig. 517) the scaphoid and lunar are always distinct, and a centrale is present in all except some of the Lemurs, the Gorilla, Chimpanzee, and Man.   A pisiform is present, and in most a radial sesamoid. As compared with that of the other Primates, the carpus of Man is short and broad ; the trapezium has a saddle-shaped articular surface turned somewhat inwards. In Man, the Chimpanzee, Gorilla, and Orang the carpus articulates exclusively with the radius ; in all the others it articulates also with the ulna.   In Man the pollex has a remarkable and characteristic freedom of movement in opposition to the other digits.

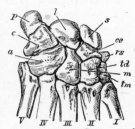

Fig. 517.—Carpus of **Baboon** (*Papio anubis*). *ce*. centrale ; *c*. cuneiform ; *l*. lunare ; *m*. magnum ; *p*. pisiform ; *r. s.* radial sesamoid ; *s*. scaphoid ; *td*. trapezoid ; *tm*. trapezium ; *u*. unciform. (After Flower.)

The human *pelvis* is remarkable for its relative breadth, for the expanded form of the ilia and the deep concavity of their inner surfaces, and for the shortness of the pubic symphysis.   In the higher Apes some of these features are recognisable, though less pronounced ; but in the lower the ilia are long and narrow, and usually curved outwards ; in the Old-World Monkeys the tuberosities of the ischia are strongly everted and roughened for the attachment of the ischial callosities.

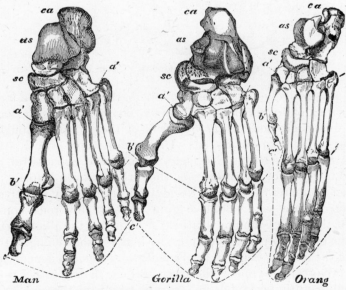

Fig. 518.—Foot of **Man, Gorilla,** and **Orang** of the same absolute length, to show the difference in proportions.   The line *a'a'* indicates the boundary between tarsus and metatarsus ; *b'b'*, that between the latter and the proximal phalanges ; and *c'c'* bounds the ends of the distal phalanges ; *as*. astragalus ; *ca*. calcaneum ; *sc*. scaphoid.   (After Huxley.)

The tibia and fibula are well developed and distinct in all. In nearly all the hallux, owing to the form and direction of the articulation between it and the internal cuneiform, is opposable to the other digits, converting the foot into a grasping organ. The human foot (Fig. 518) is distinguishable from that of the other Primates by the absence of this power of opposition and by the relative length of the tarsus, which exceeds that of the metatarsus.

ORDER CONDYLARTHRA.

This order, ranging from the Palæocene to the Eocene, is an important basal group approaching the early Creodonta in some respects, but characterised by the foreshadowing of hoofs—*i.e.*, they are on the " ungulate " line of evolution rather than on the " unguiculate." There is also a tendency for the third toe

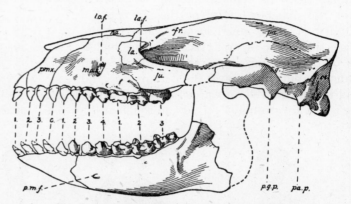

FIG. 519.—Skull of **Hyopsodus.** (After Matthew.)

to become progressively larger than the others, thus producing a mesaxonic, as compared with a paraxonic, foot. These two characters suggest that the Perissodactyla arose from some early members of the group, although no direct ancestor has so far been discovered. The tooth pattern of such a form as the Condylarth *Ectocion*, itself an Eocene form too late to be ancestral, could easily be modified into that of *Hyracotherium*, the earliest known Horse.

The chief character of the early Condylarths are mostly negative ones, as is to be expected in any very primitive group. The omnivorous, non-predacious character of the teeth is unlike what was evolving in the allied Creodonts, and there is none of the specialised features, such as the shortening of the jaws and reduction of the incisors found in the Primates. There is a general resemblance to the Insectivores, but none of the specialisations of that order is observable. The astragalus (an important bone, see Fig. 609) is of the creodont-carnivore type, and the carpus is normally interlocking with the centrale retained (see p. 643).

In general, the Condylarthra are to be considered as primitive, and not far removed from the generalised ancestral stock of the Cretaceous period, and themselves are in a position ancestral to a number of later groups.

There are five families : the Hyopsodontidæ, Phenacodontidæ, Periptychidæ, Meniscotheriidæ, and Didolodontidæ, this last family containing only South American animals that appear to be a connecting link with the exclusively South American Litopterna.

The Hyopsodontidæ (e.g., *Hyopsodus*, Fig. 519) are the more primitive forms, and have a general resemblance to Insectivores and Primates, with one or the other of which orders *Hyopsodus*, with its sexitubercular molars and hedgehog-like skull, was formerly placed, until the discovery of its typically condylarth astragalus decided its truer position. The Mioclæninæ (*Mioclænus*) have tritubercular teeth, and both retain, among other primitive features, claws rather than hoofs and an interlocking carpus.

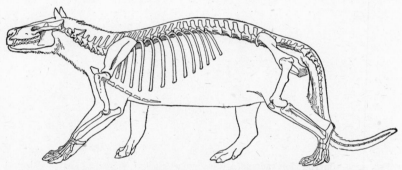

FIG. 520.—**Phenacodus primævus.** (American Museum of Natural History.)

The Phenacodontidæ contain several genera, among which are *Tetraclænodon*, which, in having blunt claws rather than hoofs, somewhat bridges the gap between the Condylarths and Creodonts, and *Phenacodus* (Fig. 520), its direct descendant, which has become specialised in having a serially arranged carpus and by the loss of the clavicle. *Ectocion*, an Eocene genus, has, as already mentioned, a dentition approaching that of the early Horses. In this family the feet are, as in the others, pentadactyle, but with a progressive tendency to tridactylism, to digitigradism, and to a broadening of the ungues into small flat hoofs.

The Periptychidæ (e.g., *Periptychus*, *Conacodon*, *Ectoconus*) also have narrow hoofs, and are a specialised side-line with enlarged premolars and multicuspid molars, which prevent them from appearing as ancestral to any later forms. Their earlier members are closely akin to the Hyopsodontidæ.

The Meniscotheriidæ (*Meniscotherium*, *Pleuraspidotherium*) retain a very primitive foot structure, but have become specialised in their very selendont molars.   On this ground they have been considered as ancestral to the Hyra-coidea, though satisfactory proof is still lacking.

The Didilodontidæ, with primitive bunodont molars and simple premolars, are on the line leading to the early Litopterna, such as *Diadiaphorus*.

ORDERS PANTODONTA AND DINOCERATA.

These two orders are sometimes classed together as a single order, the Amblypoda, but there are differences in structure that entitle them to be separated.   Both in all probability arose from some early condylarthrous stock, but diverged from one another on specialised lines of foot-structure and dentition.

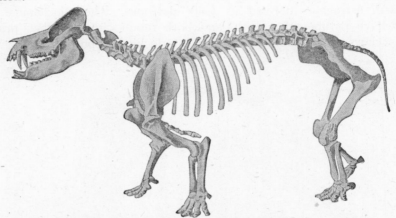

FIG. 521.—**Coryphodon radians.**   (*Cambridge Natural History.*)   (After Osborn.)

The Pantodonta comprise the families Pantolambdidæ and Coryphodon-tidæ.   *Pantolambda*, a Palæocene genus, represents a more primitive stage leading to *Coryphodon* (Fig. 521), the terminal genus of the Lower Eocene, which attained the size of a Rhinoceros.   The feet have the carpals serially arranged, and the toes tend to become short and stout as an adaptation to weight.   The teeth are present in full series, and the canines large.   The upper molars are triangular, and in *Pantolambda* have three cusps; in *Coryphodon* the pattern evolves into an aberrant type of bilophodont tooth.   The order became extinct during the early Eocene, and left no successors.

The Dinocerata, or Uintatheria, were heavy, stump-footed animals reaching a large size.   The skull is characterised by the presence of three pairs of bony horn-cores placed on the nasals, parietals, and on the maxillæ just over the enlarged spear-like upper canines.   The molar teeth are bilophodont like those of *Coryphodon* superficially, but with the two ridges converging on the inner side. Any resemblance between the two forms is due to convergence rather than to any close affinity.   The Dinocerata also died out at the close of the Eocene without successors. Examples are *Loxolophodon* (*Tinoceras*), *Uintatherium* (*Dinoceras*), *Eobasileus* (Fig. 522).

SOUTH AMERICAN " UNGULATA."

In South America there was an evolution of " Ungulates " of great diversity of form and of a range in time from the Palæocene to as late a period as the Pleistocene. They are grouped provisionally in four orders which have no connection with one another beyond some remote Condylarth ancestor. Although there are on occasions superficial resemblances to animals in other parts of the world, as, for instance, the curious convergence in foot-structure of certain Litopterna and the Horses or the proboscidean characters of the Pyrotheria, these four orders in reality have no outside relationships, and each pursued a specialised line of evolution of its own.

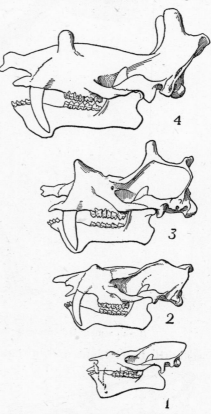

ORDER LITOPTERNA.

This is a small order, consisting of two families, the Macraucheniidæ and Proterotheriidæ. The genus *Macrauchenia* (Fig. 523) had a three-toed foot with well-developed lateral toes, the neck was long and camel-like, and the skull peculiar in the position of the nasal openings, which are placed far back on the upper surface of the skull, suggesting the presence in life of a proboscis. Of the Proterotheriidæ a series of genera show

FIG. 522.—Skulls of **Uintatheria.** 1. *Bathyopsis*; 2. *Elachoceras*; 3. *Uintatherium*; 4. *Eobasileus*. (After W. B. Scott.)

an evolution which closely parallels that of the Horses. *Notodiaphorus*, an Oligocene form, has three toes with the lateral toes stout and still resting on the ground—about the stage, that is, of *Mesohippus* among the Horses. *Diadiaphorus* (Fig. 524), in the Miocene, has the lateral toes much reduced, and can be compared with *Miohippus*, while *Thoatherium*, also Miocene, is monodactyl to a greater degree even than the modern Horse, in that the splint-bones are reduced to mere nodules of bone. (See Fig. 599, p. 645.)

The dentition of these animals has the perissodactyle-like feature of molarisation of the premolars, but, unlike the Horses, the teeth remain per-

FIG. 523.—**Macrauchenia.**
(From a mounted specimen in the American Museum of Natural History.)

sistently brachydont and, although there is a superficial resemblance in the molar pattern with the earlier Horses, there are differences in detail, and the tooth- and foot-structure combined are never in phase with any genus of Horses, so that there is no real danger of confusion.

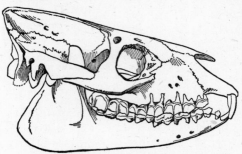

FIG. 524.—**Diadiaphorus.**   (From W. B. Scott.)

ORDER NOTOUNGULATA.

This order is larger and more varied, including the most typical and abundant South American herbivorous mammals throughout the Tertiary. Artiodactyls and Perissodactyls were there absent until the Pleistocene, and their places were taken by Notoungulates. The latter became extinct after South America was united to North America in the Pliocene, and more progressive herbivores from the North took their place. There are four principal groups of

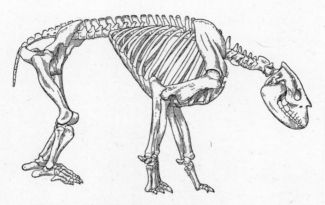

FIG. 525 A.—**Homalodotherium.** (After Riggs.)

Notoungulata. The sub-order Notioprogonia (Arctostylopidæ, occurring in Asia and North America, the only non-South American Notoungulates; Henricosborniidæ; Notostylopidæ) includes small and primitive forms, confined to the Palæocene and Eocene. Some of them closely resemble the Condylarthra, and probably show the origin of the Notoungulates from that group. The Entelonychia (Homalodotheriidæ) (Fig. 525 A) developed into large forms with clawed feet resembling those of the Chalicotheres, and became extinct towards the end of the Miocene or beginning of the Pliocene. The Toxodonta (Notohippidæ, Toxodontidæ) also reached considerable size, the genus *Toxodon* (Fig. 525 B) of the Pleistocene being as large as a rhinoceros. The typical toxodonts had large cropping incisors and strongly curved hypsodont molar teeth. The fourth suborder, Typotheria (Typotheriidæ, Hegetotheriidæ, Interatheriidæ,

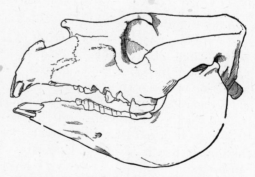

FIG. 525 B.—**Toxodon.** (After W. B. Scott.)

etc.) also developed enlarged incisors and hypsodont molars, but were mostly of small size, and some of them must have resembled rabbits in appearance and habits.

Order Astrapotheria.

This order includes only two families, but in spite of a resemblance in general aspect, these are so different in basic structure that they are referred to two sub-orders :—

Trigonostylopoidea (with the family Trigonostylopidæ) and Astrapotherioidea (Astrapotheriidæ). The typical genus, *Astrapotherium* (Fig. 526), of Miocene age, was a large animal with a disproportionately large head, provided with great canine tusks and with retracted nasals suggesting the presence of a proboscis. The premolars were reduced and the molars greatly enlarged but not hypsodont, the whole dentition suggestive of the Amynodont Rhinoceroses.

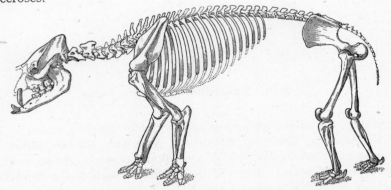

Fig. 526.—**Astrapotherium magnum.**   (From Scott, after Riggs.)

Order Pyrotheria.

The Pyrotheres are known from a single family (Pyrotheriidæ), with a short history from Eocene (*Carolozittelia*) to Oligocene (*Pyrotherium*). *Pyrotherium* was a large, elephant-like animal with a proboscis and with two pairs of large incisor tusks in the skull and one pair in the lower jaw. Each of the posterior premolars and molars has two sharp transverse crests, somewhat as in Kangaroos, Tapirs, Deinotheres, and some other groups. It has been maintained that the Pyrotheres were allied to the Mastodons and Elephants, but it is now believed that the resemblance is convergent, and that Pyrotheres, like other South American Ungulates, developed there from condylarth-like ancestors.

Order Carnivora.

The modern Carnivores are difficult to characterise. There is, in fact, only one feature constant throughout the group, and that is the fusion of the scaphoid, lunar, and centrale in the carpus. Other characteristic features, however, are the universal retention of the full number of incisors and the well-developed canines. The post-canine dentition always shows a certain amount of reduction and a rather wide range of adaptive radiation, as is described below. The digits of the feet are usually five, and are never reduced to less than four, and the toes are armed with sharp claws which are often retractile. The brain is well developed.

The present radiation of Carnivores may be said to start mainly in the Oligocene period, but the line can be traced backward through late Eocene Canidæ to the Creodont Miacidæ of the Palæocene, until it becomes merged in the basal Creodont-Insectivore stock from which so many orders arose.

Living Carnivora are divided in the first place into two sub-orders : the Fissipedia, all essentially land-living animals, with toes separate ; and the Pinnipedia, forms adapted to marine life, with the toes bound together by skin to form paddles. The Fissipedia are classified on a number of anatomical characters, such as the shape of the bulla and the presence or absence of an alisphenoid canal in the skull, but the most useful guide is the pattern of the molar teeth and the presence or absence of a modification of two teeth, always the first lower molar and the last upper premolar, into flesh-cutting shears known as the *carnassials* (Fig. 528).

There are seven families, of which the Canidæ (Dogs, Wolves, and Foxes) occupy a central position. The dentition is complete except for the absence of the last lower molar. The carnassial teeth are well developed and the upper molars are bluntly triangular in pattern (Fig. 527[1]). There are only four toes on the hind feet, and the claws are non-retractile.

On one side of the Canidæ may be ranged the Viverridæ (the Civet Cats) Hyaenidae and Felidae. Here the dentition always shows some reduction in the number of molar teeth, both upper and lower; carnassials are well developed and the upper molar is a narrow triangle sharp on the inner border (Fig. 527[2]). There are normally five toes with semi-retractile claws. An anal scent-gland is a common feature.

The Hyænidæ (Hyænas) have a molar dentition reduced to one in each section of the jaws, and the first premolar is likewise lost. The carnassials are well developed. The upper molar is reduced to a thin slip transversely placed and sharp on the inner side (Fig. 527[3]). The teeth as compared with those of the Felidæ are blunter and coarser, an adaptation to carrion-feeding and bone-crushing. There are never more than four toes on the hind foot and the claws are non-retractile. The tympanic bulla has internally a rudimentary septum which partially divides it. *Proteles*, the " Aard Wolf " of South Africa, is an aberrant insectivorous form with the teeth reduced to simple cones.

The Felidæ (Lions, Tigers, and Cats) (Fig. 527[4]), with very well-developed carnassials, show the greatest molar reduction of all these teeth, being even more reduced in size than those of the Hyænas. The premolars are also reduced both in number and in size to three above and two below. In some extinct

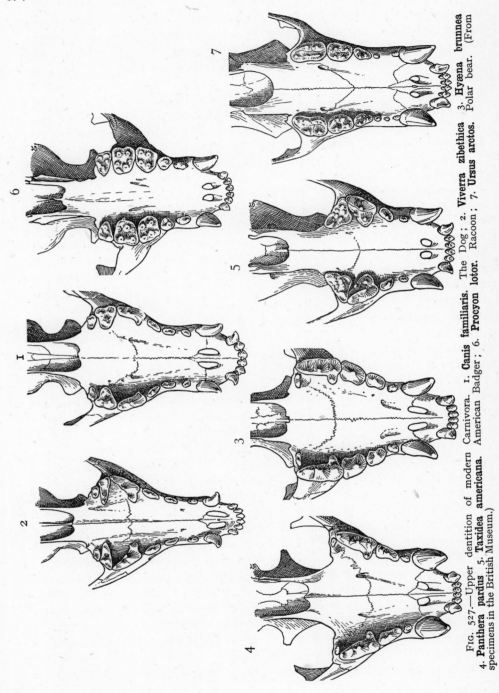

Fig. 527.—Upper dentition of modern Carnivora. 1. **Canis familiaris.** The Dog; 2. **Viverra zibethica.** 3. **Hyæna brunnea**. 4. **Panthera pardus** 5. **Taxidea americana.** American Badger; 6. **Procyon lotor.** Racoon; 7. **Ursus arctos.** Polar bear. (From specimens in the British Museum.)

Felidæ such as *Smilodon* reduction goes even further, this animal having only two premolars and a vestige of one molar in the upper jaw and one premolar and one molar in the lower. As a compensation, however, the carnassials are enormous, and the canines are exceptionally developed. The claws are completely retractile, and the tympanic bulla is smooth and inflated externally, and is divided inside by a complete septum. On the other side of the Canidæ are the Mustelidæ, Procyonidæ, and Ursidæ.

The Mustelidæ (Stoats, Otters, Skunks, Martens, Wolverines, etc.) form a large group characterised by the post-carnassial upper molar which, instead of being triangular, is expanded on the inner side (Fig. 527^5), sometimes, as in the European Badger (*Meles taxus*), very much so. The dental formula varies somewhat, but is not much reduced, except that there are never more than two molar teeth. The claws are not retractile and the tympanic bulla is not inflated and has no inner septum.

The Procyonidæ (Racoons, Kinkajou, Panda, etc.) are American in distribution, with the exception of the Panda (*Ælurus fulgens*) and the "Spectacled Bear" (*Æluropus melanoleucus*), both Oriental. The dentition, except for the loss of an anterior premolar and the last molar, shows little reduction. Carnassials are not developed as shearing-teeth and the upper molars are round in outline instead of triangular (Fig. 527^6). The claws are non-retractile. The Kinkajou (*Potos caudivolvus*) is a fruit-eating animal in which the crown surface of the molar teeth is degraded to a flat surface only obscurely tuberculated, and with a prehensile tail—a feature unique among carnivores.

The Ursidæ (Bears) have a fully plantigrade foot and non-retractile claws. Like the Procyonidæ, the shearing carnassial teeth are not formed. The molar teeth are large, elongated, and much tuberculated (Fig. 527^7), the dentition, except for the last molar, is unreduced. The tympanic bulla is flat.

The Fissipede Carnivores are often separated into two super-families: the Arctoidea (or Canoidea), including the Canidæ, Procyonidæ, Mustelidæ, and Ursidæ, and the Æluroidea (or Feloidea), the Viverridæ, Hyænidæ, and Felidæ.

The Pinnipedia (Seals, Sea-Lions, and Walrus) do not appear until the Miocene. They show little external resemblance to the land-living Carnivores, owing to their adaptation to an aquatic life and fish-eating diet. The feet, which have the full number of five digits, are enclosed in a web of skin. The proximal elements of the limbs are shortened, the distal, especially those of the hind limb, are lengthened. The first digit of the hand is the longest, and the first and fifth digits of the hind foot are equal in length and longer than the middle ones. In the wrist the carnivore feature of a coalesced scaphoid and lunar is present. The dentition differs from that of the Fissipedia in that the incisors are always less than three in each half of the jaws. There are usually four premolars and only one molar, all consisting of a conical, sometimes compressed, single crown, which may have, in addition, an anterior and posterior additional cusp.   There is no development of carnassial teeth.   The facial part of the skull is abbreviated, the cranial elongated.

There are three families.   In the Otariidæ (Eared Seals) the pinna of the ear is present, though small, and the hind legs can be turned forward for progression on land.   The Odobænidæ (Walrus) lack an external ear, but have the same arrangement of the hind feet as the Otariidæ. The upper canines form exceptionally large tusks.   The Phocidæ (Seals) also lack an external ear, but have the hind limbs turned permanently backwards, bound up with the short tails, and are useless for land locomotion (Fig. 535 A).

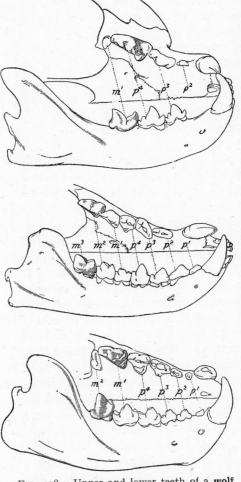

All these modern Carnivores in the course of time replaced an older group, a sub-order known as the Creodonta, which, until its final extinction at the dawn of the Miocene, were the dominant flesh-eating mammals, and themselves had a radiation into four superfamilies. Of these the earliest, known from the Lower Palæocene, were the Arctocyonoidea (Procreodi) (Arctocyonidæ and Triisodontidæ), small animals primitive in their general structure, with low skulls, small brains, and with a complete dentition.   Carnassial teeth were not as yet developed and the molars were usually of the tuberculo-sectorial pattern.   The limbs and body were long and slender, with a long tail, the feet pentadactyle and plantigrade.   From this centralised and unspecialised assembly arose,

FIG. 528.—Upper and lower teeth of a **wolf** (top figure) ; **Hyænodon** (middle figure) and **Oxyæna** (lower figure) showing the different arrangement of the carnassial teeth. The carnassials are shaded.   (After Matthew.)

mostly during the Palæocene, the three remaining superfamilies, the Mesonychoidea, Oxyænoidea, and Miacoidea, which are classified chiefly by the presence or absence of carnassial teeth and, further, by a difference in the particular teeth which become the carnassials when present.

The Mesonychoidea [Acreodi] (Mesonychidæ), like the Arctocyonoidea, developed no carnassials, but the cusps of the cheek-teeth become broad and blunt, and in some of the later forms develop a hypocone. The possession of a mesaxonic foot and a tendency to develop small hoofs on the rather wide and fissured terminal phalanges instead of claws suggest that some offshoot of this family gave rise, during the early Eocene, to the Artiodactyla.

The Oxyænoidea [Pseudocreodi] (Oxyænidæ and Hyænodontidæ) are characterised by having " false " carnassials, in the sense that they are never the same pair of teeth, the fourth upper premolar and first lower molar, as those in the Miacoidea and modern Carnivores. In the Oxyænidæ the carnassials are the first upper and second lower molars, in the Hyænodontidæ the second upper and third lower molars (Fig. 528). The two families in their day were the most successful of the earlier radiation, and gave rise to some large forms, though *Andrewsarchus*, a Mesonychid from the Lower Oligocene of Mongolia, reached the largest size of all, with a skull three feet in length.

The remaining super-family the Miacoidea [Eucreodi] (Miacidæ) originated in the mid-Palæocene, and expanded through the Eocene to transform into the radiation of the modern Carnivores during the Oligocene. The carnassials were developed from the fourth upper premolar and the first lower molar, and, like the true carnivores, in contradistinction to other Creodonts, the terminal phalanges are not fissured. The scaphoid and lunar bones, however, are still free in the carpus.

Skeleton of the Carnivora.—In the Carnivora the atlas is very large, with wing-like lateral processes. The neural spine of the axis is elongated and compressed, the odontoid conical. The other cervical vertebræ have small spines and large transverse processes. There are twenty or twenty-one thoracolumbar vertebræ. The most anterior thoracics have long, slender, backwardly-sloping spines. In the posterior thoracics large metapophyses and anapophyses are developed. The transverse processes of the lumbar vertebræ are extremely long and the spines short. The sternum is long and narrow, composed usually of eight or nine pieces. The sternal ribs are almost uncalcified.

In the *skull* of the Carnivora vera (Figs. 529 and 531) there are prominent sagittal and lambdoidal crests. The temporal fossæ are very deep; the orbits are not separated from them by bone. The relative development of the facial region varies in the different groups; in the Bears and their allies, and in the Dogs, it is elongated; in the Cats it is very short. The zygoma is strong and greatly arched outwards. The glenoid cavity is in the form of a transverse groove, to the shape of which the transversely elongated condyle is adapted. In the Cats there is a large rounded tympanic bulla (Fig. 530), the cavity of which is divided into two parts—anterior and posterior—by a septum, the anterior containing the auditory ossicles and the opening of the Eustachian tube; the bony auditory meatus is short; the paroccipital is closely applied to the posterior surface of the tympanic bulla. In the Dogs the septum of the bulla is incomplete, the auditory meatus short, and the paroccipital process not applied to the bulla. In the Bears and their allies

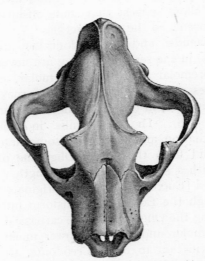

FIG. 529.—Skull of **Tiger** (*Felis tigris*). (After Blainville.)

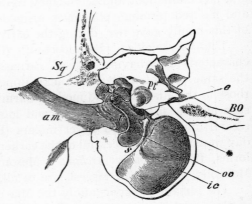

FIG. 530.—Section of the left auditory bulla of **Tiger** (*Felis tigris*). * aperture of communication between the two chambers into which the cavity of the bulla is divided; *a. m.* external auditory meatus; *B. O.* basi-occipital; *e.* Eustachian tube; *i. c.* the inner chamber; *o. c.* the outer chamber; *Pt.* periotic; *s.* septum between the two chambers; *Sq.* squamosal. (After Flower.)

(Fig. 532) the bulla is usually less dilated, and the septum is absent or only represented by a ridge, while the bony auditory meatus is elongated.

The cranium in the Pinnipedia (Fig. 535) is broad and rounded, rather

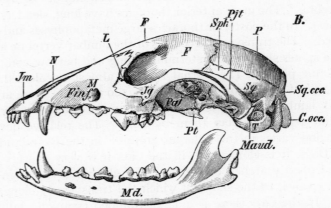

FIG. 531.—Lateral view of skull of **Dog** (*Canis familiaris*). *C. occ.* occipital condyle; *F.* frontal; *F. inf.* infra-orbital foramen; *Jg.* jugal; *Jm.* premaxilla; *L.* lachrymal; *M.* maxilla; *Maud.* external auditory meatus; *Md.* mandible; *N.* nasal; *P.* parietal; *Pal.* palatine; *Pjt.* zygomatic process of squamosal; *Pt.* pterygoid; *Sph.* ali-sphenoid; *Sq.* squamosal; *Sq. occ.* supra-occipital; *T.* tympanic. (From Wiedersheim's *Comparative Anatomy*.)

compressed from above downwards.   The orbits are large and approach near
to one another.

In the Carnivora vera the spine of the *scapula* is situated at about the middle
of the outer surface of the bone.   The acromion is usually well developed, some-

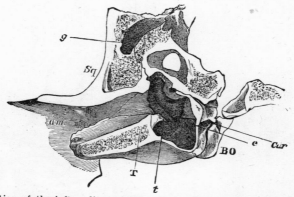

FIG. 532.—Section of the left auditory bulla and surrounding bones of a **Bear** (*Ursus ferox*).
a. m. external auditory meatus; *B. O.* basi-occipital; *Car.* carotid canal; *e.* Eustachian canal;
Sq. squamosal; *T.* tympanic; *t.* tympanic ring.   (After Flower.)

times with a metacromion.   The coracoid process is very small.   The clavicle
is never complete, sometimes entirely absent.   There is a supra-condyloid
foramen in the Cats and some of the other groups, not in the Dogs or Bears.

The scaphoid and lunar are united (Fig. 533).   There is no separate cen-

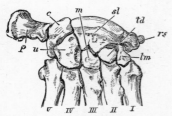

FIG. 533.—Carpus of **Bear**
(*Ursus americanus*).   *c.* cuneiform; *m.* magnum; *p.* pisiform;
r. s. radial sesamoid; *s. l.* scapho-
lunar; *td.* trapezoid; *tm.* trapezium; *u.* unciform.   (After Flower.)

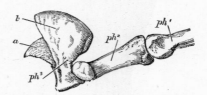

FIG. 534.—The phalanges of the
middle digit of the manus of the **Lion**
(*Felis leo*).   *ph*[1]. proximal phalanx;
ph[2]. middle phalanx; *ph*[3]. ungual
phalanx; *a*, the central portion forming
the internal support to the horny claw;
b, the bony lamina reflected around the
base of the claw.   (After Flower.)

trale.   Usually a radial sesamoid is present.   There are five digits, though the
pollex may be reduced in size, as in the Dog, and it is vestigial in the Hyæna.

The *pelvis* is long and narrow.   In the tarsus all the ordinary bones are
developed.   The hallux is fully formed in the Bears, etc., but shorter than the
other digits.   In the Cats and Dogs it is represented only by a vestige of the
metatarsal.

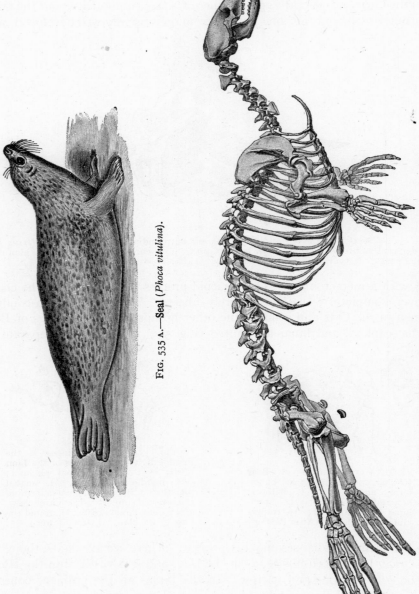

FIG. 535 A.—**Seal** (*Phoca vitulina*).

FIG. 535 B.—Skeleton of **Seal** (*Phoca vitulina*). (After Blainville.)

In the Pinnipedia (Fig. 535) both acromion and coracoid are short, and the scapula is curved backwards; there is no clavicle. The bones of the fore-limb are short and stout; the humerus has a prominent deltoid crest; there is no foramen above the inner condyle. The ulna is greatly expanded. at its proximal, the radius at its distal, end. The manus is broad and expanded. The scaphoid and lunar are united to form a scapho-lunar. The ungual phalanges are nearly straight, slender, and pointed. The ilia are short; the symphysis pubis is short and without firm union of the bones. The femur is short, thick, and flattened. The fibula and tibia are commonly ankylosed proximally. The calcaneum is short and usually without a distinct calcaneal process; the lateral digits are usually the longest.

FIG. 536.—**Killer** (*Orca gladiator*). (After True.)

ORDER CETACEA.

Modern Whales first occur, with an apparent suddenness, in the early part of the Miocene, with all the cetacean peculiarities of skeleton fully adapted to their completely marine life, and so far advanced in evolution as to hide those characters which would give information as to their original land-living ancestors. An earlier Eocene evolution (the Archæoceti), of uncertain relationship to modern forms, hardly tells us more, except for some slight indication of a possible Creodont ancestry.

Modern Cetacea are characterised by the adaptation of many of their anatomical characters to their special mode of life. Some of these structures are new, some are normal mammalian structures much modified, and some are entirely lost. Examples in the first category are: the formation of a thick layer of fat, the " blubber "; the horizontally expanded tail-flukes (Fig. 536); the dorsal fin; the breaking up of certain arteries into *retia mirabilia*; the intranarial epiglottis, the whalebone or " baleen " of the Whalebone Whales;

the extra digits (hyperdactyly) and extra phalanges (hyperphalangy, Fig. 537), both means of enlarging the surface of the paddle, are a common feature in the order. Of characters that have been modified from the normal may be mentioned the great obliquity of the diaphragm and its powerful musculature; the enclosure of the proximal elements of the fore-limb inside the body, and the alteration of the hand to a skin-covered paddle; the peculiar shape of the scapula, with its well-developed forwardly directed achromion process and absence of spine; the non-lobulated liver and lungs, and the division of the stomach into as many as four digestive regions. The whole

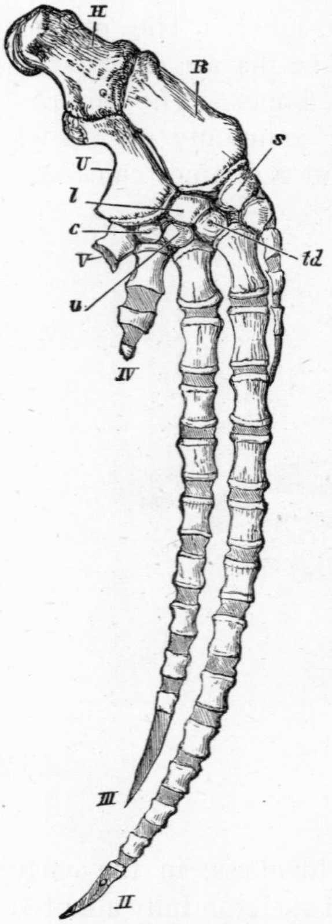

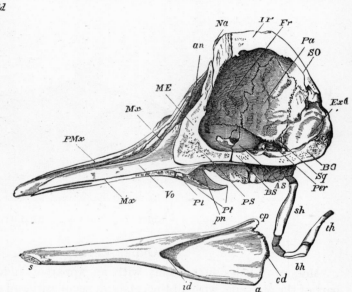

FIG. 537.—Dorsal surface of bones of the right anterior limb of **Globicephalus melas,** the round-headed Dolphin showing hyperphalangy. c. cuneiform; H. humerus; l. lunar; R. radius; s. scaphoid; td. trapezoid; U. ulna; u. unciform. (From *Cambridge Natural History*.) (After Flower.)

FIG. 538.—Skull of **Dolphin** (*Globiocephalus*), sagittal section. a. angle of mandible; an external nares; A. S. ali-sphenoid; bh. basi-hyal; B. O. basi-occipital; B. S. basisphenoid; cd. condyle of mandible; c. p. coronoid process; Ex. O. ex-occipital; Fr. frontal; I. P. inter-parietal; ME. mesethmoid; Mx. maxilla; Na. nasal; Pa. parietal; Per. periotic; Pl. palatine; P.Mx. premaxilla; p. n. posterior nares; P.S. pre-sphenoid; Pt. pterygoid; s. h. stylo-hyal; S. O. supra-occipital; Sq. squamosal; t. h. thyro-hyal; Vo. vomer. (After Flower.)

skeleton is naturally much modified. The skull has a greatly elongated facial and dorsoventrally compressed facial portions, the nasal openings, often asymmetrical, are placed far back on the upper surface of the head; the tympanic bulla is loosely attached, and the cranial bones in general are much modified in shape (Fig. 538). In the vertebral column the cervical vertebræ are shortened, compressed, and, except in the Platanistidæ, are fused together into one mass (Fig. 539). The sternum is reduced. The features that have been lost are : hair, except for a very few facial bristles ; finger-nails, except for traces in the fœtus ; external ears ; all skin-glands ; the lachrymal duct and nictitating membrane in the eye ; the tubercles of the ribs ; the odontoid process and the articulating processes (zygapophyses) between the vertebræ ; the entire sacrum and, except for traces, the hind-limbs. Of all mammals the Cetacea show the greatest deviation from the normal.

The order falls into three sub-orders : the Archæoceti, Odontoceti, and the Mystacoceti. The first-named sub-order consists of three families of primitive whales : the Protocetidæ, Zeuglodontidæ (or Basilosauridæ), and Dorudontidæ. The Protocetidæ (*Protocetus* and *Prozeuglodon*) are known from the Middle and Upper Eocene of Egypt, and are of some interest in that the dentition in *Protocetus* (Fig. 540) still shows a division into three incisors, a canine, three premolars, and three molars. The cheek-teeth have become elongated and sectorial, but one at least—the third premolar—has retained an

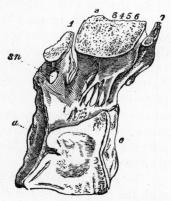

FIG. 539.—Section through middle line of united cervical vertebræ of **Greenland Right Whale (Balæna mysticetus)**. *a.* vertebræ of Greenland Right Whale (**Balæna mysticetus**). *a.* articular surface for condyle ; *e.* ephysis of seventh cervical ; *sn.* foramen in atlas for first spinal nerve ; 1-7, arches of cervical vertebræ. (After Flower.)

inner tubercle and is somewhat reminiscent of a creodont tooth. *Prozeuglodon* has evolved still further, and the anterior teeth are simple cones, and the posterior, which, however, are still two-rooted, are elongated, with secondary serrations. For the rest the skull and skeleton, as far as is known, have ad-

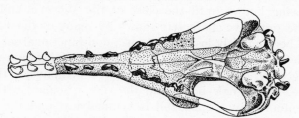

FIG. 540.—Palatal aspect of skull of **Protocetus.**

vanced a long way towards the Cetacean type. The Zeuglodontidæ (*Zeuglodon*, Fig. 541) became unusually elongated, and were clearly a side-line, the Dorudontidæ (*Dorudon*) were shorter-bodied and persisted till the end of the Oligocene. While the Archæoceti are definitely Whales, they are more primitive in some respects. The head, for instance, has the front part elongated, as in other Whales, but the cranial part is not compressed and the skull-bones bear a more normal relationship to one another that is the case in later forms.

The Odontoceti, or " Toothed Whales," are represented at the present day by the Iniidæ and Platanistidæ, Fresh-water Dolphins of South America and the Orient which retain a larger number of primitive characters than do other Whales, as, for instance, the free cervical vertebræ, each of considerable length ; the interlocking processes of the thoracic vertebræ ; the double-headed anterior ribs ; the relatively simple hand with no increase in the number of digits or phalanges, etc. The Physeteridæ (*Physeter*, the Sperm Whale), Ziphiidæ (*Ziphius, Hyperoodon, Mesoplodon*, " Beaked Whales," " Bottlenose," etc.) whales with a much-reduced dentition ; the Delphinidæ (a large group of many genera including Porpoises, Dolphins, the " Narwhale," etc.).   The Agorophoridæ and Squalodontidæ are two extinct families, the first Oligocene and the second Miocene.

The general characters of this sub-order are the possession of teeth, which with the exception of the Ziphiidæ, are numerous and homodont.   Whalebone is not formed.   The skull shows a varying degree of asymmetry ; the external

FIG. 541.—**Zeuglodon** from Romer, after Gidley.

nostril is single ; the upper jaw is broad posteriorly, and in part overlaps the frontal bones.   The anterior ribs usually have both capitulum and tuberculum. The sternum is formed of two or more sternebræ.   The mandibular rami are flat and united by a firm symphysis.

The Mystacœti or " Whalebone " whales appeared later in time, the modern families not being known until the close of the Miocene, and the sub-order has none of the primitive characters shown by many of the Toothed Whales. All teeth have been entirely lost except for a non-functional set in the embryo, and their place has been taken by the characteristic whalebone ; the mandibular rami are strongly arched and are not united by a symphysis ; the sternum has become reduced to a single bone, and the ribs articulate with the vertebræ by the tuberculum only.   The skull is symmetrical and the external nasal opening is double.

The group is classified in three families : the Cetotheriidæ, a Miocene evolution in which the compression of the skull had not proceeded as far as in the later forms ; the Balænopteridæ (" Fin-Whales," e.g., *Balæna mysticetus*, the Greenland Whale ; *Neobalæna marginata*, the " Pigmy Whale " ; and the Balænopteridæ (*Balænoptera*, the " Rorquals " ; *Megaptera*, the " Humpback " ; *Rachianectes*, the " Grey Whale," etc.).

Skeleton of Cetacea.—In the Cetacea the cervical region (Fig. 542) (*cerv.*) is always very short, and the constituent vertebræ are often completely fused together into a continuous bony mass (Fig. 539), or the atlas alone may be separated from the rest; but sometimes all the vertebræ are complete and separate. In the latter case they have small arches and long transverse processes consisting of two narrow bars with a wide space between them. The epiphyses are very distinct discs which often remain separate from the bodies up to a late period. The neural spines are well developed. The zygapophyses are not well developed, and are absent in the posterior portion of the trunk. In the absence of hind limbs there is no sacral region. The caudal region consists of numerous vertebræ beneath which, opposite the intervertebral spaces, are a series of chevron bones (*chev.*).

In the Whalebone Whales only one pair of ribs articulates with the sternum, and none articulates with the body of the vertebra, but only with the transverse processes. In the Toothed Whales only a small number are connected with the sternum, sometimes through the intervention of intermediate ribs, and a few of the anterior only, in most cases, articulate with the bodies of the vertebræ; but in some a greater number articulate with both transverse processes and bodies by distinct tubercles and heads.

The *sternum* varies in shape. Sometimes it consists of a presternum and a series of several sternebræ without xiphisternum; sometimes (Fig. 543)

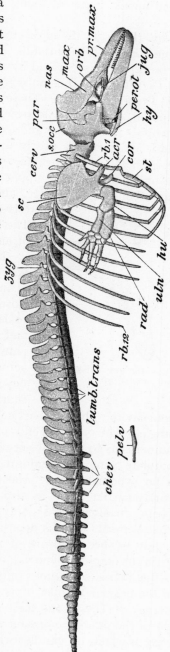

Fig. 542.—Skeleton of **Porpoise** (*Phocæna communis*). *Acr.* acromion process of scapula; *cerv.* united cervical vertebræ; *chev.* chevron bones; *cor.* coracoid process; *hu.* humerus; *hy.* hyoid; *jug.* jugal; *lumb. trans.* lumbar transverse processes; *max.* maxilla; *nas.* nasal; *orb.* orbit; *par.* parietal; *pelv.* vestige of pelvis; *per.ot.* periotic; *pelv.* vestigial pelvis; *pr.max.* premaxilla; *rad.* radius; *rb. 1,* first rib; *rb. 12,* twelfth rib; *sc.* scapula; *s. occ.* supra-occipital; *st.* sternum; *uln.* ulna; *zyg.* prezygapophysis.

it is a continuous plate of bone, occasionally with median notches or fontanelles.

In the *skull* (Fig. 538) the brain-case is rounded, the jaws greatly elongated, often unsymmetrical. The parietals (*Pa.*) do not meet in the middle line above in most Cetacea, being separated by the supra-occipital (*S. O.*) and an inter-parietal (*I. P.*); there is thus no sagittal suture. A large supra-orbital plate is developed from the frontal. There are large and stout zygomatic processes of the squamosal, but the jugals are extremely small. In all the recent forms the maxilla (*Mx.*) is very large and extends backwards to overlap a good deal of the frontal, and forwards nearly to the extremity of the snout; while the premaxillæ (*P.Mx.*), which are long narrow bones, bound but a very small part of the oral border of the upper jaw. The nasals (*Na.*) are very small. The tympanic bone is very large, and is sometimes fused with the periotic (Mystacoceti), sometimes not (Odontoceti). The lower jaw is remarkable for the absence of an ascending ramus.

The *scapula* in most of the Cetacea is very broad and flat, expanded into the shape of an open fan. The spine is usually situated close to the anterior border, sometimes coalescent with it. The acromion is curved and flat, the coracoid also compressed and parallel with the acromion. In some, both acromion and coracoid are absent. There is never any trace of a clavicle. The humerus is short and very stout; the head freely movable

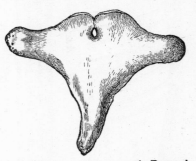

Fig. 543.—Sternum of **Rorqual** (*Balænoptera musculus*). (After Flower.)

in the glenoid cavity; the distal articulating surfaces are flat and oblique, meeting at an angle. The proximal ends of the radius and ulna are so firmly united with the humerus as to allow of very little movement; at the distal end there are no complete synovial membranes. The manus is extremely modified. There are no synovial joints; the carpus is in some (Whalebone Whales) almost entirely cartilaginous, as also are the metacarpals and phalanges—the cartilages being coalescent or separated by intervals of fibrous tissue: in some of the carpal elements bone is deposited. In the Toothed Whales the carpals are completely ossified, and are of polygonal form: the phalanges are also ossified, with incomplete synovial articulations. In the Cetacea there are sometimes five digits, sometimes only four: a few species have considerably more than the normal number of phalanges—sometimes as many as fourteen (hyperphalangy). The second digit is usually the longest.

Vestiges of the *pelvis* are present in the form of a pair of long narrow bones (Fig. 542, *pelv.*) which lie parallel with the spinal column some little distance below the region where the chevron bones begin: these appear to represent the ischia. A second pair of smaller bones which lie close to these in the Whalebone Whales are apparently vestiges of the femora, and there may be additional vestiges representing the tibiæ.

ORDERS PERISSODACTYLA AND ARTIODACTYLA.

These two orders were formerly grouped together as the " Ungulata vera," and distinguished from other hoofed animals which were called the "Subungulata." This classification no longer holds, and the two orders are considered to be entirely separate, and to have arisen from different pre-Eocene ancestors. A comparison of a typical Perissodactyl and Artiodactyl, such as a Horse and a Cow, shows a number of anatomical differences sufficient to prove that the two orders are fundamentally different.

In the skeleton the most noticeable difference lies in the structure of the feet, from which the orders take their names. In the Horse the axis of the foot passes down the third digit, in the Cow it passes between the third and fourth digits. The first is a mesaxonic foot, the second paraxonic (p. 644). The utmost reduction that can take place in the number of toes in a Perissodactyle is three. (The Horse, although functionally one-toed, is anatomically three-toed, with the second and fourth toes represented by the splint bones.) In the Artiodactyles the number of toes, as in the Cow, can be reduced to two—the third and fourth. The tarsus shows points of difference. The shape of the astragalus (p. 649, Fig. 609) is in each case diagnostic and, apart from the fusion of several of the tarsal bones in some Artiodactyles which never occurs in the Perissodactyla, the artiodactyle cuboid always has an articulating surface with the calcaneum, which is distinctive (Figs. 602, 608).

Among other differences the following may be quoted as examples. The Perissodactyle has a third trochanter on the femur, twenty-two or twenty-three dorso-lumbar vertebræ, and a peg-like odontoid process on the axis vertebra. The Artiodactyle lacks a third trochanter, has uniformly nineteen dorso-lumbar vertebræ, and a spout-like odontoid process.

Some, but not all, Perissodactyles and Artiodactyles have a complete post-orbital border. When this is present, its composition differs in the two orders. In the Horse (Fig. 544) a process of the squamosal runs between processes of the frontal and jugal. In the Cow (Fig. 545) the posterior rim of the orbit is completed by the frontal and jugal processes alone, and the squamosal is excluded. In the dentition the trend of evolution in the Perissodactyla has finally resulted in almost complete molarisation of the premolars, in the Artiodactyla all premolars except occasionally the fourth are simpler than the molars. True horns with a bony horn core never occur in the Perissodactyla. Artiodactyla usually have a gall-bladder and a more or less complicated ruminating stomach. These structures never occur in the Perissodactyla.

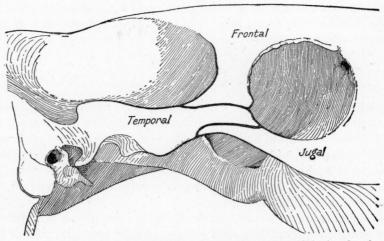

FIG. 544.—Part of Horse's skull, showing the structure of the jugal arch.
For temporal read squamosal.   (After Wood-Jones.)

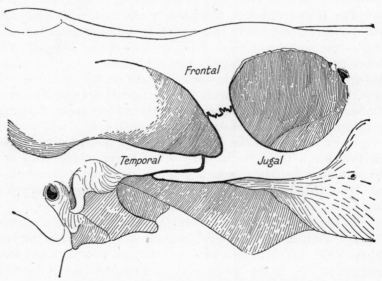

FIG. 545.—Part of Cow's skull, showing the structure of the jugal arch.
For temporal read squamosal.   (After Wood-Jones.)

Both orders occur definitely for the first time in the Lower Eocene. The
Artiodactyla still flourish in some abundance.   The Perissodactyla, on the other
hand, are much reduced from their former numbers and, but for protection,
some might soon become extinct.

ORDER PERISSODACTYLA.

This order arose from some member of the Condylarthra, and by the beginning of the Eocene had already divided into its five main lines of evolution : the Equoidea (Equidæ and Palæotheriidæ) ; Rhinocerotoidea (Rhinocerotidæ and Lophiodontidæ) ; Tapiriidea (Tapirs) ; Titanotheroidea (Titanotheriidæ) and Chalicotheroidea or Ancylopoda (Chalicotheres).

With the main ordinal features as mentioned above held in common, these five sub-orders, the earliest representatives of which show a good deal of resemblance to one another, began to evolve on adaptive lines of their own, so that the terminal species of each sub-order acquired each a very different external appearance. The different trends of evolution are concerned chiefly with the structures of the feet and the teeth. If the teeth of *Hyracotherium*, the earliest known Horse ; of *Homogalax*, a Tapir ; of *Eotitanops*, a Titanothere ; and of *Hyrachyus*, a Rhinoceros, be compared, it can be seen that all start on the same general plane, with low crowned teeth, with premolars simpler than the molars, and with the six original cusps of the upper molars still clearly traceable. Closer examination of the molars, however, shows that beginnings of differences which ultimately lead to great differences in the final result (Fig. 546). In *Hyracotherium*, which has the most primitive teeth of any Perissodactyle, the protoconule and metaconule are only just beginning to elongate towards the paracone and metacone, and these two outside cusps are beginning to elongate in the anterio-posterior to form the beginning of an ectoloph. In *Eotitanops* the intermediate cusps and the hypocone do not progress, but tend to disappear, the protocone is large and remains bunoid, while the paracone and metacone form a precociously enlarged ectoloph with a strongly marked W outer border. The Chalicotheres have a similar type of tooth-structure. *Homogalax* shows already the tapiroid structure of a bilophodont tooth in the joining of the protocone, protoconule, and paracone into an anterior transverse crest and the hypocone, metaconule, and metacone into a corresponding hinder crest ; the ectoloph is hardly developed. *Hyrachyus*, the earliest Rhinoceros, is like the Tapir in forming transverse crests, but the ectoloph is more strongly developed and is produced into a characteristic metaloph behind.

The Horses gradually evolved very hypsodont teeth, the Rhinoceroses rather less so, but in both cases a deposit of cement was acquired in the deep valleys between the cusps though to a much less degree in the Rhinoceroses. All other Perissodactyles retained more or less brachydont teeth in which cement was not formed.

In all Perissodactyla the premolars are at first simpler than the molars. During the course of evolution all the premolars, with the exception of the first, invariably became molariform.

In foot-structure the Horses became functionally monodactylous. The Titanotheres, Tapirs, and Rhinoceroses show a less degree of reduction, while the

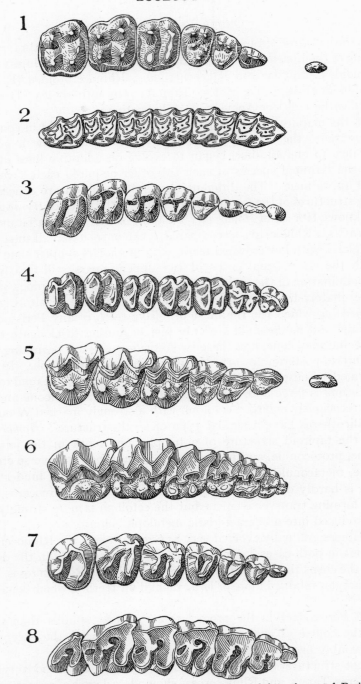

FIG. 546 —Right upper molars and premolars of early and late forms of Perissodactyla. 1, **Hyracotherium** and 2, **Horse**.   3, **Homogalax** and 4, **Tapir**.   5, **Eotitanops** and 6, **Titanotherium**. 7, **Hyrachyus** and 8, **Rhinoceros**.

Chalicotheres evolved a very aberrant foot-structure of their own. Details of the tooth-structure for each sub-order are given in Fig. 546.

Sub-order Equoidea.

The Horses present one of the most completely known phylogenies of any Vertebrates. In a condensed form it is as follows. There was a progressive increase in size and in height from the ground, due to a lengthening of the distal elements of the limbs, an adaptation to an increase in speed. In the feet, starting from a condition with four toes in the front-foot (there is no trace of a first digit, or thumb, in any Perissodactyle) and three sub-equal toes in the hind-foot, together with traces of the first and fifth digits, represented by nodules of bone, a gradual change took place whereby the central digit in both feet became progressively longer and stouter, the lateral digits became thinner, failed to reach the ground, and finally became reduced to splint-bones. The ulna and fibula became reduced to their proximal halves only and progression, at first sub-digitigrade, became unguligrade. In the skull the profile of the top of the head became changed from a straight to a convex line, and the facial part in front of the orbits became elongated. Up to the stage of *Mesohippus* the post-orbital bar was incomplete; after that stage it became complete and progressively stouter. The teeth progressed from a brachydont and almost bunodont to a very hypsodont condition, with an increasing complication of pattern, and the molars eventually acquired a coating of cement on the out-side of the tooth as well as in the deep hollows between the cusps. The canines became proportionally smaller, and the premolars, at first simpler than the molars, gradually became molariform and, in size, ultimately actually larger than the molars. A cingulum round the cheek-teeth, characteristic of the earliest forms, was soon lost.

A series of species can be selected to show these changes (Fig. 547), but the picture thus presented is only a partial one. Evolution did not proceed by a series of large jumps from the earliest type to the modern Horse—the progress was gradual. Moreover, there was not a single line of evolution of one genus succeeding another, but a continual branching off of side-lines, the majority of which, after varying periods of existence, became extinct (Fig. 548). It is not always easy, among these branches, to trace the actual line of descent of the living Horses, though a reasonable approximation to the truth is probable.

Horses appeared first, with other Perissodactyla, in the Lower Eocene of Europe and North America in the genus *Hyracotherium* (the American species being placed in the genus *Eohippus*, which is not really distinguishable). In Europe during the Eocene there was an expansion of lines from *Hyracotherium*, all of which became extinct by the Oligocene at latest. These show varying rates of evolution, some, such as *Lophiotherium*, having the premolars pre-cociously molarised, others on the contrary, while increasing in size remained

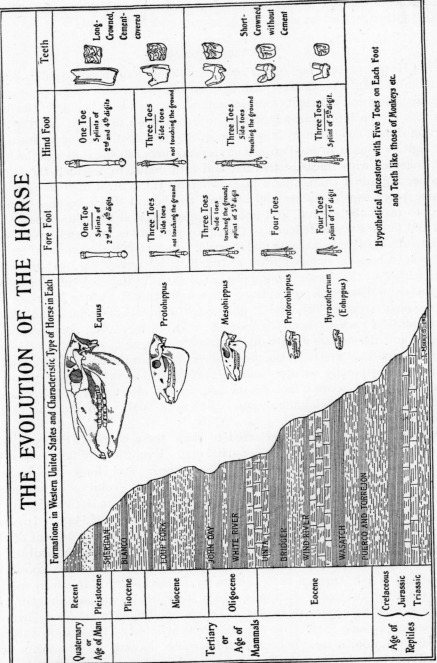

FIG. 547.—(After W. D. Matthew.)

non-progressive in their teeth. One group, the Palæotheres, departed alto-gether from a normal horse-evolution, and ended up in the Oligocene (*Palæo-therium*), the size of a Rhinoceros, with the lateral toes unreduced, with molarised premolars and a dentition comparable to a much later horse such as *Anchi-*

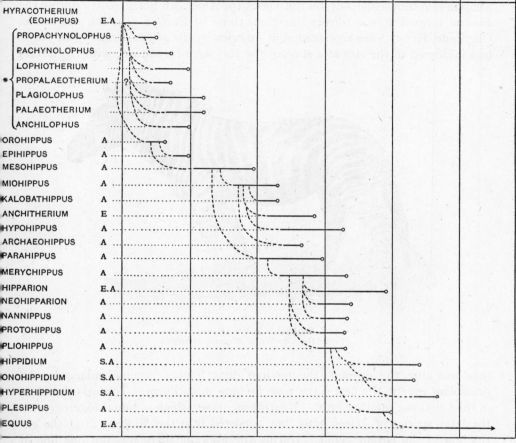

		EOCENE	OLIGOCENE	MIOCENE	PLIOCENE	PLEISTOCENE	RECENT
HYRACOTHERIUM (EOHIPPUS)	E.A						
PROPACHYNOLOPHUS							
PACHYNOLOPHUS							
LOPHIOTHERIUM							
PROPALAEOTHERIUM							
PLAGIOLOPHUS							
PALAEOTHERIUM							
ANCHILOPHUS							
OROHIPPUS	A						
EPIHIPPUS	A						
MESOHIPPUS	A						
MIOHIPPUS	A						
KALOBATHIPPUS	A						
ANCHITHERIUM	E						
HYPOHIPPUS	A						
ARCHAEOHIPPUS	A						
PARAHIPPUS	A						
MERYCHIPPUS	A						
HIPPARION	E.A						
NEOHIPPARION	A						
NANNIPPUS	A						
PROTOHIPPUS	A						
PLIOHIPPUS	A						
HIPPIDIUM	S.A						
ONOHIPPIDIUM	S.A						
HYPERHIPPIDIUM	S.A						
PLESIPPUS	A						
EQUUS	E.A						

FIG. 548.—*E*, European. *A*, North American. *S.A.*, South American. *, side lines of small horse-like animals derived from **Hyracotherium** and confined to European Eocene and Early Oligocene without leaving any successors. The presumed relationships of the American genera are based on work by W. D. Matthew. (*Quarterly Review af Biology*, 1926.)

therium, and with recessed nasals showing the possession during life of a tapir-like proboscis. In all these cases the stage of evolution was out of phase, either too advanced on one character or too retarded in another to be directly ancestral to later horses. No further horses occurred in Europe until the Miocene.

Meanwhile in North America *Hyracotherium* (or *Eohippus*), of which genus a considerable number of species has been described, evolved by small increments in height and by a progressive molarisation of the premolars, so that by the Middle Eocene a new genus, *Orohippus*, can be recognised. In the Upper Eocene *Epihippus* replaced *Orohippus*, which is still more advanced. It is, however, questionable if it is a direct descendant of *Orohippus*, and there is here a gap in our knowledge, but, on the whole, the American horse genera during the Eocene formed a more direct line than those of Europe. In the succeeding Oligocene, Horses were represented in America by the genus *Mesohippus*, which had increased to the size of a sheep ; the feet were three-toed, with the lateral

FIG. 549.—**Burchell's Zebra** (*Equus burchelli*).
(From the *Cambridge Natural History*.)

toes touching the ground, the median digit having become enlarged. All premolars except the first have now become molariform. Towards the close of the Oligocene another genus (*Miohippus*) arose, which is found together with the later species of *Mesohippus*, but persisted into the Miocene after the extinction of the parent genus. During the Miocene there was not one line of Horses but several existing side by side, all of them derivable from *Miohippus*— e.g., *Kalobatippus*, *Archæohippus*, *Hypohippus*, and *Anchitherium* (a genus which suddenly appears in Europe as an immigrant from North America). All these side-lines became extinct, but another genus, *Parahippus*, derived directly from *Mesohippus* persisted till the end of the Miocene, and during that time gave rise to the genus *Merychippus*. In this genus the teeth rapidly elongated in the sockets and there was formed a heavy deposit of cement not only between the cusps, but on the outside of the tooth as well. *Merychippus* in turn gave rise to a number of lines, including the world-wide genus *Hipparion*, and to *Protohippus* and *Pliohippus*, which at the end of the Pliocene produced the genus *Plesippus*, the direct ancestor of the modern Horse.

In South America at the close of the Pliocene and during the Pleistocene there was a separate evolution of Horses represented by the genera *Hippidium*, *Onohippidium*, and *Parahipparion* (*Hyperhippidium*), all derived from *Pliohippus*, and characterised by very long and slender nasal bones. These genera did not survive the Pleistocene. During the Pleistocene all Horses in North and South America became extinct, and the sub-order was carried on in the Old World. At the present time, apart from domestic breeds, the only wild Equidæ are represented by *E. prezevalskii* of Central Asia, *E. asinus*, the Wild Asses of Africa. *E. hemionus*, *E. onager*, and *E. hemippus*, three species

FIG. 550.—**Indian Rhinoceros** (*Rhinoceros indicus*).
(From the *Cambridge Natural History*.)

of Oriental Wild Asses, and finally four striped species of Africa *Equus* (or *Hippotigris*) the Zebras (Fig. 549).

The table (Fig. 548) gives a list of the genera of Equoidea, their appearance in time, their distribution, and relationships.[1]

Sub-order Rhinocerotoidea.

The Rhinoceroses are reduced now to five species : *R. unicornis* (the one-horned Indian Rhinoceros) (Fig. 550), *R. sondaicus* (the Javan Rhinoceros, also one horned), *R. sumatrensis* (the Sumatran Rhinoceros, two-horned and the smallest living species), *R. bicornis* (the African Rhinoceros, two-horned), and *R. simus* (the " white," or Square-lipped Rhinoceros of Africa, also two-

[1] For fuller details and for slightly different views as to the actual line of descent of the modern Horses, see W. D. Matthew (no. 101) and O. Abel (no. 86). For an account of the Horses of North America from the Oligocene onwards see H. F. Osborn (no. 107).

horned). During the Oligocene to the Pleistocene periods the rhinoceroses formed a large, varied, and important group. The characteristic tooth-structure has already been mentioned. The feet are never reduced to less than three functional toes on each foot. Two or one horns may be present, or they may be entirely absent. In some cases horns were confined to the males.

The sub-order, soon after its beginning in the Lower Eocene, divided into four main lines of evolution : the Hyrachyidæ (the most primitive forms), Hyracodontidæ (light cursorial animals), Amynodontidæ (characterised by a great reduction of the premolars and enlargement of the molars). These three families became extinct during the Oligocene period, while the fourth, the Rhinocerotidæ, beginning in the Eocene, spread out into many lines during the Oligocene and subsequent periods until the Pleistocene, after which time the sub-order became much reduced. The Rhinoceroses were a very polymorphic family, and there is still much uncertainty as to their classification and as to the line of evolution of the living forms. In certain cases genera can be dis-tinguished by some peculiar character, as, for instance, *Elasmotherium*, a large Pleistocene animal with a large forwardly directed fronto-nasal horn and with the enamel of the cheek-teeth much folded ; *Baluchitherium*, a Miocene rhinoceros with persistantly primitive teeth and procumbent lower incisor tusks, the largest known land animal standing eighteen feet high at the shoulder ; *Chilotherium*, a Pleistocene genus with an unusually broad symphysis of the lower jaws, etc.

The Lophiodontidæ were members of an Eocene to Oligocene evolution with characters intermediate between the Tapirs (with which they are sometimes placed) and the Rhinoceroses. The cheek-teeth were bilophodont, like the Tapirs, but with a metaloph more like that of the Rhinoceroses.

Sub-Order Tapiroidea.

During the Eocene period a number of small tapiroid forms evolved, which, like the European Eocene horse-lines, became extinct. A line, however, can be traced leading to the living forms, although the number of genera and species is comparatively few. The forest-living and solitary habits of Tapirs have no doubt militated against their frequent preservation as fossils.

Originally the distribution of the group was widespread over the Old and New Worlds, but now it is restricted to one species in the Old World (*Tapirus indicus* of the Malay Peninsula, Borneo, and Sumatra), and to four New World species (*Tapirus americanus* (Fig. 551), and *roulini*, and *Elasmognathus bairdi* and *dowi*).

Of all living Perissodactyla, the Tapirs are the least specialised. The feet have stout digits, four in front and three behind, the third digit in each case being somewhat enlarged. The skull has no trace of a post-orbital bar, the anterior nasal openings are enlarged and recessed, and the nasal bones small and pointed upwards in correlation with the proboscis, which is characteristic of the group. The teeth are persistently brachydont and without cement. The molar teeth are bilophodont and devoid of any complication in the way of extra cusps or crests. Modern Tapirs seem to have stayed in a stage of evolution proper to the Miocene period.

Sub-Order Titanotheroidea (or Brontotheroidea).

The Titanotheres [1] in their day were a large and important group and, although known chiefly from North America, had actually a wide distribution, species having been found in Mongolia, Burma, and one in Europe. The sub-order was polyphyletic, and a number of lines developed with differences of

FIG. 551.—American **Tapir** (*Tapirus terrestris*).   (From the *Cambridge Natural History*.)

proportion in the skull, skeleton, and teeth, but in many cases showing also parallel development in unrelated lines in the bony nasal " horns."

The terminal species attained to a great size, as much as eight feet at the shoulder, but in spite of some specialisation of shape, all remained essentially undeveloped. The brain remained small for the size of the body, the skull long and low, and the feet retained four rather unmodified digits in front and three behind. The dentition (Fig. 546) was evolved in a direction that appears to be inadaptive and incapable of chewing hard grasses, a condition that may have played a contributing part in the extinction of the sub-order. In the upper molars the protocone remained a round but large cusp, the hypocone the same but smaller, the protoconule and metaconule disappeared, while the para- and metacones became greatly enlarged, and together formed a high, W-shaped outer wall. The premolars remained rather small and less molarised than in other Perissodactyla.

[1] For a very full account of these animals see H. F. Osborn, " The Titanotheres of Ancient Wyoming, Dakota and Nebraska." Two volumes. Washington, 1929.

The earliest Titanotheres to appear were *Lambdotherium*, a genus that left no successors, and *Eotitanops*, both of the Lower Eocene; through the Middle and Upper Eocenes there arose a number of phyla until the sub-order culminated in the Lower Oligocene in such large animals as *Brontotherium* (Fig. 552), *Embolotherium*, *Megacerops*, and others. In North America none is found later than the Lower Oligocene, but some, found in Mongolia, have per-

FIG. 552.—*A*. **Brontotherium leidyi**. *B*. **B. platyceras**. (After Osborn.)

sisted into the Middle Oligocene after which time the Titanotheres appear to have come to an end.

Sub-Order Chalicotheroidea or Ancylopoda.

This sub-order shows much resemblance to the last in tooth-structure and pattern, but is characterised by an unusual foot-structure for a Perissodactyle. There are three functional toes on each foot, the front foot bearing, in addition, a splint of the fifth digit. The digits are subequal, and the toes bear, instead of hoofs, strong claws which resemble those of some of the Edentata.

Examples are known from the Eocene to the Pleistocene from North America (e.g., *Eomoropus, Moropus*) ; and from Europe, Asia, and Africa (e.g., *Chalicotherium* (Fig. 553), *Macrotherium, Schizotherium*).

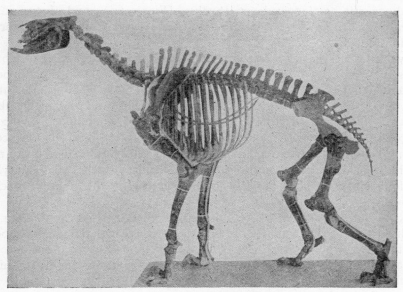

Fig. 553 A.—**Chalicotherium.**

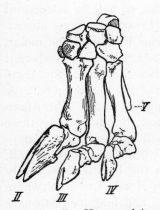

Fig. 553 B.—**Moropus elatus,** left fore foot. (After Scott.)

ORDER ARTIODACTYLA.

This order, the chief ordinal characters of which have already been mentioned, is represented at the present time by such animals as Pigs, Peccaries, Hippopotami, Camels, Giraffes, Sheep, Oxen, Deer, Antelopes, etc. In the past there were, in addition, many forms that have become extinct, and the order, as a whole, is larger and more varied than the Perissodactyla, and the division between its sub-orders deeper and more marked.

While the classification of the living forms into two main sections—the " bunodonts " (Pigs, Peccaries, and the Hippopotami) and the " selenodonts " (the remainder of living Artiodactyles)—presents no great difficulty, to discover their origin and relationships to one another and to the many important extinct forms is by no means easy, and there is at present no complete agreement as to the correct position of some of the families.

The earliest known Artiodactyla are represented by the genera *Diacodexis* and *Homacodon* of the Lower Eocene, very primitive animals with the upper molars still in the tritubercular condition, but whose paraxonic feet and diagnostic artiodactyle astragalus (Figs. 604 and 606) at once betrays their true zoological position. They form part of the super-order of Bunodonta.

A working classification of the order, based on a combination of foot- and tooth-structure, is as follows. There are four super-orders—the Bunodonta, Ancodonta, Tylopoda, and, largest of all, the Pecora. The Bunodonta are characterised by having rounded cusps on the teeth, and are further divided into two superfamilies, the Dichobunidoidea, Dichobunidæ (*Diacodexis*, *Homacodon*, *Dichobune*, etc., none of which persisted beyond the Oligocene at latest). The teeth of these animals vary from the tritubercular up to molars with the typical six cusps, and the Entelodontidæ (which had didactyl feet) with four cusped upper molars. Some species of this family reached a large size.

The second superfamily, the Suoidea, is characterised by having more specialised teeth. The canines are triangular in section and at times become stout tusks; the molar teeth, while retaining bunoid cusps, have secondary cusps added to the original pattern. This group contains the Tagassuidæ or Dicotylidæ (the Peccaries), the Suidæ (Pigs), and the Hippopotamidæ. The feet always have four toes.

The Ancodonta, a sub-order now entirely extinct, consists of four-toed animals with teeth that range from a buno-selenodont to a fully selenodont pattern, and from five to four cusps, the hypocone invariably being absent. The position of the protocone, usually on the anterior border of the molar, has in one family—the Cainotheriidæ—migrated to the hinder border, where it takes up the normal position of the hypocone. The four families of the Ancodonta are : the Anthracotheriidæ, animals from the size of a rabbit up to large species, as *Anthracotherium ingens*, the size of a hippopotamus. The Anoplotheriidæ are a family not far removed from the last, but have only three functional toes, very elongated premolars, and small canines. The Cainotheriidæ, with peculiar molar teeth, as just mentioned, are a group of small, rabbit-sized animals with four short toes, of which the lateral ones barely reach the ground. The Oreodontidæ, a family entirely North American, where it had a long range from the Eocene to the Pliocene, had four toes, strongly selenodont teeth, and the first lower premolar functioning as a canine, the canine being incisiform. In some the last premolar became molariform.

The sub-order Tylopoda, or Camels, form a clearly defined section. Starting with the Eocene genus *Xiphodon* and the small, but obvious Camel, *Poebrotherium*, of the Oligocene, the characters of the group appeared quite early. The feet became precociously didactyl, and the development of the fore and hind digits proceeded at an equal rate. The carpals and tarsals, unlike those of the Pecora, have never fused, while the metacarpals and metatarsals soon fused into a cannon bone whose distal ends gradually became divergent, with smooth, unkeeled, articular surfaces for the phalanges.

The dentition is peculiar in the living species. In the upper jaw there is the full number of incisors in the young state, but in the adult only the third is retained as an isolated recurved tooth similar in pattern to the upper and lower canines. The full number of lower incisors is retained as procumbent spatulate teeth. The premolars are reduced to the last two, and are small. The molars are very hypsodont, and their four cusps selenodont. In the neck vertebræ the vertebral artery takes the unusual course of piercing the anterior part of the transverse process, instead of traversing its whole length in the usual manner. The ruminating stomach is rather simpler than that of the Pecora, but is characterised by the possession of water-cells (Fig. 628, p. 666).

The sub-order is now reduced to two species of Camel, *Camelus dromedarius,* the one-humped Arabian form, which is no longer to be found in the wild state, and *C. bactrianus,* the two-humped Bactrian Camel of Turkestan. In South America the representatives are the Llama, Huanaco, and Alpaca, all smaller animals without the hump, and all included in one genus, *Auchenia.* The sub-order seems never to have been a large one, but there have been described several genera, some of them—as *Alticamelus,* a "Giraffe-necked" form—off the main line of descent.

The sub-order Pecora, or "ruminants," forms a very large and diverse group characterised by a few characters held in common, as, for instance, the total loss of the upper incisors. The upper canine is also usually lost, but, in the rarer cases where it persists, it is much enlarged. Flat, spatulate lower incisors are all present, as is the lower canine, which has the same shape as the incisors, and is closely pressed against them. The premolars are smaller than the molars, and the latter have four crescentic cusps. The feet always have a cannon bone. The lateral toes are usually lost and the feet absolutely didactyl. In some cases the second and fifth toes remain, but are never complete (Fig. 601, p. 647). In this group the ruminating stomach attains its highest development of four complete chambers (Fig. 628, p. 666) and horns, of which there are several types, though not always present, reach their greatest pitch of structure and size.[1]

The main divisions of the Pecora, ranking as superfamilies, are the Traguloidea (Chevrotains), Cervoidea (Deer), Giraffoidea (Giraffes), and Bovoidea (Prongbucks, Sheep, Goats, Antelopes, Oxen, etc.).

The Traguloidea are a number of families now represented only by four species of the Oriental genus *Tragulus,* the "Chevrotains" or "Pigmy Deer."

[1] See Childs Frick, "Horned Ruminants of North America." Bulletin, American Museum, New York, 1937, for examples of the variety of horn pattern.

These are the most primitive of living deer, and are characterised by the possession of much-enlarged upper canines and feet that are less highly evolved than the feet of other members of the Pecora, in that the lateral toes of both feet are still complete, though slender as is the fibula. The navicular, cuboid, and entocuneiform bones of the tarsus, however, are fused together. The odontoid process of the atlas vertebra is conical, and not spout-like. The stomach has only three instead of four compartments. As a rule there are no horns, but they were present in at least one of the extinct families, the Protoceratidæ.

The Cervoidea, dating from the Miocene, and perhaps even earlier, are contained in a single family, the Cervidæ. They are characterised by having deciduous horns or antlers confined, with one exception—the Reindeer—to the males. Horns are absent in only two instances : *Moschus* and *Hydropotes*. The lateral toes are nearly always present, but are never complete. In some the distal extremities of the metacarpals are retained (Telemetacarpal condition), and in others, including most of the Old-World Deer, the proximal elements alone persist (Plesiometacarpal condition). In both cases the phalanges are much reduced in size and do not touch the ground. The skull has two orifices for the lachrymal duct and a very large antorbital vacuity. There is no gall-bladder except in *Moschus*.

Moschus and *Hydropotes* are two rather aberrant forms in an otherwise fairly compact family. *Moschus*, the Musk Deer, is placed by itself in a separate subfamily, the Moschinæ. It is hornless, and the male has large upper canines, and a gall-bladder is present. *Hydropotes*, the Chinese Water-Deer, although placed in the second subfamily, the Cervinæ, differs from them in being hornless and in having large upper canines like *Moschus*, but in all other respects is a true Deer. Of the Cervinæ there are many genera still living in the Old and New Worlds, but none in Africa south of the Sahara.

In the Giraffoidea the horns are non-deciduous, always covered with hair, and are simple and unbranched, except in an extinct side-line represented by a few Pliocene genera such as *Vishnutherium*, *Sivatherium*, and *Bramatherium*, which had hair-covered palmated antlers. The upper canines are absent, as are all traces of lateral digits, not even the lateral hoofs persisting. The humerus has a characteristic double bicipital groove. The group may be traced from the Miocene Palæomerycidæ, and is now represented by the Giraffe and Okapi.

The Bovoidea are a compact group with well-defined characters. There are no upper canines or incisors, and there is only one orifice to the lachrymal duct. The lateral toes are completely absent except for the persistence of small horny hoofs in which there may be a nodule of bone. A gall-bladder is present. Horns are universally present in both sexes and, with the partial exception of the Prongbuck, are never shed. They are never branched, but are of many shapes : curved or spiral, smooth or round. They consist of a bony horn core covered with the horn proper, which is formed of a substance allied to hair.

There are two families : the Antilocapridæ, or Prongbucks of North America, which are separated from the rest because the outer horn has a backward prong and this horn is shed at irregular intervals. The remainder, the Bovidæ, consist of a large number of forms divided into subfamilies whose boundaries are not always very clearly definable.

FIG. 554.—**Hippopotamus** (*Hippopotamus amphibius*). (From the *Cambridge Natural History*.)

ORDER PROBOSCIDEA.[1]

Except for a remote connection with the Sirenia and Hyracoidea, the Proboscidea occupy an isolated position. At an early period of their history they acquired a number of peculiar adaptive characters which at once clearly distinguish them from other mammals, although they have retained to the present day several persistently primitive features, such as, for example, the pentadactyle hand and foot, a brain in which the cerebellum is uncovered by the cerebral lobes (which are, however, well convoluted), permanently abdominal testes, and a double vena cava.

Most, if not all, of the specialised features of the skeleton can be attributed to the interaction of three main factors : namely, the proboscis, or " trunk," the peculiar tusks and dentition, and the great size and weight of the body— all features that arose early in the evolution of the order.

The long, prehensile trunk, reaching nearly to the ground, made possible

[1] For a very full account of the Proboscidea see H. F. Osborn " Proboscidea," American Museum, 1936.

the great shortening of the neck, and this, in turn, gives a mechanical advantage in the support of the combined weight of the proboscis, skull, and tusks, which may weigh as much as 175 pounds for a single tusk in the African Elephant. At the same time an enlargement of the area of the skull becomes necessary for the insertion of muscles and ligaments of the neck, and this has been brought about by a separation of the inner and outer tables of many of the bones of the skull, in particular the frontals and parietals (Fig. 555). To avoid undue weight, the spaces between the tables of bone are filled with air-cells and, incidentally, this has caused an obliteration of most of the sutures between the bones.

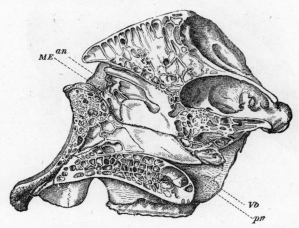

FIG. 555.—Section of skull of **African Elephant** (*Elephas africanus*), to the left of the middle line. *an.* anterior nares; *ME.* mesethmoid; *pn.* posterior nares; *Vo.* vomer. (After Flower.)

The presence of the proboscis has induced a shortening of the facial region, a recession of the nasal opening towards the top of the head, and a reduction in size of the nasal bones similar to the condition seen in the Tapirs, but to a greater degree. To carry the great weight of the head and body, the legs, simple in their general plan, have become pillar-like, with a loss of angulation, the carpals and tarsals are serial and compressed and, while the hand and foot are still pentadactyle, the digits are short, stout, and united by skin, with each toe ending in a small hoof. Progression is digitigrade, the back of the digits being supported by an elastic pad of tissue. In the fore-limb the ulna and radius are permanently crossed in the position of pronation, and the ulna is unique in having its distal articulation with the carpus larger than that of the radius. The pelvis has broad ilia and is vertical in direction, an adaptation found in many heavy-bodied animals. Clavicles are absent.

The dentition is highly characteristic. In more recent Elephants the upper tusks, which are the second pair of incisors, are the only ones to persist, the lower incisors having disappeared during the Mastodont stage of evolution. Nor is there any enamel left except for a small cap on the point of the tusk, which soon becomes worn off. Premolars have not persisted beyond the Mastodont stage. Of the six cheek-teeth the three anterior are milk-teeth, which are soon worn down and pushed out at a very early period in the Elephant's life by the three large molars. The remainder of the animal's life is served by the three molars in each half of the upper and lower jaws. There are

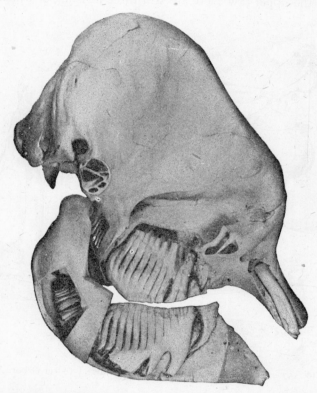

FIG. 556.—Skull of a young Indian elephant dissected to show the developing teeth. (From a specimen in the University Museum of Zoology, Cambridge.)

never more than two of the molars in use at one time in each section of the jaws owing to their size, peculiar structure, and method of growth. They consist of a number of deep plates of enamel-covered dentine bound together by cement. The teeth while forming lie at an angle to those in use and are at a higher level in the upper and lower jaws (Fig. 556). As they slide down into the position of wear they push the anterior teeth forwards until, after being nearly worn down, they fall out.

There are four sub-orders: the Mœritheroidea, Deinotheroidea, Mastodontoidea, and Elephantoidea, distinguished by differences in the arrangement of the tusks and in the pattern and degree of complexity of the molar structure (Figs. 560, 561, 562).

The Mœritheroidea (*Mœritherium*, Upper Eocene and Lower Oligocene of Egypt) are the most primitive proboscideans, showing some points of similarity to the Sirenia, but are probably not directly ancestral to the Elephants. The dentition, while showing the beginning of proboscidean characters, is less highly specialised. In the upper jaw there are still three incisors, of which the second

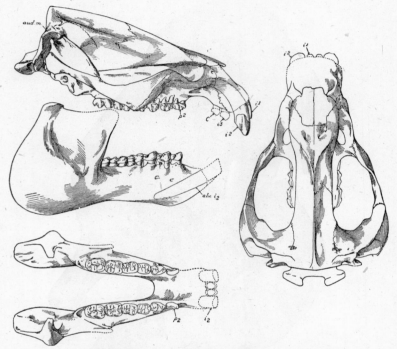

FIG. 557.—**Mœritherium.**   Skull and lower jaws.   (After Osborn.)

pair are enlarged as tusks, a canine, three premolars, and three molars. The lower jaw has only two pairs of incisors, the second being enlarged as tusks, and lacks the canine (Fig. 557). The molars are bilophodont, except the third, which shows the beginning of a third ridge.

The Deinotheroidea (*Deinotherium*, Fig. 559) (Upper Oligocene—Pliocene of Europe and Asia) are characterised by the absence of upper tusks and the presence of a pair of downwardly turned lower tusks. The molar-teeth are partly bilophodont and partly trilophodont.

The Mastodontoidea are a large and polyphyletic group with many described families, genera, and species. The upper tusks are large, downwardly

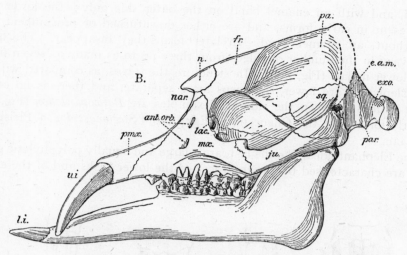

FIG. 558.—Skull of **Palæomastodon.** (After Andrews.)

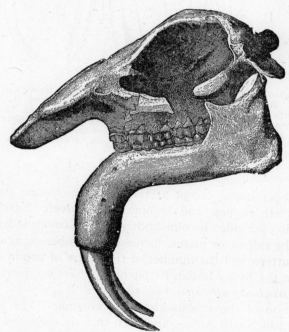

FIG. 559.—**Dinotherium giganteum.** Side view of skull. $\frac{1}{15}$th natural size.
(From Zittel's *Palæontology*, after Kaup.)

turned, and with an enamel band on the outer side only; the lower tusks are present in early forms, and are either downturned or procumbent with, or without, an enamel band. In later forms they disappear. The molar-teeth vary in the number of ridges from three up to as many as seven (in the third lower molar) (Fig. 561). In structure the ridges, as compared with the true Elephants, are lower, the cusps more separate, and there is no cement in the valleys between the ridges. Examples are *Palæomastodon* (Fig. 558), an early form from the Oligocene of Egypt, and *Stegomastodon* a Pleistocene form, etc.

The Elephantoidea, like the last, are a large and equally polyphyletic group. They are characterised by the total loss of the lower tusks and of the enamel

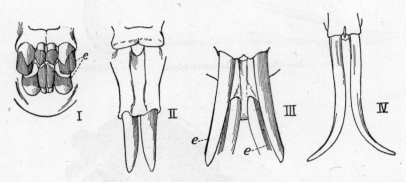

FIG. 560.—Fundamental arrangement of the tusks, or second incisors in the four sub-orders of Proboscidea. I. **Mœritherium,** the first pair of incisors are present, the second pair forming small tusks and both pairs covered by enamel (*e*). II. **Deinotherium.** The upper incisors are lost, the lower downturned and bent backwards. No enamel. III. **Rhynchotherium** (a mastodont). Enamel bands remain (*e*) on the outer sides of the upper-lower tusks. IV. **Elephas.** Lower tusks much reduced or, usually, lost. Upper incisors form large tusks. The enamel except in very early forms is lost. (After Osborn.)

on the large upper tusks, except at the tip in the young stage. The ridges of the molar-teeth deepen and become progressively flattened into plates, and the cusps in each ridge become obliterated. Cement is laid down between the plates. The ridges, or plates, increase in number to as many as twenty-seven. The pattern and the number of ridges are of use in classification, as, for example, in the living Indian Elephant (*Elephas maximus*, Fig. 562 B) and the African (*Loxodonta africana*, Fig. 562 A).

The migration of the Proboscidea is interesting. The group appears to have originated in North Africa, and then to have migrated to Asia, whence a second radiation took place, some spreading over all Asia and Europe to North, and finally, South America, while some returned to Africa to spread over that continent.

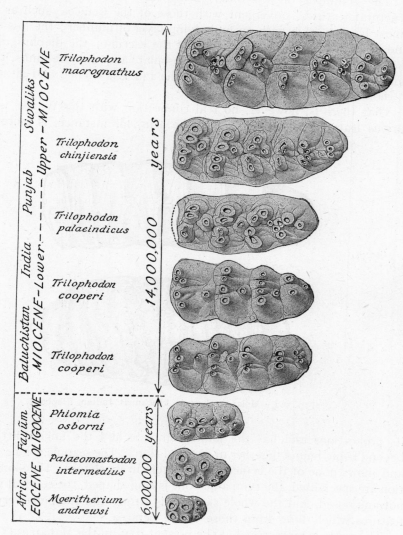

FIG. 561.—Evolution of the molar tooth in Mastodonts. (After Osborn.)

Order Sirenia.

The Mammals of this order, being fully aquatic, present a number of structural features convergent with those of the Cetacea, such as the thick, almost hairless, skin with an underlying layer of blubber ; the loss of external hind-limbs ; of an external ear, and of the sacrum ; the diaphragm, like that of the Cetacea, is oblique and very muscular, and the fore-limbs, though less highly modified, are paddle-like, and the tail is flattened and either rounded or rhomboidal in outline.

That there is, however, no real connection with the Whales is shown by various features. The skeleton of the arm, for instance, is more normal in

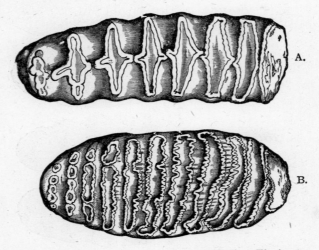

Fig. 562.—Molar teeth of A. African, B. Indian, Elephant.

its proportions and has the joints complete and the fingers little modified, beyond being bound together in a web of skin. The scapula is long and narrow, and shows none of the cetacean characters in its shape. The skull and dentition are specialised, the tympanic bone is ring-shaped, the cervical vertebræ are not ankylosed, and the whole skeleton is strong and the bone very dense—all features which differ from those of the Cetacea.

The order is represented at the present day by the Manatees (*Trichechus* = *Manatus*), which live in the fresh waters, or along the coasts of South America and Africa, and the Dugong (*Dugong* = *Halicore*) (Fig. 563) of the Oriental and Australian coasts. A third genus and species, Steller's Sea Cow (*Hydrodamalis* = *Rhytina*), of the North Pacific, only became extinct during the eighteenth century.

The Manatee and Dugong differ in some respects, and are placed in separate families. In the Manatee (Fig. 564) the cheek-teeth are covered with enamel and are bilophodont, somewhat like those of the Proboscidea. There is a large number of them, up to twenty in each half of the upper and lower jaws. They are, however, not all in use at any one time, but are continuously replaced from the hind end. The premaxillary region is small and little deflected. There are only six cervical vertebræ. The fingers have the remains of nails. The Dugong, on the other hand, has a reduced dentition as far as the grinding-teeth are concerned, never having more than six, and even these are somewhat degenerate and without pattern. The premaxillary region is, however, enlarged into a down-turned rostrum, and bears, in the male, a pair of stout tusks. The anterior part of the mandible is covered by a horny pad, under which can be found traces of the lower incisors. There are no nails on the fingers, and there are the normal seven cervical vertebræ.

The earliest Sirenia have been found in the Prorastomidæ of the Middle Eocene of Egypt (*Eotheroides* = *Eotherium*) and of the West Indies (*Prorastomus*). The site of origin of the order, therefore, and of its ancestral form is unknown. The *Prorastomidæ* have a complete eutherian dentition, a rostrum but slightly enlarged, the tusks small, and although the hind-limbs have already gone, the pelvis is but little reduced, and the family is clearly more primitive, and structurally ancestral to later forms. From the Miocene onwards several genera have been described diverging along different lines, but all showing a progressive reduction of the pelvis. All these are united in a sub-order, the Trichechiformes, to distinguish them from a second sub-order, the Desmostyliformes, which are represented by a sole family and genus *Desmostylus*, found in Miocene deposits

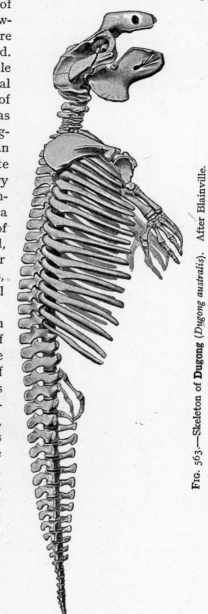

FIG. 563.—Skeleton of **Dugong** (*Dugong australis*). After Blainville.

of the Pacific coasts of North America and Japan. Its chief characteristic
lies in the peculiar dentition. There are two procumbent lower incisors, the
upper being small or absent. The molars are columnar and formed of a
number of closely appressed cylinders covered with a thick layer of enamel.

Skeleton of Sirenia.—In the Sirenia (Fig. 563) the cervical vertebræ do
not coalesce, with the exception of two of them in the Manatee. In the
Manatee there are only six cervical vertebræ, and the neural arches are sometimes incomplete. In the trunk the thoracic vertebræ are numerous; all

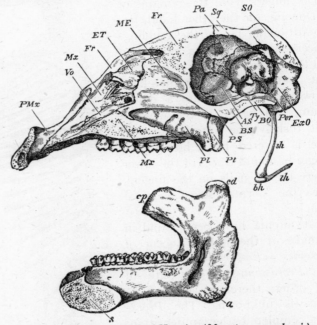

FIG. 564.—Section of skull of **Manatee** (*Manatus senegalensis*).
In addition, *ET.* ethmo-turbinal; *Ty.* tympanic. (After Flower.)

have well-developed facets for the heads of the ribs, and well developed zygapophyses. The caudal vertebræ are numerous, depressed, with wide transverse
processes. The ribs are numerous, but few of them are connected with the
sternum. The sternum is a broad bone not composed of distinguishable
segments.

The *skull* (Fig. 563) is characterised by its extreme hardness. The cranial
cavity is rather long and narrow as compared with that of the Cetacea.
Although the supra-occipital (*S. O.*) is produced forwards on the upper surface
of the skull for a considerable distance, it does not separate the parietals
(*Pa.*) from one another. The frontals develop broad supra-orbital plates.
The zygoma is stout. As in the Cetacea, the external nares are very wide,

but they are relatively farther forwards. The nasals are rudimentary. The tympanic and periotic are readily separable from the other bones. There are enormous premaxillæ in the Dugongs. The mandible has a well-developed ascending ramus and coronoid process (*c. p.*).

The *scapula* of the Sirenia is much more like that of the terrestrial mammals than the scapula of Cetacea, and is nearer that of the Seals; it is narrow and curved backwards. The spine is situated about the middle; the acromion is directed downwards. The coracoid is fairly well developed, and of a conical shape. The clavicle is absent, as in the Cetacea. The skeleton of the arm also departs less from the ordinary mammalian type than in the Cetacea. The radius and ulna are ankylosed at their extremities. The carpus has seven bones in the Manatee: the pisiform is absent. In the Dugong coalescence takes place between the carpal bones, so that the number of ossifications is reduced in the adult. There are five digits, all of which possess the normal number of phalanges.

The *pelvis* is represented by a pair or more of vestiges widely separated from the spinal column, and having a vertical position: they probably represent the ilia.

ORDER HYRACOIDEA.

The Hyracoidea show a most curious mixture of primitive and specialised characters, and some, in addition, in which they seem to resemble several different orders of mammals. The living forms of " Coneys " are all small, rather rabbit-like animals of North Africa and Western Asia, and are included in a single family, the Procaviidæ (= Hyracidæ) with the genera *Procavia* (*Hyrax*) and *Dendrohyrax*, the latter being semi-arboreal forms.

The feet are plantigrade, with four toes and a vestige of the hallux on the front-, and three on the hind-foot; the third toe is longer than the others, and all end in small flat hoofs, except the second digit of the hind-foot, which has a curved claw. The centrale persists in the carpus and the astragalus (Fig. 609) differs in shape from that of any other mammal, in that the malleolus of the tibia has a large flat bearing on it. The clavicle is absent. In the skull are several peculiar features. The post-orbital process arises largely from the parietal, and the post-orbital bar is complete in *Dendrohyrax* (Fig. 565), but not in *Procavia* (Fig. 566). The jugal is a very stout bone, and extends backwards to take as large a share in the glenoid cavity as in any Marsupial. The periotic and tympanic are ankylosed together, but not to the squamosal, the tympanic forms a bulla and has a spout-like external auditory meatus. The seventh cervical vertebra is sometimes pierced by the vertebral artery. The scapula is triangular, as in Artiodactyla, and lacks the acromion. There are as many as twenty-two dorsolumbar vertebræ. The radius and ulna are partially crossed, as in the Proboscidea.

The dentition consists of a single pair of large curved upper incisors grow-ing from persistent roots like those of Rodents, but which are triangular in section, canines are absent, and there are four premolars and three molars, which are lophodont, and in pattern look like the teeth of a rhinoceros in miniature.   In the lower jaw there are two pairs of incisors, which are spatulate

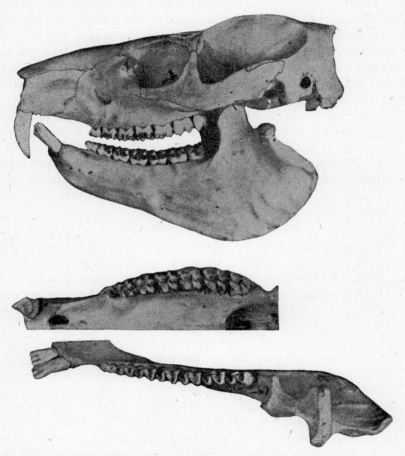

FIG. 565.—**Dendrohyrax.**   Skull, upper and lower dentitions.   The arrow in the lower
jaw points to a foramen.

and comb-like, as in some Lemurs. The lower jaw has a foramen which pierces the coronoid just behind the last molar, as in the South American Typotheres.

There is no gall-bladder, but the cæcum has a pair of cæcal pouches, which are unknown in any other mammal.   The testes are abdominal.   There is a dorsal gland on the back analogous to that found in the Peccaries.   With this curious mixture of characters it is not easy to suggest what are the affinities or what the origin of this order. It has been stated that there is a remote affinity with the Proboscidea and Sirenia.[1]

The order is known as far back as the Oligocene of Egypt, where *Saghatherium* and *Megalohyrax* have been found. Both are hyracoid in dentition, but neither appears to be on the direct line of evolution; the latter form was of considerably larger size than the modern forms. *Myohyrax* comes from the Lower Miocene of Egypt and *Pliohyrax* from the Lower Pliocene of Greece. The order appears to have originated, like the Proboscidea, in North or Central Africa, but until some representatives can be found in Eocene deposits, little light can be thrown on the problem of their origin.

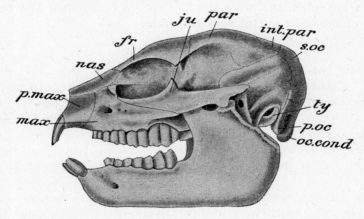

FIG. 566.—Skull of **Hyrax (Procavia).** The suture between the frontal and parietal has been by an error made to run behind the post-orbital process.

ORDERS BARYTHERIA AND EMBRITHOPODA.

These two orders have to be formed to receive each a single species of mammals. Of the Barytheria (*Barytherium*, from the Upper Eocene of Egypt) little is known beyond a lower jaw with bilophodont teeth, except the third molar, which is trilophodont, and a procumbent tusk-like incisor. The dentition is somewhat like that of *Deinotherium*, but the humerus, almost the only bone discovered, is not proboscidean in shape.

Of the Embrithopoda (*Arsinoitherium*, from the Lower Oligocene of Egypt) the complete skeleton is known. This shows a heavy animal the size of a rhinoceros, with massive limbs and stumpy, five-toed feet. The skull is remarkable for the presence of a pair of large, forwardly directed nasal horns placed side by side and united at their bases, and a pair of quite small frontal horns. The dentition is complete and is without diastemata. The canines are incisiform and the cheek-teeth hypsodont, the molars bilophodont.

[1] For details see Gregory, " The Orders of Mammals " (No. 94).

Beyond a faint suggestion in the molar pattern of some Hyracoid affinity, nothing can be said as to the relations of this peculiar animal.

ORDER TILLODONTIA.

An archaic order, of which specimens are found only in the Lower and Middle Eocene of North America. *Esthonyx, Anchippodus, Tillotherium* are the only described genera. *Tillotherium*, the last member to survive, reached the size of a Bear. There are two pairs of incisors, of which the first are small, the second much enlarged, rootless, and rodent-like. The condyles of the jaws, however, are transverse, and entirely unlike the condition found in the rodents. The canines are small, the premolars and molars brachydont and bunodont. The origin of the order is still very uncertain.

ORDER TÆNIODONTIA.

This order, of which representative are known from the Palæocene (*Conoryctes, Calamodon, Onychodectes, Psittacotherium*, etc.) to the Middle Eocene (*Stylinodon*), is, like the Tillodonts, a very obscure one.

Earlier forms are primitive and somewhat insectivore-like in having a complete dentition and enamel-covered teeth. *Stylinodon*, the last survivor, had more definite characters in its very hypsodont, rootless teeth, with the enamel confined to bands at the sides. These teeth are peg-like and without molar pattern.

Both the Tillodontia and Tæniodontia appear to have become specialised early on side lines which were, comparatively speaking, of short duration.

ORDER RODENTIA.

The Rodents can be clearly diagnosed by a characteristic arrangement of their dentition for the two purposes first of gnawing and then of chewing their food. The order, with nearly three thousand living species described, is at the present time numerically the largest of all the mammalian groups. No Rodent reaches, or ever has reached, any great size, the Capybara (*Hydrochoerus*), which is of the size of a small Pig, being the largest living form, but one which may have been exceeded by two extinct species of Beavers (*Trogontherium* and *Castoroides*). Most Rodents are rather small, and some such as the Harvest Mouse (*Mus minutus*), are among the smallest known mammals. The distribution of the group is world wide, and many species such as the Lemming (*Myodes lemmus*) and many species of Rats and Mice, can exist in almost incredible numbers, and are of economic importance from the damage they do to crops and stores and as the assistant-carriers of disease.

The characters of the order are as follows. There is never more than a single pair of upper incisors, with the exception of one section, the Duplici-dentata, where there is a small second pair, as is mentioned below. The incisors are chisel-shaped in wear, owing to the absence of enamel on the posterior surface. Having persistently open roots, they grow throughout life, and are always of great size. Canines are never present, and there is a wide

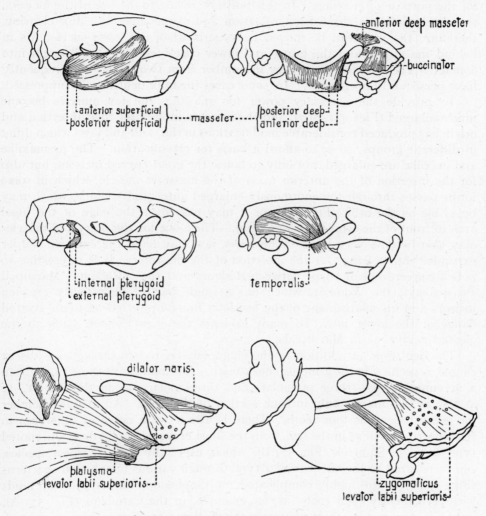

Muscles of Mastication

FIG. 567.—Jaw muscles of the rat.   (After E. Chase Green.)

diastema between the incisors and the cheek-teeth into which the cheeks can be tucked so as to separate the front part of the mouth from the hind during the process of gnawing. This habit of gnawing, universal in the group, has induced noticeable modifications not only of the teeth, but of the whole skull and jaws. The glenoid cavities for the condyles of the lower jaws are elongated in a fore-and-aft direction, an adaptation which enables the jaws to be moved forwards, and thereby the upper and lower incisors to be brought into contact for the purpose of gnawing. In this position, owing to the size of the incisors, the cheek-teeth are thrown out of action and cannot operate. For chewing, therefore, the jaws can be moved backwards when the lower incisor fits in behind the upper, and the upper and lower cheek-teeth can be brought into contact. The grinding-teeth vary in number from two to six, and frequently have persistently open roots. In some cases the milk dentition is suppressed.

To provide the necessary power for gnawing, the jaw-muscles become much enlarged (Figs 451, 567), and the increase in area for their insertion and origin has produced considerable modifications in the skull and jaws which differ in different groups, so as to afford a basis for classification. The premaxillæ and maxillæ are enlarged, not only to house the great curved incisors, but also for the insertion of the anterior mass of the masseter muscle, which in some forms passes through the enormously enlarged antorbital vacuity, which may be as big as the orbit (Fig. 568), or it may pass over the edge of the jugal arch in front of the orbit (Figs. 569, 570). The fossæ for the pterygoid muscles may also become very large. The lower jaw may have the external border expanded into a flange for the insertion of the masseter. It is interesting to note a convergence in shape between Rodents and the " Rodent " Marsupial *Phascolomys*, the Wombat, which has a single pair of persistently growing incisors and an enlargement of the masseter muscle inserted on to an everted flange of the lower jaw. In many Rodents the jugal extends back to the glenoid cavity, as in Marsupials.

The dentition, in addition to the characteristic rodent incisor and absent canine, is peculiar in the grinding cheek-teeth. The number of these varies from a maximum of six—three premolars and three molars, as in the Rabbit—to as few as two molars only in each section of the jaws. An average number for many rodents is four teeth. There is also a wide range of difference in the pattern as well as in the size, from the short crowned brachydont and rooted type, as in the Squirrels (Fig. 571 B), which, especially in the earliest species, can be referred to the tritubercular type through various bilophodont patterns (Fig. 571 C) to the highly complicated multilophodont and hypsodont kinds with permanently open roots, as, for example, in the Capybara (Fig. 571 A).

As to the rest of their anatomy, the Rodents are not highly specialised. They are, for the most part, unguiculate, pentadactyle, and plantigrade. A clavicle is usually present and, as in all herbivorous mammals, the cæcum tends to be large. The brain is little convoluted, and the cerebellum is not covered by the cerebral lobes.

The order is divided into two sub-orders of very unequal size : the Duplicidentata and Simplicidentata. The Duplicidentata (or Lagomorpha) containing

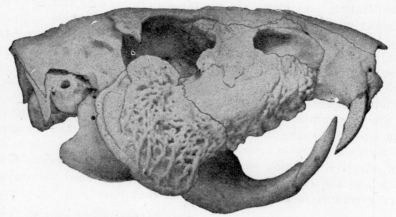

FIG. 568.—Skull of **Cœlogenys paca,** showing enlarged antorbital vacuity.

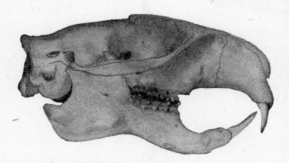

FIG. 569.—Skull of **Thryonomys swinderanus.** The antorbital vacuity is not enlarged.

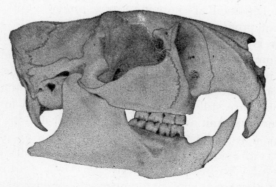

FIG. 570.—Skull of **Pedetes caffir,** with enlarged antorbital vacuity which does not transmit the masseter muscle.

the Hares, Rabbit, and Pikas, are separated from the rest in having a small pair of upper incisors in addition to the main pair placed just behind them (Fig. 449). The infraorbital foramina are always small, the incisive foramina large, and the tail is very short. The molar-teeth grow from persistent pulps, and three premolars are present.

There are only two families: the Leporidæ (Hares and Rabbits), and the Ochotonidæ (Pikas), both known from the Oligocene onwards.

The Simplicidentata, which have only a single pair of upper incisors, form the great bulk of Rodents and, as might be expected from their numbers and variety, their classification is somewhat complicated. There is a considerable range of adaptive radiation which has brought about a diversity of shape. Some, such as the Beavers, are amphibious, with flattened swimming-tails, some are burrowers to such an extent that they have acquired a mole-like

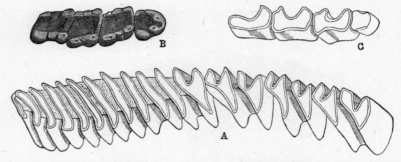

FIG. 571.—Molar teeth of Rodents. A. Capybara (**Hydrochœrus**). B. Squirrel (**Sciurus**). C. **Ctenodactylus**. (From *Cambridge Natural History*, after Tullberg.)

appearance, as *Spalax* or *Georhychus*. The Squirrels are tree-living, and the Anomaluridæ (the " Flying " Squirrels) have proceeded a step further by the possession of parachuting membranes closely resembling those of the " flying " Marsupials. The Dipodidæ are hopping forms, somewhat like the Kangaroos in their method of progression.

The sub-order is divided into three infra-orders, chiefly on the arrangement of the jaw-muscles—the Sciuromorpha, Myomorpha and Histricomorpha —and there are many superfamilies, families, and genera described.

The Sciuromorpha are the more primitive Rodents, in that two upper and one lower premolars are still retained, and the antorbital foramen is not enlarged, and does not transmit any part of the masseter muscle, which either still arises from the jugal arch alone or, at most, has a slip of its anterior superficial section attached to the side of the face in front of the orbit. The fibula often remains free, but may be fused with the tibia. There are five superfamilies: the Sciuroidea (Squirrels, Gophers, Chipmunks, etc.) ; the Aplodontoidea (*Aplodontia*, the " Sewellel," the Ischyromyidæ, Eocene, and Oligocene Rodents) ;

the Castoroidea or Beavers; the Geomyoidea (a purely North American group including the Pocket Gophers, etc.), and the Anomaluroidea (*Anomalurus*) the West African " Flying Squirrel ", and *Pedetes*, the Cape " Jumping " Hare (Fig. 570), which is of interest in that there is a large infra-orbital opening, which, however, does not transmit any part of the masseter muscle, so that the skull in this respect resembles that of the Myomorpha structurally, but not functionally).

The Myomorpha (Rats, Mice, Jerboas, etc.) are characterised by the superficial portion of the masseter muscle passing forwards in front of the orbit, while the median portion runs, via the orbit, through the enlarged infra-orbital opening to be attached to a depression, often deep, on the side of the face. The tibia and fibula are always fused.

The Histricomorpha (Porcupines, Guinea-pigs, Cavies, etc.) have the infra-orbital canal enlarged to the greatest extent of all, and the median portion of the masseter is enlarged at the expense of the anterior superficial portion, which does not extend on to the face, but retains its more primitive attachment to the jugal arch. The tibia and fibula remain separate.

Skeleton of the Rodentia.—Among the Rodents the Jerboas are exceptional in having the cervical vertebræ ankylosed. Generally, as in the Rabbit, the transverse processes of the lumbar vertebræ are elongated. As in the Ungulata, the sacrum usually consists of one broad anterior vertebra followed by several narrower ones. The caudal region varies in length in the different families; in some it is very short, but it is elongated in many (the Porcupines, Squirrels, and Beavers). The sternum of the Rodents has a long and narrow body; sometimes there is a broad presternum; the posterior end is always expanded into a cartilaginous xiphisternum.

The *skull* is elongated, narrow in front, broader and depressed behind. The nasal cavities are very large, especially in the Porcupines, with air sinuses in the upper part. In some the optic foramina fuse into one. An interparietal is often present. Paroccipital processes are developed. The orbit and the temporal fossa are always continuous. The nasal bones are large, and the nasal apertures are terminal or nearly so. The premaxillæ are always very large. A remarkable feature of the skull is the presence in many of a large opening corresponding to the infra-orbital foramen. The middle part of the zygoma is formed by the jugal; the latter often helps to bound the glenoid cavity, as in the Marsupials. The palate is short, and the anterior palatine foramina large. The periotic and tympanic may become ankylosed together, but not to the neighbouring bones. The coronoid process of the mandible is sometimes rudimentary or absent; the angle is often produced into a process.

The scapula of the Rodentia is generally long and narrow. The spine sometimes has a metacromion process and a long acromion. The coracoid process is small. The clavicle varies as regards its development. Vestiges

of the sternal end of the coracoid are sometimes distinguishable. There is considerable variation in the bones of the arm and fore-arm. The radius and ulna are in most instances distinct, though in close and firm apposition. The scaphoid and lunar are usually united; the centrale is sometimes present, sometimes absent. The pelvis and femur vary greatly. Sometimes there is a third trochanter. The fibula is sometimes distinct, sometimes fused with the tibia. In the Jerboa the metatarsals of the three digits are fused together (see Fig. 603).

ORDER XENARTHRA.

This order, part of the old order Edentata after the removal as separate orders of the Tubulidentata and Pholidota, consists almost entirely of South American animals, a few late Tertiary forms alone having penetrated into North America. The living members of the order, together with a number of extinct relatives, form the sub-order Xenarthra, and a second sub-order, the Palæanodonta, contains more primitive and entirely extinct genera.

The Xenarthra, in spite of considerable differences in shape and appearance,

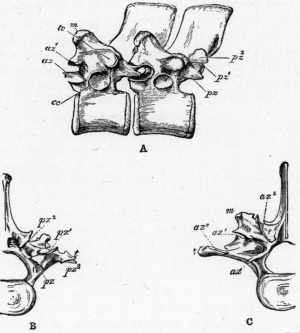

FIG. 572.—Vertebræ of the Great Anteater (*Myrmecophaga jubata*). *A.* Side view of twelfth and thirteenth thoracic vertebræ; *B.* posterior view of the second lumbar; *C.* anterior view of the third lumbar. *az.* anterior zygapophysis; *az.*[1], [2], [3], extra zygapophyses; *c. c.* facet for capitulum of rib; *m.* metapophysis; *pz.* posterior zygapophysis; *pz.*[1], [2], [3], additional posterior zygapophysis; *t.* transverse process; *te.* facet for tuberculum of rib. (From *Cambridge Natural History*, after Flower.)

are united by certain specialised characters which show them to belong to a single natural group. Enamel is entirely absent from the teeth, except in an Eocene Armadillo, *Utatetus*, in which small enamel caps were just persisting. In all the others the teeth (see p. 659) are transformed to pillar-like and persistently growing stumps (the Armadillos), and may be reduced in number (the Sloths) or altogether absent (the Great Ant-eater). One of the most noticeable characters is that the posterior dorsal and lumbar vertebræ (Fig. 572) have an extra pair of zygapophyses, a condition found elsewhere only in the Snakes. Among other specialised characters are the frequent reduction, or absence, of the zygomatic arch, the frequent fusion of the coracoid process to the front border of the scapula so as to enclose a large foramen (Fig. 573),

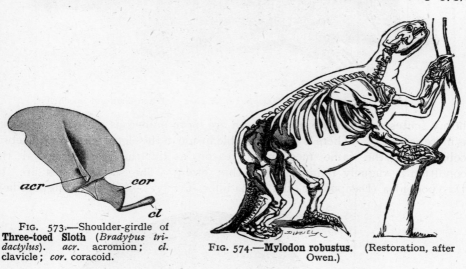

FIG. 573.—Shoulder-girdle of **Three-toed Sloth** (*Bradypus tridactylus*). *acr.* acromion; *cl.* clavicle; *cor.* coracoid.

FIG. 574.—**Mylodon robustus.** (Restoration, after Owen.)

and the articulation of several of the anterior caudal vertebræ to the ischium so as to produce an unusually long ischio-sacral region. The low type of brain, on the other hand, and the persistently abdominal testes are primitive. All Edentata have heavily clawed feet.

By adaptive radiation, the Xenarthra have evolved into such very different kinds of animals that they have to be separated into two infra-orders, the Pilosa and Loricata, and each of these again into a number of superfamilies. The Pilosa are the superfamilies Megalonychoidea, an extinct group comprising the Megatheriidæ (*Megatherium*), the Megalonychidæ (*Megalonyx*), and Mylodontidæ (*Mylodon*, (Fig. 574), *Scelidotherium*); the Myrmecophagoidea (Myrmecophagidæ *Myrmecophaga*, the Great Ant-eater, and *Tamandua* the Lesser Ant-eater), and the Bradypodoidea (Bradypodidæ, *Bradypus*, the Three-toed Sloth with nine cervical vertebræ and *Cholœpus*, the Two-toed Sloth with six cervicals. These two species, except for the Manatee among the Sirenia, are the only mammals that have not the typical number of seven cervical vertebræ).

These forms, in addition to the ordinal characters, are united by being covered with hair, in contradistinction to the infra-order Loricata, which show a feature, unusual in Mammals, of a covering of bony plates on which lie

FIG. 575.—**Tatu Armadillo** (*Dasypus sexcinctus*).   (After Vogt and Specht.)

horny scutes.   In this group the teeth are more numerous and the jugal arch is more complete.   There is a considerable fusion of the elements of the vertebral column for the same mechanical reason as in the Chelonia, and the condition is vaguely reminiscent of that group.   The superfamilies are the Dasypodoidea (Dasipodidæ, the Armadillos, Fig. 575, and the Peltephilidæ) ;

FIG. 576.—**Glyptodon clavipes.**   (After Owen.)

the extinct Glyptodontoidea (Glyptodontidæ, e.g., *Glyptodon*, Fig. 576, and its relatives *Panocthus*, etc.).

The Palæanodonta (*Palæanodon*, Palæocene to Lower Eocene, *Meta-cheiromys*, Middle Eocene, *Epoicotherium*, Oligocene) come from North America. Although aberrant and specialised in some directions, such as the possession of an enamel-covered canine—a unique feature for an Edentate—the Palæano-donts may be regarded as representing an offshoot of the ancestral edentate line. The dentition is specialised in the reduction of the teeth in number and in their degenerate condition, but the vertebræ have not acquired the Xenarth-ran peculiarity of extra zygapophyses, and there is no ischio-caudal symphysis.

The Sloths (*Bradypodidæ*, Fig. 577) are more completely adapted, in the structure of their limbs, to an arboreal life than any other group of the

FIG. 577.—Unau, or Two-toed Sloth (*Cholæpus didactylus*).
(After Vogt and Specht.)

Mammalia. They have a short, rounded head, the ears with small pinnæ, and long, slender limbs, the anterior much longer than the posterior, with the digits, which are never more than three in number, long, curved, and hook-like, adapted for enabling the animal to hang and climb, body downwards, among the branches of trees. In the Three-toed Sloth there are three toes in both manus and pes; in the Two-toed Sloth there are only two in the manus, three in the pes. The tail is rudimentary. The body is covered with long, coarse hairs, which differ from those of other mammals in being longitudinally fluted. On these hairs grows abundantly an alga, the presence of which gives a greenish tinge to the fur.

VOL. II.   2 S

The ordinary Ant-eaters (*Myrmecophagidæ*) have a greatly elongated snout, with the mouth as a small aperture at its extremity, small eyes, and the auditory pinna sometimes small, sometimes well developed. There are five digits in the fore-foot, of which the third has always a very large curved and pointed claw, rendering the manus an efficient digging organ. The toes of the hind-foot, four or five in number, are sub-equal, and provided with moderate-sized claws. In walking, the weight of the body rests on the dorsal surfaces of the second, third, and fourth digits of the manus and on a thick callous pad on the extremity of the fifth, and in the pes, on the entire plantar surface. The tail is always very long, and is sometimes prehensile. The body is covered with long hair. In the Two-toed Ant-eater (*Cycloturus*) the muzzle is short; there are four toes in the manus, of which the second and third only have claws, that of the third being the longer; the pes has four sub-equal clawed toes, forming a hook not unlike the foot of the Sloths; the tail is prehensile.

In the Armadillos (*Dasypodidæ*, Fig. 575) the head is comparatively short, broad, and depressed. The number of complete digits of the fore-foot varies from three to five; these are provided with powerful claws, so as to form a very efficient digging organ. The hind-foot always has five digits with smaller claws. The tail is usually well developed. The most striking external feature of the Armadillos is the presence of an armour of bony dermal plates; this usually consists of a scapular shield of closely-united plates covering the anterior part of the body, followed by a series of transverse bands separated from one another by hairy skin, and a posterior pelvic shield. In the genus *Tolypeutes* these bands are movable, so that the animal is enabled to roll itself up into a ball. The tail is also usually enclosed in rings of bony plates, and a number protect the upper surface of the head.

Skeleton of Xenarthra.—In the Armadillos more or fewer of the cervical vertebræ are ankylosed together both by their bodies and by their neural arches. In the lumbar region the metapophyses are greatly prolonged—longer than the transverse processes—and support the bony carapace. A remarkable peculiarity of the spinal column in the Armadillos is the fusion of a number of the anterior caudal vertebræ with the true sacrals to form the long sacrum, containing as many as ten vertebræ altogether. The caudal region is of moderate length; there are numerous chevron bones (Fig. 586). In *Manis* and *Myrmecophaga* the neck-vertebræ are not united. In the posterior-thoracic and the lumbar regions of *Myrmecophaga* there are developed complex accessory articulations between the vertebræ: the sacrum contains, in addition to the true sacral vertebræ, a number derived from the caudal region.

In the Sloths none of the cervical vertebræ are ankylosed together; but in the Three-toed Sloths (Fig. 577) there is an important divergence from ordinary Mammals in the number of vertebræ in the cervical region, there being nine or ten instead of seven; while in one species, the Two-toed Sloth (*Cholœpus hoffmanni*), there are only six. The neural spines of all the vertebræ are very short. A number of the anterior caudal vertebræ are united firmly, though not quite fused, with one another and with the true sacrals.

In the Armadillos the sternal ribs, which are sub-bifid at their sternal ends, are ossified, and articulate with the sternum by means of well-developed

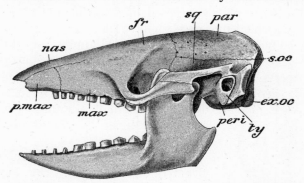

FIG. 578.—Skull of **Armadillo** (*Dasypus sexcinctus*). Letters as in Figs. 579—580. In addition, *peri.* periotic.

synovial articulations. In the American Ant-eaters there are similar synovial joints, and the sternal ends of the sternal ribs are completely bifid. In the Sloths the sternum is long and narrow, and there are no synovial joints. In front the sternal ribs are ossified and completely united with the vertebral

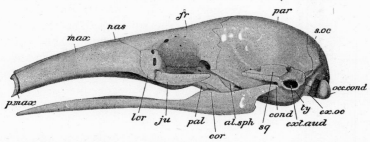

FIG. 579.—Skull of **Ant-eater** (*Myrmecophaga*), lateral view. *al. sp.* ali-sphenoid; *cond.* condyle of mandible; *cor.* coronoid process of mandible; *ex. oc.* ex-occipital; *ext. aud.* external auditory meatus; *fr.* frontal; *ju.* jugal; *lcr.* lachrymal; *max.* maxilla; *nas.* nasal; *occ. cond.* occipital condyle; *pal.* palatine; *par.* parietal; *p.max.* premaxilla; *s. oc.* supra-occipital; *sq.* squamosal; *ty.* tympanic.

ribs, but behind they are separated from the latter by intermediate ribs which are less perfectly ossified.

In the Armadillos the *skull* (Fig. 578) is broad and flat, the facial region triangular. The tympanic (*ty.*) is in some developed into a bulla. The bony auditory meatus is in some cases elongated. The zygoma is complete. The pterygoids are small, and do not develop palatine plates. The mandible has a well-developed ramus with a prominent coronoid process and a well-marked angular process.

In the American Ant-eaters (Fig. 579 and 580) the skull is extremely long and narrow—the facial region being drawn out into a long, narrow rostrum, with the external nares at its extremity. The olfactory fossæ are greatly developed. The rostrum is composed of mesethmoid, vomer, maxillæ, and nasals—the premaxillæ being very small. The zygoma is incomplete, and the orbit is not closed behind by bone, the post-orbital processes of the frontal being entirely absent. The pterygoids (*pter.*), in all but *Cycloturus*, develop palatine plates. There is no bony auditory meatus. The mandible is entirely devoid of ascending ramus—consisting of two long and slender horizontal rami, with a very short symphysis.

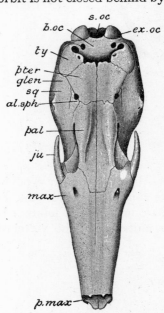

FIG. 580.—Skull of **Ant-eater** (*Myrmecophaga*), ventral view. Letters as in Fig. 579. In addition, *b. oc.* basi-occipital; *glen.* glenoid surface for mandible; *pter.* pterygoid.

In the Sloths (Fig. 581) the cranial region is elevated and rounded, the facial short; the frontal region is elevated, owing to the development of extensive frontal air-sinuses. The premaxillæ are small, and not firmly connected with the maxillæ, so that they are commonly lost in the macerated skull. The jugal (*ju.*) develops a strong zygomatic process which bifurcates behind into two branches, neither of which is connected with the rudimentary zygomatic process of the squamosal, so that the zygomatic arch remains incomplete. There are, at most, the rudiments of post-orbital processes of the frontals. The pterygoids develop vertical laminæ and form no palatine plates. The ascending ramus and coronoid process of the mandible are both well developed.

In the American Ant-eaters and Armadillos the bones of the *fore-limb* are short and powerful. The scapula in the Ant-eaters is broad and rounded; the anterior border unites with the coracoid process so as to convert the coraco-scapular notch into a foramen. In the middle of the spine there is a triangular process: a ridge on the post-spinous fossa presents the appearance of a second spine. The fibres of origin of the sub-scapularis muscles extend on to the outer surface as far forward as this ridge, so that the part of the outer surface behind the ridge corresponds to a part of the sub-scapular fossa, which in other Theria is co-extensive with the inner surface. Except in *Cycloturus* the clavicles are rudimentary. All the carpal bones are distinct.

In the Armadillos the scapula (Fig. 582) has an extremely prolonged acromion (*acr.*), sometimes articulating with the humerus. A ridge (*sp'.*)

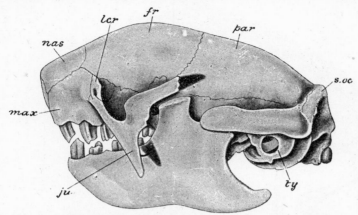

FIG. 581.—Skull of **Three-toed Sloth** (*Bradypus tridactylus*). Letters as in Fig. 579.

representing a second spine is present. The clavicle is well developed. The humerus is short and powerful, with well-developed processes and ridges, and with a foramen above the inner condyle (*entepicondylar foramen*). The carpus consists of the ordinary eight bones.

In the Sloths (Fig. 583) the arm bones are comparatively long and slender. A coraco-scapular foramen is formed as in the Ant-eaters. In the Three-toed Sloths (Fig. 573) the acromion (*acr.*) is at first connected with the coracoid process, but becomes reduced and loses the connection; in the Two-toed Sloth the connection persists. The clavicle (*cl.*) is not directly connected internally with the sternum; externally it is directly connected with the coracoid process—a condition observed in no other Mammal. The humerus is very long and slender; so are the radius and ulna, which are capable of a certain amount of movement in pronation and supination. In the carpus (Fig. 584) the trapezoid and magnum are united in *Bradypus*, distinct in *Cholœpus*: in the former the trapezium is usually fused with the rudimentary first metacarpal. The first and fifth metacarpals are

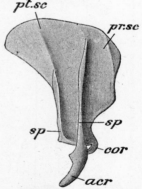

FIG. 582.—Shoulder-girdle of **Armadillo** (*Dasypus sexcinctus*). *acr.* acromion; *cor.* coracoid process; *pr. sc.* prespinous fossa; *pt. sc.* postspinous fossa; *sp.* spine; *sp'.* ridge probably marking the anterior limit of origin of the subscapularis muscle.

represented only by rudiments. The proximal phalanges of the three digits are early ankylosed with the corresponding metacarpals, so that it might readily be supposed that one of the ordinary bones of each digit was absent.

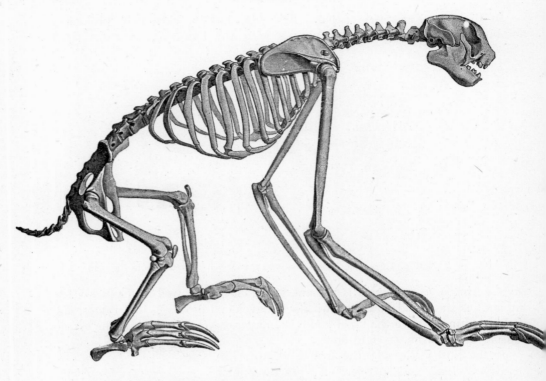

FIG. 583.—Skeleton of **Three-toed Sloth** (*Bradypus tridactylus*). (After Blainville.)

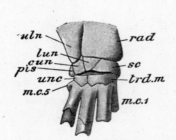

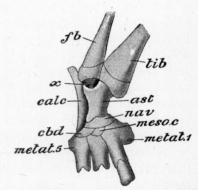

FIG. 584.—Right manus of **Three-toed Sloth**. *cun.* cuneiform; *lun.* lunar; *m. c. 1*, first metacarpal; *m. c. 5*, rudiment of fifth metacarpal; *pis.* pisiform; *rad.* radius; *sc.* scaphoid; *trd. m.* trapezoid and magnum united; *uln.* ulna; *unc.* unciform.

FIG. 585.—Pes of **Three-toed Sloth**. *ast.* astragalus; *calc.* calcaneum; *cbd.* cuboid; *fb.* fibula; *mesoc.* mesocuneiform; *metat. 1*, vestige of first metatarsal; *metat. 5*, vestige of fifth metatarsal; *nav.* navicular; *tib.* tibia; *x*, peg-like process at distal end of fibula.

The pelvis of the American Ant-eaters is elongated, with a short symphysis pubis. The ischia unite with the spinal column. There is no third trochanter. The tibia and fibula are nearly straight, and parallel with one another. In *Cycloturus* the pes is modified to form a climbing organ.

In the Sloths the pelvis is short and wide; the spines of the ischia unite with the anterior caudal vertebræ so that a sacro-sciatic foramen is formed as in Ant-eaters. The femur is long and slender; it is devoid of third trochanter. The tibia and fibula are also long and slender. At its distal end (Fig. 585) the fibula develops a peg-like process (*x*) which fits into a depression in the outer

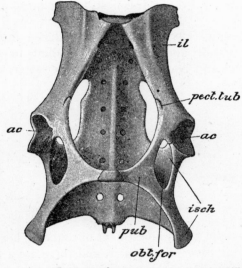

FIG. 586.—Pelvis and sacrum of **Armadillo** (*Dasypus sexcinctus*). *ac.* acetabulum; *il.* ilium; *isch.* ischium; *obt. for.* obturator foramen; *pect. tub.* pectineal tubercle; *pub.* pubis.

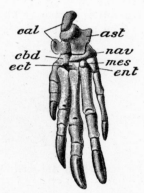

FIG. 587.—Pes of **Armadillo** (*Dasypus sexcinctus*). *ast.* astragalus; *cal.* calcaneum; *cbd.* cuboid; *ect.* ecto-cuneiform; *ent.* ento-cuneiform; *mes.* meso-cuneiform; *nav.* navicular.

face of the astragalus. The calcaneal process is extremely prolonged in *Bradypus,* in which there is a tendency to ankylosis between the tarsal bones, and the proximal phalanges ankylose with the metatarsals.

In the Armadillos the pelvis (Fig. 586) is extremely long, and both ilia and ischia are firmly fused with the spinal column. The femur has a prominent third trochanter. The bones of the pes (Fig. 587) are normal.

ORDER PHOLIDOTA.

This order contains the living Pangolins or " Scaly Ant-eaters " of tropical Africa and Asia. The most noticeable character is the covering of imbricating horny scales over the head, body, and tail, between which grow a few scattered hairs. Teeth are entirely absent, as also is the jugal arch and clavicle. The skull is long and cylindrical, and there is no division between the orbits and temporal fossæ. The tongue is very long.

There is only one genus, *Manis* (Fig. 588), and about seven species have been described. The limbs are short and strong, with five digits, the hind-feet are plantigrade, the fore-feet provided with strong curved claws and, in walking, the weight rests on the upper and outer side of the fourth and fifth toes.

What resemblance there is to the edentate *Myrmecophaga* is probably due to convergent adaptation. Nothing sure is known of the past history of the Pholidota beyond a few remains in the European Tertiary, of which the earliest is a doubtful Oligocene species. While, therefore, a remote connection with the American Edentata is not absolutely ruled out, it is best, for the present, to keep the Pholidota as a separate order.

In the Scaly Ant-eaters (*Manis*, Fig. 588) the head is produced into a short, pointed muzzle. The limbs are short and strong, with five digits in each foot. The upper surface of the head and body, the sides of the latter, and

FIG. 588.—**Scaly Ant-eater** (*Manis gigantea*). (From the *Cambridge Natural History*.)

the entire surface of the tail are covered with an investment of rounded, horny, epidermal scales. The lower surface is covered with hair, and there are a few coarse hairs between the scales. In walking, the weight rests on the upper and outer side of the fourth and fifth toes of the manus and on the sole of the pes.

ORDER TUBULIDENTATA.

Of the early history of the Aard Varks (*Orycteropus*, Fig. 589) of South Africa even less is known, although here again there are some signs of them in the European Tertiary. The body is thick-set, the head produced into a long muzzle. The fore-limbs are short and stout, with four toes, the palmar surfaces of which are placed on the ground in walking. The hind-limb is five-toed. The body is covered with thick skin with scattered hairs. *Orycteropus* lives on Termite Ants, and has a long tongue and small mouth. There are, however, from four to five peg-like teeth, which have a peculiar structure. There is no enamel, but a coating of cement and a body of vasodentine, which in the pulp-chamber is perforated by tubes, from which character the order takes its name.

The relationship of the order is very problematical—it has clearly nothing to do with the Edentata or Pholidota. The structure of the rather primitive brain is stated to show some resemblance to *Anoplotherium*, an Eocene Artiodactyl. Extinct examples are rare. *Orycteropus gaudryi* has been found in the Lower Pliocene, but it and a few fragments assigned to the order from the Oligocene and Miocene throw no light on the problem.

FIG. 589.—**Aard-vark** (*Orycteropus capensis*). (After Vogt and Specht.)

GENERAL ORGANISATION OF MAMMALS.

Integument and General External Features.—Nearly all Mammals are covered with hairs (Fig. 590) developed in *hair-follicles*. Each hair (Fig. 591) is a slender rod, and is composed of two parts, a central part or *pith* (*M*) containing air, and an outer more solid part or *cortex* (*R*) in which air does not occur; its outermost layer may form a definite cuticle (*O*). Commonly the cortical part presents transverse ridges so as to appear scaly. In one case only, viz., Sloths, is the hair fluted longitudinally. The presence of processes on the surface, by which the hairs when twisted together interlock firmly, gives a special quality to certain kinds of hair (wool) used for clothing—the *felting* quality as it is termed. A hair is usually cylindrical; but there are many exceptions: in some it is compressed at the extremity, in others it is compressed throughout; the latter condition is observable in the hair of negroid races of men. The fur is usually composed entirely of one kind of hair; but in some cases there are two kinds, the hairs of the one sort very numerous and forming the soft fur, and those of the other consisting of longer and coarser hairs scattered over the surface. Examples of a hairy covering of this kind are seen in the case of Ornithorhynchus and the Fur-Seals.

A hair, like a feather, is formed from the epidermis. The first rudiment of a developing hair (Fig. 592) usually takes the form of a slight downwardly projecting outgrowth, the *hair-germ* (*grm.*), from the lower mucous layer of the epidermis, beneath which there is soon dis-

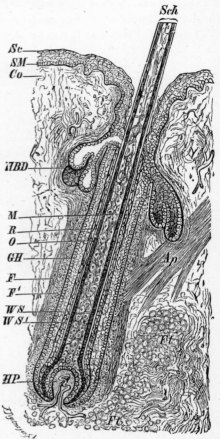

FIG. 591.—Longitudinal section through a hair (diagrammatic). *Ap*, band of muscular fibres inserted into the hair-follicle, *Co*, dermis; *F*, external longitudinal, and *F'*, internal circular fibrous layer of follicle; *Ft*, fatty tissue in the dermis; *GH*, hyalin membrane between the root-sheath and the follicle; *HBD*, sebaceous gland; *HP*, hair-papilla with vessels in its interior; *M*, medullary substance (pith) of the hair; *O*, cuticle; *R*, cortical layer; *Sc*, horny layer of epidermis; *SM*, Malpighian layer of epidermis; *WS*, *WS'*, outer and inner layers of root-sheath. (From Wiedersheim's *Comparative Anatomy*.)

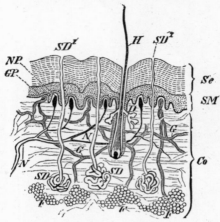

FIG. 590.—Section of human skin. *Co*, dermis; *D*, sebaceous glands; *F*, fat in dermis; *G*, vessels in dermis; *GP*, vascular papillæ; *H*, hair; *N*, nerves in dermis; *NP*, nervous papillæ; *Se*, horny layer of epidermis; *SD*, sweat-gland. *SD¹*, duct of sweat-gland; *SM*, Malpighian layer. (From Wiedersheim's *Comparative Anatomy*.)

cernible a condensation of the dermal tissue to form the rudiment of a *hair papilla* (*pp.*). In some Mammals, however, the dermal papilla makes its appearance before the hair-germ. The hair-germ, which consists of a solid mass of epidermal cells, elongates, and soon its axial portion becomes condensed and cornified to form the shaft of the hair, while the more peripheral cells go to form the lining of the hair-follicle, becoming arranged in two layers, the *inner* and *outer root-sheaths* (sh. *1*, sh. *2*). The epidermal cells in immediate contact with the hair-papilla retain their protoplasmic character and form the *hair-bulb* (*blb.*), by the activity of which the further growth of the hair is effected. Soon the upper end of the hair-shaft grows out beyond the surface of the epidermis, and the projecting part eventually becomes much longer than that which lies embedded in the follicle. At the same time the follicle grows downwards into the dermis. During its growth the hair is nourished by the blood-vessels in the dermal hair-papilla, which projects into its base.

Modifications of the hairs are often found in certain parts. Such modified hairs are the elongated hairs of the tails of some Mammals, *e.g.*, most Ungulates; the eyelashes of the eye-lids, which are stronger than the ordinary hairs; and sensitive hairs, or *vibrissæ*, about the snout. In some Mammals the hairs in part assume the form of spines, viz., in Tachyglossus, the Hedgehogs, and the Porcupines.

The coating of hairs is scanty in some Mammals, and is virtually absent in the Cetacea and Sirenia. In such cases the skin is greatly thickened, as in the Elephants, etc.; or, as in the Cetacea, an underlying layer of fat performs the function of the hair as a heat-preserving covering.

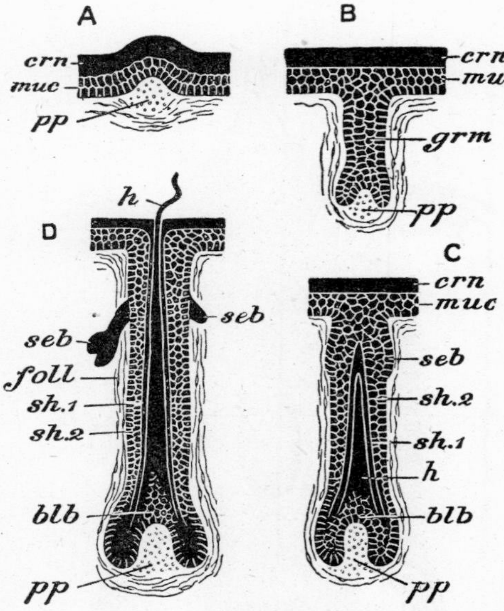

In Manis (Fig. 588) the greater part of the surface is covered with large, rounded, over-lapping horny scales of epidermal origin, similar in

Fig. 592.—Four diagrams of stages in the development of a hair. *A*, earliest stage in one of those Mammals in which the dermal papilla appears first; *B, C, D*, three stages in the development of the hair in the human embryo. *blb.* hair-bulb; *crn.* horny layer of the epidermis; *foll.* hair-follicle; *grm.* hair-germ; *h.* extremity of hair projecting on the surface in *D*; *muc.* Malpighian layer of epidermis; *pp.* dermal papilla; *seb.* developing sebaceous glands; *sh. 1, sh. 2*, inner and outer root-sheaths. (After Hertwig.)

their mode of development to those of reptiles. A similar phenomenon is seen in the integument of the tail of *Anomalurus*—a Flying Rodent. The Armadillos (Fig. 578) are the only Mammals in which there occurs a bony *dermal exoskeleton*.

Also epidermal in their origin are the horny structures in the form of nails, claws, or hoofs, with which the terminations of the digits are provided in all the Mammalia except the Cetacea. And the same holds good of the horny portion of the horns of Ruminants. The horns of the Rhinoceros are also epidermal and have the appearance of being formed by the agglutination of a number of hair-like horny fibres.

Cutaneous glands are very general in the Mammalia, the most constant being the *sebaceous glands* (Figs, 590, *D*; 591, *HBD*), which open into the hair-follicles, and the *sweat-glands* (Fig. 590, *SD*). In many Mammals, there are, in addition, in various parts of the body, aggregations of special glands secreting an odorous matter.

The *mammary glands*, by the secretion of which the young are nourished, are

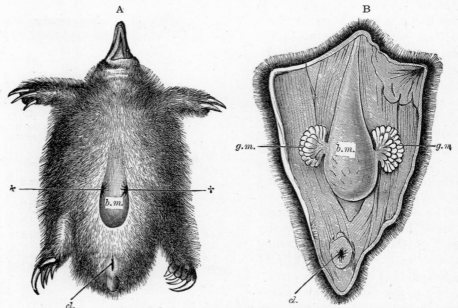

FIG. 593.—**Tachyglossus aculeata.** *A*, lower surface of brooding female; *B*, dissection showing a dorsal view of the marsupium and mammary glands; † †, the two tufts of hair projecting from the mammary pouches from which the secretion flows; *b. m.* brood-pouch or marsupium; *cl.* cloaca; *g. m.* groups of mammary glands. (From Wiedersheim's *Comparative Anatomy*, after W. Haacke.)

specially developed cutaneous glands. In the Prototheria they differ somewhat widely from those of the rest of the Mammalia in structure, and they also differ in the absence of teats. They consist of two groups of very large tubular follicles, the ducts of which open on the ventral surface. In Tachyglossus (Fig. 593) the two areas on which the ducts open become depressed towards the breeding season to give rise to a pair of pouches—the *mammary pouches*. A large brood-pouch or *marsupium* is subsequently formed, and the egg is deposited in this. When the young animal is hatched it is sheltered in the posterior deeper part of this marsupium, while in the shallower anterior part lie the mammary pouches. In Ornithorhynchus mammary pouches are indicated only by extremely shallow depressions, and no marsupium is developed.

In the higher Mammals, when the mammary glands are first developed (Fig. 594), a depression (*mammary pouch*) is formed, from the floor of which branching cylindrical strands of epidermis grow inwards to give rise to the glands. At a later stage there is developed around the opening or openings of the mammary ducts a prominence, the *teat* (Fig. 594), the wall of which may be formed of the mammary pouch area alone (Marsupials, Rodents, Primates), or, with greater or less reduction of the latter, mainly from the surrounding integument. In the latter case the teat may have a wide central canal. The number and situation of the teats vary in the different groups.

Endoskeleton.—The spinal column of Mammals varies in the number of vertebræ which it contains, the differences being mainly due to differences in

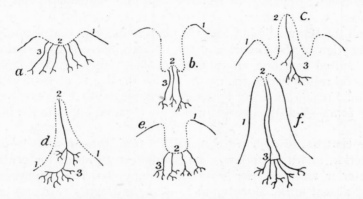

FIG. 594.—Diagrams of the phylogenetic development of teats. *a*, primitive condition corresponding to the condition in Tachyglossus ; *b*, Wallaby (*Halmaturus*) before lactation ; *c*, Opossum (*Didelphys*) before lactation ; *d*, Opossum during lactation ; this diagram stands also for the Mouse and Man ; *e*, embryonal, and *f*, full-grown cow. *1*, integumentary wall ; *2*, mammary area, the broken line represents the mammary pouch ; *3*, milk-ducts. (After Max Weber.)

the length of the tail. The various regions are very definitely marked off. In the *cervical* region the first two vertebræ are modified to form the *atlas* and *axis*. Owing to the absence of distinct cervical ribs, the posterior cervical vertebræ are much more sharply marked off from the anterior thoracic than is the case in Reptiles and Birds. The vertebræ of the cervical region have double transverse process (or a transverse process perforated at the base by a foramen which transmits the vertebral artery) in all except the last with certain exceptions, such as many Masupials, some Rodents, Hyrax and the Hippopotami, where the seventh cervical vertebra is also perforated. The lower portion of the transverse process in certain cases (*e.g.*, seventh and sometimes some of the others in Man) arises from a separate ossification, and this is regarded as evidence that the lower part, even when not independently ossified, represents a cervical rib. Seven is the prevailing number of vertebræ in the cervical region ; there are only three exceptions to this—the Manatee, Hoffmann's Sloth, and the Three-toed Sloth (*cf.* p. 626). The number of *thoracic* and *lumbar* vertebræ is not so constant ; usually there are between nineteen and twenty-three. Hyrax has a larger number of thoraco-lumbar vertebræ than any other mammal—from twenty-nine to thirty-one.

The thoracic vertebræ have *ribs* which are connected, either directly or by intermediate ribs, with the *sternal ribs*, and through them with the *sternum*. Each rib typically articulates with the spinal column by two articulations —one articular surface being borne on the head and the other on the tubercle. The tubercle articulates with the transverse process, and the head usually with an articular surface furnished partly by the vertebra with which the tubercle is connected, and partly by that next in front ; so that the head of the first thoracic rib partly articulates with the centrum of the last cervical vertebra.

In all the Mammalia in which the hind-limbs exist, that is to say, in all with the exception of the Sirenia and the Cetacea, there is a *sacrum* consisting of closely united vertebræ, the number of which varies in the different orders. The *caudal* region varies greatly as regards the degree of its development. In the caudal region of many long-tailed mammals there is developed a series of *chevron bones*—V-shaped bones, which are situated opposite the inter-vertebral spaces.

The centrum of each vertebra ossifies from three centres [1]—a middle one, an anterior, and a posterior. The middle centre forms the centrum proper ; the anterior and posterior form the epiphyses. The epiphyses are almost entirely absent in the Monotremes, and in the Dugong (*Sirenia*) have not been detected. Between successive centra is formed a series of discs of fibro-cartilage—the *inter-vertebral discs*—represented in lower Vertebrates only in Crocodiles and Birds. The anterior and posterior surfaces of the centra are nearly always flat.

The *sternum* consists of a number of segments—the *presternum* in front, the *mesosternum*, or *corpus sterni*, composed of a number of segments or *sternebræ* in the middle, and the *xiphisternum* behind. The sternum is formed in the fœtus in great part by the separating off of the ventral ends of the ribs. Some of the Cetacea and the Sirenia are exceptional in having a sternum composed of a single piece of bone. The sternal ribs, by which the vertebral ribs are connected with the sternum, are usually cartilaginous, but frequently undergo calcification in old animals, and in some cases early become completely converted into bone.

The *skull* of a Mammal (Fig. 595) contains the same chief elements and presents the same general regions as that of the Sauropsida, but exhibits certain special modifications. A number of the bones present in the skull of Sauropsida

---

[1] Usually the two centres of ossification which form the neural arches also contribute to the formation of the bony centrum.

are not represented, or, at all events, not certainly known to be represented definitely by separate ossifications in the mammalia. Such are the supra-orbital, the pre-frontal, the post-orbital, the ecto-pterygoid and the quadrato-jugal. The bones of the skull, with the exception of the auditory ossicles, the lower jaw, and the hyoid, are all immovably united together by means of sutures.

The palatine bones develop *palatine plates* separating off a posterior nasal

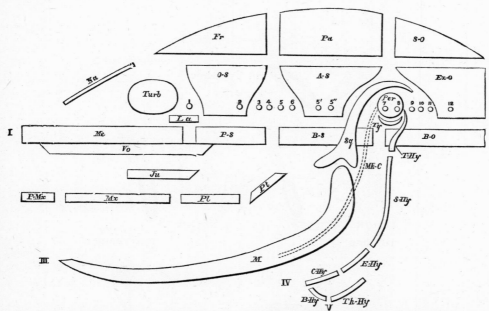

FIG. 595.—Diagram of the relations of the principal bones of the Mammalian skull. **A-S.** ali-sphenoid; **B-Hy.** basi-hyal; **B-O.** basi-occipital; **B-S.** basi-sphenoid; **C-Hy.** cerato-hyal; **E-Hy.** epi-hyal; **Ex.-O.** ex-occipital; *Fr.* frontal; *Ju.* jugal; *La.* lachrymal; *M.* mandible; **ME.** mesethmoid; *Mx.* maxilla; *Na.* nasal; **O.-S.** orbito-sphenoid; *Pa.* parietal; **Per.** periotic; *Pl.* palatine; **P.-S.** pre-sphenoid; *PMx.* premaxilla; *Pt.* pterygoid; **S-Hy.** styo-hyal; **S-O.** supra-occipital; *Sq.* squamosal; **T-Hy.** tympano-hyal; **Th-Hy.** thyro-hyal; **Turb.** turbinal; *Ty.* tympanic; *Vo.* vomer. (**Thick type**—replacing bones; *italics*—investing bones.) The numbered circles indicate the points of exit of the cranial nerves; 1, olfactory; 2, optic; 3, oculo-motor; 4, trochlear; 5, 5', 5", the three divisions of the fifth nerve; 6, abducent; 7, facial; 8, auditory; 9, glosso-pharyngeal; 10, pneumogastric; 11, spinal accessory; 12, hypoglossal. (After Flower.)

passage from the cavity of the mouth, a condition found among the living Sauropsida only in the Crocodilia, and, to a less extent, in the Chelonia and some Lizards.

The *zygomatic arch* is a strong arch of bone formed partly of the squamosal, partly of the jugal, and partly of the maxilla : in position it represents the upper temporal arch of Amphibia and Sauropsida, but is differently constituted (*see* p. 376). The *orbit* in the skull of some mammals is completely enclosed by bone, constituting a well-defined cavity ; in others it is not completely surrounded by bone behind, and so communicates freely with the *temporal fossa* which lies behind it.

The *periotic* bones (*pro-otic*, *opisthotic*, and *epi-otic*) are not separately represented in the skull of mammals. Part of the periotic mass sometimes projects on the exterior at the hinder part of the lateral region of the skull, and is the *mastoid* portion ; the rest is commonly called the *petrous* portion of the

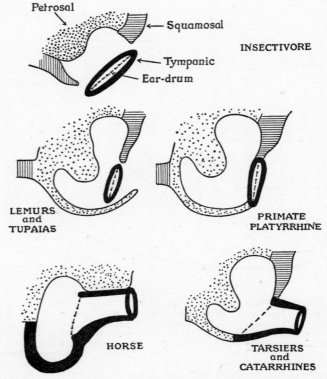

FIG. 596.—Diagrams of tympanic cavity of certain mammals. The tympanic bone is black ; the petrosal dotted, the squamosal horizontally shaded and the basi-occipital vertically shaded.

periotic, and encloses the parts of the internal ear—the mastoid portion containing only air-cells. The *tympanic* bone, which represents the angular of Sauropsida, sometimes forms a long tube, sometimes only a mere ring of bone. In other cases it not only gives rise to a tube for the external auditory meatus, but also forms the *bulla tympani*, a dilated bony process containing a cavity.

The tympanic cavity, in which lie the ear-bones, is hollowed out of the petrosal. In the primitive condition, as can be seen at the present time in some of the Marsupials, Insectivores, Edentates, etc., this chamber has no bony covering, and the tympanic bone (*ectotympanic*) is an open ring lying loosely and supporting the ear-drum. When, as in most cases, a bony covering is formed, this structure is termed the " *bulla*." It is not always formed in the same way in different groups. In those Marsupials in which a bulla is present it is always made from the ali-sphenoid, the tympanic forming the external auditory meatus. In the Primates it is formed chiefly by an outgrowth of the petrous bone, which may either grow round the tympanic ring so as to enclose it, as in the Tupaiidæ and Lemuridæ (Fig. 596), where it lies free in the cavity, or, as in the Lorisidæ and Platyrrhine Monkeys, it joins on to the edge of the tympanic ring, which thus forms part of the bulla-wall and acts as the opening of the middle ear, while in the Tarsioid and Catarrhine Monkeys it is further produced outwards to form a bony tube—the external auditory meatus. In other Mammals the tympanic, as a rule, forms most of the bulla, but the entotympanic, squamosal, ali-sphenoid, and basi-sphenoid may also take some part either in the formation of the bulla or as supporting elements.

The *occipital* region presents two condyles for the articulation of the atlas.

The *mandible* consists in the adult of one bone, the equivalent of the *dentary* of Sauropsida, on each side—the two rami, as they are called, being in most mammals closely united at the symphysis. The mandible articulates with an articular surface formed for it by the *squamosal* bone, below the posterior root of the zygomatic arch.

The *hyoid* consists of a body and two pairs of *cornua—anterior* and *posterior* ; of these the anterior pair are usually longer, and consist of several bones, the most important and most constant of which is the *stylo-hyal*, connected usually with the periotic region of the skull. The posterior cornua or *thyro-hyals* are usually much smaller.

The ratio borne by the capacity of the cranial cavity to the extent of the facial region varies greatly in the different orders. The greater development of the cerebral hemispheres in the higher groups necessitates a greater development of the corresponding cerebral fossa of the cranium. This is brought about by the bulging upwards, forwards, and backwards of the cranial roof, resulting in a great modification in the primitive relations of certain of the great planes and axes of the skull (Fig. 597). Taking as a fixed base line the *basi-cranial axis*—an imaginary median line running through the basi-occipital, basi-sphenoid, and pre-sphenoid bones—we find that the great expansion of the cerebral fossa in the higher mammals leads to a marked alteration in the relations to this axis (1) of the *occipital* plane or plane of the foramen magnum ; (2) of the *tentorial* plane or plane of the tentorium cerebelli (a transverse fold of the dura mater between the cerebral hemispheres and the cerebellum) ; and (3) of the *ethmoidal* plane or plane of the cribriform plate of the ethmoid. In the lower Mammals (*A*) these are nearly at right angles to the basi-cranial axis. In the higher groups, by the bulging forwards and backwards of the cranial roof, the occipital and tentorial planes incline backwards and the ethmoidal forwards, until all three may become approximately horizontal. At the

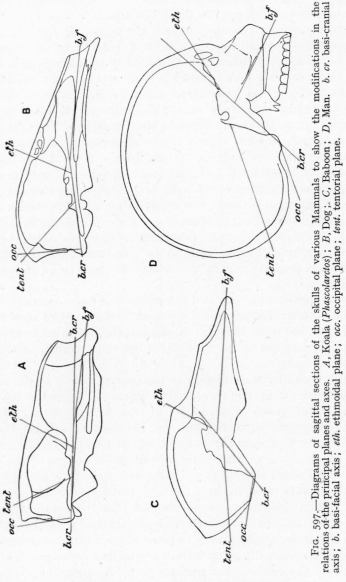

Fig. 597.—Diagrams of sagittal sections of the skulls of various Mammals to show the modifications in the relations of the principal planes and axes. *A*, Koala (*Phascolarctos*); *B*, Dog; *C*, Baboon; *D*, Man. *b. cr.* basi-cranial axis; *b.* basi-facial axis; *eth.* ethmoidal plane; *occ.* occipital plane; *tent.* tentorial plane.

same time there is produced a change in the relations of the basi-cranial axis to the *basi-facial axis*—a line passing along the axis of the face between the mesethmoid and the vomer. In the lower forms the angle at which the basi-facial axis, when produced, meets the basi-cranial is an exceedingly open one; in the higher forms, owing to the downward inclination of the facial region, this angle decreases in size, though it is never reduced to less than a right angle.

The *pectoral arch* of the mammalia has fewer distinct elements than that of the Sauropsida. The coracoid, which in the latter is a large bone, taking a share at its dorsal end in the bounding of the glenoid cavity, and at its ventral end articulating with the sternum, is never present, in the adult, as a distinct bone. In the young of many mammals it appears to be represented by a small ossification which enters into the glenoid facet; but this very soon coalesces with the scapula. The coracoid process, which is a separate ossification in the young mammal, and, though in most instances completely fusing with the scapula and with the smaller coracoid element, is sometimes recognisable as a distinct element up to a late period (many Marsupials, Sloths), appears to correspond to the bone called epicoracoid in the Prototheria (*vide* p. 529). In fœtal Marsupials the coracoid is represented by a well-developed cartilaginous element which extends inwards and meets the rudiment of the sternum.

In the scapula a *spine* is nearly always developed, and usually ends in a freely-projecting acromion-process. It is developed, unlike the main body of the scapula, without any antecedent formation of cartilage, and is perhaps to be compared with the *cleithrum*, an investing bone occurring in some Amphibia and Reptilia (p. 338). A *clavicle* is well developed in many mammals, but is incomplete or absent in others; its presence is characteristic of mammals in which the fore-limbs are capable of great freedom of movement. In the embryo of the mammals there is, in the position of the clavicular bar, a bar of cartilage, which coalesces with its fellow in the middle line. The cartilaginous tract thus formed segments into five portions—a median, which coalesces with the presternum, two small inner lateral, which unite with the clavicles or are converted into the sterno-clavicular ligaments, and two long outer lateral, which give rise to the clavicles. The median and inner lateral portions appear to correspond to the episternum of Reptiles and Prototheria. An additional small cartilage may represent the inner portion of the precoracoid of Amphibia. A piece of cartilage at the outer end of the clavicle proper is sometimes distinguishable—the *meso-scapular segment*. The three elements of the *pelvic arch* unite to form a single bone, the *innominate*. The ilia unite by broad surfaces with the sacrum; the pubes, and sometimes the ischia, unite in a *symphysis*. All three may take a share in the formation of the acetabulum, but the pubis is usually shut out by a small *cotyloid bone*. In the shank the inner or *tibial* element is always the larger; the *fibula* may be rudimentary. A large sesamoid bone—the *patella*—is almost universally formed in close relation to the knee-joint.

The most primitive type of extremity is the *plantigrade*, with five sub-equal digits, with a flexible carpus and tarsus, and with the bones " interlocking "

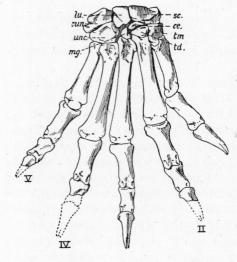

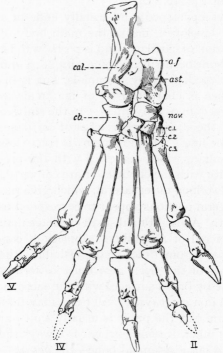

FIG. 598.—Carpus (upper) and tarsus (lower figure) of **Tritemnodon agilis.** *a. f.* astragalar foramen; *ast.* astragalus; *cal.* calcaneum; *cb.* cuboid; *ce.* centrale; *cun.* cuneiform; *c.* 1, 2, 3, ento-, meso- and ectocuneiforms; *lu.* lunar; *mg.* magnum; *nar.* navicular; *sc.* scaphoid; *td.* trapezoid; *tm.* trapezium. (After Matthew.)

(e.g., *Tritemnodon,* Fig. 598, and many primitive Mammals). From a generalised pattern of this sort many modifications have been derived. As an increasing adaptation to speed, the *cursorial* patterns proceed through the subdigitigrade to the digitigrade, and finally to the unguligrade condition as the extreme adaptation along this line. It is accompanied by an increase in the length of the digits, either along the axis of the third toe—the *mesaxonic* pattern— or between the third and fourth toes—the *paraxonic* pattern. An early stage of a mesaxonic foot can be seen in the Condylarth *Tetraclænodon,* and its final stage in the Horse or the Litopterna (Fig. 599) where a functionally one-toed condition has been reached, although morphologically three-toed, the second and fourth toes still being represented by splint bones. The paraxonic hand and foot, of which an early stage can be seen in the Creodont *Mesonyx* (Fig. 600), has the axis passing between the third and fourth digits, which enlarge at an equal rate. The second and fifth toes, on the other hand, become equally reduced, and the first toe disappears. The final result can be seen in the more advanced Artiodactyla—*e.g.,* a Cow or Sheep—where there is a complete reduction to two toes and a fusion of the two metapodials into the characteristic "cannon bone" (Fig. 601). The bones of the carpus and tarsus, while retaining the characters of the interlocking type, are arranged to allow great flexion in the fore-and-aft direction, but little in the lateral. In many Artiodactyles there is a fusion of some of the bones of the tarsus (Fig. 602).

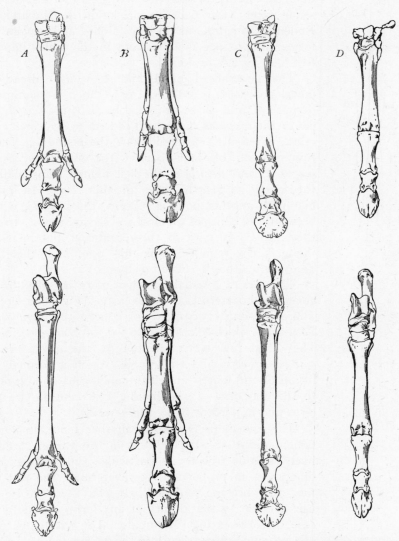

FIG. 599.—Fore and hind feet of Horses and Litopterna showing convergence. *A.* **Mery-chippus**, three toed stages ; *B.* **Diadiaphorus**, three toed stages ; *C.* **Pliohippus**, single toed stages, *D.* **Thoatherium**, single toed stages. (Redrawn after Matthew.)

In bulky animals such as the Elephants, Dinocerata, etc., the carpals and tarsals become serially arranged with a great loss of flexibility, and the digits, while not reduced in number as a rule, become short and stout. Special habits, such as hopping—the Kangaroos, *Macroscelides* among Insectivores, *Dipus* and *Alactaga* are among the Rodents (Fig. 603) ; swimming—*e.g.*, the Cetacea, Sirenia, Seals, etc. ; flying—*e.g.*, the Bats and to some extent the parachuting kinds of Marsupials and Rodents ; digging, as in the Moles and several other forms, all produce modifications in the limbs, hands, and feet more or less profound.

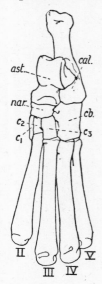

The generalised hand and foot has already been mentioned (see p. 80, Fig. 65). In the mammals the carpus contains three proximal bones (Figs. 601, 604, 605, 606) : the *scaphoid, lunar* and *cuneiform*, to which is added on the outer side a sesamoid bone, the *pisiform*. The distal row consists of four bones : the *trapezium, trapezoid, magnum*, and *unciform*, the last named being a fusion of the fourth and fifth bones of this row. In primitive mammals another bone is present, the *centrale*, which lies between the bones of the first and second rows. In reptiles there can be as many as three centralia, but in mammals there is never more than this one, and this usually disappears either by fusion or loss.

The tarsus is usually rather more modified from the generalised pattern than is the carpus (Figs. 602, 607, 608). There are only two proximal bones : the *astragalus* and *calcaneum*, which correspond to the scaphoid and cuneiform. The distal row is represented by the *ecto-, meso-*, and *ento-cuneiforms*, and the *cuboid*, which is formed by the fusion of the fourth and fifth cuneiforms and corresponds to the unciform of the hand. The centrale becomes a large and important bone, the *navicular*.

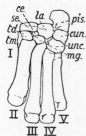

Fig. 600.— Paraxonic carpus and tarsus of *Mesonyx*. *ast.* astragalus; C_1, $_2$, $_3$, ento-, meso- and ectocuneiforms; *cal.* calcaneum; *cb.* cuboid; *cun.* cuneiform; *lu.* lunar; *mg.* magnum; *nav.* navicular; *pis.* pisiform; *sc.* scaphoid; *d.* trapezoid; *tm.* trapezium; *unc.* unciform.

The astragalus is also, in another sense, an important bone, because its shape differs in the various orders, but itself remains true to its particular type, subject only to differences in proportion, however much the rest of the foot may become modified. It can therefore be a very useful guide to the affinity of any form, especially in the case of some extinct Mammals. The astragalus consists of a proximal grooved surface the *trochlea*, which articulates proximally with the tibia and fibula, a *neck* and a *head* of varying shape which articulates with the navicular, and sometimes with the cuboid as well. In many early forms an *astragalar foramen* is present near the upper border of the trochlea. This foramen usually diappears in later mammals, but still occurs sporadically, as, for example, in *Orycteropus*.

The main modifications of the astragalus are as follows. In the Condy-larth–Creodont–Carnivore group the tibial trochlea is more or less grooved, obliquely pitched, with the inner (tibial) crest lower than the outer (fibular), or even absent ; the neck is distinct and the head convex (Fig. 609 A). In the Insectivora the trochlea is broad and shallow, but with well-defined crests of equal height, the neck is oblique and oval in section, the head convex (Fig. 609 B). The Primate astragalus (Fig. 609 D) has a concavo-convex trochlear

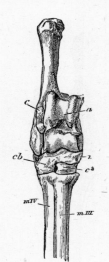

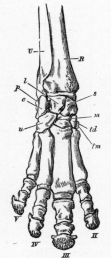

FIG. 601. —Bones of manus of **Red Deer** (*Cervus elaphus*). m^2. m^5. vestigial second and fifth meta-carpals ; *R.* ra-dius. (After Flower.)

FIG. 602.—Dor-sal surface of right tarsus of **Red Deer** (*Cervus elaphus*). *a.* astragalus ; *c.* cal-caneum ; *cb.* cuboid ; c^3. conjoined ecto-and meso-cunei-form ; *mIII, mIV,* third and fourth metatarsals ; *n.* na-vicular. (After Flower.)

FIG. 603. —Hind foot of **Dipus.**

FIG. 604.— Bones of the manus of **Tapir** (*Tapirus indicus*). *c.* cunei-form ; *l.* lunar ; *m.* magnum ; *p.* pisi-form ; *R.* radius ; *s.* scaphoid ; *td.* trapezoid ; *tm.* tra-pezium ; *U.* ulna ; *u.* unciform. (After Flower.)

surface, broader at the neck end than above, a somewhat oblique neck and a convex head. In the Rodents the general appearance is like that of the Insecti-vores, except that the trochlea extends backwards to the posterior margin of the bone (Fig. 609 E). In the Perissodactyla (Fig. 609 H, I) the trochlea is deeply grooved and oblique, the neck short, and the head flattened. In the earlier forms there is a very small astragalo-cuboid facet which, in more advanced forms, especially in the rhinoceroses and titanotheres, becomes larger, though never to the extent that it does in the highly characteristic artiodactyle astragalus, where the trochlea is deeply grooved in a straight line with the head and neck, and with well-marked facets for both the cuboid and navicular (Fig. 609 F, G).   In this type also the sustentacular facet on the medial aspect, which articulates with the calcaneum, is a single large and flat surface instead of being divided, as in other astragali.

Other bones of the carpus and tarsus have their distinguishing characteristics, if rather less obvious than those of the astragalus, as, for example,

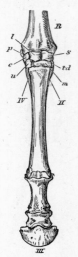

Fig. 605.— Bones of the manus of **Horse** (*Equus caballus*). *c.* cuneiform; *l.* lunar; *m.* magnum; *p.* pisiform; *R.* radius; *s.* scaphoid; *td.* trapezoid; *u.* unciform; *II, IV,* vestigial second and fourth metacarpals. (After Flower.)

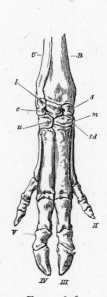

Fig. 606.— Bones of manus of **Pig** (*Sus scrofa*). *c.* cuneiform; *l.* lunar; *m.* magnum; *R,* radius; *s.* scaphoid; *td.* trapezoid; *U.* ulna; *u.* unciform. (After Flower.)

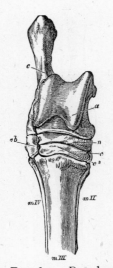

Fig. 607.—Dorsal surface of right tarsus of **Horse** (*Equus caballus*). *a.* astragalus; *c.* calcaneum; *cb.* cuboid; *c.* united meso- and ento-cuneiform; c^3. ecto-cuneiform; *n.* navicular; *mII, IV,* vestigial second and fourth metatarsals; *III,* third metatarsal. (After Flower.)

Fig. 608.—Dorsal surface of right tarsus of **Pig** (*Sus scrofa*). *a.* astragalus; *c.* calcaneum; c^3. ecto-cuneiform; c^2. meso-cuneiform; *mII—V,* metatarsals; *n.* navicular. (After Flower.)

the artiodactyle cuboid, which shows a constant difference from the cuboid of all other Mammals in having a facet on its outer border for the calcaneum.

The external form of the limbs and the mode of articulation of the bones vary in the different orders of the Mammalia, in accordance with the mode of locomotion.   In most the habitual attitude is that which is termed the *quadrupedal*—the body being supported in a horizontal position by all four limbs. In quadrupedal mammals the manus and pes sometimes rest on the ventral surfaces of the entire metacarpal and metatarsal regions as well as on the phalanges—when the limbs are said to be *plantigrade*; or on the ventral surfaces of the phalanges only (*digitigrade*) ; or on the hoofs developed on the terminal phalanges (*unguligrade*). Many of the quadrupeds have the extremities prehensile, the hand and foot being converted into grasping organs. This is most marked in quadrupeds that pass the greater part of their life among the branches of trees, and in the Sloths the modification goes so far that both hands and feet are converted into mere hooks by means of which the animal is enabled to suspend itself body downwards from the branches of trees.

Certain mammals, again, have their limbs modified for locomotion through the air. The only truly *flying* Mammals are the Bats and the so-called " Flying Foxes," in which the digits of the fore-limb are greatly extended so as to support a wide delicate fold of skin constituting the wing. In other so-called flying

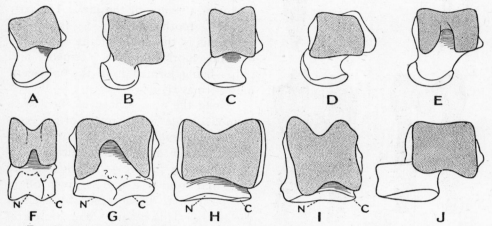

FIG. 609.—Astragali of certain mammals. *A.* a condylarth ; *B.* an insectivore ; *C.* a carnivore ; *D.* a primate ; *E.* a rodent ; *F.* an average artiodactyle ; *G.* **Hippopotamus** ; *H.* **Rhinoceros** ; *I.* **Equus** ; *J.* **Hyrax** ; *N.* navicular ; *C.* cuboid facets. The trochlea is shaded.

Mammals, such as the Flying Squirrels, and Flying Phalangers, there is no active flight, and the limbs undergo no special modification ; the flying organ, if it may be so termed, in these cases being merely a parachute or *patagium* in the form of lateral flaps of skin extending along the sides of the body between the fore- and hind-limbs.

Further, there are certain groups of *swimming* mammals. Most mammals, without any special modification of the limbs, are able to swim, and some of the quadrupeds, such as the Tapirs and Hippopotami, spend a great part of their life in the water. But there are certain mammals in which the limbs are so specially modified to fit them for an aquatic existence—assuming the form of flippers or swimming paddles—that locomotion on land becomes almost, if not quite, impossible. Such are the Whales and Porpoises, the Dugongs and Manatees, and, in a less degree, the Seals and Walruses.

Digestive Organs.—*Teeth* are present in nearly all Mammals, but in some they are wanting in the adult condition (Whalebone Whales and Ornithorhynchus). In Tachyglossus teeth are not present even in the young. In some of the Ant-eaters teeth are developed in the foetus and are thrown off *in utero*—the adult animal being devoid of them.

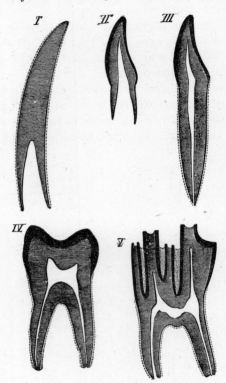

Teeth, as already explained in the general account of the Craniata, are developed partly from the epidermis and partly from the underlying dermis. In the Mammals each tooth is lodged in a socket or alveolus in the jaw. The part of the tooth developed from the epidermis is the enamel; the remainder of the tooth—dentine, cement and pulp—being formed from the subjacent mesodermal tissue.

Along the oral surface of the jaw is formed a ridge like ingrowth of the ectoderm—the *dental lamina* (Fig. 611, *lam.*). The position of this is indicated externally by a groove—the *dental groove* (*gr.*), and from it a bud is given off in the position to be occupied by each of the teeth. This becomes constricted off as a conical cap of cells—the *enamel-organ*—which remains in continuity with the dental ridge only by a narrow isthmus. This cap-like form is brought about by the development of a papilla of condensed dermal tissue—the *dental papilla* (*pap.*), which pushes upwards against the enamel-organ. On the surface of this papilla, in contact with the enamel-organ, the cells (*odontoblasts*) become arranged into a layer having the appearance of an epithelium—the *dentine-forming layer*. The cells of the enamel-

FIG. 610.—Diagrammatic sections of various forms of teeth. *I*, incisor or tusk of Elephant with pulp-cavity persistently open at base; *II*, human incisor during development, with root imperfectly formed, and pulp-cavity widely open at base; *III*, completely formed human incisor, with pulp-cavity opening by a contracted aperture at base of root; *IV*, human molar with broad crown and two roots; *V*, molar of the Ox, with the enamel covering the crown deeply folded, and the depressions filled up with cement; the surface is worn by use, otherwise the enamel coating would be continuous at the top of the ridges. In all the figures the enamel is black, the pulp white, the dentine represented by horizontal lines, and the cement by dots. (After Flower and Lydekker.)

organ form two layers, of which that in contact with the dental papilla assumes the character of a layer of long cylindrical cells—the *enamel-membrane* (*en. m.*); the more superficial layer consists of cubical cells. Between the two the remaining cells of the enamel-organ become modified to form a kind of connective tissue—the *enamel-pulp* (*en. plp.*).

The connective tissue immediately surrounding the entire rudiment of the

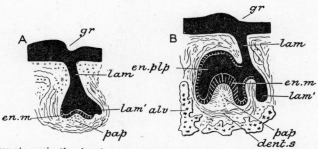

FIG. 611.—Two stages in the development of the teeth of a **Mammal** (diagrammatic sections). *alv.* bone of alveolus; *dent. s.* dental sac; *en. m.* enamel-membrane; *en. plp.* enamel-pulp; *gr.* dental groove; *lam.* dental lamina; *lam'.* part of dental lamina which grows downwards below the tooth-germ; *pap.* dental papilla. (After O. Hertwig.)

tooth becomes vascular and forms a distinct investment—the *dental sac* (*dent. s.*); from this blood-vessels extend into the papilla.

Ossification begins by the formation of a cap of dentine (Fig. 612 *dent.*), produced by the dentine-forming cells, and of a layer of enamel (*en.*) on the surface of this, produced by the cells of the enamel membrane. To these additional layers are added until the crown of the tooth becomes fully developed. The substance of the dental papilla gives rise to the pulp. As the tooth elongates, it projects on the surface and eventually breaks through the mucous membrane of the gum, the remains of the enamel-organ becoming thrown off. The cement is formed by the ossification of the connective-tissue of the dental sac.

In the teeth of most mammals distinct *roots* are formed, each with a minute opening leading into the pulp-cavity (Fig. 610, *III—V*); but in

FIG. 612.—Diagrammatic section showing the development of the milk- and permanent teeth of **Mammals.** *alv.* bone of alveolus; *dent.* dentine; *dent. s.* dental sac; *en.* layer of enamel; *en. m.* enamel-membrane of milk-tooth; *en. m².* enamel-membrane of permanent tooth; *en. plp.* enamel-pulp of milk-tooth; *gr.* dental groove; *lam.* dental lamina; *n.* neck connecting milk-tooth with lamina; *pap.* dental papilla of milk-tooth; *pap².* dental papilla of permanent tooth. (After O. Hertwig.)

some there are no roots, the pulp-cavity being widely open below (*I*), and the tooth constantly growing from the base as it becomes worn away at the crown; such teeth are said to have *persistent pulps*.

Usually Mammals have two distinct sets of teeth developed, the milk and

permanent dentitions, but sometimes there is only one, and accordingly we distinguish *diphydont* and *monophyodont* dentitions : in nearly all of the latter, however, another set is developed, though the teeth early become absorbed or

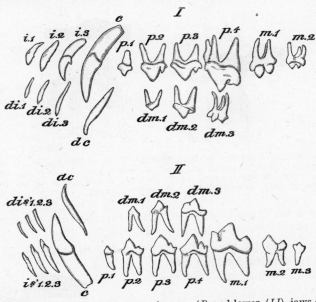

Fig. 613.—Milk- and permanent dentition of upper (*I*) and lower (*II*) jaws of the **Dog** (*Canis familiaris*), with the symbols by which the different teeth are commonly designated. (After Flower and Lydekker.)

remain in the condition of functionless vestiges ; and in a considerable number of groups it has been found that more than two sets of teeth are formed, only one, or at most (in diphyodont forms) two, of these sets become fully developed. The milk-teeth in mammals with typical diphyodont dentition

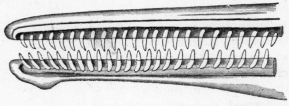

Fig. 614.—Upper and lower teeth of one side of the mouth of a **Dolphin** (*Lagenorhynchus*) illustrating the homodont type of dentition in a Mammal. (After Flower and Lydekker.)

sometimes disappear at an early stage, and sometimes do not become replaced by the permanent teeth till long after birth. Some mammals have the teeth almost indefinite in number, *e.g.*, the Dolphins and Porpoises, in which they are all uniform (*homodont*) and not divided into sets (Fig. 614). In the typical dentition there are forty-four teeth, viz., three incisors on each side, one canine, and seven premolars and molars above and below. The incisors (Fig. 612, *i.*) of the upper jaw are to be distinguished as being the teeth that are lodged in the premaxillæ; the incisors of the lower jaw are the teeth that are placed opposite to these. The upper canine (*c.*) is the most anterior tooth of the maxilla, situated on or immediately behind the premaxillo-maxillary suture, and has usually a characteristic shape. The lower canine is the tooth which bites in front of the upper canine. The premolars (*p.*) are distinguished from the molars by having milk predecessors (*d.m.*), but the first premolar is, except in the Marsupials, nearly always a persistent milk-tooth; the molars (*m.*) have no teeth preceding them, and are sometimes looked upon as persistent teeth of the first set. The various sets of teeth are also usually distinguishable by their shape. As a rule the incisors have cutting edges; the canines are pointed and conical; the premolars and molars have broad surfaces with ridges and tubercles for crushing the food, and may have from two to four roots.

The crown-surface of the molar teeth of mammals shows a wide range of pattern which, used with caution and with the possibility of convergence duly borne in mind, is of great use in classi-fication. With very few exceptions these patterns can be expressed as modifications of a relatively simple type, and this type itself can be ex-plained as a modification from a simple

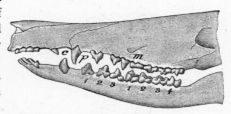

Fig. 615.—Teeth of **Bandicoot** (*Perameles*). (After Owen.)

ancestral reptilian cone. This basal type of mammalian molar pattern is termed the *tritubercular*, with respect to the upper molar and *trituberculo-sectorial* with respect to the lower. The theory of its origin, due originally to Cope, and subsequently added to and amended by Osborn, is known universally as the *Cope–Osborn theory of trituberculy*. The theory in its present-day form will be more easily understood if a brief and condensed history of its origin is first given.

Cope noticed that the molar teeth of the earliest mammals commonly possessed a triangular crown with three main cusps or tubercles, and that later forms tended to have molars with from four to six tubercles, and these he regarded as derived from the earlier triangular type. Osborn greatly de-veloped this hypothesis and, on the assumption that the principal cusps are homologous throughout the mammalia, gave them names that have been in universal use ever since. Osborn's view as to the method of origin of the individual cusps, which has since been modified in some important respects, was as follows (Fig. 616). Starting with a simple reptilian cone, this was assumed to have elongated in an antero-posterior direction and two subsidiary cones to have arisen one on the front and one on the hind border, thus producing a triconodont tooth. These two cusps were then supposed to have rotated in opposite directions in the upper and lower jaws to form triangular or *tritubercular* teeth. The apex of the triangle, or *trigon*, points inwards in the upper tooth and outwards in the lower. The cusp at the apex of the triangle, being supposed to represent the original reptilian cone, was named the *protocone* in the upper and *protoconid* in the lower tooth.[1]

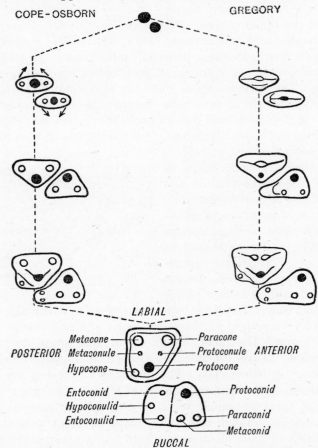

FIG. 616.—Diagram comparing the original Cope–Osborn theory of the tritubercular origin of molar teeth with its modification by Gregory. At the top the two black circles represent an upper and lower reptilian cone as the starting point. The black circles in the other teeth represent the protocone of the upper and protoconid of the lower tooth, respectively.

---

[1] The suffix *-id* designates a cusp on the lower molar. Of the other two cusps, the antero-external was named the *paracone* and the postero-external the *metacone*. A fourth cusp arising later on the cingulum on the postero-internal side, termed the *hypocone*, produce a quadri-tuber-cular tooth, and by the evolution of two smaller intermediate cusps, an anterior, the *protoconule*, and a posterior, the *metaconule*, the six cusped tooth, which underlies the molar pattern of so many mammals, comes into being. Like the upper, the lower molar consists of a triangle, or *trigonid*, and in addition a posterior shelf, the *talonid*, on which a number of cusps arise to produce the trituberculo-sectorial pattern, termed the *entoconid*, *hypoconulid*, and *hypoconid*.

At a very early stage criticism was directed against the view that the proto-cone of the mammalian tritubercular tooth represents the original reptilian cone largely because in ontogeny it is not the first cusp to be formed, nor is there any known evidence to support the hypothesis of the rotation of the sub-sidiary cusps to form the triangles. Within the premolar series, and still more in the milk-molar series, there is usually a transition from behind forwards from a tooth that resembles a molar in many respects to one that is more like a canine or an incisor. If the single cusp of the canine is traced back-wards through the successive teeth, it is seen to correspond to the paracone of the molar, and not to the protocone.[1] The protocone of the molar is repre-sented on the more anterior teeth as an inner shelf at the base, or is even completely absent, and it was therefore thought probable that this cusp is secondary in origin to the paracone, a statement which is consistent with the embryological evidence. Further evidence for the same theory is found in the fact that in some groups the premolars evolve from simple peg-like teeth to a molariform condition,[2] and in this evolution the original cusp becomes the paracone of the molar rather than the protocone.

Subsequent discovery of other early mammalian dentitions has given rise to a more probable explanation of how the molar pattern arose, which makes use of Osborn's original cusp terminology with certain modifications in the interpretation of their origin, of which the most important is that the term *protocone* is understood to represent not the original reptilian cone, but a secondary cusp, which arises on the internal border of the upper molar. The *protoconid*, on the other hand, does represent the original main cusp. The original reptilian cusps therefore, both in the upper and lower jaws, lie on the outer border, and the hypothesis of reversal of the triangles is no longer required.

To return to the probable evolution of the triangle of main cusps. Although the vast majority of Cænozoic mammalian teeth are derivatives of the tritubercular type, certain primitive mammals have teeth of a somewhat different pattern. Some of them have *zalambdodont* teeth, in which the metacone is not distinct from the paracone and the protocone is very small (Fig. 617). Others have *dilambdodont* teeth, in which the paracone and meta-cone are V-shaped, well separated, and placed near the middle of the tooth. Both these types can be traced very far back in time, and they have probably not been derived from the tritubercular type, although they must have had a common origin with it. Some idea of what the common ancestor was like is given by the Insectivore *Deltatheridium pretrituberculare* (Fig. 617), from the Cretaceous of Mongolia. Here the upper molar is a narrow triangle, on which there is a small cusp in the position of the protocone and two closely applied

[1] This is the essence of the " premolar analogy " theory.
[2] This process is called the *molarisation* of the premolars.

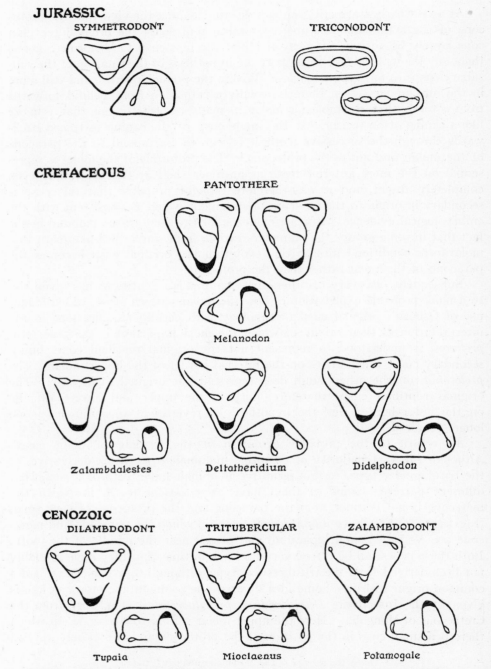

JURASSIC
SYMMETRODONT   TRICONODONT

CRETACEOUS
PANTOTHERE

Melanodon

Zalambdalestes   Deltatheridium   Didelphodon

CENOZOIC
DILAMBDODONT   TRITUBERCULAR   ZALAMBDODONT

Tupaia   Mioclaenus   Potamogale

FIG. 617.—Diagrams of the right upper and lower molar tooth of various primitive mammals. In the Cretaceous and Cenozoic examples the protocone and protoconid are coloured black.

cusps in the centre, the paracone and metacone.[1] From the evidence of *Deltatheridium* it has been suggested that a single cusp in the tooth of ancestral Mammals became divided into two to give rise to the paracone and metacone of later forms. This original undivided outer cusp is called the *amphicone*.

Still earlier in time, the molar of a mesozoic Pantothere (Fig. 617) is a transversely elongated tooth with a main inner and outer cusp, together with some smaller cuspules. It has been supposed that the inner main cusp in the protocone and the outer main cusp the amphicone. This view, however, is open to criticism, because the inner cusp is the highest on the tooth and seems to correspond to the main cusp of the premolars and the canine, as does the paracone, rather than the protocone, in other Mammals. The various mesozoic Mammals show a great variety of molar pattern, the relation of which to modern types is still a matter of discussion.[2]

It is certain that, in whatever manner the tritubercular tooth may have arisen, the subsequent sexi-tubercular tooth has been derived from it. This is borne out by an enormous amount of direct fossil evidence, and it is possible to show that such diverse tooth-patterns as that of an Artiodactyl, a Perissodactyl, or a Carnivore can be derived from the tritubercular type.

Further terms are in use to designate different parts of a tooth. If the cusps remain separate and rounded, the tooth is termed *bunoid*, if they join to form ridges, these ridges are termed *lophs*, and the tooth is *lophodont*. A tooth with crescentic cusps is *selenodont*. Any tooth may have a combination of these characters, in which case it is called *buno-lophodont*, *buno-selenodont*, etc. Additional pillars such as can be seen in the molar of a Horse, or on the outer border or *ectoloph* of many teeth, are called *styles*—e.g., the *proto-*, *meso-* and *meta-style*, etc. A tooth with a low crown is termed *brachydont*, and with a high crown and deep socket termed *hypsodont*.

As has already been stated, the crown pattern of the teeth of Mammals is largely used as a guide to their affinities. Generally speaking, it is a fairly dependable one, and starting from the more primitive and generalised forms of dentition, such as is shown by the early Insectivores, Creodonts, and Condylarths, the major groups of Mammals usually have trends of evolution on their own recognisable lines. Thus, for example, the Carnivora, the Artiodactyla, the Perissodactyla have all ultimately acquired dental patterns which are sufficiently distinctive. Other groups, such as the Proboscidea, Cetacea, and Xenarthra, have patterns that are both distinctive and diagnostic. At the same time exceptions occur, due presumably to some unusual and specialised

---

[1] There are, further, some small cusps on the external cingulum, cusps such as these frequently exist in early small Mammals with zalambdodont or dilambdodont molars. Whether such cusps are always homologous is open to doubt. It must be understood that the original tritubercular tooth may have had small cusps additional to the principal named ones.

[2] For a discussion of this question, and a full account of the history of the tritubercular theory, see W. K. Gregory (no. 96) and for details of the mesozoic forms, G. G. Simpson (no. 111), P. M. Butler (no. 89) in the appendix on literature.

kind of food, such as in *Proteles*, an insect- and worm-eating Hyæna, or *Potos*, a fruit-eating Procyonid, both of which animals have their dentition modified away from the usual carnivore type. These two are examples of a dentition that has degenerated, but there are many instances of tooth resemblance, more or less close, among unrelated animals due to convergence, the result of similar feeding habits. Thus a permanently growing gnawing incisor is not absolutely diagnostic of a Rodent, but can be found in more than one Primate, as, for instance, *Chiromys* (*Daubentonia*) (Fig. 511), in *Tillotherium* and even in an Artiodactyle such as *Myotragus*. A bilophodont form of molar tooth occurs in many diverse orders of mammals. The lophodont molar of the Hyracoids shows a curious resemblance to that of the Rhinoceros, to quote but a few examples. The difficulty of being certain as to the true affinity of some mammals on the evidence of the teeth alone increases when the earlier and more primitive forms are considered, and to decide whether a Palæocene or an Eocene tooth is to be ascribed to an Insectivore, a Primate, a Condylarth, or a Creodont is difficult, and sometimes in the present state of our knowledge is impossible. Precaution therefore must be taken against regarding as evidence of affinity a similarity of pattern, which may be the result of convergence due to a similarity of habit.

A comparison of the wide adaptive radiation of the teeth of the Marsupials into insectivorous, carnivorous, rodent, and herbivorous types of dentition with those of Placental Mammals of corresponding habits is instructive.

The number of the various sets of teeth in the jaws is conveniently expressed by a *dental formula*, in which the kind of tooth (incisor, canine, pre-molar, molar) is indicated by the initial letter (*i.*, *c.*, *p.*, *m.*), and the whole formula has the arrangement of four vulgar fractions, in each of which the numerator indicates the teeth of the upper, the denominator those of the lower jaw. Thus:

$$i. \ \frac{3 \cdot 3}{3 \cdot 3}, \ c. \ \frac{1 \cdot 1}{1 \cdot 1}, \ p. \ \frac{4 \cdot 4}{4 \cdot 4}, \ m. \ \frac{3 \cdot 3}{3 \cdot 3} = 44 \ ;$$

or, in a simpler form, since the teeth of the right and left sides are always the same,

$$i. \ \frac{3}{3}, \ c. \ \frac{1}{1}, \ p. \ \frac{4}{4}, \ m. \ \frac{3}{3} = 44.$$

Tachyglossus has no teeth at any stage. In Ornithorhynchus teeth are present in the young and are functional for a time, but they are thrown off when the animal is about a year old ; vestiges of an earlier dentition have been detected. The function of teeth is performed in the adult by broad horny plates, one on each upper and one on each lower jaw (Figs. 474, 475).

The Marsupials have the milk-dentition in a degenerate condition. Germs of milk-teeth are developed, but with the exception of one—the last premolar—these remain in an imperfect state of development, though they persist, as functionless vestiges, to a comparatively late stage.

In the adult dentition of the Marsupials the number of incisors in the upper and lower jaws is always dissimilar, except in *Phascolomys*. With regard to the arrangement of these teeth, the order falls into two series, termed respectively the *diprotodont* and the *polyprotodont*. In the former (Figs. 618, 619) the two anterior incisors are large and prominent, the rest of the incisors and the canines being smaller or absent. On the other hand, in the polyprotodont forms (Figs. 620, 621), which are all more or less carnivorous, the incisors are numerous and sub-equal and the canines large. There are typically three premolars and four molars. A good example of the diprotodont arrangement is the Kangaroo (*Macropus*, Fig. 619), which has the dental formula—

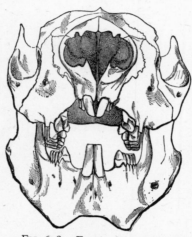

FIG. 618.—Front view of skull of **Koala** (*Phascolarctos cinereus*), illustrating diprotodont and herbivorous dentition. (After Flower.)

$$i. \frac{3}{1}, c. \frac{1}{0}, p. \frac{2}{2}, m. \frac{4}{4} = 34.$$

The canine is very small and early lost. Of the polyprotodont forms the Australian Dasyure or Native Cat (Fig. 492) has the formula—

$$i. \frac{4}{3}, c. \frac{1}{1}, p. \frac{2}{2}, m. \frac{4}{4} = 42;$$

and the American Opossum (*Didelphys*) (Fig. 621)—

$$i. \frac{5}{4}, c. \frac{1}{1}, p. \frac{3}{3}, m. \frac{4}{4} = 50.$$

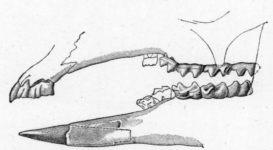

FIG. 619.—Teeth of **Great Kangaroo** (*Macropus major*). (After Owen.)

The Xenarthra, though not by any means all toothless, always have some defect in the dentition; when teeth are present in the adult the anterior series is absent and the teeth are imperfect, wanting roots and devoid of enamel. The tooth-characters differ widely in the different groups. In the Sloths there are five teeth above and four below on each side; no second series is known.

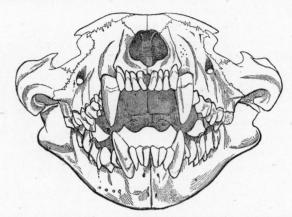

FIG. 620.—Front view of the skull of **Tasmanian Devil** (*Sarcophilus ursinus*), showing polyprotodont and carnivorous dentition. (After Flower.)

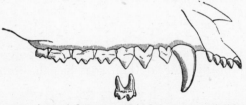

FIG. 621.—Teeth of upper jaw of **Opossum** (*Didelphys marsupialis*), showing the condition typical of marsupials, in all of which there is no succession except in the last premolar, the place of which is occupied in the young animal by a molariform tooth represented in the figure below the line of the other teeth. (After Flower and Lydekker.)

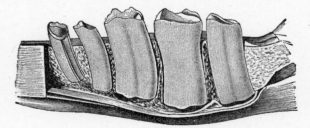

FIG. 622.—Section of lower jaw and teeth of **Orycteropus.** (After Owen.)

In the American Ant-eaters there are no teeth in the adult. In the Armadillos, on the other hand, the teeth are numerous, though simple and rootless, and, in one genus at least, two series occur. In the Scaly Ant-eaters there are no teeth. In the Tubulidentata or Cape Ant-eaters (Fig. 622) again, there are numerous teeth which are heterodont and diphyodont, and have a peculiar structure, being perforated by numerous minute, parallel, vertical canals; the pulp of each tooth, entire at its base, is divided distally into a number of parallel columns.

In the Ungulata the dentition is heterodont and diphyodont, and the teeth are very rarely devoid of roots. In the Artiodactyla the premolars and molars differ from one another in pattern; the first upper premolar is almost always without a milk predecessor. The Pigs (Fig. 623) are among the very

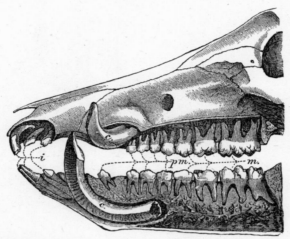

FIG. 623.—Left lateral view of the dentition of the **Boar** (*Sus scrofa*), the roots of the teeth being exposed. (After Flower and Lydekker.)

few recent Mammalia which possess what has been referred to as a typical dentition: the formula of the completed dentition is—

$$i. \frac{3}{3}, \; c. \frac{1}{1}, \; p. \frac{4}{4}, \; m. \frac{3}{3} = 44.$$

The incisors of the upper jaw are vertical, those of the lower greatly inclined forwards. The canines are greatly developed, especially in the male, and grow from persistent pulps; both the upper and lower are bent upwards and outwards and work against one another in such a manner that the upper wears on its anterior and external surface, the lower at the extremity of the posterior surface. The premolars are compressed, with longitudinal cutting edges, and the molars are provided with numerous tubercles or cusps arranged for the most part in transverse rows (bunodont type). The first permanent premolar has no predecessor, the formula of the milk dentition being—

$$i. \frac{3}{3}, \; c. \frac{1}{1}, \; m. \frac{3}{3} = 28.$$

In the typical Ruminants there are no teeth on the premaxillæ, the incisors of the lower jaw and the canines, which resemble them in shape, biting against a thickened callous pad on the opposed surface of the upper jaw, and the upper canines are also usually absent; there are three premolars and three molars in both upper and lower series, all characterised by the presence of column-like vertical folds of enamel, the interstices between which may be filled up with cement—the worn surface of the tooth presenting a pattern of the selenodont type (Fig. 610, *V*). In the Camels there are a pair of upper incisors and a pair of large canines in each jaw.

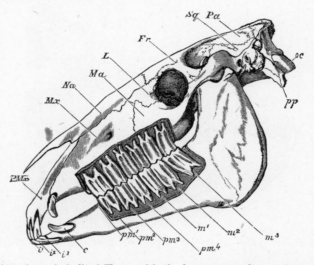

FIG. 624.—Side view of skull of **Horse** with the bone removed so as to expose the whole of the teeth. *c.* canine; *Fr.* frontal; *i¹. i². i³.* incisors; *L.* lachrymal; *Ma.* jugal; *Mx.* maxilla; *m¹. m². m³.* molars; *Na.* nasal; *o. c.* occipital condyle; *Pa.* parietal; *p. m¹.* situation of the vestigial first premolar, which has been lost in the lower, but is present in the upper jaw; *pm². pm⁴. pm¹.* remaining premolars; *Pmx.* premaxilla; *p. p.* par-occipital process; *Sq.* squamosal. (After Flower and Lydekker.)

In the Perissodactyla the molars and premolars form a continuous series of large teeth with ridged or complexly-folded crowns, the posterior premolars often differing little in size and structure from the molars. In the Horse (Fig. 624) the formula is—

$$i. \frac{3}{3}, c. \frac{1}{1}, p. \frac{4}{4}, m. \frac{3}{3} = 44,$$

but the first premolar is a small tooth which soon becomes lost. A fold of the enamel dips downwards (*i.e.*, towards the root) from the extremity of the incisor teeth like the partly inverted finger of a glove; the canines are small in the female, and may not appear on the surface. There is a wide interval in both jaws between the canines and premolars. The premolar and molar teeth present a complicated pattern due to folds of the enamel, which differ in their arrangement in the upper and lower jaws; their roots become completed only at a late period.

In the Hyracoidea the dental formula is—

$$i. \frac{1}{2}, c. \frac{0}{0}, p. \frac{4}{4}, m. \frac{3}{3} = 34.$$

The upper incisors are not unlike the larger pair of the Rabbit in shape, though prismatic and pointed, instead of compressed and chisel-like; they grow from persistent pulps. The outer incisors are elongated, inclined forwards, and tri-lobed at the extremities. The premolars and molars form a continuous series, separated by an interval from the incisors, and in pattern closely resemble those of some of the Perissodactyla.

The Elephants (Fig. 562) have an extremely specialised dentition. There are no canines and no lower incisors. The single pair of upper incisors are developed into the enormous tusks (Fig. 610, I), which grow continuously

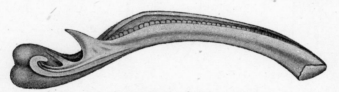

FIG. 625.—Left lower jaw of fœtus of **Balænoptera rostrata,** inner aspect, showing teeth natural size. (After Julin.)

from persistent pulps throughout the life of the animal; they are of elongated conical form, and usually become curved. The tusks are composed of solid dentine, enamel occurring only on the apices, and becoming early worn away. The molars (Fig. 562) are very large, and their worn surfaces are marked with prominent transverse ridges; there are six molars altogether on each side, but only one or two are functional at once, the more posterior moving forward and taking the place of the more anterior as these become worn out.

When teeth are developed in the Cetacea they are nearly always numerous, homodont, and monophyodont: in the Sperm-Whales they are confined to the lower jaw. In the Whalebone Whales, though teeth are developed in the fœtal condition (Fig. 625), they become lost either before or soon after birth, and they are succeeded in the adult by the plates of baleen or whalebone (Fig. 626), which, in the form of numerous triangular plates, hang vertically downwards from the palate.

Of the Sirenia, the Dugong and Manatee have a heterodont dentition; in Rhytina teeth were absent. In the two former Sirenians there are incisors and molars with a wide diastema between them. In the Manatee there are two rudimentary incisors on each side, both in the upper and the lower jaw; these disappear before the adult condition is reached. There are altogether eleven molars on each side above and below, but not more than six of these are in use at once, the more anterior when worn out being succeeded by the more posterior. They have enamelled crowns with transverse ridges, and are preceded by milk-teeth. In the Dugong there are no incisors in the mandible of the adult, and only one tusk-like pair in the upper jaw, large in the male—in which they grow from persistent pulps, little developed in the female and remaining concealed in their sockets. In the young there are rudimentary

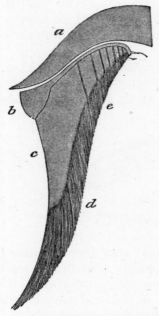

FIG. 626.—Section of upper jaw of **Balænoptera** (*a*), with baleen-plates (*b*, *c*) frayed out at their free edges (*d*, *e*). (After Owen.)

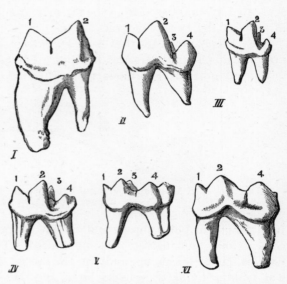

FIG. 627.—Left lower carnassial teeth of **Carnivora.** *I*, **Felis**; *II*, **Canis**; *III*, **Herpestes**; *IV*, **Lutra**; *V*, **Meles**; *VI*, **Ursus.** *1*, anterior lobe (paraconid) of blade; *2*, posterior lobe (protoconid) of blade; *3*, inner cusp (metaconid); *4*, talon (hypoconid). (After Flower and Lydekker.)

incisors in the mandible, and also a rudimentary second pair in the upper jaw. There are either five or six molars on each side, both in the upper and lower jaws. These are cylindrical teeth, devoid of enamel, and with persistent pulps.

In the Carnivora vera (Fig. 627) the dentition is complete, heterodont, and diphyodont, and all the teeth are provided with roots. The incisors are relatively small, chisel-shaped teeth; there are nearly always three of them on each side, in both upper and lower jaws. The canines are always large and pointed. The presence of carnassials, consisting of the last premolar in the upper and the first molar in the lower jaw, is typical. In front of the carnassial the teeth are compressed and pointed; behind it they have broad surfaces. In the Cat family (*Felidæ*) the formula is—

$$i. \frac{3}{3}, c. \frac{1}{1}, p. \frac{3}{2}, m. \frac{1}{1} = 30.$$

The lower carnassial is thus the last of the series. In the Dogs (Canidæ) the formula is usually—

$$i. \frac{3}{3}, c. \frac{1}{1}, p. \frac{4}{4}, m. \frac{2}{3} = 42,$$

and in the Bears (Ursidæ) it is the same. (For the pattern of the molar teeth see Fig. 527.)

In the Pinnipedia there are always fewer than $\frac{3}{3}$ incisors, and carnassials are not developed. The premolars and molars have a compressed, conical, pointed form. The prevailing dental formula of the Seals is—

$$i. \frac{3}{2}, c. \frac{1}{1}, p. \frac{4}{4}, m. \frac{1}{1} = 34.$$

In the Walrus the adult formula is—

$$i. \frac{1}{0}, c. \frac{1}{1}, p. \frac{3}{3}, m. \frac{0}{0} = 18.$$

The upper canines take the form of large, nearly straight tusks.

In the large order of the Rodents the dentition is remarkably uniform, and, in all its general characters, resembles what has already been described in the Rabbit. But the second, smaller pair of incisors of the upper jaw is present only in the Hares and Rabbits; the number of premolars and molars varies from—

$$p. \frac{0}{0}, m. \frac{2}{2} \text{ to } p. \frac{3}{2}, m. \frac{3}{3},$$

and they may develop roots.

In the Insectivora the dentition is heterodont, complete, and diphyodont. All the teeth are rooted. There are never fewer than two incisors on either side of the lower jaw. The canines are not of large size. The crowns of the molars are beset with pointed tubercles.

In the Chiroptera the dentition is complete, and the teeth are all rooted. There is a milk-series which differs entirely from the permanent teeth. In the insectivorous Chiroptera (Bats) the molars are provided with pointed cusps, while in the frugivorous forms ("Flying Foxes") they are longitudinally grooved or excavated.

In the Primates the teeth are heterodont and diphyodont, and always form roots. There are almost invariably two incisors on each side in each jaw, and, in all but the Hapalidæ, three molars. The dental formulæ of the various families have been given in the synopsis of the classification. The dentition of Man differs from that of the rest of the order in the teeth forming a continuous series not interrupted by a diastema, and in the comparatively small size of the canines.

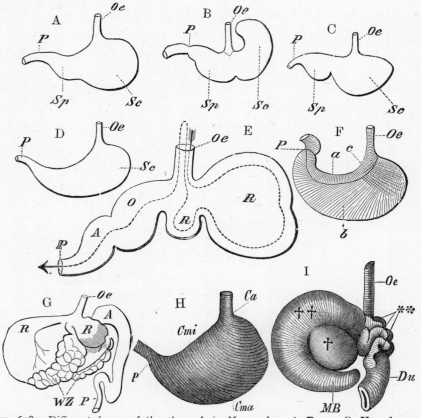

FIG. 628.—Different forms of the **stomach** in Mammals. *A*, **Dog** ; *B*, **Mus decumanus** ; *C*, **Mus musculus** ; *D*, **Weasel** ; *E*, scheme of the **ruminant** stomach, the arrow with the dotted line showing the course taken by the food ; *F*, **human** stomach, *a, b, c*, muscles on inner side ; *G*, **Camel** ; *H*, **Tachyglossus aculeata** ; *I*, **Bradypus tridactylus**. *A*. (in *E* and *G*) abomasum ; *Ca*. cardiac end ; *Cma*. greater curvature ; *Cmi*, lesser curvature ; *Du*. duodenum ; *MB*, cæcum ; *O*, psalterium ; *Oe*. œsophagus ; *P*. pylorus ; *R*. (to the right in Fig. *E*), ††, rumen ; *R*. (to the left in Fig. *E*), †, reticulum ; *Sc*. cardiac division ; *Sp*. pyloric division ; *WZ*, water-cells ; ** duodenal pouches. (From Wiedersheim's *Comparative Anatomy*.)

The mouth in mammals is bounded by fleshy *lips*. On the floor of the mouth is situated the *tongue*, which is usually well developed, but varies in size and shape in different orders. Its surface is covered with papillæ of different forms, in association with certain of which are the special end-organs of the nerves of taste—the *taste-buds*. The roof of the mouth is formed in front by the *hard palate*, consisting of the horizontal palatine plates of the maxillary and palatine bones covered with mucous membrane. Behind the hard palate projects backwards the soft muscular fold of the *soft palate*, also with taste-buds, which divides the cavity of the pharynx into two chambers, an upper and a lower. In front of the opening, leading from the lower division of the pharynx into the larynx, is a cartilaginous plate—the epiglottis—of which rudiments only are found in certain lower vertebrates.

The *œsophagus* is always a simple straight tube. The *stomach* varies greatly in different orders, being sometimes simple, as in the majority of mammals, sometimes divided into chambers, as in the Cetacea and the Ruminants.

In the majority of mammals the stomach is a simple sac, as in the Rabbit (p. 502). But in certain groups it is complicated by the development of internal folds, and may be divided by constrictions into a number of different chambers. The complication of this organ reaches its extreme limit in

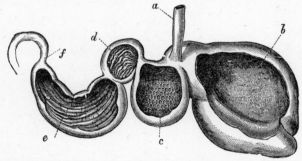

FIG. 629.—Stomach of **Ruminant** opened to show the internal structure. *a*, œsophagus; *b*, rumen; *c*, reticulum; *d*, psalterium; *e*, abomasum; *f*, duodenum. (After Flower and Lydekker.)

the ruminant Ungulata and in the Cetacea. In a typical Ruminant (Fig. 628 E, Fig. 629), such as a Sheep or an Ox, the stomach is divided into four chambers—the *rumen* or *paunch*, the *reticulum*, the *psalterium*, and the *abomasum*, or *rennet stomach*. The first of these (Fig. 629, *b*) is much larger than the rest; its mucous membrane is beset with numerous short villi. The reticulum (*c*), which is much smaller than the rumen, has its mucous membrane raised up into a number of anastomosing ridges, giving its wall the appearance of a honeycomb with shallow cells. From the aperture by which the reticulum communicates with the rumen to that with which it communicates with the psalterium runs a groove bounded by a pair of muscular ridges, which are capable of closing together in such a way as to convert the groove into a canal. The mucous membrane of the psalterium (*d*) is raised up into numerous longitudinal leaf-like folds. The abomasum (*e*), smaller than the rumen, but larger than the reticulum, has a smooth vascular and glandular mucous membrane. The œsophagus opens into the rumen close to its junction with the reticulum. The herbage on which the ruminant feeds is swallowed without mastication, accompanied by copious saliva, and passes into the rumen and reticulum, where it lies until, having finished feeding, the animal begins ruminating or chewing the cud. In this process the sodden food is returned in rounded boluses from the rumen to the mouth, and there undergoes mastication. When fully masticated it is swallowed again in a semi-fluid condition, and passes along the groove into the reticulum, or over the unmasticated food contained in the latter chamber, to strain through between the leaves of the psalterium and enter the abomasum, where the process of digestion goes on. In some Ruminants the psalterium is wanting. In the Camels (Fig. 628, G) the stomach is not so complicated as in the more typical Ruminants, there being also no distinct psalterium, and the rumen being devoid of villi; both the rumen and the reticulum have connected with them a number of pouch-like diverticula (w. z.), the openings of which are capable of being closed by sphincter muscles; in these water is stored. In the Cetacea the stomach is also divided into compartments. In the Porpoise (Fig. 630) the œsophagus (a) opens into a spacious paunch (b), the cardiac compartment of the stomach, with a smooth, thick, mucous membrane. This is followed by a second chamber (c), of considerably smaller dimensions, with a glandular mucous membrane, which is thrown into a number of complex folds. A long and narrow third, or pyloric, compartment (d, e) follows upon this, terminating in a constricted pyloric aperture, beyond which the beginning of the intestine is dilated into a bulb.

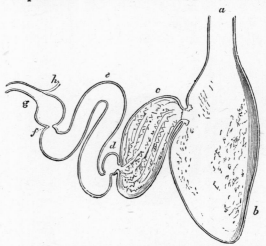

FIG. 630.—Diagrammatic section of the stomach of the **Porpoise.** a, œsophagus; b, left or cardiac compartment; c, middle compartment; d and e, the two divisions of the right, or pyloric compartment; f, pylorus; g, duodenum, dilated at its commencement; h, bile-duct. (After Flower and Lydekker.)

A cæcum, situated at the junction of the large and small intestines, is usually present, but varies greatly in extent in the different orders and families. It is much larger in vegetable-feeding than in carnivorous forms, and among the former it is those that have a simple stomach, such as the Rabbit, that have the largest cæcum. Hyrax differs from all the rest of the class in having a pair of supplementary cæca situated some distance down the large intestine. A cæcum is absent in the Sloths, some Cetacea, and a few Carnivora.

The Prototheria resemble Reptiles, Birds, and Amphibia, and differ from other Mammals in the presence of a cloaca, into which not only the rectum but the urinary and genital ducts open. In the Marsupials a common sphincter muscle surrounds both anal and urinogenital apertures and in the female there is a definite cloaca ; in nearly all the Eutheria the apertures are distinct, and separated from one another by a considerable space—the *perinæum*.

The liver (Fig. 631) consists of two parts or main divisions, right and left, incompletely separated from one another by a fissure termed the *umbilical*, owing to its marking the position of the fœtal umbilical vein. Typically each of these main divisions is divided by a fissure into two parts, so that *right lateral (rl.)* and *right central (rc.)* and *left lateral (ll.)* and *left central (lc.)* lobes are distinguishable. When a gall-bladder is present, as is the case in the majority of mammals, it is attached to, or embedded in, the right central lobe. A

fissure, the *portal*, through which the portal vein and hepatic artery pass into the substance of the liver, and the hepatic vein passes out, crosses the right central lobe near the anterior border. The postcaval lies in contact with, or embedded in, the right lateral lobe near its anterior border, and given off from this lobe, between the postcaval and the portal fissure, is a small lobe, of varying extent — the *Spigelian*. The term *caudate lobe* is applied to a process of the right lateral lobe, of considerable extent in most mammals, having the postcaval vein in intimate relation to it, and often closely applied to the kidney. A gall-bladder is usually

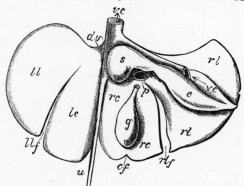

Fig. 631.—Diagrammatic plan of the liver of a **Mammal** (posterior surface). *c.* caudate lobe ; *cf.* cystic fissure ; *dv.* ductus venosus ; *g.* gall-bladder ; *lc.* left central lobe ; *ll.* left lateral lobe ; *llf.* left lateral fissure ; *p.* portal vein entering transverse fissure ; *rc.* right central lobe ; *rl.* right lateral lobe ; *rlf.* right lateral fissure ; *s.* Spigelian lobe ; *u.* umbilical vein ; *vc.* post-caval. (After Flower and Lyddeker.)

present, but is absent in the Cetacea, the Perissodactyle Ungulata, the Hyracoidea, and some Rodents.

Vascular System.—The blood of mammals is warm, having a temperature always of from 35° to 40° C. The *red corpuscles* are non-nucleated : in form they are most usually biconcave discs, always circular in outline, except in the Camilidæ, in which most of them are elliptical. The *lymphatic system* of vessels is very highly developed, ramifying richly throughout all parts of the body. In the course of this system occur numerous lymphatic glands. The special part of the lymphatic system of vessels (*lacteals*) which ramify in the wall of the intestine and absorb the fatty matters of the food combine with the lymphatic vessels from the hind-limbs and body to form a receptacle—the *receptaculum chyli*—from which a tube, the *thoracic duct*, which may be double, runs forward to open into the base of one of the great veins of the precaval system by a valvular aperture.

The general statements which have been given with regard to the *heart* of the Rabbit (p. 504) hold good for the Mammalia in general. The sinus venosus is never distinct from the right auricle : of its valves, which are more completely retained in the Edentata than in the other orders, the right gives rise to the Eustachian valve—a membranous fold, often fenestrated in the adult, extending from the right wall of the postcaval to the edge of the foramen ovale (annulus ovalis) ; while the left becomes merged in the auricular septum, helping to complete the annulus ovalis behind. Each auricle has an auricular appendix. The right auriculo-ventricular aperture has a three-lobed tricuspid valve, and the left a two-lobed bicuspid, or mitral, with chordæ tendineæ and musculi papillares. In all mammals the openings of the pulmonary artery and aorta are provided with three-lobed semilunar valves.

The single aortic arch, situated in all mammals on the left side, varies greatly in the way in which it gives off the main arterial trunks. Sometimes a single large trunk passes forward from the arch of the aorta and gives rise to both carotids and both subclavians. Sometimes there are two main trunks— *right* and *left innominate arteries*—each giving rise to the carotid and sub-clavian of its own side. Sometimes there is a right innominate giving off right carotid and right subclavian, the left carotid and left subclavian coming off separately from the arch of the aorta ; or, as in the Rabbit, an innominate may give origin to the right subclavian and both carotids, the left subclavian coming off separately.

In Monotremes and Marsupials, in most Ungulates, and in the Rodentia, Insectivora, and Chiroptera, both right and left precavals persist ; in the others the left aborts, its vestige giving rise to the coronary sinus. In the Monotremes the openings of all three cavals are provided with valves, only vestiges of which exist in the other groups. In the Monotremes all the pulmonary veins open by a common trunk. In the Metatheria and Eutheria the four veins sometimes open separately, sometimes the two veins of each side unite to form a single lateral trunk. In Tachyglossus there is an abdominal vein corresponding to that of the Frog and Lizard (pp. 323 and 368).

The following are some of the principal variations in the structure of the heart which occur in the different groups of mammals. In the Monotremes there is a deep fossa representing the fossa ovalis in the auricular septum. The auri-culo-ventricular valves depart from the structure typical of Mammals and approach the corresponding valves in the heart of Birds. In the Marsupials the fossa ovalis and annulus ovalis are absent ; in the uterine fœtus of the Kan-garoo the auricles communicate by a fissure, but all trace of this becomes lost before the adult stage is reached.

In the Cetacea, Eustachian and Thebesian valves are both absent. In

some of the Cetacea the apices of the ventricles are separated by a slight depression. In the Sirenia there is a corresponding, but much deeper and wider, cleft, so that the apex of the heart is distinctly bifid.

In the Ungulata, Eustachian and coronary valves are both absent; in some there is a cartilage or a bone—the *os cordis*—often double, at the base of the heart. The Eustachian valve is absent in most of the Carnivora. In the Pinnipedia an aperture of communications between the auricles often persists in the adult.

The **organs of respiration** resemble those of the Rabbit in the general features mentioned on p. 508.

In the Cetacea, the epiglottis and arytenoids are prolonged to form a tube, which extends into the nasal chambers and is embraced by the soft palate, so that a continuous passage is formed leading from the nasal chambers to the larynx, and giving rise to the condition of *intra-narial epiglottis*. In all the remaining orders a similar condition occasionally occurs—the epiglottis being produced upwards into the respiratory division of the pharynx behind the soft palate. In fœtal Marsupials, in which the intra-narial condition is very complete, it is obviously associated with the passive absorption of the milk, while breathing is being carried on continuously through the nostrils. Some Cetacea and Artiodactyla, etc., are exceptional in having a *third bronchus*, which passes to the right lung anteriorly to the ordinary bronchus of that side and to the pulmonary artery. In connection with various parts of the respiratory system there are cavities containing air. The connection of the tympanic cavity with the pharynx by means of the Eustachian tubes has been already mentioned. Air-sinuses, connected with the nasal chambers, extend into the bones of the skull, especially into the maxillæ and frontals, where they may reach large dimensions, and are known as the *maxillary antra* and *frontal sinuses*. Air-sacs are also developed in connection with the larynx in many of the Apes.

Nervous System.—The brain of mammals (Fig. 632) is distinguished by its relatively large size, and by the large size and complex structure of the *cerebral hemispheres* of the fore-brain.

The cerebral hemispheres of opposite sides are connected together across the middle line in all mammals, except the Monotremes and Marsupials, by a band of nerve-tissue termed the *corpus callosum*—a structure not present in the Sauropsida. The hemispheres, in all but certain of the lower and smaller mammals, are not smooth, but marked by a number of grooves or sulci separating winding ridges or convolutions. The *lateral ventricles* in the interior of the hemispheres are of large size and somewhat complex form.

The *optic lobes*, which are relatively small, are divided into four parts, and are hence called the *corpora quadrigemina*. The *pineal body* is always a small gland-like structure. Connecting together the lateral parts of the cerebellum, which, in the higher Mammals, attains a high degree of development, is a

transverse flattened band—the *pons Varolii* (*Po.*)—crossing the hind-brain on its ventral aspect.

In the Monotremes and Marsupials (Figs. 633, 634) there is no corpus callosum, while the anterior commissure (*ant. com.*) is of relatively large size,

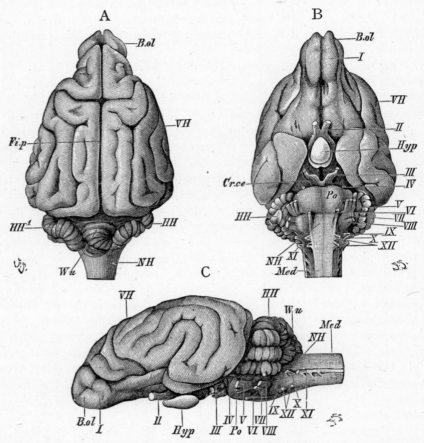

FIG. 632.—Brain of **Dog.** *A*, dorsal; *B*, ventral; *C*, lateral aspect. *B. ol.* olfactory bulb; *Cr. ce.* crura cerebri; *Fi. p.* great longitudinal fissure; *HH, HH'*, latera lobes of cerebellum; *Hyp*. hypophysis; *Med.* spinal cord; *NH*, medulla oblongata; *Po.* pons Varolii; *VH*. cerebral hemispheres; *Wu*, middle lobe (vermis) of cerebellum; *I—XII*. cerebral nerves. (From Wiedersheim's *Comparative Anatomy*.)

and, unlike the corresponding commissure in lower vertebrates, contains fibres connecting together areas of the non-olfactory regions (*neo-pallium*) of the hemispheres. The hippocampi extend along the whole length of the lateral ventricles. The layer of nerve-cells in each hippocampus gives origin, as in Eutheria, to numerous fibres, which form a layer on the surface, the *alveus*, and become arranged in a band—the *tænia hippocampi*. In the Eutheria, as we have seen in the case of the Rabbit, the tæniæ unite mesially to form the body of the fornix (see p. 510). In the Monotremes and Marsupials, on the other hand, there is no such union; the fibres of the tænia run towards the foramen of Monro, where they become divided into several sets. Of these one set, constituting the great majority of the fibres, pass into the hippocampus of the opposite side, giving rise to a *hippocampal commissure* (*hip. com.*, cf. Figs. 633 and 634), the great development of which readily leads to its being mistaken for a corpus callosum. The fibres entering into the formation of this commissure correspond, however, not to the fibres of the corpus callosum, which

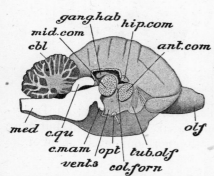

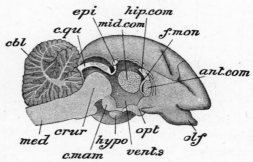

FIG. 633.—Brain of **Tachyglossus acu-leata,** sagittal section. *ant. com.* anterior commissure; *cbl.* cerebellum; *c. mam.* corpus mammillare; *col. forn.* column of the fornix; *c. qu,* corpora quadrigemina; *gang. hab.* habenular ganglion; *hip. com.* hippo-campal commissure; *med.* medulla oblongata; *mid. com.* middle commissure; *olf.* olfactory bulb; *opt.* optic chiasma; *tub. olf.* tuberculum olfactorium; *vent. 3,* third ventricle.

FIG. 634.—Sagittal section of brain of **Rock Wallaby** (*Petrogale penicillata*). *ant. com.* anterior commissure; *cbl.* cerebellum; *c. mam.* corpus mammillare; *c. qu.* corpora quadrigemina; *crur.* crura cerebri; *epi.* epiphysis, with the posterior commissure immediately behind; *f. mon.* position of foramen of Monro; *hip. com.* hippocampal commissure, consisting here of two layers continuous behind at the splenium, somewhat divergent in front where the septum lucidum extends between them; *hypo.* hypophysis; *med.* medulla oblongata; *mid. com.* middle commissure; *olf.* olfactory bulb; *opt.* optic chiasma; *vent. 3,* third ventricle.

is the commissure of the neo-pallium, but, as proved by their mode of origin, to the fibres of the fornix, and they connect together only the hippocampi, the *fasciæ dentatæ*, or specialised lower borders of the hippocampi, and an area of the hemisphere in front of the anterior commissure (*pre-commissural area*): they thus constitute an *olfactory* or *archipallial* commissure, since all these parts belong to the olfactory region of *archipallium* of the hemispheres. In the Monotremes (Fig. 633) the hippocampal commissure is only very slightly bent downwards at its posterior extremity. In most Marsupials (Fig. 634) it bends sharply round posteriorly and runs forward again, becoming thus folded into two layers, dorsal and ventral, continuous with one another at a posterior bend or *splenium*, similar to the splenium of the corpus callosum. The dorsal layer of the hippocampal commissure becomes almost completely replaced in the

Eutheria by the fibres of the corpus callosum, and the ventral part persists in the shape of the psalterium or lyra.

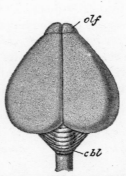

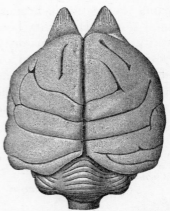

FIG. 635.—Brain of **Ornithor-rhynchus anatinus,** dorsal view (natural size). *cbl.* cerebellum ; *olf.* olfactory bulbs.

FIG. 636.—Brain of **Tachyglossus aculeata,** dorsal view (natural size).

In Ornithorhynchus (Fig. 635) the hemispheres are smooth ; in Tachy-glossus (Fig. 636) they are tolerably richly convoluted. Both genera, but more particularly Tachyglossus, are characterised by the enormous development of the

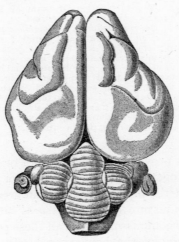

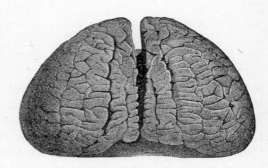

FIG. 637.—Brain of **Kangaroo** (*Macropus major*). (After Owen.)

FIG. 638.—Dorsal view of brain of **Gray's Whale** (*Cogia grayi*). (After Haswell.)

parts of the hemispheres (archipallium) connected with the olfactory sense. In the lower Marsupials there are no convolutions (Notoryctes, Koala, Phalangers), while in the higher the convolutions are numerous, though the sulci are not very deep (Macropus, Fig. 637). Among the Eutheria there is a great range in the grade of development of the brain, from the Rodents and lower Insectivores to the higher Primates. In the lower types of mammalian brain the cerebral hemispheres are relatively small, do not over-lap the cerebellum, and have smooth, or nearly smooth, surfaces. In the higher types the relative development of the hemispheres is immense, and their backward extension causes them to cover over all the rest of the brain, while the cortex is thrown into numerous complicated convolutions separated by deep sulci (Fig. 638). This development of the cerebral hemispheres reaches its maximum in Man.

The **organs of special sense** have the same general structure and arrangement as in the Sauropsida. *Jacobson's organs*, which in the Sauropsida constitute such important accessory parts to the olfactory apparatus, are well developed only in the lower groups of mammals. The *olfactory mucous membrane* is of great extent, owing to the development of the convoluted ethmo-turbinal bones over which it extends. In the toothed Cetacea alone among mammals do the nasal chambers lose their sensory functions —the olfactory nerves being vestigial or absent. The organs of taste are *taste-buds* in the mucous membrane covering certain of the papillæ on the surface of the tongue and in that of the soft palate.

In essential structure the *eye* of the Mammal resembles that of the Vertebrates in general (*see* p. 112). The sclerotic is composed of condensed fibrous tissue. The pecten of the eye of Birds and Reptiles is absent. In most Mammals there are three movable eye-

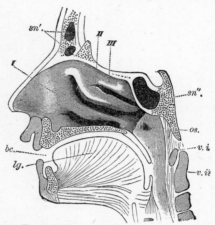

FIG. 639.—Sagittal section through the nasal and buccal cavities of the human head. *I, II, III,* the three olfactory ridges formed by the turbinals; *bc,* entrance to the mouth; *lg.* tongue; *os,* opening of Eustachian tube; *sn',* frontal sinus; *sn'',* sphenoidal sinus; *v. i,* atlas vertebra; *v. ii,* axis vertebra. (After Wiedersheim.)

lids, two, upper and lower, opaque and usually covered with hair, and one anterior, translucent, and hairless—the *nictitating membrane*. The secretions of a *lachrymal*, a *Harderian*, and a series of *Meibomian* glands moisten and lubricate the outer surface of the eye-ball and its lids. In Moles, and certain other burrowing Insectivores and Rodents, and in Notoryctes among the Marsupials, the eyes are imperfectly developed and functionless.

The *ear* of a mammal is more highly developed than that of other vertebrates, both in respect of the greater complexity of the essential part—the membranous labyrinth—and in the greater development of the accessory parts. A large external *auditory pinna*, supported by cartilage, is almost invariably present, except in the Monotremata, Cetacea, and Sirenia. This is a widely open funnel, of a variety of shapes in different groups, having the function of collecting the waves of sound. By the action of a system of muscles it is usually capable of being turned about in different directions. Enclosed by its basal part is the opening of the *external auditory passage* (Fig. 640, *Ex.*). This, the length of which varies, leads inwards to the *tympanic membrane* (*M.*), which separates it from the cavity of the middle ear or *tympanic cavity*. The wall of the external auditory passage is sometimes entirely membranous or cartilaginous, sometimes in part supported by a tubular part of the tympanic bone; in Tachyglossus it is strengthened by a series of incomplete rings of cartilage. The tympanic cavity, enclosed by the periotic and tympanic bones, communicates

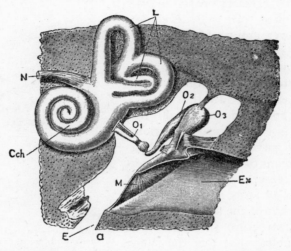

FIG. 640.—Parts of the **Human ear** (diagrammatic). *Cch.* cochlea; *E.* Eustachian tube; *Ex.* outer opening of ear; *L.* labyrinth; *M.* tympanic membrane; *N.* entrance of auditory nerve; O_1, O_2, O_3, the three auditory ossicles, stapes, incus, malleus. (After Headley.)

with the upper or respiratory division of the pharynx by a longer or shorter tubular passage—the *Eustachian tube* (*E.*). On its inner wall are the *fenestræ ovalis* and *rotunda*, and across its cavity, from the tympanic membrane to the fenestra ovalis, runs the irregular chain of auditory ossicles—the malleus (O_3), the incus (O_2) and the stapes (O_1). These vary somewhat in form in different Mammals. The stapes is usually perforated by a considerable foramen, as in the Rabbit, but, in the Monotremes, certain Marsupials, and Manis among the Edentata, approximates more towards the rod-like shape which the columella presents in Amphibians, Reptiles, and Birds. The *membranous labyrinth* (*L.*) of the internal ear of a Mammal is characterised by the special development of the *cochlea* (*Cch.*), which (except in the Monotremes) is coiled into a spiral like the shell of a Snail.

Urinogenital Organs.—The *kidneys* of Mammals are compact organs of oval shape. On the inner side is a notch or *hilus*, by which vessels and ducts enter or leave the interior of the kidney. The substance of the kidney consists of two distinctly marked portions—a central portion of *medulla*, and an outer part or *cortex*; the latter is the secreting part; the former consists of a mass of straight tubules by which the secretion is carried to the ureter. The ureter dilates as it enters the kidneys to form a chamber—the *pelvis*—into which the straight tubules of the medulla of the kidney open. The openings of the tubules are on the summits of papillæ, which are the apices of a series of pyramidal masses into which, in most cases, the substance of the kidney is incompletely divided. In many mammals, however, there is no such division of the kidney substance, and all the ducts open on the surface of a single papilla. In others again (Ox, Bears, Seals, Cetacea) the division is carried so far that the kidney is divided externally into a number of distinctly separated lobules.

The ureters in all the Theria open into a large median sac—the *urinary bladder*—situated in the posterior or pelvic part of the cavity of the abdomen. From this a median passage, the urinogenital passage or *uretha*—into which in the male the *vasa deferentia* open—leads to the exterior. Only in the Monotremes do the two ureters and the bladder all have separate openings into the urinogenital division of the cloaca.

The testes are oval bodies, which only exceptionally retain their original position in the abdominal cavity, descending in the majority of mammals through a canal—the *inguinal canal*—in the posterior part of the abdominal wall to lie in the *perinæum*, or space between the urinogenital and anal apertures, or to be received into a pendulous pouch of skin, sometimes double—the *scrotum*. The *penis*, present in the males of all mammalia, consists of two *corpora cavernosa*, firm strands of vascular tissue attached proximately to the ischia except in the Monotremes, Marsupials, and some Edentata, and a central strand, the *corpus spongiosum*, perforated by the urethral canal and often dilated at the extremity to form the *glans*. The two *vasa deferentia* continued from the epididymes, which are in close relation to the testes, join the urethal canal near the neck of the bladder, each often having connected with it, near its distal end, a sacculated reservoir—the *vesicula seminalis*. A small diverticulum of the proximal part of the urethra—the *uterus masculinus*—may be a remnant of the Mullerian duct. Surrounding this part of the urethra is a glandular mass—the *prostate gland*; and the ducts of a pair of small glands—*Cowper's glands*—open into the urethra near the base of the penis.

The *ovaries* are compressed oval bodies which retain their primary position in the abdomen, or pass backwards into its posterior or pelvic part. In the Monotremes, large Graafian follicles project on the surface of the ovary, while in other mammals the Graafian follicles are very small, and the surface of the ovary is almost smooth.

The *oviducts* have dilated funnel-like abdominal openings, the edges of which,

except in the Monotremes, are fimbriated or fringed. In the Monotremes the
two oviducts are distinct throughout their length, and open separately into a

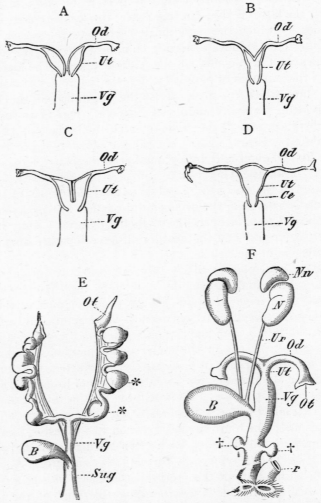

Fig. 641.—Various forms of uteri in **Eutheria.** A, B, C, D, diagrams illustrating the different
degrees of coalescence of the oviducts. A, two distinct uteri. B, bicornuate uterus. C, uterus
with a median partition. D, complete coalescence. E, female reproductive organs of one of
the *Mustelina* with embryos (**) in the uterus. F, female reproductive organs of the Hedgehog.
B, urinary bladder; *Ce.* cervix uteri (neck of uterus); *N, Nn,* kidneys and adrenal bodies; *Od.*
Fallopian *tube*; *Ot.* ostium tubæ (abdominal opening of Fallopian tube); *r.* rectum; *Sug.* urino-
genital-canal; *Ur.* ureter; *Ut.* uterus; *Vg.* vagina; ††, accessory glands. (From Wiedersheim's
Comparative Anatomy.)

urinogenital sinus. In nearly all the Theria more or less coalescence takes
place. In the Marsupials this coalescence is confined to the proximal part of

the vagina. In the Opossums (Fig. 641, A) the two oviducts are merely in close apposition at one point behind the uteri, and there is no actual coalescence. In the rest of the Marsupials (B, C) the anterior portions of the oviduct in the region (vagina) behind the uteri unite to form a median chamber which may send backwards a median diverticulum (*median vagina*, *Vg.*, *B*), and in this way communicate behind with the urinogenital passage. In the Eutheria there is a single median *vagina* (Fig. 641, *Vg.*) formed by the union of the posterior parts of the two oviducts. In some cases the two uteri (*A*, *ut.*) remain distinct ; in others their posterior portions coalesce (*B*, *C*), the anterior parts remaining separate, so that there is formed a median *corpus uteri* with two horns or

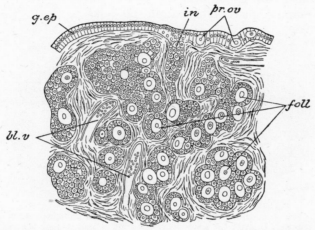

FIG. 642.—Part of a sagittal section of an **Ovary** of a new-born child. *bl. v.* blood-vessels ; *foll.* strings and groups of cells derived from the germinal epithelium becoming developed into follicles ; *g. ep.* germinal epithelium ; *in.* ingrowing cord of cells from the germinal epithelium ; *pr. ov.* primitive ova. (From Hertwig, after Waldeyer.)

cornua. In Primates and some Edentates the coalescence goes still further, there being an undivided uterus (*D*) in addition to an undivided vagina, the only parts of the oviducts which remain distinct from one another being the narrow anterior parts or Fallopian tubes. In all Mammals there is, in the *vestibule* or *urinogenital passage* through which the vagina communicates with the exterior by the aperture of the *vulva*, a small body—the *clitoris*—the homologue of the penis, and sometimes perforated by the urethral canal.

Development.—The ova of mammals (Fig. 642), like those of vertebrates in general, are developed from certain cells of the germinal epithelium. Each of these, surrounded by smaller unmodified cells of the epithelium, sinks into the stroma of the ovary, in which it becomes imbedded, the small cells forming a *Graafian follicle* (*foll.*) which encloses it. Soon spaces filled with fluid appear among the follicle cells (Fig. 643, *A*, *sp.*), and these eventually coalesce to form a single cavity. This cavity which in some mammals is crossed by strings of cells, separates an outer layer of the follicle cells—the *membrana granulosa* (*mem.*)—from the mass—*cumulus proligerus* (*disc.*)—surrounding the ovum, except on one side where they coalesce. A basement membrane is formed externally to the follicle cells, and the stroma around this becomes vascular, and forms a two-layered investment for the follicle. The cells immediately surrounding the ovum become arranged as a definite layer of cylindrical cells—the *corona radiata*. A thick membrane—the *zona radiata*—perforated by numerous radially arranged pores, into which project processes from the cells of the corona, invests the ovum ; and in many, if not in all, there is beneath this a delicate vitelline membrane. In Marsupials the ovum contains yolk which is soon extruded ; the ovum of placentals contains no yolk.

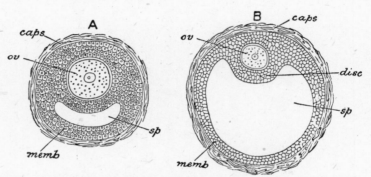

FIG. 643.—Two stages in the development of the **Graafian follicle**. *A*, with the follicular fluid beginning to appear ; *B*, after the space has largely increased. *caps.* capsule ; *disc.* cumulus proligerus ; *memb.* membrana granulosa ; *ov.* ovum ; *sp.* space containing fluid. (After Hertwig.)

As the ovum approaches maturity the fluid—*liquor folliculi*—in the cavity of the follicle increases in quantity, so that the follicle becomes greatly distended. The follicle has meanwhile approached the surface of the ovary, on which it comes to project as a rounded prominence. Eventually the middle region of the projecting part of the wall of the follicle thins out and ruptures, setting free the ovum, which passes into the Fallopian tube. On the way along the Fallopian tube fertilisation takes place, and, after becoming enclosed in an envelope of albumen (not always present), the ovum passes onwards to the uterus, there to undergo its development. In the place of the discharged ovum there is left a space which becomes filled with connective tissue to form a body known as the *corpus luteum*. If the ovum should become fertilised and proceed to develop in the uterus, the corpus luteum increases in size and persists for a considerable time : if no development takes place it disappears comparatively quickly.

With the absence of food-yolk are connected most of the differences observable between the early stages of the development of a higher mammal

(Fig. 644) and the corresponding stages in the development of a reptile or bird. One of the most striking of these is in the mode of cleavage. In the case of the large ovum of the Bird, as we have seen, the segmentation is of the incomplete or *meroblastic* type, being confined to a small disc of protoplasm—the *germinal disc* on one side of the ovum. In the Mammals, on the other hand, except in the Monotremes, cleavage is complete or *holoblastic*, the entire ovum taking part in the process of segmentation. The cleavage is nearly or quite regular, the

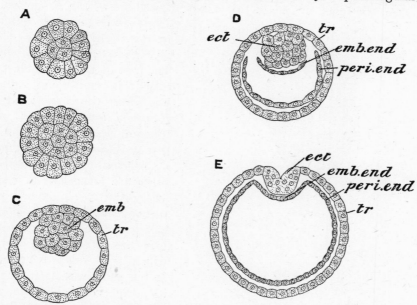

Fig. 644.—Diagram representing sections of the embryo of a **Mammal** at successive stages in the segmentation and formation of the layers. *A* and *B*, formation of enclosing layer (trophoblast) and inner cell-mass destined to give rise to the embryo; *C*, blastodermic vesicle with embryonic cell-mass (*emb.*) separated from trophoblast (*tr.*) except on one side; *D*, blastodermic vesicle in which peripheral and embryonic portions of endoderm have become established: the break here represented on each side between the two does not occur. *E*, stage in which the embryonic ectoderm has broken through the trophoblast and become joined to it peripherally.

cells into which the ovum divides being of equal, or approximately equal, size. The result, in the Eutheria, is the formation of a sphere of cells, which soon become distinguishable into an outer layer the *trophoblast*, and a central mass, the *inner cell-mass* or *embryonal knot*. In the Marsupials, so far as known, the stage of a solid cellular sphere or morula does not occur, a central cavity being present from the outset. In the Eutheria, by imbibition of liquid, a cavity, which is formed in the interior of the sphere, increases rapidly in size. The stage now reached is called the *blastodermic vesicle*. During the growth in size of the internal cavity the central mass of cells remains in contact with one side only of the trophoblast, where it spreads out as a stratum several cells deep.

From it are derived the embryonal ectoderm and the entire endoderm of the vesicle.

The outer layer is apparently the equivalent of the extra-embryonal ectoderm of the Bird and Reptile, and has been termed the *trophoblast* or *trophoblastic ectoderm*, because of the part which it plays in the nutrition of the foetus. Immediately beneath it, throughout its extent, a thin layer of flattened cells appears—the *peripheral endoderm* : this is continuous with a similar layer formed on the inner surface of the embryonic cell-mass—the *embryonic endoderm*—and is formed by outgrowth from it. The rest of the cell-mass gives rise to the *embryonic ectoderm*. The part of the trophoblast lying over this embryonic ectoderm, known as the *covering layer* or *Rauber's layer*, has a widely different fate in different Eutheria : it may thin out and disappear.

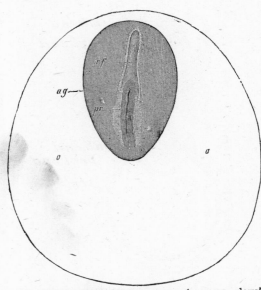

Fig. 645.—Embryonic area of seven days' embryo **Rabbit**. *ag.* embryonic area ; *o,* place of future vascular area ; *pr,* primitive streak ; *fr,* medullary groove. (From Balfour, after Kölliker.)

A *primitive knot* and *embryonic shield* are formed as in Reptiles. The primitive knot has simply the appearance of the somewhat enlarged anterior extremity of a *primitive streak* (Fig. 645, *pr.*) which is developed very much in the same way as in the Bird, its formation being due to the same cause as in the Bird, viz., active proliferation of cells leading to the development of the beginnings of the mesoderm. A dark median streak, the *head-process*, appears in front of the primitive knot, and in some Mammals there is an invagination on the surface of the latter leading to the formation of a neurenteric canal and of a notochordal canal which gives rise to the rudiment of the posterior part of the notochord In the region of the anterior part of the primitive streak, the primitive knot and the head-process, the mesoderm coalesces with the endoderm ; but there does not appear to be any breaking through into the underlying space such as occurs in Reptiles (p. 417). A *medullary groove* (*rf*) and *canal* are formed in front of the primitive streak, and a row of protovertebræ (Fig. 646) make their appearance on each side of the former. The embryo becomes folded off from the blastoderm as in the Bird, and at length the body of the young mammal is constricted off from the " yolk-sac " or *umbilical vesicle*, so that, ultimately, the two come to be connected only by a narrow yolk-stalk (Figs. 647 and 649) : the yolk-sac is a thin-walled sac containing a coagulable fluid in place of yolk.   A *vascular area* early becomes established around the embryo on the wall of the yolk-sac.

The most important of the points of difference between a mammal and a Bird, as regards the latter part of the history of the development, are connected with the fate of the *fœtal membranes*.   The amnion is in many mammals

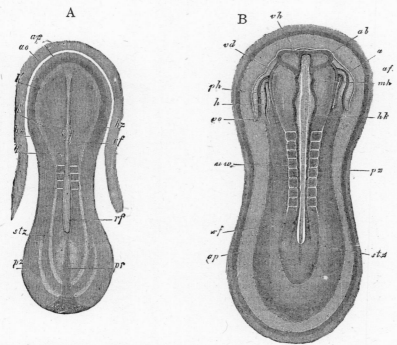

Fig. 646.—**Embryo Rabbit,** of about nine days, from the dorsal side. *a.* aorta; *ab,* optic vesicle; *af,* fold of amnion; *ao.* area opaca; *ap,* area pellucida; *h. hz,* heart; *h′, h″,* medullary plate in the region of the future fore-brain; *h″,* medullary plate in the region of the future mid-brain; *hh* and *hh‴,* hind-brain; *mh,* mid-brain; *ph,* pericardial section of body cavity; *pr,* primitive streak; *pz,* lateral zone; *rf,* medullary groove; *uw,* proto-vertebræ; *stz,* vertebral zone; *vd,* pharynx; *vo,* vitelline vein.   (From Balfour, after Kölliker.)

developed in the same way as in the Bird, viz., by the formation of a system of folds of the extra-embryonal somatopleure which arise from the blastoderm around the embryo, and grow upwards and inwards, eventually meeting in the middle over the body of the embryo, and uniting in such a way as to form two layers.   Of the two layers thus formed the outer, consisting of trophoblastic ectoderm and somatic mesoderm, simply constitutes a part of the extra-embryonic somatopleure which forms a complete investment for the entire ovum, and is known as the *chorion* or *sub-zonal membrane* (Fig. 647, *2* and *3*).

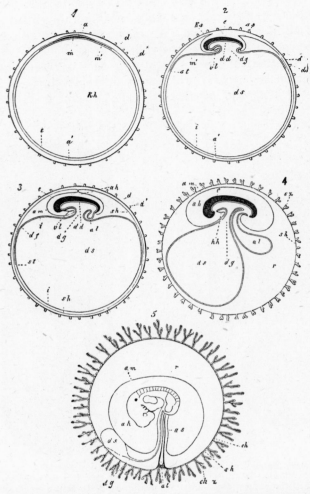

Fig. 647.—Five diagrammatic sections illustrating the formation of the **fœtal membranes** of a Mammal. In *1, 2, 3, 4* the embryo is represented in longitudinal section. *1*, Embryo with zona pellucida blastodermic vesicle, and embryonic area; *2*, embryo with commencing formation of yolk-sac and amnion; *3*, embryo with amnion about to close; *4*, embryo with villous chorion, larger allantois, and mouth and anus; *5*, embryo in which the mesoderm of the allantois has extended round the inner surface of the chorion and united with it to form the fœtal part of the placenta; the cavity of the allantois is aborted. *a*, ectoderm of embryo; *a'*, ectoderm of non-embryonic part of the blastodermic vesicle; *ah.* amniotic cavity; *al.* allantois; *am.* amnion; *ch.* fœtal part of placenta; *chz,* placental villi; *d,* in *1* zona radiata, in *2* and *3* chorion; *d',* processes of zona radiata and chorion; *dd,* embryonic endoderm; *df.* area vasculosa; *dg,* stalk of umbilical vesicle; *ds,* cavity of umbilical vesicle; *e.* embryo; *hh,* pericardial cavity; *i,* non-embryonic endoderm; *Kh,* cavity of blastodermic vesicle; *Ks.* head-fold of amnion; *m.* embryonic mesoderm; *m',* non-embryonic mesoderm; *r,* space between chorion and amnion; *sh,* subzonal membrane (chorion); *ss,* tail-fold of amnion; *st.* sinus terminalis; *sz,* villi of chorion; *vl.* ventral body wall. (From Foster and Balfour, after Kölliker.)

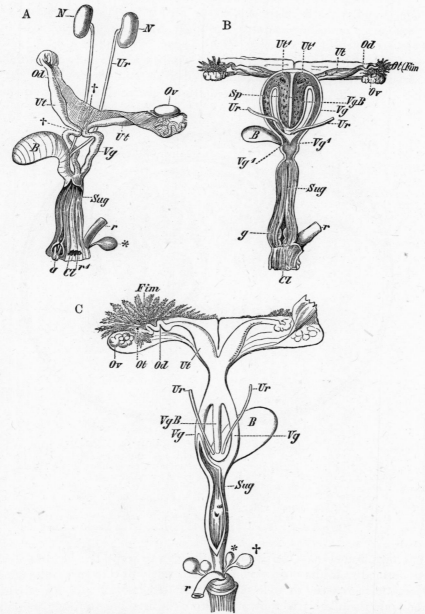

FIG. 648.—Female urinogenital apparatus of various **Marsupials.** A, **Didelphys dorsigera** (young) ; B, **Trichosurus** ; C, **Phascolomys wombat.** *B*, urinary bladder ; *Cl.* cloaca ; *Fim.* fimbriæ ; *g.* clitoris ; *N.* kidney ; *Od.* Fallopian tube ; *Ot.* its aperture ; *Ov.* ovary ; *r.* rectum ; *r*[1], its opening ; *Sug*, urinogenital canal ; *Ur.* ureter ; *Ut.* uterus ; *Ut*[1]. opening of the uterus into the median vagina (*Vg. B.*) ; *Vg.* lateral vagina ; *Vg*[1]. its opening into the urinogenital canal ; †*, rectal glands ; †, bend between uterus and vagina. (From Wiedersheim's *Comparative Anatomy.*)

In the account of the development of the Bird it has been referred to as the *false amnion* or *serous membrane*. The inner layer or true amnion, as in the Bird, forms the wall of a cavity—the *amniotic cavity* (4 and 5, *ah.*)—which becomes tensely filled with fluid (the *liquor amnii*) over the body of the embryo ; this serves the purpose of protecting the delicate embryo from the effects of shocks. As in the case of the Bird, the folds giving rise to the amnion and

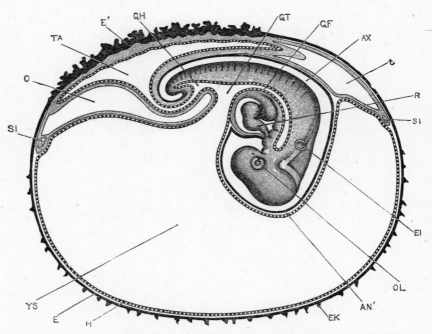

Fig. 649.—A **Rabbit** embryo and blastodermic vesicle at the end of the tenth day. The embryo is represented in surface view from the right side, the course of the alimentary canal being indicated by the broad dotted line ; the blastodermic vesicle is shown in median longitudina ; section. The great part of the tail has been removed. *AN'*. pro-amnion ; *AX*. cavity of amnion. *C*. extra-embryonic portion of cœlome ; *E*. ectoderm ; *E'*. thickened ectoderm by which the vesicle is attached to the uterus and from which the fœtal part of the placental is derived ; *EI*. auditory vesicle ; *EK*, ectodermal villi ; *GF*. fore-gut ; *GH*. hind-gut ; *GT*. mid-gut ; *H*. endoderm ; *O*, extra-embryonic cœlome ; *OL*. lens of eye ; *R*. heart ; *SI*. sinus-terminalis ; *TA*. allantoic cavity ; *YS*. yolk-sac. (From Marshall, in part after Van Beneden and Julin.)

serous membrane may consist from the first (except the head-fold, which, being formed from the pro-amnion, consists solely of ectoderm and endoderm) of somatic mesoderm as well as ectoderm (trophoblast : or mesoderm may extend into them later), so that, either from the first, or as a result of outgrowth which takes place subsequently, the chorion contains mesoderm as well as ectoderm. The ectodermal cells—trophoblast cells—of the choroin may enter into close relationship with the mucous membrane of the wall of the uterus, and send out processes or *primary villi* (Fig. 649, *EK*) by means of which the ovum becomes intimately attached, and by means of which perhaps nourishment is absorbed.

In certain mammals the history of the amnion is very different from that above described. In the Hedgehog (Fig. 650), for example, a cavity appears in the ectoderm of the embryonic area ; this is destined to give rise to the cavity

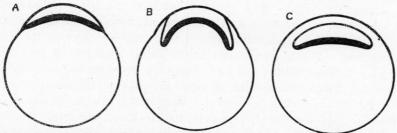

FIG. 650.—*A—C*, diagram illustrating the formation of the **amnion** and **trophoblast** in the **Hedgehog.** Only the ectoderm is represented. *A*, early stage in which the amniotic cavity has appeared, roofed over by chorionic ectoderm ; *B*, later stage in which the amniotic ectoderm is growing up below the chorionic from the edges of the ectodermal floor ; *C*, stage in which the amniotic ectoderm completely roofs over the cavity. (After Hubrecht.)

of the amnion. The ectoderm, which forms its roof, is entirely trophoblastic or chorionic ; that which forms its floor is partly destined to become amniotic ectoderm, partly embryonal ectoderm. After the mesoderm has begun to become differentiated, the margins of the amniotic part of this ectodermal floor(*B*) begin to grow upwards, giving rise to a layer which extends over the

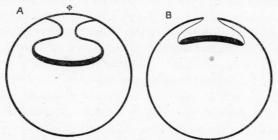

FIG. 651.—Diagram illustrating the mode of formation of the **amnion** in various Mammals *A*, commencing formation of the amnion in Mus, Arvicola, etc. The asterisk marks what corresponds to the portion of the trophoblast overlying the embryo in Fig. 650, *C*, *B*, mode of formation of the amnion in many Mammals. The portion of the trophoblast indicated by the asterisk in *A* disappears before the amniotic folds make their appearance. (After Hubrecht.)

roof on the inner side of the chorionic ectoderm and eventually (*C*) forms a complete layer—the ectodermal layer of the amnion.

In the Mole (*Talpa*) spaces appear in the layer of ectoderm of the embryonal area, and these subsequently coalesce to form a single cavity—the primitive amniotic cavity, but this has only a temporary existence, the amnion arising later by the formation of a series of folds. In *Mus, Arvicola*, and others (Fig. 651, *A*), the amnion is developed from a series of folds of the ectoderm which arise beneath the trophoblast. In other Mammals (*B*) the amnion arises in the manner already described, and the portion of the trophoblast immediately overlying the embryonic part of the ectoderm eventually disappears.

The allantois has, in all essential respects, the same mode of development as in the Bird, arising in most cases as a hollow outgrowth from the hinder part of the alimentary canal; this, growing out into the space (extra-embryonic cœlome) between the chorion and the amnion, becomes in all the Eutheria applied to the former, and unites with it to contribute towards the formation of the *placenta*. But in some cases the allantois does not at first contain a cavity, and in some (Primates) the severance between the amnion and the chorion is not completed, and the allantois arises from the outset in continuity with the latter. Sometimes, as in the Rabbit (Fig. 649), the union between the allantois (*TA*) and the chorion is limited to a comparatively small part of the extent of the latter, but in most instances the allantois spreads over the entire inner surface of the chorion, and becomes united with it throughout its entire extent (Fig. 647). Villi, into which mesoderm with blood-vessels penetrates, grow out from the surface of the chorion and are received into depressions or *crypts* in the mucous membrane of the uterus, which becomes profoundly modified. The villi branch and enter into intimate union with the uterine mucous membrane, so that a close connection becomes established between the vascular system of the fœtus and that of the parent.

The term *placenta* is applied to the entire structure by means of which this connection is brought about; the parts derived from the embryo are termed the *fœtal placenta*, those developed from the wall of the uterus the *maternal placenta*. In some mammals the union between the two is not very close, so that at birth no part of the uterine mucous membrane is thrown off; such a placenta is said to be *non-deciduate* (*semi-placenta*). In other mammals the union is closer, and at birth a part of the hypertrophied mucous membrane is thrown off in the form of a *decidua*; such a placenta is termed *deciduate* (*placenta vera*). In the Mole and the Bandicoot not only is there no decidua thrown off, but the fœtal placenta with the distal portion of the allantois does not pass out after the fœtus, but remains, and is broken up or absorbed in the uterus. Such a condition has been termed *contra-deciduate*.

In one of the simplest forms of placenta—the *discoidal*—found in the Rabbit and other Rodents (Fig. 649), the yolk-sac extends over the surface of the chorion and becomes fused with it, except in a small area on the dorsal side of the embryo. In this small area the allantois is applied to the chorion and coalesces with it, and from the membrane so formed vascular villi grow out, and are received into the uterine crypts. In most mammals, however, as already stated, the allantois becomes applied to the chorion throughout its entire extent, and thus completely encloses the embryo. Villi may be developed from all parts except the poles: when this condition persists in the fully-formed placenta, the term *diffuse* is applied. Sometimes the diffuse condition is temporary, and the completed placenta has villi disposed in a broad band or zone (*zonary* placenta). Sometimes the villi are grouped together in patches or cotyledons (*cotyledonary* placenta). In Man and the Apes the villi become secondarily restricted to a disc-shaped area of the chorion situated on the ventral side of the embryo (*meta-discoidal* placenta).

In many Mammals the yolk-sac, through the medium of the chorion, enters into a close relationship with the uterine wall, and a connection, the so-called *yolk-sac placenta*, is established through which nourishment can be conveyed to the embryo ; but this rarely persists after the true (allantoic) placenta has become established.

The stalk of the yolk-sac, with the corresponding narrowed part of the allantois and the vessels which it contains, forms the *umbilical cord* by which the fœtus is connected at the umbilicus with the yolk-sac and placenta. This is enclosed in a sheath formed by the ventral portion of the amnion. The part of the allantois which remains within the cavity of the body develops into the urinary bladder, together with a cord—the *urachus*—connecting the bladder with the umbilicus.

In the Marsupials the ovum is comparatively large. After fertilisation it becomes enclosed in a thick shell-membrane with a layer of albumen. The first cleavage of the ovum (*Didelphys*), or the fourth (*Dasyurus*), involves a separation of the embryo-forming part of its substance from that destined to give rise only to the trophoblastic ectoderm.

Fig. 652.—Mammary fœtus of **Kangaroo** attached to the teat. (Natural size.)

Further divisions take place in such a way as to give rise, not to a solid morula as in the Eutheria, but to a hollow blastodermic vesicle with a wall composed of a single layer, the cells on one side of which form the embryonic area. An allantoic placenta is not developed except in Perameles. The intra-uterine development of the fœtus is abbreviated, and birth takes place when the young animal is still relatively very small and has many of the parts incompletely formed. In this helpless condition the young Marsupial is placed by the mother in the marsupium, where it remains for a time as a *mammary fœtus* (Fig. 652), hanging passively to the teat, to which the mouth becomes firmly adherent. The milk is expressed from the mammary gland by the contraction of a muscle, the *cremaster*, and passes down the gullet of the fœtus, which is enabled to breathe unobstructedly through the nostrils by the establishment of a continuous passage from the nasal cavities to the larynx, as already described (p. 671).

In all the Marsupials, so far as known, the embryo is covered over, except in a limited area, by the compressed and expanded yolk-sac. In the majority

(Fig. 653) the allantois (*all.*) is small, and is completely enclosed with the embryo in the yolk-sac. In the Koala, however (Fig. 654), it stands out and

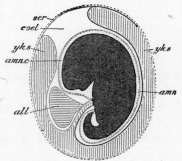

FIG. 653.—Diagram of the embryo and fœtal membranes of **Hypsiprymnus rufescens.** *all.* allantoic cavity; *amn.* amnion; *amn. c.* cavity of amnion; *cœl.* extra-embryonic cœlome; *ser.* serous membrane (chorion); *yk. s.* yolk-sac. (After Semon.)

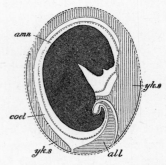

FIG. 654.—Diagram of the embryo and fœtal membranes of **Phascolarctos cinereus.** Letters as in Fig. 653. (After Semon.)

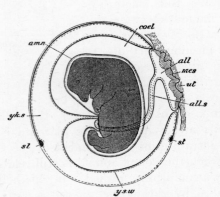

FIG. 655.—Diagram of the embryo and placenta of **Perameles obesula.** Letters as in Fig. 653. In addition, *all. s.* allantoic stalk; *mes.* mesenchyme of outer surface of allantois fused with mesenchyme of serous membrane; *s. t.* sinus terminalis; *ut.* uterine wall. (After J. P. Hill.)

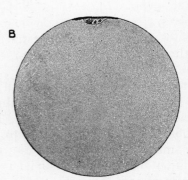

FIG. 656.—*A*, blastula stage of one of the **Theria.** *B*, transition stage between the morula and blastula in a **Monotreme.** Both represented in diagrammatic section. (After Semon.)

becomes closely applied to the serous membrane over the small area not covered by the yolk-sac; but no vascular villi are developed. In the Native Cat (*Dasyurus*) there is a well-developed yolk-sac placenta. Only in the Bandicoots (Fig. 655), so far as known, is the outgrowth of the allantois to the chorion followed by the establishment of an intimate relationship between the chorion and the uterine wall, with the formation of interlocking ridges and depressions, the whole constituting a placenta of the same essential character as that of the Eutheria, though devoid of actual villi.

The Prototheria, unlike all the rest of the Mammalia, are oviparous. In Tachyglossus only a single egg, as a general rule, is laid in a season. This is placed in a temporary marsupium, formed as already described (p. 636) in the mammary region of the ventral surface. The young animal soon emerges from the egg, and remains enclosed in the marsupium till it reaches an advanced stage of development. Ornithorhynchus develops no marsupium, and the two eggs which it produces are deposited in its burrow. In Tachyglossus the egg-shell is composed of keratin; in Ornithorhynchus it contains carbonate of lime. The ova of the Prototheria (Fig. 656) are very much larger than those of other Mammals, their greater dimensions being due to the presence of a large proportion of food-yolk. The segmentation, unlike that of all the Theria, is meroblastic, and the blastoderm eventually forms a complete investment of two layers, to the yolk. An embryonic area is differentiated at one pole, and on it appears a primitive streak with a primitive knot and head-process.

APPENDIX ON LITERATURE DEALING WITH THE CHORDATA

THE following lists are a selection of, and intended only as a condensed guide to, publications that are likely to be useful to students of the Chordata either as standard text-books or as papers in which new or important aspects of classification and of morphology have been introduced.

In several of the works quoted (which are marked with **) more detailed lists of references will be found up to the dates of their publication. In some cases references to papers dealing with particular points have been given as footnotes to the text in this volume.

GENERAL TEXT-BOOKS

1. ABEL, O. *Die Stämme der Wirbelthiere*, Berlin and Leipzig, 1919.
2. ABEL, O. *Lebensbilder aus der Tierwelt der Vorzeit*, Jena, 1922.
3. ABEL, O. *Lehrbuch der Paläozoologie*, Jena, 1920.
4. BOLK, L. and others. *Handbuch der Vergleichenden Anatomie der Wirbeltiere,*** 2 vols., Berlin, 1934.
5. BORRADAILE, L. A. *Manual of Elementary Zoology*, London, 1938.
6. DE BEER, G. A. *The Development of the Vertebrate Skull*, Oxford, 1937.
7. GOODRICH, E. S. *The Structure and Development of Vertebrates,*** London, 1930.
8. HERRICK, C. J. *An Introduction to Neurology*, Philadelphia, 1927.
9. IHLE, J. E. W. and others. *Vergleichende Anatomie der Wirbeltiere,*** Berlin, 1927.
10. KERR, J. GRAHAM. *Text-book of Embryology.* The embryology of vertebrates excluding the mammalia, London, 1919.
11. LULL, R. S. *Organic Evolution*, New York, 1936.
12. MARSHALL, A. M. and HURST, C. H. *Practical Zoology*, London, 1912.
13. MATTHEW, W. D. *Climate and Evolution*, New York Academy of Sciences, 1939.
14. REGAN, C. T. (Editor) *Natural History*, London, 1936.
15. ROMER, A. S. *Vertebrate Palæontology,*** Chicago, 1933.
16. WILDER, H. H. *History of the Human Body*, New York, 1923.
17. ZITTEL, K. VON. *Text-book of Palæontology* (English translation), Vol. II, Fishes to Birds, Eastman and Smith Woodward; Vol. III, Mammals, Smith Woodward, London, 1932.

PROTOCHORDATA

18. DELAGE, Y. and HÉROUARD, E. *Traité de Zoologie Concréte*, Vol. VII, Prochordés, Paris, 1898.
19. PIETSCHMANN and KÜKENTHAL. *Handbuch der Zoologie*, 6. I Hälfte Acrania Cephalochorda, 1929.

FISHES

20. AGASSIZ, J. L. R.   *Recherches sur les Poissons Fossiles*, Neuchâtel, 1833–43.
21. AGASSIZ, J. L. R.   *Monographie des Poissons Fossiles du Vieux Grès Rouge, ou Système Dévonien des Iles Brittaniques et de Russie*, Neuchâtel, 1844–45.
22. BROILI, F.   Weitere Fischreste aus den Hunsrückschiefern, *Sitzungsber, Bay. Acad. Wiss.*, Munich, 1933.
23. BROILI, F.   Ein Macropetalichthyide aus den Hunsrückschiefern, *Sitzungsber, Bay. Acad. Wiss.*, Munich, 1933.
24. BROUGH, J.   On Fossil Fishes from the Karroo System, and some General Considerations on the Bony Fishes of the Triassic Period, *Proc. Zool. Soc.*, London, 1931.
25. BROUGH, J.   *The Triassic Fishes of Besano, Lombardy*, British Museum, London, 1939.
26. DEAN, B.   *A Bibliography of Fishes*, 3 Vols., New York, 1916–23.
27. BEER, G. R. DE, and MOY-THOMAS, J. A.   On the Skull of Holocephali.   *Phil. Trans. Royal Soc.*, 1935.
28. EIGENMANN, C.   *Cave Vertebrates of North America, a Study in Degenerative Evolution*, Washington, 1909.
29. GOODRICH, E. S.   Vertebrata Craniata, I. Cyclostomes and Fishes in Lankester, E. R.   *A Treatise on Zoology*, IX, London, 1909.**
30. GOODRICH, E. S.   *Polypterus* a Palæoniscid, *Palæobiologica*, Vol. I, 1928.
31. GOODE, G. B. and BEAN, T.   *Oceanic Ichthyology*, Washington, 1895.
32. GREGORY, W. K.   Studies on the body-forms of Fishes, *Zoologica*, Vol. VIII, New York, 1928.
33. GROSS, W.   Histologische Studien am Aussenskelett fossilier Agnathen und Fische, *Palæontographica*, Vol. LXXXIII, Stuttgart, 1935.
34. HEINTZ, A.   Die Downtonischen und Devonischen Vertebrata von Spitzbergen II Acanthaspida, *Skr. Svalbard og Ishavet*, XXII, Oslo, 1929.
35. HEINTZ, A.   The structure of *Dinichthys*.   A contribution to our knowledge of the Arthrodira, *Am. Mus. Nat. Hist. Dean Mem.* Vol. IV, New York, 1932.
36. JORDAN, D. S.   *Fishes*, New York and London, 1925.
37. KIAER, J.   The Downtonian fauna of Norway I Anaspida, *Skr. Vidensk. Selsk. Kristiania*, VI, 1924.
38. MEEK, A.   *The Migrations of Fish*, London, 1916.
39. MOY-THOMAS, J. A.   The early evolution and relationships of the Elasmobranchs, *Biological Reviews*, XIV, Cambridge, 1939.
40. MOY-THOMAS, J. A.   *Palæozoic Fishes*, London, 1939.
41. NORMAN, J. R.   *A History of Fishes*, London, 1936.
42. REGAN, C. T.   *The Fresh-water Fishes of the British Isles*, London, 1911.
43. REGAN, C. T.   Articles on Fishes, Selachians, etc., in the 14th edition of the *Encyclopedia Britannica*, London and New York, 1929.
44. REGAN, C. T., and TREWAVAS, E.   Deep-sea Angler-fishes (Ceratioidea), *Rep. Carlsberg Ocean. Exped.* 1928–30.
45. SÄVE-SÖDERBERGH, G.   The dermal bones of the head and the lateral line system in *Osteolepis macrolepidotus* Ag. with remarks on the terminology of the lateral line system and on the dermal bones of certain other Crossopterygians, *Nova Acta R. Soc. Sci.*, Upsaliensis, 1933.
46. STENSIÖ, E. A.   *Triassic fishes from Spitzbergen*, Part I, Vienna, 1931.
47. STENSIÖ, E. A.   On the head of the Macropetalichthyids with certain remarks on the head of the other Arthrodires, *Field Museum of Natural History*, Chicago, 1925.

48. STENSIÖ, E. A. *Triassic fishes from Spitzbergen*, Part II, K. Sv. Vetensk. Akad., Stockholm, 1925.
49. STENSIÖ, E. A. Upper Devonian Vertebrates from East Greenland, *Medd. om Grønland*, København, 1931.
50. STENSIÖ, E. A. *The Cephalaspids of Great Britain*, British Museum (Natural History), 1932.
51. SYEVERTZOV, A. N. Evolution der Bauchflossen der fische, *Zool. Jahrb.*, Jena, 1934.
52. WATSON, D. M. S. The Structure of Certain Palæoniscids and the Relationships of that group with other Bony Fish, *Proc. Zool. Soc.*, London, 1925.
53. WATSON, D. M. S. The interpretation of the Arthrodires, *Proc. Zool. Soc.*, London, 1934.
54. WATSON, D. M. S. The Acanthodian Fishes, *Phil. Trans. Roy. Soc.*, London, 1937.
55. WESTOLL, T. S. On the Cheek-bones in Teleostome Fishes, *Journ. Anat.*, Cambridge, 1937.
56. WHITE, E. I. The Ostracoderm *Pteraspis* and the Relationships of the Agnathous Vertebrates, *Phil. Trans. Roy. Soc.*, London, 1935.
57. WHITE, E. I. A new Type of Palæoniscid Fish, with Remarks on the Evolution of the Actinopterygian Pectoral fins, *Proc. Zool. Soc.*, London, 1939.
58. WOODWARD, A. S. *Catalogue of the Fossil Fishes in the British Museum*, Parts I–IV, London, 1889–1901.

AMPHIBIA, REPTILES AND BIRDS

59. BEDDARD, F. E. *The Structure and Classification of Birds*, London, 1898.
60. BRONN, H. G. *Die Classen und Ordnungen des Thier-Reichs, Vögel*, von Hans Gadow und E. Selenka, VI. Abth. 4, Leipzig and Heidelberg, 1869–91.
61. BROOM, R. *The Origin of the Human Skeleton*, London.
62. BROOM, R. *The Mammal-like Reptiles of South Africa*, London.
63. EVANS, A. H. Birds, *Cambridge Natural History*, Vol. IX, London, 1899.
64. FRANCIS, E. T. B. *The Anatomy of the Salamander*, Oxford, 1934.
65. GADOW, H. Amphibia and Reptiles. *Cambridge Natural History*, Vol. VIII, London, 1901.
66. GILMORE, C. W. Osteology of the armoured Dinosauria in the United States National Museum, *Bull. U.S. Nat. Museum*, 1914.
67. GILMORE, C. W. Osteology of the carnivorous Dinosauria in the United States National Museum, *Bull. U.S. Nat. Museum*, 1920.
68. GOODRICH, E. S. On the Classification of the Reptilia, *Proc. Royal Society*, 1916.
69. HUENE, F. VON. *Die Ichthyosaurier des Lias und ihre Zusammenhänge*, Berlin, 1922.
70. LAMBRECHT, K. *Handbuch der Palæornithologie*, Berlin, 1933.
71. LULL, R. S. A revision of the Ceratopsia, *Memoir, Peabody Museum*, New Haven, 1933.
72. MOOKERJEE, H. M. On the Development of the vertebral column of Urodela, *Trans. Royal Society*, Vol. 218.
73. MOOKERJEE, H. M. On the Development of the vertebral column of Anura, *Trans. Royal Society*, Vol. 219.
74. NOBLE, G. K. *Biology of the Amphibia*, New York, 1931.
75. NOPSCA, F. The Genera of Reptiles, *Palæobiologica*, 1928.
76. SÄVE-SÖDERBERGH, G. On the Dermal Bones of the head in Labyrinthodont Stegocephalians and the classification of the Group, *Meddelelser om Grönland*, Copenhagen, 1935.

77. STEEN, MARGARET C. On the Fossil Amphibia from the Gas Coal of Nýřany and other Deposits of Czechoslovakia, *Proc. Zool. Soc.*, London, 1938.
78. SWINTON, W. E. *The Dinosaurs*, London, 1934.
79. WATSON, D. M. S. *Eunotosaurus africanus* and the Ancestry of the Chelonia, *Proc. Zool. Soc.*, London, 1914.
80. WATSON, D. M. S. On *Seymouria*, the most primitive known Reptile, *Proc. Zool. Soc.*, London, 1918.
81. WATSON, D. M. S. The Origin and Evolution of the Amphibia, *Trans. Royal Soc.*, London, 1926.
82. WETMORE, A. *A Systematic Classification for the Birds of the World*, Revised and Amended, Smithsonian Institution, Washington, 1934.
83. WILLISTON, S. W. *Water Reptiles of the Past and Present*, Chicago, 1914.
84. WILLISTON, S. W. *Osteology of the Reptiles*, ed. W. K. Gregory, Cambridge, Mass., 1925.

MAMMALS

85. ABEL, O. *Die vorzeitliche Säugetiere*, 1914.
86. ABEL, O. *Das Biologische Tragheitgesetz.* An account of the evolution of the horses in *Biologia Generalis* Band IV Lieferung 1/2, Leipzig, 1928.
87. ABEL, O. *Die Stellung des Menschen im Rahmen der Wirbeltiere*, treats of the palæontology of all primates,** Jena, 1931.
88. BEDDARD, F. E. Mammalia, *Cambridge Natural History*, Vol. X, London, 1902.
89. BUTLER, P. M. Studies of the Mammalian Dentition, *Proc. Zool. Soc.*, Series B, Vol. 1939, London, 1939.
90. CLARK, W. E. LEGROS. *Early Forerunners of Man*, An account of the anatomy of primates, London, 1934.
91. FLOWER, W. H. and LYDEKKER, R. *Mammals, living and extinct*, London, 1891.
92. FRICK, CHILDS. *Horned Ruminants of North America*, New York, 1937.
93. GREEN, EUNICE CHASE. Anatomy of the Rat. A fully illustrated manual of the anatomy, *Trans. Amer. Philos. Soc.*, Vol. XXVII, Philadelphia, 1935.
94. GREGORY, W. K. The Orders of Mammals, *Bull. Amer. Mus. Nat. Hist.*, Vol. XXVII, New York, 1910.
95. GREGORY, W. K. On the Structure and Relations of *Notharctus*, an American Eocene Primate, *Memoir, Amer. Mus. Nat. Hist.*, New York, 1920.
96. GREGORY, W. K. The Origin and Evolution of the Human Dentition, *Journ. Dental. Research*, Baltimore, 1922.
97. GREGORY, W. K. *Man's Place among the Anthropoids*, Oxford, 1934.
98. JONES, F. WOOD. *The Mammals of South Australia*, Adelaide, 1924.
99. JONES, F. WOOD. *Man's Place among the Mammals*, London, 1927.
100. MATTHEW, W. D. The Carnivora and Insectivora of the Bridger Basin, Middle Eocene, *Memoir American Museum of Natural History*, New York, 1909.
101. MATTHEW, W. D. The Evolution of the Horse, a record and its interpretation, *Quarterly Review of Biology*, Vol. I, no. 2, 1926.
102. MATTHEW, W. D. Palæocene Faunas of the San Juan Basin, New Mexico, *Trans. Am. Philos. Soc.*, Philadelphia, 1937.
103. OSBORN, H. F. *The Age of Mammals*, New York, 1910.
104. OSBORN, H. F. *Titanotheres of Ancient Wyoming, Dakota and Nebraska*, two volumes, Washington, 1929.
105. OSBORN, H. F. *Proboscidea.* A monograph of the discovery, evolution, migration and extinction of the Mastodonts and Elephants of the World, Vol. I (Vol. II in the press), New York, 1936.
106. OSBORN, H. F. *Evolution of the Mammalian Molar Teeth*, New York, 1907.

107. OSBORN, H. F. Equidæ of the Oligocene, Miocene and Pliocene of North America, *Memoir, American Museum*, 1918.
108. SCOTT, W. B. *A History of the Land Mammals of the Western Hemisphere*, New York, 1937.
109. SIMPSON, G. G. *A Catologue of the Mesozoic Mammalia in the Geological Department of the British Museum*, London, 1928.
110. SIMPSON, G. G. *American Mesozoic Mammalia*, New Haven, 1929.
111. SIMPSON, G. G. The Beginning of the Age of Mammals, *Biological Reviews*, Vol. XII, Cambridge, 1937.
112. SMITH, G. ELLIOT. *Essays on the Evolution of Man*, London, 1927.
113. TULLBERG, T. *Ueber das System der Nagethiere*, Upsala, 1899.
114. WEBER, MAX. *Die Säugetiere*, Vol. I, Anatomy; Vol. II, Systematic; Jena, 1927-28.

LIST OF PERIODICALS

Acta Zoologica. Stockholm.
American Museum of Natural History, New York.
    Bulletin.
    Memoirs.
    Novitates.
American Naturalist. New York.
Anatomical Record. Philadelphia.
Anatomischer Anzeiger. Jena.
Annals and Magazine of Natural History. London.
Archiv für Naturgeschichte. Berlin.
Auk (ornithology). Cambridge, Mass.
Biological Reviews, &c., Cambridge.
Biologisches Centralblatt. Leipzig.
British Museum (Natural History). London.
    Catalogues.
    Monographs.
    Novitates Zoologicæ.
Calcutta, Indian Museum.
    Memoirs.
    Records.
Cambridge, Mass., Harvard University.
    Bulletin of the Museum of Comparative Zoology.
    Memoirs of the Museum of Comparative Zoology.
Chicago, Field Museum. Publications in Zoology.
Copeia, New York.
Ibis (ornithology.) London.
Journal of Anatomy. London.
Journal of Animal Ecology. Cambridge.
Journal of Mammalogy. Baltimore.
Journal of the Royal Microscopical Society. London.
Journal of the Society for the Preservation of the Fauna of the Empire. London.
Linnean Society of London.
    Journal.
    Memoirs.
    Proceedings.
Nature. London.
Palæobiologica. Vienna.
Paläontologische Zeitschrift. Berlin.
Paris, Muséum National d'Histoire Naturelle.
    Archives.
    Bulletin.
Proceedings of the Biological Society of Washington. Washington.

Quarterly Journal of Microscopical Science. London.
Royal Society of London.
 Proceedings.
 Transactions.
Science. New York.
Science Progress. London.
Zeitschrift für Säugetierkunde. Berlin.
Zoogeografica. Jena.
Zoologica. New York.
Zoologische Garten, Der. Leipzig.
Zoologischer Anzeiger. Leipzig.
Zoologischer Bericht. Jena.
Zoological Record. London.
Zoological Society of London.
 Proceedings A.
 Proceedings B.
 Transactions.

INDEX

All numbers refer to pages : words in italics are names of families, genera and species : words in thick type are names of higher divisions : words in small capitals are names of examples. Numbers in thick type are numbers of pages on which there are figures : an asterisk after a number indicates a definition of the term or of the group.

PRINTED IN GREAT BRITAIN BY
RICHARD CLAY AND COMPANY, LTD.,
BUNGAY, SUFFOLK.